# THE ANNUAL
# OF
# PSYCHOANALYSIS

# THE ANNUAL
# OF PSYCHOANALYSIS

## A Publication of the Chicago Institute for Psychoanalysis

## Volume XII/XIII

International Universities Press, Inc.
New York        New York

Library of Congress Catalog Number: 72-91376
ISBN: 0-8236-0373-3
Published annually and available in print:
    Vol. I, 1973, Vol. II, 1974, Vol. III, 1975; Vol. IV, 1976; Vol. V, 1977;
    Vol. VI, 1978; Vol. VII, 1979; Vol. VIII, 1980; Vol. IX, 1981, Vol. X, 1982;
    Vol. XI, 1983

Manufactured in the United States of America

With appreciation to Fred M. Hellman, whose generosity makes the publication of *The Annual of Psychoanalysis* possible.

*Heinz Kohut, M.D.*

# CONTENTS

# III

## CLINICAL STUDIES

# IV

## APPLIED PSYCHOANALYSIS

# CONTRIBUTORS

*Michael Franz Basch, M.D.*
Training and Supervising Analyst, Chicago Institute for Psychoanalysis; Professor of Psychiatry, Rush Medical College.

*Christopher Bollas, Ph.D.*
Member of the British Psycho-Analytic Society; Honorary Non-medical Consultant to the Clinic Directorate of the London Clinic of Psycho-Analysis; Visiting Professor Instituto di Neuropsichiatria Infantile, University of Rome.

*Richard D. Chessick, M.D., Ph.D.*
Professor of Psychiatry, Northwestern University; Adjunct Professor of Philosophy, Loyola University of Chicago; Senior Attending Psychiatrist, Evanston Hospital; Corresponding Member, German Psychoanalytic Society.

*Carlton Ferrono*
Graduate Student, Committee on Human Development, University of Chicago.

*Arnold Goldberg, M.D.*
Professor of Psychiatry, Rush Medical College; Training and Supervising Analyst, Chicago Institute for Psychoanalysis.

*Meyer S. Gunther, M.D.*
Training and Supervising Analyst, Chicago Institute for Psychoanalysis.

*John M. Hall, M.D.*
Faculty, Cincinnati Psychoanalytic Institute; Faculty, International Study Center for Psychoanalytic Self Psychology; Assistant Professor of Clinical Psychiatry, University of Cincinnati, College of Medicine.

*Thomas Jobe, M.D.*
Assistant Professor and Associate Director of Residency Training, Department of Psychiatry, College of Medicine, University of Illinois at Chicago.

*Stanley M. Kaplan, M.D.*
Faculty, Cincinnati Psychoanalytic Institute; Professor, Department of Psychiatry, University of Cincinnati, College of Medicine.

*Jerome Kavka, M.D.*
Training and Supervising Analyst, Member of the Psychoanalytic Education Council, Chicago Institute for Psychoanalysis.

*Charles Kligerman, M.D.*
Training and Supervising Analyst, Chicago Institute for Psychoanalysis.

*Lotte Köhler, M.D.*
Training and Supervising Analyst, Munich; Member of the German and Swiss Psychoanalytic Association; Founder, René A. Spitz Society for the Promotion of Psychoanalysis.

*Frank M. Lachmann, Ph.D.*
Faculty Member, Senior Supervisor, and Training Analyst, Postgraduate Center for Mental Health.

*Siegmund Levarie, Ph.D.*
Professor of Music, City University of New York.

*Mark Levey, M.D.*
Instructor, Continuing Education Program, Chicago Institute for Psychoanalysis; Chief, Adult Psychiatric Clinic, Michael Reese Hospital; Clinical Assistant Professor, Pritzker School of Medicine, University of Chicago.

*Jay Martin, Ph.D.*
Research Psychoanalyst, Southern California Psychoanalytic Institute; Leo S. Bing Professor of Literature, University of Southern California; Lecturer, Department of Psychiatry and Human Behavior, University of California, Irvine.

*Arnold H. Modell, M.D.*
Training and Supervisory Analyst, Boston Psychoanalytic Institute; Clinical Professor of Psychiatry, Harvard Medical School; Psychiatrist, Beth Israel Hospital, Boston.

*Pinchas Noy, M.D.*
Training and Supervising Analyst, The Israel Institute of Psychoanalysis; Associate Professor, Department of Behavioral Sciences, Ben-Gurion University of the Negev.

*Anna Ornstein, M.D.*
Professor of Child Psychiatry; Co-Director, International Study Center for Psychoanalytic Self Psychology, University of Cincinnati, College of Medicine.

*Franco Paparo, M.D.*
Senior Consultant Psychiatrist, Mental Health Center RM3; Professor of Child Neuropsychiatry, University of Rome.

*Daphne D. Socarides, M.A.*
Doctoral Candidate in Clinical Psychology, Graduate School of Psychology, Albert Einstein College of Medicine Campus, Yeshiva University.

*Robert D. Stolorow, Ph.D.*
Professor, Graduate School of Psychology, Albert Einstein College of Medicine Campus, Yeshiva University; Training and Supervising Analyst, Institute of the National Psychological Association for Psychoanalysis.

*David M. Terman, M.D.*
Training and Supervising Analyst, Chicago Institute for Psychoanalysis.

*Vamik D. Volkan, M.D.*
Professor of Psychiatry and Director of the Division of Psychoanalytic Studies, University of Virginia Medical School; Medical Director, Blue Ridge Hospital, University of Virginia; Training and Supervising Analyst, Washington Psychoanalytic Institute.

*Jerome A. Winer, M.D.*
Instructor and Faculty Member, Postgraduate Education and Psychotherapy Doctoral Programs, Chicago Institute for Psychoanalysis; Associate Professor of Psychiatry, College of Medicine, University of Illinois at Chicago.

*Ernest S. Wolf, M.D.*
Training and Supervising Analyst, Chicago Institute for Psychoanalysis; Assistant Professor of Psychiatry, Northwestern University Medical School.

# I

# MEMORIAL

# Dedication

When *The Annual of Psychoanalysis* was founded in 1973, and Volume I appeared, the first paper was by Heinz Kohut. This position of primacy was fitting in a real and symbolic sense—for Heinz was, in my view, unquestionably the most seminal and influential psychoanalytic thinker to emerge from the Chicago Institute. An integral member of this group to the end of his life, he went on to make deeply significant contributions to every aspect of psychoanalysis—clinical, theoretical, educational, administrative—and to the broad social and cultural areas of its application. In fact his fundamental work, the development of the Psychology of the Self, not only markedly extended the range of effective psychoanalytic work in the individual but offered a meaningful intrapsychic approach to the problem of Self and Other which opened up new possibilities in the psychoanalytic understanding of society, the humanities, and the arts. That first paper, "Psychoanalysis in a Troubled World," was an expression of a passionate interest that rivaled his investment in his profound clinical contribution.

It is not possible in this brief statement to give an adequate impression of his scientific contribution, his extraordinary cultural range, or the singular charm and nobility of his character. Perhaps the succeeding pages will afford some reflection of this. It is often difficult to reach an accurate perspective on the historical significance of a powerful and creative innovator in one's own time. But it seems clear that Kohut's work, renowned throughout the psychoanalytic world and beyond, his development, out of the classical Freudian matrix, of Self Psychology, which many believe points the future direction of psychoanalysis, places him in the front rank of the few really great and original minds in our field after Freud. With pride and affection, this volume is dedicated to the honor and memory of Heinz Kohut.

CHARLES KLIGERMAN, M.D.

# Memorial for Heinz Kohut, M.D.
## October 31, 1981

Having been asked to speak for all of us who were privileged to be Heinz Kohut's colleagues in the profession of psychoanalysis, I found it difficult, indeed almost impossible, to avoid seeming hyperbolic when writing my tribute to him, for Heinz was the psychoanalyst *par excellence*.

When we were students and Heinz was our teacher, his confident, yet unassuming and always courteous demeanor endeared him to us. His devotion to the field, his grasp of its complexities, and his legendary skill at conveying what he had mastered in understandable form, all won our admiration. One needs ideals, Heinz Kohut filled that need for us.

His seemed to be that rare life in which virtue and excellence went neither unsung nor unrewarded. He did not promote himself; he was sought out by both his elders and his peers. Honor upon honor was thrust upon him—locally, nationally, and internationally. The offices to which he was elected and the positions to which he was appointed were not ceremonial ones; invariably he discharged his duties with distinction.

When in middle life his papers on the psychoanalysis of narcissistic personality disorders were first published, they received, literally, worldwide acclaim as analysts found that what he advocated worked where nothing had worked before. Simply put, Kohut demonstrated that the psychoanalytic method had wider application and greater efficacy than anyone, including Freud, had heretofore suspected. But, illustrious as they are, a recital of his accomplishments will not begin to convey what it meant to be Heinz Kohut's colleague.

A short time after I graduated from the Institute Heinz happened to ask me what I was doing, and I mentioned some papers I had written. He said he would like to see them. I sent them to him, of course, but assumed that he had requested my manuscripts only out of politeness; after all, I was but a raw recruit in an army in which he was a general—that he took notice of me at all was encouragement enough. I should have known better.

Some weeks later he asked me to spend an evening with him, and I found that he had not just read, but had studied my work and knew it as well as if it were his own. We proceeded to spend four or five hours discussing its implications and ramifications in detail to my great benefit. The generosity and wisdom with which Heinz dealt with a beginner's hopes and ambitions affected me deeply and, far beyond the substantive issues we discussed, taught me things that I will never forget about psychoanalysis and what it means to be a psychoanalyst.

This is the experience that always came to my mind when someone who knew his work but did not know Heinz personally asked me "what is he really like?". There is no end to similar stories that so many of us here and elsewhere could tell of Heinz Kohut's readiness to help anyone who took psychoanalysis seriously.

Kohut's dedication to psychoanalysis and his devotion to Freud's vision had always been unquestioned. However, after he published *The Analysis of the Self* it became clear that his clinical findings had theoretical implications which were felt as a threat by those who believe that it is not the psychoanalytic method but, rather, Freud's biological speculations that represent the foundation of psychoanalysis and that these hypotheses are immutable. Heinz always welcomed collegial discussion and scientific debate, but the opposition now mounted against him was only too often played out on a considerably lower and less edifying plane. This distressed but did not deter Heinz, and it is a measure of the man that though he had much to lose, he never compromised or temporized for the sake of expediency, no matter how great the pressure brought to bear upon him.

But Heinz did not dwell on his disappointments; in the main his was an affirmative, joyful, and triumphant life. In the last ten years he maintained an unbroken productivity, writing *The Restoration of the Self*, his just-completed book *How Does Analysis Cure?*, the many papers and addresses with which we are familiar, and the innumerable letters that made up his voluminous correspondence, all the while serving his patients, and of course teaching, always teaching. He lived to see the psychology of the self, his crowning achievement, assured of an ongoing role in the evolution of psychoanalysis.

There can be no doubt that Heinz was one of the great analysts. For years it had been evident that the biological reductionism built into psychoanalytic theory restricted our view of human development, but no one seemed to be able to revise the theory appropriately without abandoning the psychoanalytic method in the process. Heinz succeeded where all others had failed. His insights and their elaboration freed psychoanalysis from the constraints of formula and cant; strengthened and expanded psychoanalysis by showing us the indispensable role of empathy in gathering data required for effective interpretation at all levels of a patient's characterological development. Kohut's discoveries have permanently changed the ambience of the psychoanalytic situation. His findings are by now not just in books, but are so much a part of the warp and woof of the field that those who practice psychoanalysis today and those who will learn to do so in the future cannot help but be influenced for the better by them.

Viewed from the vantage point of the history of science as a whole Heinz Kohut's achievement has significance that goes far beyond even the signal contribution it makes to the practice and theory of psychoanalysis. In the seventeenth century René Descartes came to the conclusion that mind was separate from body, thereby removing religious objection to the scientific study of the latter. Almost three hundred years later Freud captured the mind for science, erasing the boundary between the sacred and the mundane. However, Freud unwittingly incorporated into his theory in the form of psychic determinism and the unequal, foredoomed struggle between instinct and culture, the ecclesiastical concept that man was destined to suffer, condemned now not by an irate God, but by biology, and this time with no hope of redemption. Heinz Kohut brought forward the evidence that the struggle between instinct and civilization is neither bedrock nor inevitable, and that when it does occur it can be corrected. Conceptual advances of this kind have a life of their own and will prevail. Already we see Kohut's ideas about the self and its development being used to reinterpret literature, sociology, philosophy, and history—that will continue. Ultimately, they will affect man's view of his nature and of his destiny, replacing the anticipation of the apocalypse and the yearning for the cataclysm with hope—hope in man and hope for mankind. Heinz Kohut's ideas live—and future generations will be shaped by them. We acknowledge Heinz Kohut as a great psychoanalyst; history will claim him for the ages as one of the great minds of our time.

As for us here assembled, our hearts go out to Betty and to Tom. We mourn the loss of a friend and count it as being our inestimable good fortune to have known and worked with one so brilliant, so dedicated, so courageous. Heinz Kohut, our colleague, and a noble man.

MICHAEL FRANZ BASCH, M.D.

# Memorial for Heinz Kohut, M.D.
## October 31, 1981

I first met Heinz Kohut in the neurology clinic of Billings Hospital in June 1941 on the eve of my medical graduation. I had worked up a case, and in walked the brand new resident to check my findings. He made an instant, indelible impression: medium height, handsome, wavy blondish hair brushed back, European style; stocky, even slightly plump. It was very hot and he was sweating and nervous in the unfamiliar world of a new hospital, but his keen, intelligent blue eyes and firm chin gave him an air of quiet authority that progressively increased along with his zest, as he discussed the case. Here was the essential Kohut: no matter what the stress at the surface, personal or creative, one always felt the calm, unruffled solidity at the core. And he could always rise to the occasion. Any intellectual challenge was an instant inspiration.

This encounter led to a friendship of forty years. I believe Robert Wadsworth, who provides the lovely music we hear today, was his first lasting American friend. I was the second. Heinz and Robert met through the musicologist Siegmund Levarie, Heinz's schoolmate from Vienna, who had preceded him to Chicago and the University.

Later Heinz and I lived on the same floor of the residents' quarters of the Home for Destitute and Crippled Children. He roomed then with Jay McCormick, and was still a neurologist. But on our Sunday walks on the Midway, after the art, the music, Viennese memorabilia, the talk inevitably turned to Freud and psychoanalysis, a subject which poured out of Heinz with irresistible enthusiasm. His idealization of Freud was complete. He also had great admiration for Anna Freud, Heinz Hartmann, and Edward Glover. And of course for his old analyst in Vienna, August Aichhorn, a legendary master of empathy.

When I returned from the war as a psychiatry resident, Heinz beamed, "now you are one of *us*," for he, too, had made the switch. This change caused some feelings of hurt and loss among the professors. Others had

9

made such a move with no great stir, but Heinz was someone special. There was an aura about him, an amalgam of intellect, charm, stability, determination, and something else that promised future significance. He had been expected to be a Mr. Scientist just as later he became Mr. Psychoanalysis. I don't believe his old chief ever forgave him.

Heinz always valued the warm friendship of his colleagues and teachers, and was pained by this reaction. This pain was to be reexperienced much more intensely years later when he introduced self psychology and its significance began to dawn on the analytic community.

But Heinz was indomitable. Never a complainer, he responded philosophically, and now in his true field, he became more zestful than ever. But not provocative. He always respected the defenses of the other doctors, and never derided their psychological blindspots as did Tom Szasz, Lester MacLean, myself, and other brash neophytes. He taught us tolerance and wisdom; he taught me not to interpret slips socially. Heinz could be ebullient and spontaneous, but never impulsive or unkind. And so the warm respect refirmed, and he retained a valued relationship with the University of Chicago for the rest of his life.

When Heinz was appointed Assistant Professor, he was absolutely elated—in a boyish kind of way. The enormous value of such an appointment to a Viennese intellectual cannot be overestimated. He ceremoniously produced a box of photos I had never seen: his parents on their honeymoon in the Piazza San Marco feeding the pigeons; Heinz as a boy with his mother, sturdy and serious; as an adolescent in a swimsuit at a lake in France, etc. He declaimed: "Here are the parents of the future Assistant Professor! Here is the future Assistant Professor at camp in France!" We laughed. In retrospect, I was the mirroring selfobject, privileged to witness one of the really great moments in Heinz's life. I am not sure his reactions to any of the numerous great honors he later won were as ecstatic as this.

He was almost as delighted some months later when he bought his first motorcar. For the first time in the impoverished years since Vienna, he could afford this American luxury—a great triumph. Naturally, we had to go on drives in this precious acquisition. One of the jaunts—to the Brookfield Zoo—often came back to my mind: we had paused to watch some posturing pink flamingos when suddenly a male swooped down on the nearest hen. Heinz frowned with elaborate seriousness: "Let's see if he behaves in a friendly fashion afterward." But the flamingo clumsily flapped his wings and flew off. Heinz shook his head sadly—"Not cultured!" This was intoned with such drollery, I was convulsed.

Later I wondered why this episode stuck with me. Then it dawned on me: this was the quintessential Kohut! First and most palpable, the marvelous sense of humor. It long preceded narcissistic transformation—it was always there. Then another lifelong trait: the conviction that culture consisted not in the moralistic proscription of selfish drives, but in their transformation through ideals. Even in this casual little joke the value system was clear.

Third, it illustrated his empathic immersion in the feelings and needs of others, here jokingly anthropomorphized. His capacity to synthesize a situation, to grasp the essential meaning, and at the same time to see original aspects was most unusual. And in this sense Heinz was always "on." Whether observing the antics of a barber, a waiter, an O'Neill character, he always had some penetrating observation. In some this ability could have become pedantic or boring, but with Heinz it was deft, humorous, and illuminating. Not always humorous: when a nurse habitually swung her keys on the locked ward, Heinz was the only one who noted that this was a cruel reminder to the patients of their incarceration. He was strongly moved by the prisoner scene in *Fidelio*.

Our student days at the Chicago Institute in the forties were spent in the atmosphere of the tensions that led to the departure of Alexander and the subsequent election of Gerhart Piers, then George Pollock, as directors of the Institute. In true Chicago tradition the crisis was weathered without a split, but during the turmoil Heinz was actively courted by both sides, neither of which was slow to recognize his extraordinary qualities. Someone else did too. The then-head social worker of the Institute, Betty Meyer, now Betty Kohut, recalls the first time she saw Heinz: she had sat in on a class of Thomas French, where one Heinz Kohut was presenting a case. She was completely dazzled by the brilliance of his exposition delivered extempore, as he nearly always did. They soon discovered their mutuality and love and in 1948 were married—a truly happy event for everyone, because if two people ever suited each other, it was Betty and Heinz. Both knew it well, spoke of it, and were extremely grateful for having found each other.

The marriage stabilized Heinz. Along with the birth of his son Tom and his Institute graduation, both in 1950, he reached his maturation as a full-fledged psychoanalyst and family man, and now his career rapidly accelerated. He soon became a member of the staff of the Institute and a training analyst. Along with Joan Fleming and Louis Shapiro he helped recast the curriculum in a form that still stands as a model of psychoanalytic education. He taught the core theory sequence for years in a manner that set the standard for every subsequent teacher. When to all this is added a clinical practice, university teaching, administrative duty at the Institute, and deep involvement in the work of the national and international psychoanalytic organizations, one is reminded of Goethe who felt a centrifugal pull in every direction, yet sensed that everything was solidly tied at the core.

At his own core, Heinz had an inner agenda of which few were then aware: while teaching the Hartmann-Kris-Loewenstein ego psychology to which he then adhered, a ferment was taking place that welded together his introspective-empathic method, his studies in creativity, and his extensive analytic experience in problems of narcissism. His soaring creativity led ultimately to the development of the Psychology of the Self, and placed him in the ranks of those scientific thinkers who shake existing paradigms and win world fame.

But I would like to return for a moment to the question of narcissism. It is no secret that Heinz had his full share of this commodity. But then we all do, or if we don't, God help us! In Heinz it was relatively unambivalent, conflict-free. It was the quality that fueled his productive creativity, his charm, his extraordinary energy. In his more exhibitionistic moments, there was a childlike joy that was irresistible. No one ever thought of Heinz as vain. These qualities were too natural a part of his personality. Even in lower-keyed moments Heinz was "on." But again, no one resented his holding center stage, not only because of his charm and humor, but also because of the extraordinary richness of content that poured forth—form and content were intrinsically entwined, leaving indelible impressions. In forty years I can scarcely remember a single conversation of more than a few minutes in which I did not learn something from Heinz.

In large groups, his capacity to talk extempore with clarity, organization, and elegance was remarkable.

This natural and precious *amour-de-soi* had been cramped by certain external influences. The rise of Hitler and the destruction of the idealized Viennese world in which he had become *persona non grata* were tremendous blows to his self-esteem. But another stifling influence came from a most curious source: his own psychoanalytic mentors. A branch of the Chicago group led by Blitzsten had an enormous interest in narcissism and made many important contributions. But despite lip service to the existence of healthy narcissism, they acted in practice as if all narcissism were pathological, a regressive obstacle to the development of object love. One of the favored ways of dealing with the typical narcissistic grandiosity was to adopt a joking, ironic stance that was supposed to kindle the patient's humor, but often slid into sarcasm, ridicule, even mockery. Many patients laughed at themselves dutifully but were really quite hurt. I am sure this stance caused Heinz a good share of pain, although he manfully went along with the rationale, and even tried the technique himself. But something in him rebelled against viewing some of the greatest creations of man as defensive,

and some of the greatest artists as "narcissistic personalities" in the pejor-
ative sense, if they had not attained a rich object love. As we all know, he
ultimately came to see that narcissism and object love have separate lines
of development, that there is a healthy phase-specific narcissism at every
developmental level, and that it becomes pathological when unempathically
responded to. And this recognition was a central determinant of Self Psychology.

I believe this creative achievement ran parallel to an ongoing self-analysis
in the same area, so that simultaneous with the emergence of the work
came an internal resolution and the final consolidation of his cohesive,
creative self. This gave him the added strength that he was soon to need
to withstand both the negative *and* the positive reactions that steadily escalated. Honor and acclaim poured in from all sides. Heinz loved it—he
always loved honors—but he kept an even keel. He had no illusions about
the nature of the overextravagant idealization of both his person and his
ideas by some of his adherents, and was not surprised by the other side of
the coin as well which sometimes brought bitter rejection. On the negative
front he had expected strong criticism from people rigidly entrenched in
the established tradition, but he was not prepared for the personal coolness
and the meanness of the attacks from old friends, and they hurt deeply.
Here, for once, Heinz's empathy failed him; he understood it all intellectually—the threat to narcissistic positions, the rivalrous envy—but he could
not resonate emotionally with the bitter snideness of some respected colleagues, because he himself was so devoid of such feelings. He never showed
a shadow of meanness or pettiness, and never retaliated in kind. With all
his sophistication, some part of him believed in the idealism of his fellow
scientists; he believed that they, like him, would take truth for granted like
an ego function, that they would be men of good will in spite of scientific
differences. Heinz was not a divisive man, and he was distressed by rifts
of this sort. He would go to the greatest lengths compatible with his dignity
to preserve a relationship with someone he valued.

But these painful aspects did not deter Heinz from pursuing the dictates
of his integrity and vision. The coolness and ill-will of former friends are
often the lot of the creative innovator. There were other prices to be paid.
When Heinz embarked on his scientific voyage he knew he had to conserve
himself for the main goal. But his cherished activities were so far-flung,
and the clamor for his time and attention so intense, that it was no easy
task for him to reduce them. Heinz loved to teach, for example, and gave
of himself to younger colleagues and students in a prodigal fashion. He
had difficulty checking himself. Yet he did so systematically, with certain
priorities, and thereby some were offended. Once when I remarked on his

enormous productivity, despite the demands of his analytic work, teaching, and organizational activities, he commented ruefully, "Yes, and do you know what I had to give up? My social life." For Heinz loved conviviality, not in the large groups to which he was often subjected, but in the small dinner parties where his Viennese wit bubbled over. However, this deprivation was mitigated by his extraordinary capacity to extract the maximum enjoyment from every moment in which he was involved. A glass of rare Trockenbeerenauslese, Verdi's *Falstaff*, Schubert or Hugo Wolf sung by Dietrich Fischer-Dieskau, and especially his doughty hikes in the country on his summer work-vacations: in Carmel, or in St. Antonin high in the Grisons in Switzerland. And of course the precious weekends in Wisconsin with Betty and her sister Gretchen Meyer.

Heinz strove to conserve his physical self as a necessary vehicle for the intellectual adventure. Some early adumbrations of his vulnerability led him to stop smoking and to lose weight to a point of such slenderness that no one would have dreamed he was once heavy. He doggedly ran a mile a day on Jackman Field, when running for health was virtually unknown in America. From coast to coast, analysts would remark with awe: Kohut runs a mile a day! It sounds funny now, but at that time it was formidable. In the end, in spite of all his efforts, Kohut's body failed to keep pace with his soaring creative self. I think only his indomitable will kept him going the last couple of years.

Heinz was ready for death. He always had a firm conviction that each person had almost an inborn agenda, a destiny to fulfill; that compared to eternity it mattered little how long one lived, provided one lived up to one's potentialities in pursuing one's ideal. If ever a man completely fulfilled his, it was Heinz. In the last months, when he was so ill, he sometimes wavered a little on two accounts:

(1) that his scientific contribution would not be sufficiently anchored for the future;

(2) that his own precious mental powers would slip.

I am certain he felt reassured on both scores. As for the first, he had developed a staunch following of able and dedicated colleagues, in Chicago and throughout the Western world, both inside and outside of the psychoanalytic family. And he had just witnessed the third of several increasingly successful conferences on the self. He had finished his third book—on the theory of therapy. When the current tensions abate, and his contributions are viewed from a more dispassionate perspective, I am convinced that Self Psychology will be seen as central in the development of psychoanalysis, a natural step after ego psychology and superordinate to it.

As for the second, his mind was sharp and clear to the end. A few days before his death, so ill he could scarcely stand, he delivered a superb half-hour address in his usual style, without notes, to an assembled conference. Then he came home to Chicago, and to familiar old Billings Hospital. The night he died, he actually felt a little better and cheerier, and played a game of Scrabble with Betty. Heinz had indeed fulfilled his own criteria, his destiny, from beginning to end. His essential work was done, he died peacefully, and, I believe, happily, perhaps even prizing that final experience in his characteristic heroic style.

When we lose a man of this great and noble quality, and a very dear friend as well, it is hard not to feel a deep sorrow. But, at a still deeper level, we can all feel a mighty joy in the celebration of a life truly fulfilled. The other side of tragic man is triumphant man, and this was Heinz.

CHARLES KLIGERMAN, M.D.

# II

# THEORETICAL STUDIES

# Transference: The Future of an Illusion

ROBERT D. STOLOROW, Ph.D. (Los Angeles)
and FRANK M. LACHMANN, Ph.D. (New York)

Of the concepts introduced by Freud to illuminate human nature, transference is the most encompassing. It occupies a pivotal position in every aspect of psychoanalysis. It is pictured as the tidal wave of the past that washes over the present, leaving its unmistakable residues. It is invoked to explain bizarre acts of aggression, painful pathological repetitions, and the tender and passionate sides of love and sex. First seen only as a resistance to psychoanalytic treatment, it was later acknowledged as its facilitator as well. Generations of analysts have sought to use transference to distinguish analyzable from nonanalyzable patients. Finally, the concept of transference has been used to disparage cures obtained by nonpsychoanalytic therapies and to excuse failures encountered in psychoanalytic treatments.

Initially, the idea of transference was applied far more modestly. Breuer and Freud (1893–1895) ascribed what we now call transference to a "false connection" made by the patient. They noted that this was both frightening to the patient and a regular occurrence in some analyses, wherein the patient transferred "on to the figure of the physician the distressing ideas which arise from the content of the analysis" (p. 302).

The image of the transference "arising" was consistent with the "archeological" model implicit in much of Freud's psychoanalytic theorizing, a model based on an "assumption that [the] patient knew everything that was of any pathogenic significance" (Bergmann and Hartman, 1976, p. 310). Writing twenty years later, Freud (1913) still conceived of psychoanalysis

This article will also appear in *Psychoanalysis: Future Directions*, ed. J. Reppen, to be published by Lawrence Erlbaum Associates, Inc., Hillsdale, N.J.

19

as a technique whereby one digs into the unconscious and clears ever deeper layers: Psychoanalysis "consists in tracing back one psychological structure to another which preceded it in time and out of which it developed" (p. 183).

The archeological model has retained some hold on the clinical understanding of transference in general. More specifically, the very early notion of a "false connection" has been preserved in considering transference a "distortion" of reality. Other explanations of transference as regression, displacement, and projection, though consistent with a dynamic viewpoint, still retain a residue of the colorful imagery of archeological expeditions. The archeological model shows many of the disadvantages of Freud's energy theory, in that psychological motivations and states are treated as though they were finite, palpable entities. How this has affected our understanding of transference was a central concern leading to this paper.

Bergmann and Hartman (1976) write:

> Following Freud's emphasis on archeology as the model for psychoanalysis, psychoanalysts tended to see their work essentially as a reconstruction of what has once existed and was buried by repression. By contrast, Hartmann (1939) sees the work of interpretation not only, or not even primarily, as that of reconstruction, but rather as the establishment of a new connection, and therefore as a new creation [p. 466].

In contrast with the archeological viewpoint, this emphasis on new connections and new creations within the therapeutic process focuses attention on the contributions of both patient and analyst. Current interest in and attention to the therapeutic alliance (Greenson, 1967), countertransference (Stolorow, Atwood, and Lachmann, 1981), intersubjectivity (Stolorow, Brandchaft, and Atwood, 1983; Atwood and Stolorow, 1984), and the analyst's contribution to the analytic process reflect a shift in psychoanalysis and in scientific thinking in general. How we study a phenomenon affects and alters it.

We turn now to a critical examination of formulations that traditionally have been employed to describe and explain transference.

## Conceptualizations of Transference

### Transference as Regression

The traditional psychoanalytic view of transference as regression was clearly enunciated by Waelder (1956): "Transference may be said to be an attempt of the patient to revive and re-enact, in the analytic situation and in relation to the analyst, situations and phantasies of his childhood. Hence, transference is a regressive process" (p. 367).

A survey of the uses of the term "regression" in psychoanalytic writings (see Arlow and Brenner, 1964) reflects the variety of ways, each with vastly different meanings and implications, in which this concept has been applied. Included are discussions of psychosexual regression, topographic regression, structural regression, genetic regression, etc. These different terms can be assigned to two general uses of the concept—regression as a diminution in the level of psychological organization and regression as retrogression along a time dimension. No doubt archaic modes of psychological organization in adults are related to the psychological organizations found in childhood. However, these archaic modes are not identical with their manifestations and occurrences in the young child. To confine the concept of regression solely to level of structuralization requires fewer unverifiable assumptions. With respect to transference, the concurrent influences of various modes and levels of organization can be addressed, with full recognition of their complex interplay, and with no assumption of a literal retrogression in time.

The assumption that adult relationships in their repetitive and conflictual aspects are isomorphic re-enactments of traumatic relationships from the early history of the individual has enabled analysts to link the current psychopathology, the course of early development including its pathological variations, and the nuances of the patient-analyst relationship, the transference. Careful observations of patients' transferences and inferences based on these have provided analysts with data for reconstructions of specific genetic sequences and for formulating an epigenetic theory. For these assumptions with respect to temporal regression to be verified, it must be demonstrated that inferences about childhood derived from adult analyses can be validated independently and that modes of mental organization characteristic of early childhood are sufficiently similar to archaic modes of organization as they emerge in adult analyses to warrant inferential leaps from one epoch in the life cycle to the other.

Major challenges to the assumption that adult psychopathology reflects temporal regressions to infantile phases of development are found in recent observations of early infancy (Brody, 1982). There is now increasing evidence that the autism of adult schizophrenic patients has no such counterpart in infancy. The postulation of an autistic phase or of an undifferentiated phase is not supported by the accumulating evidence. The adult psychopathology, therefore, cannot be accurately described as a temporal regression to an earlier normal phase (Silverman, in press). Furthermore, when it appears that the autistic adult had suffered from similar states in childhood, regression is again not an appropriate term, since the state had evidently remained present all along.

Consistent with the findings from the infancy literature is the hypothesis that the infant alternates between periods of oneness with its mother, as inferred from synchronous action patterns, and periods of disengagement (Beebe, in press; Stern, 1983). Both of these patterns are characteristic of the young infant; neither is primary or a precondition for the other. When adult psychopathology is characterized by a predominance of dependent clinging to maternal figures, this is often described as a regression to a phase of early infancy—for example, the symbiotic phase. However, prolonged or continuous periods of symbiosis are apparently neither typical nor normative for the infant. Thus, symbioticlike wishes or fantasies may characterize adult motivation and may be related to an early developmental period, but what the adult imagines, yearns for, or enacts is not identical to what is typical of the young child.

The most frequent use of the idea of temporal regression is with respect to psychosexual development. Discussions in which psychopathology is understood as a regression to oral, anal, phallic, or oedipal phases presuppose that the predominant motivational priorities of the patient are identical to those of the child in the earlier phases. There are two questionable assumptions here. The first pertains to the linearity of psychosexual development—the notion that in the adult earlier motivations are normally renounced or relinquished in favor of later ones. It is assumed that maturity requires renunciation and that, indeed, such renunciation is possible. The concept of temporal regression, therefore, implies a failure in renunciation. The second questionable assumption is that an adult whose motivations are dominated by psychosexual wishes and conflicts must be functioning like a child who is traversing the corresponding psychosexual phases.

Restricting the concept of regression to the level of psychological organization clarifies its relevance for the transference. Analysts are thereby alerted to the possibility that higher levels of organization, which include objectivity, perspective, humor, wisdom, and differentiation between self and other, though not in evidence, can potentially be revived or achieved. Analysts can also then better assess whether more archaic organizations had previously been prematurely aborted, precluded, or disavowed, so that their emergence in treatment is a developmental achievement (Stolorow and Lachmann, 1980), or whether they serve to ward off other material. In all cases, the analytic stance toward the emergence of archaic modes of organization should be to promote their integration with other, more mature modes, thereby enriching psychological functioning, rather than to insist on their renunciation or elimination.

Included in the concept of structural regression are both defensive re-vivals of archaic states and the emergence in treatment of arrested aspects of early developmental phases. In neither case can the patient be said to have actually retrogressed to an infantile period. We can only say that the patient's experiences, especially of the analytic relationship, are being shaped by archaic organizing principles, either for the purpose of defense, or in order to resume a developmental process that had become stalled.

## TRANSFERENCE AS DISPLACEMENT

The repetition compulsion and displacement are two closely related con-cepts frequently invoked to explain the occurrence of transference. To Freud (1920), the repetition compulsion, a biologically inherent attribute of living matter, provided an explanation for the ubiquity of transference phenomena. We will consider the issue of repetition in later sections. Dis-placement initially referred to a mechanism of the dream-work (Freud, 1900) and neurotic symptom formation (Freud, 1916–1917). According to Nunberg (1951), the patient "displaces emotions belonging to an uncon-scious representation of a repressed object to a mental representation of an object of the external world" (p. 1).

Assumed within this concept of displacement is Freud's economic the-ory—a cathexis being pushed along an associative path from an idea of greater emotional intensity to a more distant one of lesser intensity, from a place where discharge is conflictual and blocked to a place where dis-charge is possible. For example, hostility initially directed unconsciously toward the same-sexed parent in childhood may be displaced to a superior at work. The presumed repetitive reliving of the past in the present neither improves one's current life nor alters one's perspective on or memories of the past. On the contrary, such reliving of the past in displaced form is believed to perpetuate the archaic configuration, until it becomes engaged in the analytic transference and can be interpreted.

In our view of transference, there is nothing that is *removed* from the past and attached to the current situation. It is true that the organization of the transference gives the analyst a glimpse of what a childhood relationship was like or what the patient wished or feared it could have been like. However, this insight into the patient's early history is possible not because an idea from the past has been displaced to the present, but because the structures that were organized in the past either continue to be functionally effective or remain available for periodic mobilization. That is, these themes have either remained overtly salient throughout the patient's life prior to the beginning of treatment or have been providing a more subtle back-ground organization which the analytic process has brought to the fore.

The concept of transference as displacement has perpetuated the view that the patient's experience of the analytic relationship is solely a product of the patient's past and psychopathology and has not been determined by the activity (or nonactivity) of the analyst. This viewpoint is consistent with Freud's archeological metaphor. In neglecting the contribution of the analyst to the transference, it contains certain pitfalls. Suppose an archeologist unknowingly dropped a wristwatch into a dig. If the assumption is made that anything found in the dig must have been there beforehand, some woefully unwarranted conclusions would be reached.

TRANSFERENCE AS PROJECTION

Analysts who draw upon the theoretical ideas of Melanie Klein tend to conceptualize transference as a manifestation of the mechanism of projection. Racker (1954), for example, viewed transference as the projection of rejecting internal objects upon the analyst, whereby internal conflicts become converted into external ones. Similarly, Kernberg (1975) attributes certain archaic transference reactions to the operation of "projective identification," a primitive form of projection whose main purpose is to externalize all-bad, aggressive self and object images.

We define projection as a defensive process in which an aspect of one's self is excluded from awareness by being attributed to an external object, in order to alleviate conflict and avoid danger. To view transference phenomena solely or primarily as defensive externalizations confines the explanation of transference to only one of its many possible functions and can lead to a serious neglect of its other dimensions and multiple meanings. Once the transference is established, projection may or may not emerge as a component, depending on the extent of its prominence as a characteristic mode of defense against the subjective dangers experienced at any particular juncture.

A particular difficulty with formulations of transference as an expression of projection is that they often obscure the developmental dimension of the transference. As we have stressed elsewhere (Stolorow and Lachmann, 1980, chap. 6), projection as a defense actively employed to ward off conflict can come into play only after a minimum of self-object differentiation has been reliably achieved. Defensive translocation of mental content across self-object boundaries requires that those boundaries have been partially consolidated. When states of confusion between self and object occur in the context of an archaic transference configuration, this developmental achievement in self-boundary formation cannot be presupposed. Such archaic transference states are most often best understood not as manifestations of projective mechanisms, but rather as remnants of developmental arrests at early modes of experience in which self and object are incompletely distinguished.

## TRANSFERENCE AS DISTORTION

Implicit in the conceptions of transference discussed so far (as temporal regression, displacement, or projection) is the idea that transference involves a distortion of "reality," as the relationship with the analyst becomes cast in images from the patient's unconscious infantile past or infiltrated by the patient's endopsychic world of internal object relations. This idea was made explicit in Sullivan's (1953) concept of "parataxic distortion," a process by which a present relationship is presumed to be "warped" by earlier ones. Certain Freudian authors, too (e.g., Stein, 1966), have stated more or less directly that the goal of analysis is to correct the patient's distortions of what the analyst "knows" to be objectively real.

In another context (Stolorow and Lachmann, 1980, chap. 9), we have cautioned against certain dangers embedded in the concept of a "real" relationship between analyst and patient, of which the transference is presumed to be a distortion. Such dangers lie in the fact that judgments about what is "really true" about the analyst and what is distortion of that "truth" are ordinarily left solely to the discretion of the analyst—hardly a disinterested party. We find that therapists often invoke the concept of distortion when the patient's feelings, whether denigrating or admiring, contradict self-perceptions and expectations that the therapist requires for his own well-being.

Gill (1982), whose views on this subject we find compatible with our own, criticizes the concept of transference as distortion because it implies "that the patient is manufacturing his experience out of whole cloth" (p. 117). "A more accurate formulation than 'distortion,' " Gill argues, "is that the real situation is subject to interpretations other than the one the patient has reached . . . Indeed," he continues, "seeing the issue in this way rather than as a 'distortion' helps prevent the error of assuming some absolute external reality of which the 'true' knowledge must be gained" (p. 118). In a similar vein, Schwaber (1983) objects to the notion of transference as distortion because of its embeddedness in "a hierarchically ordered two-reality view" (p. 383)—one reality experienced by the patient and the other "known" by the analyst to be more objectively true.

Transference, fully established, is a sampling of psychic reality in purest culture. As such, it belongs to what Winnicott (1951) called "the realm of illusion," an "intermediate area of experience, *unchallenged in respect of its belonging to inner or external reality . . ."* (p. 242; emphasis added). A prime example of this respect for illusory experience is the attuned parent's attitude toward a child's transitional object. "It is a matter of agreement between us and the baby," Winnicott wrote, "that *we will never ask the question* 'Did you conceive of this or was it presented to you from without?' The important point is that no decision on this point is expected. The question is not to be formulated" (pp. 239–240; emphasis added). One could scarcely find a better description of the proper analytic (i.e., neutral) attitude for facilitating the unfolding and illumination of the patient's transference experience.

## TRANSFERENCE AS ORGANIZING ACTIVITY: A REFORMULATION

In our view, the concept of transference may be understood to refer to all the ways in which the patient's experience of the analytic relationship is shaped by his own psychological structures—by the distinctive, archaically rooted configurations of self and object that unconsciously organize his subjective universe (Stolorow, Atwood, and Ross, 1978). Thus transference, at the most general level of abstraction, is an instance of *organizing activity*—the patient *assimilates* (Piaget, 1954) the analytic relationship into the thematic structures of his personal subjective world. The transference is actually a microcosm of the patient's total psychological life, and the analysis of the transference provides a focal point around which the patterns dominating his existence as a whole can be clarified, understood, and thereby transformed.

From this perspective, transference is neither a regression to nor a displacement from the past, but rather an expression of the *continuing influence* of organizing principles and imagery that crystallized out of the patient's early formative experiences. Transference in its essence is not a product of defensive projection, although defensive aims and processes (including projection) certainly can and do contribute to its vicissitudes. The concept of transference as organizing activity does not imply that the patient's perceptions of the analytic relationship distort some more objectively true reality. Instead, it illuminates the specific shaping of these perceptions by the structures of meaning into which the analyst and his actions become assimilated.

The concept of transference as organizing activity offers an important clinical advantage over the other formulations in that it explicitly invites attention to both the patient's psychological structures and the input from the analyst that they assimilate (Wachtel, 1980). As Gill (1982) repeatedly observes, it is essential to the analysis of transference reactions to examine in detail the events occurring within the analytic situation that evoke them. The transference reactions become intelligible through comprehending the *meanings* that these events acquire by virtue of their assimilation by the patient's subjective frame of reference—by the affect-laden, archaically determined configurations of self and object that pervade his psychological life.

Another advantage of the concept of transference as organizing activity is that it is sufficiently general and inclusive to embrace the multiplicity of its dimensions, the subject to which we now turn.

## Dimensions of the Transference

### THE MULTIPLE FUNCTIONS OF TRANSFERENCE

We have suggested a reformulation of the concept of transference from one which was encumbered by the psychoeconomic viewpoint and an outdated archeological metaphor to one which emphasizes the psychological process of organizing current experience. This process occurs through the continual confluence of present events and previously formed psychological structures. Thus, what shapes an experience of a current situation, including the analytic situation, is derived from a multitude of sources in the person's history, as well as from properties of the current situation and the meanings into which these are assimilated. Transference must therefore be understood from a multidimensional perspective, on the assumption that a multiplicity of thematic structures and levels of psychological organization will have been mobilized by the analysis. Different dimensions of the transference will become salient at different points in the analysis.

The concept of transference as organizing activity is an alternative to the view that transference is the manifestation of a biologically rooted compulsion to repeat the past. In addition, transference as organizing activity focuses more narrowly on the specific patterning of experience within the analytic relationship, to which both patient and analyst contribute. Thus we have used the term in two ways. As a higher-order, supraordinate psychological principle it replaces the biological repetition compulsion. Transference is conceived, not as a biologically determined tendency to repeat the past, ad infinitum, for its own sake, but rather as the expression of a universal psychological striving to organize experience and construct meanings.

Within the narrower focus on the shaping of the analytic relationship, the transference can subserve the entire gamut of psychological functions that have been illuminated by clinical psychoanalysis. The organization of the transference can (1) fulfill cherished wishes and urgent desires, (2) provide moral restraint and self-punishment, (3) aid adaptation to difficult realities, (4) maintain or restore precarious, disintegration-prone self and object imagoes, and (5) defensively ward off configurations of experience that are felt to be conflictual or dangerous. Viewing the transference in terms of its multiple functions enables the analyst to examine, without prejudice, what is most salient in the patient's motivational hierarchy at any particular juncture.

## THE RELATIONSHIP OF TRANSFERENCE TO RESISTANCE

The relationship of transference to resistance is a complex one and has been the source of disagreements among analysts since Freud's early papers on the subject. Both Racker (1954) and Gill (1982) have pointed out that embedded in Freud's writings on transference and resistance are two distinct and contradictory theoretical models of the relationship between them. Racker's (1954) discussion of these two different viewpoints deserves quotation at some length:

> [In the first view the transference] is regarded and interpreted as a resistance to the work of remembrance, and is utilized as an instrument for remembering, but [in the second] the transference is itself regarded as the decisive field in which the work is to be accomplished. The primary aim is, in the first case, remembering; in the second, it is re-experiencing [p. 75].

> The two points of view may also be said to differ in that in the former transference is regarded predominantly as arising from resistance, whereas in the latter resistance is mainly a product of transference. In the first, the analysand repeats so as not to remember; in the second, he repeats defences (resistances) so as not to repeat traumatic or anxious experiences [pp. 75–76].

The first model of the relationship between transference and resistance, in which repetition is a defense against remembering, is a relic of Freud's archeological metaphor for the analytic process. As such, it should be abandoned as a theoretical and therapeutic anachronism. The second model, in which the experience of transference is central to the analytic process (Strachey, 1934; Gill, 1982), is compatible with our own conception of the transference as equivalent to the patient's organizing activity and as a microcosm providing therapeutic access to the patient's psychological world and history.

From this latter perspective, what is the relationship of transference to resistance? Gill (1982), embracing as we do Freud's second model of this relationship, claims that "all resistance manifests itself by way of transference" (p. 29) and that "the analysis of resistance is in effect the analysis of transference" (p. 39). He then proposes two broad categories of relationship between transference and resistance: resistance to the transference and resistance to the resolution of the transference. Resistance to the transference is further subdivided into resistance to the awareness of transference, as when transference feelings must be inferred from allusions to them in extratransference material, and resistance to involvement in transference.

Kohut (1971) also discussed resistance to involvement in transference, specifically describing resistances to involvement in archaic idealizing and mirror transferences. Such resistance, triggered by disintegration anxiety and the need to preserve a fragmentation-prone self, was seen by Kohut to arise from two sources. First, the patient may resist involvement in the transference for fear that his emerging archaic needs will meet with traumatic disappointments, rejections, and deprivations similar to those he had experienced as a child. Second, the patient may resist the transference, sensing his own structural vulnerabilities, as when a need for merger is fended off for fear of the extinction of individual selfhood.

An important implication of Kohut's over-all viewpoint for the analysis of resistance to involvement in transference is that such resistance cannot be viewed solely in terms of isolated intrapsychic mechanisms located within the patient. Resistance to the transference based on "the dread to repeat" (Ornstein, 1974) past traumas is always to some extent evoked by actions of the analyst that the patient experiences as unattuned to his emerging needs. Such "empathic failures" invariably trigger resistance because for the patient they signal the impending recurrence of traumatically damaging childhood experiences. Since resistance to involvement in transference is in part a product of the patient's organizing activity, it is actually already an expression of the transference.

Gill's second broad category of relationship between transference and resistance—resistance to the resolution of the transference—seems to us to embody an assumption that analysis seeks to enable the patient to "renounce" infantile fixations as these are worked through in the transference, and that this goal of renunciation engenders resistance. In a later section we shall present our objections to this notion that transference is to be resolved or renounced. In the present context we wish to stress that, in our view, the persistence of transference is not primarily the product of resistance. It is the result of the continuing influence of established organizing principles when alternative modes of experiencing the self and object world have not yet evolved or become sufficiently consolidated. We would thus replace Gill's "resistance to the resolution of the transference" with the concept of *resistance based on transference*. This would encompass all of the anticipated dangers and resulting constrictions of the patient's psychological life that appear in direct consequence of the transference having become firmly established, including those forfeitures of self-experience that the patient believes are necessary to maintain the analytic relationship.

## THE DEVELOPMENTAL DIMENSION OF TRANSFERENCE

Recent advances in psychoanalytic developmental psychology have highlighted the central importance of developmental transformations in the child's organizing activity, leading to the progressive articulation, differentiation, integration, and consolidation of the subjective world. The conception of transference as organizing activity can encompass this developmental dimension as an aspect of the analytic relationship in a way that earlier concepts of transference cannot. We refer to instances in which the patient seeks to establish with the analyst a nexus of archaic relatedness in which aborted structuralization processes can be resumed and arrested psychological growth can be completed. In our earlier work (Stolorow and Lachmann, 1980, chap. 9), we termed such instances "prestages" of transference, as distinguished from its more classical form in which consolidation of the subjective world is presupposed.

A major contribution to our understanding of the developmental aspect of transference was Kohut's (1971, 1977) formulation of the "selfobject transferences," wherein the patient attempts to re-establish with the analyst the idealizing and mirroring ties that had been traumatically and phase-inappropriately ruptured during the formative years, and upon which he comes to rely once again for the restoration and maintenance of the sense of self. We have come to believe that it has been a conceptual error to consider the term "selfobject transference" (or prestages of transference) to refer to a *type* of transference characteristic of a certain type of patient. Instead, we now use the phrase "selfobject transference" to refer to a *dimension* of *all* transference, which may fluctuate in the extent to which it occupies a position of figure or ground in the patient's experience of the analytic relationship (see Stolorow, Brandchaft, and Atwood, 1983). Kohut's work has illuminated the unique therapeutic importance of understanding and transforming those transference configurations in which the selfobject dimension is figure—in which, that is, the restoration or maintenance of self-organization is the paramount psychological purpose motivating the patient's specific tie to the analyst. Even when this is not the case, however, and other dimensions of experience and human motivation—such as conflicts over loving, hating, desiring, and competing—emerge as most salient in structuring the transference, the selfobject dimension is never absent. So long as it is undisturbed, it operates silently in the background, enabling the patient to confront frightening feelings and painful dilemmas.

An important implication of this conceptualization is that the analyst must continually assess the often subtly shifting figure-ground relationships among the selfobject and other dimensions of the transference that occur throughout the course of treatment. The assessment of what dimensions and psychological functions constitute figure and what constitute ground at any particular juncture of the analysis will directly determine the content and timing of transference interpretations (see Stolorow and Lachmann, 1980, chap. 9, and Stolorow and Lachmann, 1981).

A second implication of this conceptualization is that the selfobject or developmental dimension of transference must be included in any effort to delineate the process of cure in psychoanalysis. We shall return to this issue in a later section.

## Transference and the Therapeutic Process

### THE ANALYST'S CONTRIBUTION TO THE TRANSFERENCE

While a review of the voluminous literature on the role of the transference in the therapeutic relationship would take us beyond the intentions of this paper, two broadly contrasting positions can be outlined. On the one hand, transference has been understood as emanating entirely from the patient. The belief, implicit in the archeological model, that the patient makes a "false connection" or engages in "distortion" exemplifies this position. The analyst who adheres to this view will exercise care lest the transference become "contaminated." The recommendation that the analyst must avoid offering any gratification of the patient's infantile wishes will be strictly followed, so that these "frustrated" wishes can then emerge from repression and gain verbal expression. Abstinence is equated here with neutrality, on the assumption that the active frustration of the patient's wishes and needs constitutes a "neutral" act that neither colors the transference nor affects how these wishes and needs become manifest in the therapeutic relationship. Even Strachey's (1934) oft-quoted position that only transference interpretations are mutative is consistent with this viewpoint, because it implies that nontransference interpretations and other behaviors of the analyst will not alter the transference neurosis.

It is our view, by contrast, that any action, nonaction, or restrained action of the analyst can affect the transference on a variety of levels of psychological organization, according to its meanings for the patient. Furthermore, the analyst's attitudes and responses will influence which dimensions of the transference predominate at any given time. The relentlessly abstinent analyst, for example, who believes that the patient's infantile wishes must be exposed and renounced, will obstruct the developmental or self-object dimension of the transference, and may in addition evoke intense conflicts over primitive hostility—an artifact of the therapeutic stance (Wolf, 1976). On the other hand, the analyst who strives actually to fulfill the patient's archaic needs may impede the development of more advanced modes of organization in the transference.

A second position, which arose in opposition to the view that transference is derived solely from the psychology of the patient, recommends that the analyst acknowledge his "actual" contribution to the transference. A typical example might involve a patient who reveals that he felt the analyst was angry with him during the prior session. An analyst who adheres to this second position might privately review the events of the previous session and determine for himself whether, indeed, he may have directly or indirectly conveyed annoyance to the patient. He might then acknowledge the "reality" of the patient's perception and then proceed to analyze the patient's reactions.

A disadvantage of the first position is that it requires the patient to relinquish his organizing principles and psychic reality in favor of the analyst's. We object to the second view because, like the first, it places the analyst in the position of evaluating the veracity of the patient's perceptions, and the patient's experience is validated only because it coincides with that of the analyst. At its worst, this approach can tip the therapeutic balance in the direction of making the analyst's "reality" an explanation for the patient's reactions. The danger here lies in endowing the patient's perceptions with "truth" and "reality," not through the analytic process, but through the analyst's confirmations.

Our own view is different from each of the two positions described above. When transference is conceptualized as organizing activity, it is assumed that the patient's experience of the therapeutic relationship is always shaped by *both* inputs from the analyst and the structures of meaning into which these are assimilated by the patient. We therefore make a sharp distinction between the concept of abstinence, a relic of drive theory, and the analytic principle of neutrality. The latter we define as an attitude of inquiry which seeks understanding of the patient's expressions from within the perspective of the patient's subjective frame of reference. From this neutral vantage point, the actuality of the patient's perceptions of the analyst is neither debated nor confirmed. Instead, these perceptions serve as points of departure for an exploration of the meanings and organizing principles that structure the patient's psychic reality.

This investigatory stance will itself have an impact on the transference. The patient's feeling of being understood, for example, can revive archaic oneness or merger experiences, which in turn may produce therapeutic effects (Silverman, Lachmann, and Milich, 1982). This brings us once again to the developmental dimension of the transference and its therapeutic action.

## TRANSFERENCE CURES

An understanding of the developmental or selfobject dimension of the transference sheds new light on the role of transference in the process of psychoanalytic cure. Once established, the selfobject dimension of the transference is experienced to some degree by the patient as a "holding environment" (Winnicott, 1965), an archaic facilitating context reinstating developmental processes of psychological differentiation and integration that had been aborted and arrested during the patient's early formative years (Stolorow and Lachmann, 1980, chap. 9). Thus, when protected from protracted disruptions, the transference bond in and of itself can directly promote a process of psychological growth and structure formation. In our view, therefore, the singular importance of analyzing the patient's experiences of ruptures in the transference bond may not lie solely or even primarily in the transmuting internalizations that are thought to result (Kohut, 1971). Rather, the therapeutic action of such analysis may derive primarily from its impact in consistently mending the broken archaic tie and thereby permitting the arrested developmental process to resume once again.

We are contending that it is the transference, especially in its developmental or selfobject dimension, that lends to interpretations their *mutative* power. Consider, for example, the transference context in which a traditional resistance analysis takes place (see Stolorow, Brandchaft, and Atwood, 1983). Experienced analysts know that clarifying the nature of a patient's resistance has no discernible therapeutic result unless the analyst is also able to identify the subjective danger or emotional conflict that makes the resistance a felt necessity. It is only when the analyst shows that he knows the patient's fear and anguish and thereby becomes established to some degree as a calming, containing, idealized selfobject—a *new* object separate and distinct from the dreaded parental imagoes—that conflictual regions of the patient's subjective life can emerge more freely.

The term "transference cure" has traditionally been applied pejoratively to indicate that a patient has "recovered" because of the unanalyzed influence of an unconscious instinctual tie to the analyst. What we are stressing here, in contrast, is the ubiquitous curative role played by the silent, at times unanalyzed selfobject dimension of the transference. We hold that every mutative therapeutic moment, even when based on interpretation of resistance and conflict, includes a significant element of selfobject transference cure.

RESOLUTION OF TRANSFERENCE

What is the ultimate fate of the transference in a successful psychoanalysis? Various authors have recommended that in the termination phase of an analysis the transference (especially the positive transference) must be resolved or dissolved through interpretation. Usually this means that the infantile wishes toward the analyst must be renounced.

The analytic relationship is a peculiar one in many respects. It is unique in that it is formed for a specific purpose—a therapeutic purpose for one of the participants. The requirement that it should end without residual transference feelings remaining seems to us to be unwarranted. Indeed, attempts to eliminate all traces of the transferences that have evolved in the course of analysis can adversely affect and even derail an otherwise successful treatment. Often it is believed that the transference must be dissolved for the sake of the patient's autonomy and that any residual transference feelings would constitute an infantilizing element, potentially undermining independence and object choices. In contrast, when transference is viewed as an expression of a universal human organizing tendency, analysis aims not for renunciation, but rather for the acceptance and integration of the transference experience into the fabric of the patient's analytically expanded psychological organization. The transference, thus integrated, greatly enriches the patient's affective life and contributes a repertoire of therapeutically achieved developmental attainments.

With regard to so-called infantile wishes, needs, and fantasies, it has never been adequately demonstrated that they can or should be renounced. Within an expanded and more evolved psychological organization, they can be welcomed, just as any valued possession can find a place on the mantelpiece, to be used on special occasions. The remaining love and hate for the analyst, including their archaic roots, can thus be acknowledged and accepted, without their having either to be requited or negated, or presumed to constitute an interference with the patient's current living. Ordinarily, after treatment has ended, the residual analytic transference will gradually recede from its pre-eminent position, relatively central in the patient's psychological world, to a position where it serves as a bridge to a more complex, differentiated, and richly experienced life.

## Conclusion

The future of transference analysis lies in the concept of organizing activity. According to this viewpoint, transference in its essence refers neither to regression, displacement, projection, nor distortion, but rather to the assimilation of the analytic relationship into the thematic structures of the patient's personal subjective world. Thus conceived, transference is an expression of the universal psychological striving to organize experience and create meanings. This broad conceptualization of transference holds numerous advantages over earlier ones. It can encompass the multiple dimensions of transference, including especially its developmental dimension, and it sheds light on the relationship of transference to resistance. It clarifies the contributions of both analyst and patient in shaping the patient's experience of the therapeutic relationship. It illuminates the role of the transference in the process of psychoanalytic cure and in the patient's life after analysis is completed. Most importantly of all, the concept of transference as organizing activity, by encouraging an unwavering inquiry into the patient's subjective frame of reference, opens a clear and unobstructed window to the patient's psychological world, and to its expansion, evolution, and enrichment.

## REFERENCES

Arlow, J. & Brenner, C. (1964), *Psychoanalytic Concepts and the Structural Theory*. New York: International Universities Press.
Atwood, G. & Stolorow, R. (1984), *Structures of Subjectivity: Explorations in Psychoanalytic Phenomenology*. Hillsdale, N.J.: Analytic Press.
Beebe, B. (in press), Mother-infant mutual influence and precursors of self and object representations. In: *Empirical Studies of Psychoanalytic Theories*, ed. J. Masling, vol. 2. Hillsdale, N.J.: Erlbaum.
Bergmann, M. & Hartman, F. (1976), *The Evolution of Psychoanalytic Technique*. New York: Basic Books.
Breuer, J. & Freud, S. (1893–1895), Studies on Hysteria. *Standard Edition*, 2. London: Hogarth Press, 1951.
Brody, S. (1982), Psychoanalytic theories of infant development and its disturbances: A Critical evaluation. *Psychoanal. Quart.*, 51:526–597.
Freud, S. (1900), The Interpretation of Dreams. *Standard Edition*, 4 & 5. London: Hogarth Press, 1953.
———— (1913), The Claims of psycho-analysis to scientific interest. *Standard Edition*, 13:165–190. London: Hogarth Press, 1955.

———— (1916–1917), Introductory lectures on psycho-analysis. *Standard Edition*, 15 & 16. London: Hogarth Press, 1963.
———— (1920), Beyond the pleasure principle. *Standard Edition*, 18:3–64. London: Hogarth Press, 1955.
Gill, M. (1982), Analysis of Transference, vol. 1. *Psychological Issues*, Monogr. 53. New York: International Universities Press.
Greenson, R. (1967), *The Technique and Practice of Psychoanalysis*. New York: International Universities Press.
Hartmann, H. (1939), *Ego Psychology and the Problem of Adaptation*. New York: International Universities Press, 1958.
Kernberg, O. (1975), *Borderline Conditions and Pathological Narcissism*. New York: Aronson.
Kohut, H. (1971), *The Analysis of the Self*. New York: International Universities Press.
———— (1977), *The Restoration of the Self*. New York: International Universities Press.
Nunberg, H. (1951), Transference and reality. *Internat. J. Psycho-Anal.*, 32:1–9.
Ornstein, A. (1974), The dread to repeat and the new beginning: A contribution to the psychoanalysis of the narcissistic personality disorders. *This Annual*, 2:231–248. New York: International Universities Press.
Piaget, J. (1954), *The Construction of Reality in the Child*. New York: Basic Books.
Racker, H. (1954), Considerations on the theory of transference. In: *Transference and Countertransference*. London: Hogarth Press, 1968, pp. 71–78.
Schwaber, E. (1983), Psychoanalytic listening and psychic reality. *Internat. Rev. Psycho-Anal.*, 10:379–392.
Silverman, D. (in press), Some proposed modifications of psychoanalytic theories of early childhood development. In: *Empirical Studies of Psychoanalytic Theories*, ed. J. Masling, vol. a. Hillsdale, N.J.: Erlbaum.
Silverman, L., Lachmann, F., & Milich, R. (1982), *The Search for Oneness*. New York: International Universities Press.
Stein, M. (1966), Self-observation, reality, and the superego. In: *Psychoanalysis—A General Psychology*, ed. R. Loewenstein. New York: International Universities Press, pp. 275–297.
Stern, D. (1983), The early development of schemas of self, of other, and of various experiences of "self with other." In: *Reflections on Self Psychology*, ed. J. Lichtenberg & S. Kaplan. Hillsdale, N.J.: Analytic Press.
Stolorow, R., Atwood, G., & Lachmann, F. (1981), Transference and countertransference in the analysis of developmental arrests. *Bull. Menninger Clin.*, 45:20–28.
———— ———— & Ross, J. (1978), The representational world in psychoanalytic therapy. *Internat. Rev. Psycho-Anal.*, 5:247–356.
———— Brandchaft, B., & Atwood, G. (1983), Intersubjectivity in psychoanalytic treatment: With special reference to archaic states. *Bull. Menninger Clin.*, 47:117–128.
———— Lachmann, F. (1980), *Psychoanalysis of Developmental Arrests: Theory and Treatment*. New York: International Universities Press.
———— ———— (1981), Two psychoanalyses or one? *Psychoanal. Rev.*, 68:307–319.
Strachey, J. (1934), The nature of the therapeutic action of psychoanalysis. *Internat. J. Psycho-Anal.*, 15:127–159.
Sullivan, H. S. (1953), *The Interpersonal Theory of Psychiatry*. New York: Norton.
Wachtel, P. (1980), Transference, schema, and assimilation: The relevance of Piaget to the psychoanalytic theory of transference. *This Annual*, 8:59–76. New York: International Universities Press.
Waelder, R. (1956), Introduction to the discussion on problems of transference. *Internat. J. Psycho-Anal.*, 37:367–368.
Winnicott, D. (1951), Transitional objects and transitional phenomena. In: *Through Paediatrics to Psycho-Analysis*. New York: Basic Books, 1975, pp. 229–242.

———— (1965), *The Maturational Processes and the Facilitating Environment*. New York: International Universities Press.
Wolf, E. (1976), Ambience and abstinence. *This Annual*, 4:101–115. New York: International Universities Press.

*April 1983*

# On Selfobject Countertransference

## LOTTE KÖHLER, M.D. (Munich)

That Heinz Kohut opened up new fields of understanding in psychoanalysis with the concept of selfobject has been recognized by both advocates and critics of the psychology of the self. In *The Analysis of the Self* Kohut (1971) not only defined the concept of the selfobject transference but went on to delineate the countertransference that may be mobilized in the analyst as a result of the selfobject transference. In his work with Ernest Wolf (Kohut and Wolf, 1978) these concepts were expanded. Wolf (1979) suggested that in analogy to the differentiation between object-instinctual transferences and selfobject transferences, one should also differentiate countertransferences in which the analyst falls in love with or competes with his patient from *selfobject countertransferences* in which the analyst experiences the patient as a part of his self.

It is my view that our growing understanding of the dynamics of the infant-caregiver relationship and of the patient-analyst relationship can be enriched by our recognition of these transferences and countertransferences. This paper is an attempt at such an application. It should be regarded as an opening exploration, one which, it is hoped, will stimulate further investigation and intellectual exchange.

## Prototypes of Countertransference in the Relation of Child and Caregiver

Psychic development is no longer studied by considering the growing infant as an isolated individual. The interaction between child and caregiver is

This paper is dedicated to the memory of Heinz Kohut, M.D. It was translated from the German by Daniel Niederland.

39

conceived of as an *indivisible system* in the process of growth and differentiation. Investigations such as *The Effect of the Infant on Its Caregiver* (Lewis and Rosenblum, 1974) are examples of this approach. Further studies deal with reciprocal rhythms, feed-forward and feed-back cycles, and organizing mechanisms between child and caregiver (for example, Brazelton and Als, 1979). Of special importance in this context is the work of Louis W. Sander and his colleagues (1962, 1975), who consistently observed the "mother-child system" and described the development of the child's self-organizing core within this matrix.

The basis of Sander's theory is that every living organism is actively self-regulating and at the same time exists in intimate exchange with its life-supporting environment. In his view, neither the self-regulating individual nor the influences coming from its environment can be considered separately. As Sander writes (1975), "The content of behavior must be accounted for in a specific context" (p. 135). The mother, with her individual personality, and the child, with its innate qualities, form a system in which certain regulations and mutual adaptations develop. The regulative equilibrium of the mother-child system is disturbed by the maturing processes of the child. This necessitates a new adaptation by the mother as well as by the child on a more complex and more differentiated level. Sander described a series of seven characteristic "issues" which are negotiated between mother and child in the first 36 months of the child's life and which lead to the development of the child's self-organizing core. As illustrations, I would like to discuss briefly the first three issues formulated by Sander. They show quite clearly that the child triggers emotional impulses in the mother which affect her attitude and behavior toward her child. Prototypes of countertransferences aroused in the analyst by the patient can be seen to a certain extent here. Because the mother emotionally still experiences her child as a part of her self, i.e., as a selfobject, during the child's first months of life, the mutual exchanges in this early phase are particularly relevant to the understanding of selfobject countertransference.[1]

ISSUE I: BASIC REGULATION (FIRST THREE MONTHS OF LIFE)

The first issue is the establishment of certain basic regularities and rhythms to which mother and child become accustomed, such as the circadian sleep-wake rhythm, the nursing cycle, or regular procedures such as bathing or diapering. If this is done successfully, a certain periodicity of the child's different states will be achieved, whereby the child attains a first level of coordination in its multiple physiological subsystems.

[1] This does not mean, of course, that there would not also be selfobject countertransferences on the oedipal level.

The issue is to what extent the mother grasps the cues coming from her child and brings them into synchronization with her own notions, needs, and other commitments. One has only to think of the difference between feeding at regular intervals and feeding at the child's demand. A certain phase synchrony with respect to the periodicities of relative activity and quiescence develops between the mother and the child. This represents a second level of coordination, but this time in the regulatory mother-child system and not solely in the individual infant.

One of the special features of every mother-child pair is the degree to which the child is able to determine certain sectors of its own regulation that would otherwise be determined by the mother. The mother's nursing activities affect the state of the child, which, in turn, reflects back on the mother. If the mother empathically understands the cues coming from her child and responds to them, her child will give her the feeling that she is a good mother who knows her baby, knows what it needs and how to comfort it, etc. Her self-confidence as a mother is thereby strengthened. Conversely, if the baby does not behave according to her expectations, this disappointment will cause feelings of anxiety and insecurity in the mother. Sander notes that the degree of harmony between mother and child depends at least partially on the extent to which the mother can view her child as an individual with its own distinct characteristics, and the extent to which she projects her own expectations and ideas onto it and uses it—so to speak—as a selfobject in the service of her self. With each individual mother, the mixture of these two attitudes determines the areas in which infant needs will be met by appropriate response or by inappropriate stimulation or lack of response.

## ISSUE II: MUTUAL ACTIVATION (CA. THIRD TO SIXTH MONTH)

The reciprocal coordination between mother and child increases in various ways which lead to mutual activation. "Smiling play" is especially important. Some children smile—without any specific trigger—a few days after birth. But when the mother is able actively to elicit this smile she is delighted. The child seems to be experiencing a feeling of joy and delight that is evident of a successful social link and an interpersonal "fitting together." The child's means of expression include not only smiling, but also joyful kicking and tossing when the mother comes, various vocalizations, turning its head toward the mother, and the like. Thus the child can show that the mother's actions, such as feeding, bathing, and fondling her baby, make it feel happy. And the mother's feeling of being a good mother is confirmed.

ISSUE III: INITIATIVE (CA. SEVENTH TO NINTH MONTH)

The child is learning to crawl and creep now, and its own initiative, which could already be observed occasionally during the smiling play, is increasing. It begins to explore the world. The strength of its goal-directed intentionality becomes particularly evident when its aims are blocked. The mother experiences a bifurcation of her child's impulses: toward her and away from her. This sign of growth may produce ambivalent feelings in the mother. She finds her child aggressive, no longer good and obedient, and she thinks the child is rejecting her. Or she is happy about the child's new impulses and encourages its activities. Her reaction will have its effect. It is also important whether a somewhat stable harmony of rhythms was achieved in the two preceding phases, for then the child's exploratory impulses will develop more easily, i.e., the new impulses do not have to be directed toward stabilizing or restoring labile rhythms.

The issue that has to be negotiated between mother and child in this phase revolves around the following question: "To what degree will the initiative of the infant be successful in establishing areas of reciprocity in the interchange with the mother?"

Sander (1962) gives the following example to illustrate the first, almost subliminal, goal-directed activities of the child:

> a 7½-month-old boy is being spoonfed on his mother's lap. He takes the food readily; all goes smoothly. After some time, he seems to want a brief respite from taking the mouthfuls of food. The mother waits until he is ready again. A couple of times he puts his head back and looks directly up at her. The mother seems extremely delighted and—excited by this contact—returns his gaze, then pulls herself away and offers him the next spoonful.

It seems that the child perceives those initiatives which lead to a reciprocal exchange with the mother as different from those which are unsuccessful. Anticipation plays a role. It is clear that each mother will react differently to the initiatives of her baby.

Sander describes the "battle of initiative" between a mother-child pair which had experienced a satisfactory initial adaptation and a delightful early period of social smiling play. The "battle" starts when the boy becomes capable of pulling himself to the edge of his carriage at the age of 4½ months. The mother fears he might fall out. At the age of about 8 months, the pediatrician suggests introducing solid food. The boy refuses. He gags and spits. The mother is disgusted. He cries and screams, has fits. He wants to walk, but the mother puts him in his high chair. He does not want to sit, bangs his head, and screams. The mother picks him up, but he continues crying. The mother is frustrated because she cannot effect any improvement. Again she puts him in his high chair and gives him a toy "to shut him up," but nothing can stop him from crying.

   This baby, who had been one of our most attractive infants in his fourth and fifth months, lost all signs of spontaneous pleasurable affect in the early part of his second year of life. He was completely defeated by his mother in this early struggle. . . . The threat which the initiative of her infant posed for this mother was revealed by the fact that she suddenly went to work for 4 months, leaving the 7-month-old baby in the care of her husband. . . . [She returned home again because the husband was yielding to the baby's demands.] The self-assertion usually seen in the early part of the second year of life submerged. In a follow-up at the age of 5½ years he showed a striking passivity and almost an avoidance of investment in the few activities he could begin himself [pp. 140–141].

These examples should suffice to give an impression of how Sander conceives of the phase- and personality-specific interaction between mother and infant. Even though Galenson (Panel, 1980) stated that the existing psychoanalytic theories on psychosexual development, object relations, and ego development offered no satisfying possibility for a progressive understanding of such interactions, I would like to point out that Kohut's concept of the selfobject matrix in which the self develops could offer the possibility of a psychoanalytic explanation for the events of early childhood. What can the concepts of the selfobject or the selfobject matrix and self-selfobject relationship contribute to the understanding of the early mother-child relationship?

When Sander, together with Pavenstedt, undertook a longitudinal investigation of mother-child pairs in 1954, his question was whether the development of the child would be influenced by the mother's attitude toward it. His hypothesis was that children whose mothers recognize them as separate individuals would be better developed and more advanced at the age of six than children whose mothers projected fixed ideas and notions onto them.

Furthermore, Sander's findings show that children whose mothers empathically grasped their individual needs and states and acted accordingly were more likely to thrive; conversely, development was impaired when this was not the case. We see this clearly in the spoon-feeding example as well as in the battle of the high chair.

Translated into the language of self psychology, this means that the child who has the best chance is the one whose mother is a phase-adequate selfobject, who can respond to the child empathically, and who simultaneously respects its developing self as a center of its own initiative.

Is this just another example of old wine in new bottles, or can the application of the concepts of self psychology contribute something new? I think this approach is potentially very promising. The findings of direct child observation are limited and incomplete because the child's internal experiences can only be inferred from its external behavior. But if we observe the mother-child pair as a system, then at least the conscious and unconscious impulses, motivations, and reactions of one partner—the mother—avail themselves to us.

Sander's findings clearly show that the mother's self-confidence depends on whether her child is developing well, whether she is familiar with it and knows how to treat it, and whether she can comfort it. Her self-confidence is undermined if the child does not behave according to her expectations. She becomes frustrated if she does not succeed in establishing eye contact with her baby or in bringing it to smile. Thus, not only does the mother mirror her child, but the child also mirrors its mother. The mother needs her child as a selfobject. In the positive instance, the child's reactions help the mother become aware of her own behavior; in the negative instance, the mother projects her ideas and expectations onto her child. There is a great danger of not doing justice to its potential and impairing its development.

A case described recently by Beebe and Sloate (1982) illustrates the catastrophic results that arise when a mother is not able to accept the impulses and expressions of her child as being independent but, instead, imposes upon it ideas shaped by her own needs.

The "caretaker-mother" was an academic coming from a well-to-do family. The relationship to her own mother had been disturbed. In spite of psychotherapy during adolescence she suffered a psychotic episode following the break-up of a love affair during college. She was nevertheless later able to complete her studies with distinction. Following many years of a childless marriage, a 3-week-old girl, Dorothee, was adopted. The childhood problems of the adoptive mother were reactivated and caused her to seek therapeutic help when the child was three months old.

It was obvious that this mother had no empathic grasp of the child's needs and could not understand its expressions. The shared delight of a mother and infant in tune with one another was minimal. One indicator of the existing dissonance was that the mother was not able to provide periods of sustained gaze and face-to-face contact. During the office sessions the infant would from time to time begin to smile at the mother spontaneously in a very appealing manner. It was difficult for the therapist not to respond to that. The mother, however, could not notice the child's overtures to begin an exchange. The attempt at contact broke off again. Not only then did the mother not grasp the infant's needs and states. Her inability and clumsiness in handling the baby could be seen in many instances. It thus might happen that the mother was singing to the child, but did not stop when the baby began fussing or crying. Her only response was to say "shut up." Whereas the therapist could establish normal eye and social contact with the child and also could soothe it, the mother was not able to do so.

The distress of the child was interpreted by the mother as being purposeful or malevolent. "Each instance of fuss, cry, averted gaze or lack of responsivity was construed as an accusation or persecution by the infant rather than as the expression of its own needs. She was jealous and enraged whenever the baby smiled at others, construing these smiles as proof that they were preferred over her." It was the child's function to confirm to her that she was a good mother. As the child failed in doing so, the stage was already set at the age of 3 to 4 months for the infant to be experienced as a persecutory object. This in turn raised fears and wishes in the mother to kill her baby.

In spite of some improvement through the therapy, which consisted mainly in advising and teaching the mother, the child, by the age of 7 months, began to frequently bite its mother in the face. It had temper tantrums, lying on the floor, screaming and kicking around. This rage-filled relationship was dramatically manifested in the "refuelling" (Mahler et al., 1975) situation. Although able to ask for mother's attention and soothing by either crying or hitting at her, once mother responded, Dorothee rejected her. As soon as mother lifted Dorothee into her arm or placed her on her lap, she would immediately struggle to be relieved. . . . Dorothee's relationship with her mother worsened as she desperately sought to maintain some affective contact. This now took the form of violent physical attacks, in which she bit and scratched at her mother's face. The child had not learned to modulate affects, be they positive or negative ones. Its reactions were aggressive behavior, retreat, or "tuning out." On its second birthday it had made only a few single-word utterances. There was almost no symbolic play.

Because of this development, a treatment was also begun with the child. The unfolding and elaboration of Dorothee's wish to be a baby and a game, "baby is sick," played a central role in the therapy. Dorothee chose the therapist's upholstered footstool as her bed. She wanted the therapist to cover her and give her the bottle. While she was being fed with the bottle, she looked directly at the therapist's face, and the therapist returned a steady gaze. The lagging development was made up for. When Dorothee was 30 months old, she spoke complete sentences, and when she was 33 months old, she drew a human face, which she named after herself. After eight months of therapy, the "baby is sick" game changed to "baby goes to sleep." "She requested the sustained gaze of an oriented, soothing, feeding, and admiring mother. In brief, Dorothee sought to obtain from the therapist the full spectrum of maternal stimulation and soothing that had been missing during her infancy period" [pp. 603–619].

The mother's explanations are reminiscent of Melanie Klein's (1950) ideas regarding the paranoid position. According to her theory, the three-month-old child wishes to hurt and to destroy the mother and her breast, supposedly because of an inborn, destructive, aggressive drive which is directed at the mother. It may be not too far-fetched to suppose that the unconscious countertransferences of M. Klein facing children like Dorothee were similar to the feelings of Dorothee's mother and that she then took the secondary consequences of the primary derailment of dialogue between mother and child as the model for her theory. We don't know Dorothee's experience, but we know how Dorothee is experienced by her mother, who is not able to soothe her and to acknowledge her as an individual separate from her. The child who is different from the mother's expectations becomes a persecuting object for her, and she develops death wishes against it. The child's subsequent behavior seems to confirm Klein's presumption of innate destructive aggression. But this is contradicted by the fact that during the entire treatment a "normal" affectionate relationship between the therapist and the child existed and the child expressed tenderness and attachment as soon as an empathic object was at its disposal. One can draw the conclusion that the child's aggression was neither genuine nor innate (one should also bear in mind that the child was adopted and not the mother's own) but, rather, a result of the fact that the mother could not look upon the child as a center of its own initiative. The child was her selfobject. She experienced the child as a part of herself. It had the function of mirroring her and confirming that she was a good mother. When her expectations remained unfulfilled, she responded with increased misunderstanding, aversion, and aggression, like the mother of the child in the high chair.

While in the case of Beebe and Sloate the child was needed as a mirroring selfobject, other examples from observations of mothers and children indicate that mothers (or parents) need their children as idealized selfobjects to make up for deficiencies in their own selves. Stierlin (1973) described this problem under the heading of "Delegation."

## Selfobject Countertransference

How, then, are the experiences of the caretaker, in a system of infant and caretaker that is disturbed, repeated in the analysis of patients with narcissistic personality disorders? We are all too familiar with the counter-transferences which may be mobilized in the analyst as a result of the selfobject transference. Kohut (1971) pointed to them in *The Analysis of the Self*. The analyst may feel threatened by dissolution of the self as a result of the patient's merger wishes. The analyst may be bored, unable to engage himself or herself emotionally. It may be difficult for him to pay sustained attention if he feels he is not being personally recognized and is being addressed by a patient who has developed an alter-ego transference and is therefore not mentioning everything that is going on inside him because he assumes that the analyst knows it anyway. The analyst may suffer from having to serve "only" as a mirror rather than being experienced as a complete person. In the idealizing transference, as well, the analyst may not feel that he is being experienced as he really is. The analyst's own unfulfilled unconscious notions of grandiosity may be awakened. What all these specific forms of countertransference have in common is the fact that the analyst, in the selfobject transference, is treated by the patient as if he were a part of the latter, while the analyst himself feels that he is a separate independent person, a center of his own initiative. Kohut describes the ways in which the analyst may react to such provocations if he is unaware of them, and the ways in which the course of the transference may thereby be hindered or destroyed.

Ernest Wolf (1979) explained that the various forms of transference —namely, oedipal love and rivalry impulses, on the one hand, and selfobject transferences with narcissistic personality disorders, on the other—have their parallels in the various forms of countertransferences. He coined the term *selfobject countertransferences* for those countertransferences in which the patient becomes a selfobject to the analyst, that is, in which the analyst uses the patient in the service of his self or experiences him as a part of his self. With this, Wolf (1979) introduced a new concept into psychoanalysis and illustrated it with the following case.

The patient was a medical doctor, whose mother had died during his infancy. Following this loss he spent several years in institutions. During this time he had learned to elicit positive experiences of being mirrored by being a good boy, an eagerly compliant and helpful child.

During the analysis a close friend of the patient became seriously ill and the patient attempted to give medical care to him. It was worked out that his excessive involvement was motivated more by his need to be the good boy who is caring rather than by his concern for his friend's welfare. Shortly thereafter he reported in the analysis that he had convinced his friend to accept the care of another physician who hospitalized the friend.

The analyst directed his interpretations to the aspect of separation.

(The patient had always been sensitive to separations.) However, no special reaction could be observed. The next day, the patient complained of waking up with a great deal of anxiety, and now he was feeling depressed. The patient, who was usually dressed very decently, was now wearing a clashing color combination. The analyst had the impression that the patient was in a state of a so-called "minifragmentation." He asked himself how he might have misunderstood the patient during the last hour. It finally turned out that the patient had expected that the analyst would be pleased, if he stopped taking care of his friend. He had behaved as the good boy and he had wished for a confirming mirroring response. Furthermore, the acknowledgment of the analyst would have meant to him acceptance by the selfobject as worthy to share in the idealized selfobject's power and righteousness [pp. 588–589].

Wolf notes that the analyst was fixated on the idea of separation, which was based on the analyst's own archaic selfobject needs. As a result, he partly lost his empathy and was not in full contact with the patient. He responded to the part of the patient that was anxiously occupied with separation, not to the patient as a whole person.

Wolf's example throws light on a point of view that is reached by proceeding from the selfobject concept: the analyst experiences the patient as a part of his self. In contrast, if one were to take the point of view that analyst and patient are separate personalities one would assume in this case a projective identification of the analyst with the patient. In any case, this example illustrates the danger of explaining what *the analyst* feels is important without grasping empathically what the patient is concerned with.

Kohut (1971) states that a selfobject is either used in the service of the self or is experienced as a part of the self. In selfobject countertransference, as described by Wolf, the analyst is experiencing the patient as a part of his self. I would like to discuss a further possibility: that in selfobject countertransference the analyst uses the patient in the *service* of his self.

The financial aspect of this process, as is well-known, often stands in the way of the archaic self-selfobject relationship between patient and analyst as an extraneous element. But how else might the analyst use the patient as a selfobject? Which of the analyst's narcissistic needs would the patient have to satisfy? How might the analyst need his patient to maintain his own self-esteem?

## IDEALIZING SELFOBJECT COUNTERTRANSFERENCES

In an idealizing selfobject countertransference, the analyst feels aggrandized if he analyzes a gifted or successful patient. The patient's notions of grandiosity may be assessed as being real because the analyst feels comfortable with them. This would be an example of collusion. One used to speak of analysts being in love with their patients. This somewhat colloquial expression comprises not only tender or sexual desires, but also admiration. Supposing that an analyst admires his patient, one must distinguish whether in this case he acknowledges, respects, and values his patient's potential as center of his own initiative, or uses his patient's grandiosity to buttress his own feelings of self-esteem. In the latter case, the patient will be overburdened by the selfobject-countertransference expectations of his analyst. The patient cannot afford any failure or breakdown without causing anxiety in his analyst or threatening his self-confidence. For the patient, this may mean a replication of childhood experiences in which, for example, the mother became anxious at any sign of weakness in the child and the child thus always had to be in top form in order not to disturb its mother's psychological equilibrium.

## ALTER-EGO COUNTERTRANSFERENCES

Alter-ego countertransference is especially apt to occur in training analysis, where it is often assumed that the candidate holds the same analytic ideals and views as his analyst. It can also develop if the patient and his analyst belong to the same social class or share the same political or religious convictions. Relatively similar familial patterns or personal histories shared by the analyst and the patient can lead the analyst to see the patient as his alter-ego, as may have been the case in Wolf's example cited above.

## MIRROR COUNTERTRANSFERENCES

As an example of mirror countertransferences I would like to designate those countertransferences in which the analyst needs to have the patient confirm that he is a good analyst, namely, by showing improvement. The replication of the mother-child system can be seen quite clearly here. The analyst takes on the role of the mother—one who wants to be a good mother and who would like to see her child prosper, who responds with joy to her child's progress. With this she gives the child the feeling that it can be a source of pleasure for her. This results in a mutual reinforcement, a feed-forward cycle. This kind of countertransference may be increased by certain personal features of the analyst—the very features that also motivated him to choose his profession. They are basically associated with notions of grandiosity. They may, for example, reflect a desire to help the weak and the sick, the unfortunate and those who have failed. In an extreme case, they can lead to a savior complex. Becoming an analyst may serve a desire to become immersed in, or even merge with, another psyche in order to understand and grasp it. With the more directively oriented therapists, another factor may be the wish to reorient the patient, to put him on the right track, to enable him to use his abilities in a better way, and to free him of obsolete defense mechanisms that inhibit him. There is a heavy burden on the analyst when the patient does not respond to his efforts over a long period of time, when the analysis is stalemated by a chronic negative therapeutic reaction, when the patient does not give the analyst the feeling of being a good analyst. The interpretation in such cases often is, "the patient is not granting the analyst success." This is an objective but not an empathic view which presupposes that the patient could do otherwise. In fact what is happening is that a childhood drama is recurring. The patient is no better understood than he was as a child, in this case because he has not fulfilled the selfobject expectations of his analyst, who feels offended and frustrated by him. The patient's familiar vicious circle is intensified. He seems to be ruining anything good that is offered him or rejecting it outright. But is not the patient's rage an expression of his self-assertiveness toward the analyst, who has told him something that is not true? Is not his rage an expression of his despair at having once again been misunderstood? Is not his rage, in addition, a compensation for the feelings toward the early childhood objects, which he could not afford to have at that time without risking the loss of the little affection that remained? When Sander describes how the autonomy and self-assertiveness of the child in the high chair are crushed, our sympathies lie with the child. But when we have aggressive and sensitive patients, our own narcissistic needs for self-justification prevent us from understanding their misery. Only with great difficulty can we accept our own inability to help them improve.

Now another problem which plays a great role in narcissistic relationships will become clear. The patient wants to see his reality validated by the analyst, but the analyst in turn is frustrated if the patient does not validate his expectations. It is not only a question of the analyst's feeling that he is conducting a good analysis; it is also a question of the analyst's expectations as to the possible future development of his patient. One should bear selfobject countertransference in mind and listen carefully if, during a long phase of working through, when all efforts at interpreting seem to be in vain, the analyst becomes impatient, and words such as "not" or "still" enter his thoughts or even crop up in his interpretations. "Why *can't* the patient . . . , why *doesn't* he act differently, why does he see this and *not* that . . ." Or, "Why is the patient *still* hanging on to old gratifications? Why does he *still* have his old anxieties?" In such cases, one must consider that the analyst has certain expectations regarding the patient's development —even if they are very well-meant—that do not do justice to him.

Consider the following example: A thirty-year-old female patient with even, articulate, and very beautiful features but with an insecure and shy demeanor went into analysis because of acute states of anxiety and occasional depersonalization, which hindered her in practicing her profession. She was one of those patients who had sound ego functions but an unstable self. The patient was born on her parents' estate in East Prussia shortly before the end of the war; she was their second daughter. The parents had ardently hoped for a son to carry on the family name, and this all the more, after the grandfather, the patron of the family, had died a few days prior to the patient's birth. Her father was in the war. When she was a year and a half old, the family fled from their home in a dramatic escape, and three months later, a brother was born.

Early on in the analysis, the patient had spoken of family pictures and said that there were some photographs of the children's baptismal ceremonies. However, the emotional significance of these pictures came out only in the fifth year of analysis and caused a significant turn. At the baptismal ceremony of the elder sister, everyone was dressed in white and was cheerful; but at the patient's baptism, they were all dressed in black and were sad. The patient attributed this difference in mood to *herself*. Since she had not experienced mutual delight with her mother (Sander's second issue), she assumed that people were obviously displeased with the way she was. From an early age, she had adapted herself, had been more sensible than her older sister, and had become the confidante of her mother, who overburdened her with all her problems, in particular her marital problems. In a certain way, she became the mother of her mother. On the other hand, she was a "problem child." The mother had to go through special procedures in order to feed her. She had a bad appetite. In the preliminary consultation, she very deliberately expressed reproaches and hate toward her thoughtless and insensitive mother. There was no mutual joy between mother and daughter. She was not thriving well and thus showed the mother that she was a bad mother. The mother, on her part, showed no joy over her child. There may have been some truth in what the patient had felt about everyone wearing black at her baptism.

My emotions and patience were often taxed by this patient during the phase of working through in the analysis. The degree of my often irritated responses showed me that a countertransference was at work here, which warned me and made me become careful with explanations, especially those concerning aggression. The patient played down her problems with an overexaggerated timid and frail voice; she was brave and yet deeply unhappy; she controlled herself, although she had me as a stable and attentive object and selfobject at her disposal. She was also a "problem child" for

me; she did not improve. She did not give me the joy of experiencing that
I was a good analyst. I understood (from the objective viewpoint) the very
feebly concealed denials of her complaints as masochistic. The patient, who
was so brave and worked so strenuously in the analysis, explained in a
reserved and controlled voice, which in reality was full of despair, how she
was being mistreated and exploited by the people close to her. But she said
this was due to her. She said this, even though I sat there patiently hour
after hour conducting an analysis with her. My feeling was that her lam-
entations and self-accusations were referring to me, and the patient's hopelessness also took hold of me. At the same time, I noticed that I was
becoming impatient. These emotions indicated my identification with the
patient and my selfobject countertransference.

I considered a number of possible explanations. Was there a personal
problem? Did the patient have a similarity to me or to somebody close to
me? It could also be conceived that the patient directed her aggression
toward herself in a masochistic fashion. If this were the case, the entire
spectrum of the dynamics of masochism would have been open to interpretation.[2] Another possibility would be that the patient made me sense
the aggression she herself did not dare to express, so that I would become
aggressive for her. Or was this a negative therapeutic reaction, as Asch
(1976) describes, in which the patient, with suppressed whining and la-
menting, expresses the ambivalent relationship to the hated but needed
mother? As an analyst who considers defense mechanisms, I could also see
the self-accusations as a defense against accusations that are aimed at the
objects and at the analyst. In reality, the patient's childhood objects had
not been empathic, and her present objects exploited her. I did not exploit
her. Why could she *not* execute the therapeutic dissociation of the ego
(Sterba, 1934) and realize that I was unlike her objects? All these considerations and interpretations brought me nowhere. Only the concept of
selfobject countertransference helped me progress.[3]

Why was the patient's hopelessness so hard for me to bear? If I view the
patient and myself as a mother-child pair, then she is the baby and I am
the helpless mother. I do not know how to deal with the baby. It whimpers
and cries, and it is not developing well. The patient becomes depressive
and gets on my nerves because I simply cannot find a way to satisfy her.
It is a *narcissistic mortification* that I am not capable of helping another
person. The patient reproaches me, as does the child the mother, with "you
are not helping me, you can't help me, nobody can help me." The narcis-

[2] An indication of latent homosexual problems, which one could also theoretically consider,
was not evident in the material.

[3] I owe the following observation to Heinz Kohut, who supervised the case for several hours
in 1978.

sistic mortification of not being able to help makes me furious. Recognizing my countertransference kept me from letting my anger become involved in contrast to the mother who had intensified the vicious circle of the child's hopelessness with anger, reproaches, and withdrawal. What I provided for the patient was more of a corrective experience than analysis. My feeling of being unable to help her remained.

Some analysts would say that the patient was making me helpless in order to demonstrate her superiority. Others would say that she was making me feel her own helplessness. And still others would try to pass the buck onto the patient and say that she was not granting me success and was making all my efforts seem in vain.

I am afraid that all such explanations are protective interpretations aimed at preserving the analyst's integrity, which is being threatened. One will arrive at a different conclusion when one realizes that the interaction (as between mother and child) between analyst and patient, as a *system*, has broken down.

When she was still very young, the patient had been forced by her mother into the role of caring for her brother and sister and, later, for the mother herself. Neglecting her own interests and needs, which were hardly conscious to her any more, she cared for the people close to her. My countertransference showed that the same pattern also formed in the transference, only somewhat camouflaged. When *I* was frustrated because the patient did not improve, when *I* wanted her to improve, then *I* wanted something from her—she was supposed to deliver the proof that I was a good analyst. I was on the receiving end. Thus the roles in the analysis were also reversed. But the patient had a right to demand that I see and bear her suffering. Only that gave her the feeling that her self was being accepted in its wholeness, and not only in its well-adjusted and helpful side.

The following episode from an advanced stage of this analysis shows further misunderstandings and pitfalls caused by transference and countertransference. The patient had developed a triangle relation, in which she believed that she had to choose between me and a friend of hers. Although she feared losing me if I was not her favored object, she ventured to take steps toward autonomy. When she learned that I—contrary to her mother—was not holding onto her, she was enormously relieved and grateful. During one session, she told me in an irritating manner of the severe maltreatment she had been exposed to by her objects, but which, she said, had been her fault. I interpreted completely on the level of object-instinctual drives, explaining to her that she was angry at her objects.

In reality, I myself was furious that she was *still* suffering so. *I* could not bear her putting up with everything, and I explained to her that she had aggressions which were suppressed. In a certain way, my interventions took on the character of a reproach, like, "Why *can't* you defend yourself?" Afterward, I had the feeling that I had gotten rid of my aggressions but that I had not also understood the patient correctly. In the next session, she came and said that something had not been right the last time. I confirmed this by telling her I had had the same impression.

It became evident that a certain degree of object constancy had been achieved in the course of the long analysis. The patient no longer fragmented, she became neither aggressive nor depressive, she did not get any symptoms or miss any sessions. She could explain to me what had happened. She had come to the last session too early. She was so grateful to me, for she felt that, in contrast to her objects, I was not abusing her. She had passed by a florist's and had thought of buying me a bouquet, a bouquet of her favorite flowers, namely, pale violet asters. But then she began to doubt herself. Would I like the flowers? Would other patients bring me nicer flowers? Would I prefer stronger colors? Basically, her thoughts revolved around the lack of certainty as to whether she *herself* was welcome, whether I would be pleased and delighted by the flowers she liked most. These thoughts made her very aggressive, and she came to the session with these aggressions.

Even with the greatest empathy, it would have been difficult to grasp the true meaning of her provocative behavior. My countertransference prevented me from holding back with interpretations. The patient had complained about the objects who had mistreated her, as well as about herself thereby putting the blame on herself. What she had said was true, but in a totally different sense than I had assumed. She had been mistreated not through actions, but as a result of the lack of cheerful mirroring of her whole person, and she logically traced this deficit back to herself. The mere thought that this could also happen to her with me produced a suppressed narcissistic rage. It was not an object-instinctual animosity toward other objects or toward me arising from the momentary triangle situation. The child in the patient thought: "I like you, I need you. Why don't I see a gleam in your eyes? Why don't you smile back when I smile? My smile is disappearing now; I will put up with everything." The analyst in her selfobject countertransference thought: "Why is the patient sad? Why does she *still* tolerate everything? Why *doesn't* she defend herself? After being in analysis for such a long time, she really ought to have oedipal hate impulses toward the analyst." (Some analysts believe that one has to raise the patient to the oedipal level as soon as possible.)

The lesson to be learned from this episode is that when dealing with patients with selfobject transferences, one must be extremely careful with explanations, on the level of object-libidinal or aggressive conflicts, even when the analysis is already at an advanced stage. In the areas where the child had little or no opportunity of self-regulation or where the early dialogue between mother and child broke down, the results are afterward explained by the child and later by the patient in a causally and secondary-process-like manner. But this explanation is found out at a much later level of development—the earlier level has been forgotten and lost. To interpret the material on this false level is to misunderstand the patient.

Finally, I would like to consider the question whether selfobject countertransferences have their foundation in the analyst's person, or whether they are brought about by the patient and can thus be used diagnostically. This question applies in fact to all kinds of countertransferences. Of course, every analyst has his weak spots and personal narcissistic idiosyncrasies, and they may endanger his work, if they are unconscious. Some of them may be very difficult to detect, as they are ego syntonic and belong to the usual or normal motivations of one who chooses a healing profession. The more we learn about the processes to which Kohut made such an important contribution with the concept of the selfobject, the easier it may become to discover facets of the analyst's personality and narcissism which may interfere with his analytic work. In spite of these components of the self-object countertransference, which may have their basis in unconscious attitudes and personality features of the analyst, I believe that the countertransference mobilized inside him is pathognomonic for the patient—it is a replication of the patient's childhood experiences, and as such it can be used in the analysis as a valuable tool for understanding his psychodynamics.

In this article I have attempted to expand the concepts of countertransference and selfobject transference in the direction of selfobject countertransference as initiated by Wolf (1979). I have expressed my hope that this may spark further investigation. The phenomenon of countertransference has been described by many authors as for instance Freud (1910), Heimann (1950), Gitelson (1952), Spitz (1956), Annie Reich (1960), Kernberg (1965), Racker (1968). The concept of selfobject countertransference adds a new dimension. It deserves further elaboration in depth as to its advantages, limits, and heuristic value. Following Kohut's suggestion, "that Sander's work in particular (e.g., 1975) promises to enrich self psychology and, in turn, to be enriched by it" (1980, p. 475), I have tried to show that infant research conceiving of child and caretaker as an indivisible system in the progress of growth on the one hand and analytic research on the line of Kohut's concepts of selfobject transference and selfobject relations may mutually increase understanding.

# REFERENCES

Asch, S. (1976), Varieties of negative therapeutic reactions and problems of technique. *J. Amer. Psychoanal. Assn.*, 24:383–407.

Beebe, B. & Sloate, P. (1982), Assessment and treatment of difficulties in mother-infant attunement in the first three years of life. *Psychoanal. Inquiry*, 1:601–623.

Brazelton, B. T. & Als, H. (1979), Four early stages in the development of mother-infant organization. *The Psychoanalytic Study of the Child*, 34:349–369. New Haven: Yale University Press.

Freud, S. (1910), The future prospects of psychoanalytic therapy. *Standard Edition*, 11:139–152. London: Hogarth Press, 1957.

Gitelson, M. (1952), The emotional position of the analyst in the psychoanalytic situation. *Internat. J. Psycho-Anal.*, 733:1–10.

Heimann, P. (1950), On countertransference. *Internat. J. Psycho-Anal.*, 31:81–84.

Klein, M. (1950), *Contributions to Psychoanalysis*. London: Hogarth Press.

Kohut, H. (1971), *The Analysis of the Self*. New York: International Universities Press.

——— (1980), Reflections. In: *Advances in Self Psychology*, ed. A. Goldberg. New York: International Universities Press, pp. 473–554.

——— Wolf, E. (1978), The disorders of the self and their treatment. *Internat. J. Psycho-Anal.*, 59:413–426.

Lewis, M. & Rosenblum, L. (eds.) (1974), *The Effect of the Infant on Its Caregiver*. New York: John Wiley.

Mahler, M., Pine, F., & Bergman, A. (1975), *The Psychological Birth of the Human Infant*. New York: Basic Books.

Panel (1980), New knowledge about the infant from current research; Implications for psychoanalysis, L. Sander, reporter. *J. Amer. Psychoanal. Assn.*, 28:181–198.

Racker, H. (1968), The countertransference neurosis. In: *Transference and Countertransference*. New York: International Universities Press, pp. 105–126.

Reich, A. (1960), Further remarks on countertransference. *Internat. J. Psycho-Anal.*, 41:389–395.

Sander, L. W. (1962), Issues in early mother-child interaction. *J. Amer. Acad. Child Psychiat.*, 1:141–166.

——— (1975), Infant and caretaking environment: Investigation and conceptualization of adaptive behavior in a system of increasing complexity. In: *Explorations in Child Psychiatry*, ed. E. J. Anthony. New York: Plenum Press, pp. 129–166.

Spitz, R. A. (1956), Countertransference. *J. Amer. Psychoanal. Assn.*, 4:256–265.

Sterba, R. (1934), The fate of the ego in analytic therapy. *Internat. J. Psycho-Anal.*, 15:117–126.

Stierlin, H. (1973), Interpersonal aspects of internalizations. *Internat. J. Psycho-Anal.*, 54:203–213.

Wolf, E. (1979), Transferences and countertransferences in the analysis of disorders of the self. *Contemp. Psychoanal.*, 15:577–594.

*February 1984*

# Self Psychology and the Neuroses

## ERNEST S. WOLF, M.D. (Chicago)

A science, as it grows and matures, moves from a description and classification of relatively gross phenomena to a theory-bound understanding of theory-selected data. In psychology, the step from the description of gross behavior patterns to a focused scrutiny of underlying unconscious structures and their dynamics is the equivalent, for example, to the shift in neuroanatomy from overtly visible organs and gross structures to the microscopic study of postulated hidden pathways that often can be made visible only by the action of certain specific stains.[1]

To make the hidden visible, to make the unconscious conscious —microanatomy and micropsychology were never very far apart in Freud's attempt to penetrate into the mysteries of nature, including, of course, that of his own "demon," as he sometimes referred to it. Charcot, Janet, and Breuer had taught Freud that hysterical phenomena were not merely the result of inborn constitutional weakness but could be explained as a dynamic process. They had transformed the medieval view of hysteria into a first scientific theory of neurosis "when once they had replaced the 'demon' of clerical phantasy by a psychological formula" (Freud, 1893, p. 22).

The early decades of psychoanalysis were practically synonymous with

[1] In fact, it may not be altogether an unconnected coincidence that the neurologist who invented one of these stains to visualize and study otherwise invisible nerve-tracts also was the genius who invented a method to conceptualize and study otherwise unconscious mental pathways. Ernest Jones has commented that the English translation of Freud's "A New Histological Method for the Study of Nerve-Tracts in the Brain and Spinal Cord," published in *Brain* in 1884, was the first paper by Freud that Jones had ever come across. It was just about a hundred years ago that Freud changed the course of our civilization by changing the course of his scientific life from an investigation of the microanatomy of neurons to an investigation of the micropsychology of the neuroses. In October 1883 Freud's successful experiments with a solution of gold chloride helped him overcome his chagrin at having just broken the ring that Martha had given him, and he began to apply the new stain to the study of structures.

the study of the psychoneuroses. Hysteria, anxiety neurosis, phobia, and obsessive-compulsive neurosis were the most frequent diagnostic labels attached by Freud to the patients who provided him with the data from which he constructed his theories. The study of dreams, humor, the parapraxes of everyday life and, especially, of the artifacts of culture, such as religion, art, and literature, brought forth a plethora of further data that fitted the conceptualizations derived from neurotic pathology. Indeed, a closely knit web of interrelated concepts made it possible for psychoanalysis to encompass a multiform of human experiences in an elegant all-covering theory.

But gradually, as more and more patients with diverse types of psychopathology came under the psychomicroscope of analytic scrutiny, data began to accumulate that could be brought under the cover of then-existing psychoanalytic theory only by uncomfortably stretching the conceptual fabric. Freud himself was not entrenched in his theoretical positions and was able to leap quickly into new hypotheses when new data forced the surrender of cherished old beliefs. In our time we have had to do the same, not only to survive as a legitimate scientific enterprise, but also to be able to respond adequately to the apparently changed psychopathology of many of our patients. I cannot escape the observation that where I used to see patients with hysterical conversions or obsessive-compulsive rituals as their chief complaint I now see many more patients who complain of the inadequacy of their relations to family and friends or of the inability to experience a sense of worthwhile accomplishment, or whose once-energetic life has been sapped into an empty depression. Perhaps, the patient with a typical symptom neurosis no longer consults the psychoanalyst, or, to be more precise, no longer finds his way into my analytic consulting room. Nowadays he may sometimes be seen in emergency rooms or treated by the family doctor. I get the impression that in the main symptom neurotics have disappeared only from the upper-middle-class urban scene and are not yet extinct in more rural or in religiously fundamentalist milieus.

Instead of the traditional neurotic, today's urban patient presents in the modern but different garb of culturally acceptable emotional illness to gain admittance to the mental-health professional who is perceived as the provider of societally sanctioned soothing and support. We attach a variety of diagnoses to these patients, usually some variation of personality disorder or character disorder if they are judged to be treatable by psychoanalysis. The handy wastebasket-label "borderline" usually designates psychotherapeutically treatable but not analyzable pathology. The observed phenomenon of the multiplication of the character disorders antedates, of course, the advent of self psychology by several decades. The near disappearance of the symptom neuroses is of more recent date. I can clearly remember a number of so-called classical hysterics and obsessive-compulsives that I treated during my psychiatric training in the early fifties. This shift to a preponderance of the character disorders had already been noticed by Fenichel who commented in 1945:

there has been a fundamental change in the clinical picture of the neuroses during the last decade. In the classic neuroses an integrated personality was suddenly disturbed by inadequate actions or impulses. In modern neuroses, however, it is not a question of dealing with a hitherto uniform personality that is merely disturbed by some immediate event but, rather, with one that is patently torn or malformed, or at any rate so involved in the illness that there is no borderline between "personality" and "symptom." Instead of clear-cut neurotics, more and more persons with less defined disorders are seen, sometimes less troublesome for the patients themselves than for their environment [pp. 463–464].

Fenichel also was candid in stating that psychoanalytic therapy in the case of character disorders meets with special difficulties. However, he was not discouraged and, following Freud, reiterated that since psychoanalysis cannot alter the individual constitutionally its effectiveness thus remains limited; however, it may change the patient into what he would have become had his life circumstances been more favorable (pp. 539–540). It is interesting to note that only 77 pages of Fenichel's massive 703-page opus were devoted to the character disorders. I would imagine that if he were rewriting his book today he would give a much larger portion to the character disorders and would elaborate greatly on the studies of the life circumstances which he and Freud held to be so pivotal in the development of treatable aspects of neurotic illness.

Much of the development of psychoanalytic science during the last decades can be said to have been stimulated by the clinical and the theoretical challenges posed by the problem of treating these character neuroses. These trends have led to an elaboration of ego psychology, to an enrichment of object-relations theory, and to the emergence of Kohut's self psychology. It is with the last of these, the self-psychological reconceptualization of the neuroses, that I will be concerning myself in the remainder of this essay.

I will not attempt a historical survey of these developments here but do think it important to point up the two main considerations that led to Kohut's reformulations. These were both theoretical and clinical. The first of these was Kohut's recognition that empathy defined as vicarious introspection, i.e., as a mode of observation attuned to the inner life of man, was the *sine qua non* of any psychoanalytic—as distinct from other psychologies—set of observations. Therefore, any psychoanalytic theory must somehow in its structure reflect the crucial fact about its field of observation, namely, that we are not observing an object "out there" in the world, like other sciences do, but are observing introspectively an "inner state." Parenthetically, I might add that we can learn to perform this examination of our subjectivity just as objectively as the extrospective scientist examines the world around him (Kohut, 1959, 1982).

The second of the main considerations that led Kohut to his reconceptualization of the neuroses was his clinical experience with the many patients who did not respond to the classical psychoanalytic approach. Initially, this led Kohut to formulate the category of narcissistic personality disorders as distinct from the neurotic conditions. In 1978 we summarized as follows:

> . . . the psychoanalytic investigation of certain frequently encountered patients led to the recognition of a definable syndrome which at first appeared to be related to the psychoneuroses and neurotic character disorders. It was clear from the outset that these patients are characterized by a specific vulnerability: their self-esteem is unusually labile and, in particular, they are extremely sensitive to failures, disappointments and slights. It was, however, not the scrutiny of the symptomatology but the process of treatment that illuminated the nature of the disturbance of these patients. The analysis of the psychic conflicts of these patients did not result in either the expected amelioration of suffering or the hoped-for cessation of undesirable behavior; the discovery, however, that these patients reactivated certain specific narcissistic needs in the psychoanalytic situation, i.e., that they established "narcissistic transferences," made effective psychoanalytic treatment possible. . . . As the understanding of the symptomatology, core psychopathology, and treatment of the narcissistic personality disorders increased, in particular via the investigation of the narcissistic transferences, it became clear that the essence of the disturbance from which these patients suffered could not be adequately explained within the framework of classical drive-and-defense psychology. In view of the fact that it is a weakened or defective self that lies in the center of the disorder, explanations that focused on conflicts concerning either the libidinal or the aggressive impulses of these patients could illuminate neither psychopathology nor treatment process. . . . The decisive steps forward in the understanding of these disorders . . . were made through the introduction of the concept of the selfobject . . . [Kohut and Wolf, 1978, pp. 413–414].

The selfobject concept has become the cornerstone of theorizing and of the clinical application of self psychology. For example, during the earliest phases of development the neonate is engaged in an interactive relationship with its caretakers. Those functions of the relationship with the caretakers that evoke and maintain in the infant the experience of selfhood are defined as selfobject functions. As a terminological shorthand these caretakers are often designated "selfobjects." However, strictly speaking, selfobjects are not objects but self-evoking functions performed by objects through their relationship to the emergent self.

Over time the numerous intersecting experiences of self-evoking relationships with a matrix of selfobjects leave a relatively enduring pattern of memory traces of these relationships which in interaction with inborn potentials precipitate as an enduring configuration, i.e., a psychological structure. The word "structure" here may be misleading in that it suggests something fixed in space. It is, however, still a useful figure of speech to indicate that as an enduring configuration psychological structure has a history, i.e., a past, a present, and a future. This structure is associated with the experience of selfhood and, therefore, has been designated as the self. The self, a psychological structure in the sense just described, refers to the enduring configuration evoked and maintained by selfobject relations. The self is the organizational nucleus of the personality. The healthy and fully structured cohesive self is experienced with a sense of confident well-being, i.e., as a healthy sense of selfhood. The word "structured" here is no more than a metaphor for the enduring qualities of the self and connotes no fixed and formed entity. It is difficult to define the self precisely, but as a working description I would suggest that the self consists of a cluster of evoked potentialities—the inborn potentials that can be evoked by appropriate selfobject relations—which manifest as a disposition toward certain patterns of action. Prominent among these action patterns are those that are designed to elicit or even compel potential human selfobjects to continue to perform those selfobject functions that will maintain and enhance the cohesion of the self. It is interesting to note how often the self has recourse to nonhuman substitutes when selfobject relations with persons are not available or blocked by defenses.[2]

The sustaining selfobject functions fall into two groups, the mirroring and the idealizing selfobject relations. The self that emerges from the sustaining selfobject matrix may be said to be well integrated, cohesive, vigorous, and harmoniously organized. Or it may be disintegrating, fragmented, enfeebled, chaotically torn, or even empty. Again, it is well to remind ourselves here that these qualities are metaphorical descriptions designed to evoke workable hypotheses. These metaphors are derived from introspected experience, either directly or vicariously through empathy, and they allow one to think psychologically. They are not to be confused with the concrete qualities of extrospectively perceived structures in the

---

[2] By nonhuman substitutes I mean primarily fetishistic objects that by their close association to human selfobjects come to serve as a substitute that is more predictable and reliable. Yet the mechanistic predictability prevents live interaction and growth.

world of objects around us. Let me add that such metaphorical conceptualization is sanctioned by scientific usage. As Freud (1926) said:

> In psychology we can only describe things by the help of analogies
> [*Vergleichungen*]. There is nothing peculiar in this; it is the case elsewhere
> as well. But we have constantly to keep changing these analogies, for
> none of them lasts us long enough [p. 195].[3]

I may seem to have wandered a long way from the psychoneuroses, the
subject of this essay. But it is necessary to define as clearly as possible the
framework of self psychology before attempting to describe in self-psychological terms what is so clearly defined in terms of classical psychoanalysis.

Both self psychology and classical analysis agree in seeing the phenomena
of the neuroses and character disorders as manifestations of the personality's reaction to pathological interaction between the organism and its
environment. In other words, the personality is determined not by either
nature or nurture but by both.

These two psychologies differ, however, in postulating the cause or origin
of the sexual or aggressive driveness that may occur as part of the pathological outcome. Classical psychoanalytic theory proposes a universal and
ubiquitous sexual instinct which after a period of infantile development
reaches the oedipal phase where it inevitably comes into sharp conflict with
parental authority because of its instinctually determined object, the parent
of the opposite sex. Castration anxiety and repression are the normally
expected outcome. Self psychology recognizes the same development of
infantile sexuality into the oedipal phase with the same sensual lusting for
the parent of the opposite sex. However, self psychology also stresses that
this oedipal constellation occurs within the framework of the child's selfobject relations with his or her parents and that the outcome, whether
neurosis-producing struggle or relatively conflict-free transition into eventual healthy adult sexuality, depends on the quality of these selfobject
relations with the parents. Thus, while in classical formulations castration
anxiety is unavoidable and usually *causes* repression as well as neurotic
symptom formation, self psychology takes the view that castration anxiety

---

[3] My use of the term "metaphor" here as analogous to Freud's *Vergleichungen* calls for some
justification. *Vergleichungen* comes closest in English to "comparisons." However, exact terminology is elusive not only in translation but also in proper English usage. The *Princeton
Encyclopedia of Poetry and Poetics* (1972, p. 490) states: "The nature and definition of metaphorical terms and of the relations between them have both been matter for much speculation
and disagreement. It is unlikely therefore that a more specific definition will at first be
acceptable. The metaphorical relation has been variously described as comparison, contrast,
analogy, similarity, juxtaposition, identity, tension, collision, fusion"; in choosing the term
"metaphor" I have tried to stay within the poetic spirit of Freud's *Vergleichungen*.

and its neurotic sequelae are not inevitable but *symptoms* caused by the breakdown of the cohesive self structure subsequent to faulty selfobject relations between the oedipal child and its oedipal selfobjects. Psychoneuroses, according to this view, are conceptualized as a particular subcategory of the disorders of the self.

Let us now spell out in somewhat greater detail the developmental vicissitudes as the little boy enters the oedipal phase, assuming that the child enters this crucial developmental phase with a relatively intact and cohesive self. The mother becomes the object of his phallic-erotic strivings while the father becomes a rivalrous object who is targeted for hostile-destructive impulses. At the same time both parents are not only objects of these phase-appropriate strivings, but are also selfobjects, i.e., the child requires a particular kind of selfobject response to maintain the cohesion of its self. The multiplicity of possible polyphonic responses cannot be encompassed in a brief survey such as this, but I think one can point to some characteristic response patterns that may facilitate the integration of the maturing sexuality into the constitution of the developing self. In contrast, other response patterns may tend to fragment the child's self with the thus-liberated sexuality manifesting as distorted disintegration products that eventuate in neurotic sequelae. In the first instance the boy experiences a heightened sensuality and even some erotic excitement which may be accompanied by some mild anxiety because of the novelty of the experience and the required adjustment to a new relationship to the oedipal parents. He therefore requires the kind of selfobject responses that allow the integration of the erotically tinged object strivings without weakening the self: for example, the father can support the youngster by showing his pride in this "chip off the old block." Such proud mirroring by the father also permits the child to gain further cohesion through merger with the idealized selfobject, the father. Few children would misunderstand such camaraderie as an invitation to acting out. The mother, on her part, also can good-naturedly admire her "little man" without undue overstimulation.

But, perhaps more important than these admittedly difficult selfobject responses is the absence of faulty responses that would be destructive to the still-fragile self of the child. I have in mind the counteraggression often evoked so easily in the insecure father by the challenging youngster. Nor would the mother make a contribution to her boy's emerging masculinity by being either coldly rejecting or warmly seductive in response to his flirtatious sensuality. As we all have had many occasions to observe, it is not difficult to crush a child's budding self. The anxiety that we have observed so often in these instances is disintegration anxiety, not castration anxiety. The fragmentation of the self is followed by the emergence of lifelong patterns of distorted sexuality, the driveness around which a "pseudo-self" reorganizes with much manifest castration anxiety, repression, and defenses leading to the characteristic symptom formation of the psychoneuroses. Kohut (1982), in a posthumous paper, has summarized these conceptualizations as follows:

> Under normal circumstances we do not encounter drives via introspection and empathy. We always experience the not-further-reducible psychological unit of a loving self, a lusting self, an assertive self, a hostile-destructive self. When drives achieve experiential primacy, we are dealing with disintegration products: in the realm of Eros, the fragmenting self watching helplessly as it is being replaced by a feverishly intensified pleasure experience, by the ascendancy of a pleasure-giving erogenic zone, and thus of the drive over the self; or, in the realm of Thanatos, the fragmenting self watches helplessly as it is being replaced by a feverishly intensified rage experience, by the ascendancy of a destructive and/or self-destructive orgy, and thus, again, of drive over the self [p. 401].

A number of questions remain. In my hypothetical case of the little boy entering the oedipal phase and its vicissitudes I assumed an intact and cohesive self. But how valid is this assumption? How often is the self structure already compromised by the vicissitudes that befall selves during their formation and during the vicissitudes of traversing the shoals of preoedipal encounters with the preoedipal selfobjects? These and other questions can be answered not by recourse to theoretical speculation but only by the evidence obtained in future empirical research.

We need to remember, however, that in empirical research we need and use data, and it is only with the guidance of some theoretical frame that we can sift data from innumerable observations. Let me illustrate with a brief example of how theory determines the selection of data. A patient opened an analytic session by announcing that she had had a sexual dream and that she was tempted to tell it in minute detail. She appeared to be rather anxious and actually never did tell the dream in all its sexual detail during the ensuing hour. If my theory would have told me to listen for evidence of the activity of the sexual instincts, then I would have had to consider that my empathic data regarding her anxiety were the outcome of her being caught up in a conflict between some instinctual activity and some countervailing force. Similarly, I would have had to conclude that her reluctance actually to tell me about the sexual events in the dream was the result of this conflict between drive and defense.

But if my theory tells me to look for evidence of her self experience then I have to conceptualize my explanations in answer to the question: what does this person—not this instinct—want or need from *me*? And how has it come about that she is so anxious while she tells *me*? Selfobject theory directs me to think about either her or her instinctual life not in isolation but within the context of her as a person addressing me as another person. And, of course, within the context of her experiencing herself and me I will notice not only evidence of her selfobject needs—e.g., unconscious needs for me as a selfobject to sustain the cohesion of her self—but also other needs and wishes, such as using me as an object for her sexual driveness or wishing to destroy me because in some way she experiences me as threatening her self, particularly by making her feel helpless. And I am likely to notice also much conflict—not only or even primarily instinctual conflict, to be sure—but conflict involving self assertion vis-à-vis selfobjects or vis-à-vis the environment.

Though pure symptom neurosis has become uncommon we do see many patients who exhibit discrete neurotic symptoms against a backdrop of narcissistic pathology. In doing psychoanalytic treatment one can always observe both selfobject transferences and neurotic transferences. The majority of patients—in my clinical experience—present with complaints that appear related to difficulties in self-esteem regulation as a consequence of chronically faulty selfobject relations. They are unable to form enduring and satisfying relationships with the people to whom they look for the human closeness that every person needs. The presenting symptoms usually are a mixture of autoplastic depressions, anxieties, irritations, resentments, and absent or inappropriate affect states: they feel lonely and unhappy. Their behavior may manifest as an alloplastic attempt to compel the environment to yield the needed selfobject responses that will banish the unbearable misery of self fragmentation and emptiness. It may range from the loudly obnoxious arrogance of the infantile selfobject demand when it is expressed by an adult to the shy timidity of defensively repressed and disavowed self assertion; it may surface in narcissistic rage directed homicidally against others who are perceived as threatening narcissistic injury or suicidally against the unbearably injured and helpless self.

A smaller group of patients present with the kind of symptoms that traditionally have been termed the psychoneuroses: anxiety, phobias, hysterical conversion symptoms, obsessive-compulsive thinking and rituals. Many of these turn out to be disorders of the self, i.e., narcissistic personality disorders or narcissistic behavior disorders or borderline states or, very rarely, psychoses. In a small number of patients the vulnerability of the self may be relatively minor and inconspicuous while the neurotic conflicts resulting from Oedipus-complex pathology may manifest more or less prominently in the symptoms of a classical psychoneurosis. However, even in this latter group the transference will reflect the vicissitudes of self cohesion and self fragmentation. In the view of self psychology the etiology of the neurosis is to be found in the developmental history of the self and its selfobject relationships rather than in any inherent qualities of the instinctual drives.

As already stated, all patients manifest both selfobject and neurotic symptomatology, especially in the transference. In psychoanalytic treatment we can distinguish two kinds of patients with neurotic symptoms, or, to be more precise, two typical courses an analysis may take. The first group consists of patients who initially came into analysis for the treatment of more or less severe narcissistic personality disorders. As these analyses proceed toward a satisfactory conclusion with a manifestly strengthened self I often begin to recognize oedipally structured neurotic transferences. These oedipal transferences make their first appearance in these analyses either as the termination phase is approached or during the termination phase. It is as if there had been a preoedipal developmental arrest, as if as a result of the analysis the arrested development had become remobilized. These analysands seem never to have had the experience of a childhood oedipal phase before, and they traverse it toward the end of their analyses *de novo* with the analyst. The quality of the transference challenge to the analyst, however, is less intense, not as serious but more playful than that of similarly structured oedipal transferences during the analysis of patients with primarily neurotic features against a diffusely inconspicuous background of selfobject disturbance. These analysands present from the very beginning of the analysis with prominent neurotic symptoms. Rarely, however, do they exhibit the typical symptom neurosis of classical psychoanalytic literature.

According to Kohut the sequence of developmental vicissitudes that brought the neurotic constellation into existence is reversed during analysis. That is, by analyzing from the surface down, the castration anxiety becomes manifest first. Then, as one penetrates deeper into the underlying vulnerability of the self, the disintegration anxiety becomes more prominent. Thus the analysis of the oedipal transferences precedes that of the selfobject transferences. In my own practice I have not been able to see such an orderly process of analysis which reverses the developmental sequence. My own experience has been mostly with analysands whose oedipal transferences appeared *de novo* near or during the termination phase. I cannot be certain whether my not having been able to duplicate Kohut's observations here represents the particular selection of patients that I have worked with or whether some countertransference blindness of mine has skewed my perceptions. Obviously, we need much more research.

A few words are in order about the conceptualization of the treatment process. Let us recall that the psychopathology of a self disorder consists of a defective self, and the symptomatology consists of the (1) affective experiences of a weakened or fragmented self, and (2) the behavioral manifestations resulting from these. Among the frequently experienced affects are anxiety, depression, shame, boredom, irritability, narcissistic ragefulness, etc. Among the frequently observed behaviors are all kinds of sexual or aggressive acting out, perversion, delinquency, addiction, lying, stealing, exhibitionistic behaviors, etc. All these behaviors, of course, can occur at times also in relatively normal and healthy people. What gives them the mark of a symptom of a disorder of the self is that they are almost desperately and imperatively used to safeguard some remnant of self-esteem. For instance, one patient was irresistibly driven to cruise and make a homosexual pickup whenever a particular kind of social rebuff was experienced as a painful withdrawal of selfobject sustenance with resulting partial fragmentation of the self. The pickup would become a transient emergency selfobject that would tide him over the crisis of severe fragmentation anxiety until he had restored the cohesion of his self through other responsive selfobject relationships.

Since the psychopathology is a weakened self, the aim of treatment is to strengthen the self. In psychoanalysis the process of strengthening occurs via the transference through interpretation. In a well-conducted analysis, i.e., in an analytic ambience of nonjudgmental empathic understanding, the archaic unsatisfied selfobject needs focus on the analyst as more or less conscious and more or less defended-against demands. The analytic therapist will, of course, not attempt gratification but will try to understand empathically the nature and origin of the demands. Though initially this feels good to the patient, sooner or later it is insufficient either because the frustration seems too harsh or the therapist just does not seem to understand. The transference relationship, which is a selfobject relationship, becomes disrupted, tension replaces harmony, and there may even be some acting out. In analyzable cases the therapist can restore the disrupted transference by interpretation of the factors having caused the disruption. Usually, such an interpretation must include not only the contemporary dynamics of the analytic relationship but also the analogous genetic precursors that one has been able to reconstruct or remember. A successful interpretation not only heals the relationship but also lifts it to a new level of mutual understanding. The archaic selfobject need is replaced by a reciprocal empathic resonance (Wolf, 1983). The therapist understands his patient better. More importantly, however, the patient has gained some, if ever so slight, empathic understanding of the therapist, his analytic actions, and his choice of interpretation over gratification. *Pari passu* the patient gains a similar slight inkling of an insight and understanding into the actions of the archaic parent, or, to be more precise, into how and why the past was experienced in just such a particular and hurtful way. Thus the patient becomes more empathic with himself also, and he may finally begin to accept that despised injured self which had been hiding all these years.

## Summary

In summary, the child enters the oedipal phase needing particular kinds of responses from the oedipal selfobjects, usually the parents. When the parent fails in these selfobject functions, the child's self suffers the disintegrating experiences that may and often do result in the distortion of the normal conflicts that occur during the oedipal phase into the pathological conflicts that have been called the Oedipus complex. This Oedipus complex, seen by self psychology as secondary to insults to the oedipal self, results in the neurotic drives, neurotic defenses, neurotic symptoms—the classical neuroses that psychoanalysis has investigated so well during the first century of its scientific development.

### REFERENCES

Jones, E. (1953), *The Life and Works of Sigmund Freud*, vol. 1. New York: Basic Books.
Fenichel, O. (1945), *The Psychoanalytic Theory of Neurosis*. New York: Norton.
Freud, S. (1893), Charcot. *Standard Edition*, 3:9–24. London: Hogarth Press, 1962.
——— (1926), The question of lay analysis. *Standard Edition*, 20:179–258. London: Hogarth Press, 1959.
Kohut, H. (1959), Introspection, empathy and psychoanalysis: An examination of the relationship between mode of observation and theory. *J. Amer. Psychoanal. Assn.*, 7:459–483.
——— (1982), Introspection, empathy, and the semi-circle of mental health. *Internat. J. Psycho-Anal.*, 63:395–407.
——— Wolf, E. S. (1978), The disorders of the self and their treatment: An outline. *Internat. J. Psycho-Anal.*, 59:413–425.
*Princeton Encyclopedia of Poetry and Poetics* (1972), Princeton, N.J.: Princeton University Press.
Wolf, E. S. (1983), Empathy and countertransference. In: *The Future of Psychoanalysis*, ed. A. Goldberg. New York: International Universities Press, pp. 309–325.

*November 1983*

# Self Preservation and the Preservation of the Self

ARNOLD H. MODELL, M.D. (Waban, Mass.)

The calm assurance and optimism that marked the period of ego psychology have given way to our present condition in which psychoanalysis is constantly challenging itself from within its own ranks. The theoretical premises of metapsychology have been considered by some psychoanalysts to be in serious disarray; others consider metapsychology a useless relic of Freud's materialistic intellectual history. There is an active debate concerning what the philosophers call the "placement" of psychoanalysis —whether it is a science or a branch of history, hermeneutics, or linguistics. The impetus for this turmoil does not arise only from philosophical or intellectual considerations but has, I believe, a definite empirical, that is clinical, base; I believe that our patients have been changing and that the model of the neurosis on which some of our theoretical assumptions have been based has in part become antiquated. It is these clinical issues that will be the focus of this presentation.

My assertion that the forms of the neuroses are continually changing is not something that can be proven by a clinician. It would take a sociologist of the stature of Durkheim (1897) to demonstrate for neurosis what he did for suicide—that its frequency transcended considerations of individual psychopathology. Although my opinion is unprovable, I am in agreement with Kohut (1977) that there has been an actual increase in the number

An earlier version of this paper was presented at the symposium on "Narcissism, Masochism, and the Sense of Guilt in Relation to the Therapeutic Process," held at the Letterman General Hospital, San Francisco, May 14–15, 1983, sponsored by the Department of Psychiatry, Letterman General Hospital; the Mount Zion Psychotherapy Research Group; and the Extension Division of the San Francisco Psychoanalytic Institute. The paper was also presented to the Washington Psychoanalytic Institute on January 13, 1984.

of narcissistic neuroses; that there has in fact been a change in the ecology of narcissism, although the character types described are by no means of recent vintage. But though I am unable to prove my assertion, I firmly believe that the neuroses are a barometer of historical change, that the current interest in narcissism follows from an actual increase in the so-called narcissistic disorders, which in turn is not the result of chance but has been thrust upon us by social forces which we can only dimly perceive (Samitca, 1981; Modell, 1983). The flamboyant, hysterical symptoms, those anesthesias and paralyses of Freud's day, are all but extinct in the consultation rooms of the urban psychoanalyst although they may well persist in other cultural settings.

The term "narcissism" has unfortunate connotations arising from its mythic origins. In the myth, of course (in Graves's [1955] version) Narcissus fell in love with his own reflection and was so tortured by the wish to possess what he could not possess that he eventually stabbed himself to death. Although the myth describes self love, our recent experience with the psychoanalysis of the so-called narcissistic personality has taught us that the term is misleading because what we call narcissistic is not primarily erotic but is a reaction to a disturbance between the self and the human protective environment, what Winnicott (1965) called the "holding environment." The connotations of eroticism and self-absorption inherent in the myth of Narcissus have prevented us from recognizing that *narcissism is the end result of conflict between the self and the affirming or negating human environment.* Kohut also understands narcissism to stand apart from this erotic series, but in contrast to Kohut (1977) I have emphasized that self psychology is a psychology of conflict, as I shall later describe (Modell, 1984b). In a larger sense it reflects one's sense of safety in the world.

The issue is further beclouded by certain theoretical assumptions which may have become invalid because of the knowledge we have acquired of the narcissistic neuroses, the knowledge that the conflict between the ego and the external world cannot be used to distinguish the psychoses from the neuroses. For in addition to intrapsychic conflict the narcissistic disorders involve conflict that can be placed within the context of a two-person psychology. We have learned that psychotic-like defenses related, for example, to fears of losing one's autonomy and separateness, of being swallowed up by the other, which we initially observed in the psychoses, can now also be observed within this group of narcissistic neuroses (Green, 1975). These phenomena are not to be judged psychotic as there is no concurrent loss of reality testing. What is more, the people we term narcissistic cover a broad spectrum, from those who are frankly ill to those who are socially very effective and successful.

In contemplating a change in the model of the neuroses we are forced to consider the relation between this new arena of conflict, that between the self and the environment, and the more traditional source of conflict in the neuroses—the Oedipus complex, which may also be active in the so-called narcissistic personality. I shall consider later the complex interplay between these two sectors of the personality.

The relationship between the self and the human environment is in part mediated through the sphere of affects; states of nonrelatedness are one type of response to disturbances in the holding environment. States of nonrelatedness may be characterized by the noncommunication of affects or by the display of essentially false affects that serve not as a communication but as a manipulation of the affective response in the other. We are all aware of patients who induce in us a feeling that there are not two people present in the consulting room, who fill up the hours with talk, but whose words are essentially shorn of their affective meaning. Sometimes sessions may be filled with *Sturm und Drang* and yet empty, in fact, of genuine affects. This is not to imply any conscious attempt to mislead, but it should be understood as an unconscious defense in which an affective response is elicited in the other so that it will be reflected back into the patient who otherwise feels empty and dead. When someone is not relating to me I often feel sleepy and bored, and although we may all respond in our own particular way, I believe it is axiomatic that when we are continually in the presence of someone who is physically near us but not relating, we will experience a profound affective reaction (Modell, 1975a, 1980, 1981, 1984b).

I have used the metaphor of the cocoon to describe the patient's endo-psychic perception of this state of nonrelatedness (Modell, 1976). A cocoon is like a fortress, yet it is self-sufficient and requires no further nourishment; it has the capacity for further growth but is in a state of suspended animation. To follow the analogy further, although it is walled off it needs to be attached to something. What I am describing is a state of omnipotent self-sufficiency—the belief that one does not need anything from others, which is an illusion that may paradoxically deny an extreme dependency. The people I am describing may not be able to give freely or receive affection; they may be truly isolated within their fortress so that they neither hear nor receive anything from the outside. Some of my patients describe themselves as being encased in a plastic bubble, a mummy case or, as Sylvia Plath perceived it, a bell jar. As one penetrates further into this phenomenology, one learns that the illusion of self-sufficiency is reinforced by a magical belief that they occupy a protected sphere, removed from the dangers of the world, removed from the possibility of death, disease, and misfortune, that they are not "really in the world." In this sense they have achieved an illusion of invulnerability; they cannot be surprised, influenced, or controlled.

This kind of character formation has been understood as a response to trauma. This is explicit in Winnicott's (1965) work and more recently in Kohut's (1977) contribution. In considering the issue of trauma there is no escape from Freud's "complemental series," that is, the complementary influences of those autonomous forces arising within the personality and those traumatic influences imposed upon the personality from the environment. At different periods Freud himself varied the emphasis that he attributed to the role of trauma vis-à-vis purely internal influences, initially emphasizing environmental trauma, then fantasy, and later, after 1920, returning to a consideration of the influence of trauma. Sulloway (1983) has suggested that with the publication of "Beyond the Pleasure Principle" Freud (1920) attributed greater weight to the traumatic etiology of neuroses, seeing this as consistent with the workings of the repetition compulsion.

We also know that ever since Freud learned that he had been misled by believing in his patient's fantasies of seduction by their caretakers, psychoanalysts have guarded themselves against any naïve belief in the stories their patients tell them. We have become distrustful of our reconstructions. (Spence [1982] has carried this distrust to its logical extreme.) Of course there are no definitive guidelines that enable us to separate fantasy from historical fact. All we can say with certainty is that our reconstructions correspond to the patient's psychic reality. With our growing experience with narcissistic personalities our understanding of trauma has broadened to include not only a single event but the effect of more cumulative interaction between the child and its caretakers (Khan, 1963; Winnicott, 1965; Kohut, 1977). In the reconstruction of these traumas, whether or not the patient's parents behaved precisely as they have been reported cannot be judged with any assurance. In spite of all these disclaimers, I tend to believe in certain reconstructions. For what we accept as the truth is not what the patient first presents to us, but is a picture that emerges only gradually after considerable resistance has been overcome. The initial portrait of a parent may be idealized and negative features denied in order to preserve an illusion of protection, and a truer picture may take many months or in some cases several years to emerge.

Although significant failures of the parental holding environment do occur, and what we term narcissism is in part a response to these traumas, narcissistic disorders may also reflect unspecified social forces, so that individual trauma alone cannot account for the adult neurosis. I am merely suggesting that we are always re-examining the balance between internal and external forces, and that in the narcissistic personality one cannot avoid the impression that certain experiences have proved to be traumatic. But it is also possible that certain issues may be selectively emphasized because of a restructuring of memory that occurs in adolescence and adult life. It has long been recognized that our memories behave very much as the Russians write their histories, that is, in accordance with current and immediate requirements.

Much of what we call narcissism is really a system for self-preservation. We know that in human development, as is true of other species, the parents stand as a buffer between the young and a potentially dangerous environment. Information concerning this environment is usually transmitted through speech charged with a certain quota of affect. We have only to recall the observations of Anna Freud and Burlingham (1944) during World War II that young children remained calm during bombing raids if their mothers were not unduly anxious. In a literal sense, the communication of affect between parent and child is vital for the survival of the child. What we can reconstruct from our case histories is nothing as dramatic as the reaction to a bombing raid, but something that is more subtle and insidious. Among patients who are significantly narcissistic it is a common pattern for one parent to have been emotionally absent for significant periods of time and hence simply not there to communicate. Such a parent may disguise this absence through the communication of affects that are essentially false and misleading, such as "everything is wonderful, dear." In some cases intelligent children will correctly observe that their parents are "off." In some instances a child may sense that a parent is in fact crazy, although this fact may not be acknowledged either within or without the family. In other instances a parent may be correctly judged to be silly or fatuous, that is, lacking good social judgment (Modell, 1975a, 1981). These parents, then, become unreliable sources of information about the external world, and so create a secondary world that is at odds with the child's growing appreciation of social reality. George Orwell (1968), in his memoir of life in an English boarding school, described his reaction to a punishment as: ". . . a deeper grief which is peculiar to childhood and not easy to convey: a sense of desolate loneliness and helplessness, of being locked up not only in a hostile world but in a world of good and evil where the rules were such that it was actually not possible for me to keep them" (p. 334).

Besides being an unreliable source of information concerning the world, some parents may also ignore the child's right to his or her own autonomy, and fail to acknowledge him as a separate being. This leads to a failure to grant a right to privacy, a right to control one's bodily functions and to retain an area of mind that is secret and cannot be found.

The response to these relative failures in the parental holding environment is a precocious maturation, as if the child were saying to himself: "I
cannot rely on my mother's judgment, therefore I have to be a better
mother to myself." There is then a turning away from the caretakers and
the establishment of an illusory system of self-sufficiency—the cocoon. In
the face of actual helplessness this system needs to be buttressed by grandiose and omnipotent illusions. It is in this sense that I understand narcissism: the preservation of the self is a manifestation of self-preservation.
Affects are the markers of this process: nonrelatedness signifies a giving
up, a turning away; if affects are object seeking, as I believe them to be,
nonrelatedness signifies that there is no object to be had. This state of
nonrelatedness, playing the game of compliance or introducing false affects, serves also to hide what is genuine and real (Modell, 1980). It serves
to protect what Winnicott called the true self from being shattered by an
unempathic response.

What happens when someone with this type of defensive organization
enters into psychotherapy or psychoanalysis? Problems of safety or the
entrustment of the self to another become paramount. If the trauma has
been severe these issues may occupy the treatment to the exclusion of
anything else, and may do so for months and even years. If treatment
proves to be successful, if there is still a willingness to try again, the therapeutic setting will function as a new holding environment. Therapeutic
gains may still occur in states of nonrelatedness; one can have an object
tie—sometimes of great intensity—and still not relate. I have used the visual
metaphor in describing this as a sphere within a sphere (Modell, 1980);
the patient may still be contained within his own omnipotent self-sufficiency
and yet be held by the larger sphere of the therapeutic environment. The
idealization of the therapist, which may or may not be openly acknowledged, is, I believe, derived from the wished-for illusion that someone now
stands between the self and the dangerous world. I have described this as
a form of transitional relatedness emphasizing the illusion of protection
(Modell, 1968). Kohut has referred to some of the same phenomena using
the term "selfobject."

This clinical description is intended to illustrate some aspects of the
phenomenology of narcissism in contrast to what has been considered the
classical model of the neurosis. I have already alluded to the role of trauma
in the narcissistic neuroses. There is also implicit in these neuroses a blur-
ring of the boundaries between self and object, a condition we first encountered through our treatment of psychoses. In describing a new model
of the neuroses we now have to consider the Oedipus complex (Panel, in
press) and the related subject of transference. The belief that the Oedipus

complex is at the center of the neuroses has been, until recently, an almost unquestioned assumption. Freud (1905) stated: "The Oedipus complex is the nuclear complex of the neuroses, and constitutes the essential part of their content. It represents the peak of infantile sexuality, which, through its after-effects, exercises a decisive influence on the sexuality of adults. Every new arrival on this planet is faced by the task of mastering the Oedipus complex; anyone who fails to do so falls victim to neurosis" (p. 226n).

We know that Kohut questioned the centrality of the Oedipus complex, proposing that it is the disturbance of the self rather than the Oedipus that is at the center of the narcissistic personality. We know also that this idea is not entirely new, but we are all indebted to Kohut for so forcibly confronting us with this issue. What I described earlier under the heading of narcissism is a mixture of wishes, fears, and defenses related to the autonomy and separateness of the self, and Kohut has tended to view this as part of a selfobject transference. However, I have come to think that the general term "transference" may obscure the fact that what we observe is conceptually of quite a different order from the transference neuroses in which the Oedipus complex is at the center. The uniformity of these manifestations, the fact that they recur repeatedly in such a broad range of people, suggests that we are witnessing the working through of developmental conflicts concerning self/object differentiation (see also Mahler, 1967) and the related issue of the protection afforded by the human environment. This is in sharp contrast to the variegated, highly personalized transference neuroses which reflect an externalization of imagos derived from the Oedipus complex. Therefore the existence of a transference neurosis can be thought of as an operational marker for the Oedipus complex.

Now, I have said that this working through of developmental conflict related to self/object differentiation may occupy an analysis for years to the exclusion of conflicts derived from the Oedipus complex. In some individuals a genuine transference neurosis does in fact emerge, frequently with an emphasis on the negative Oedipus complex. In others, derivatives of the Oedipus never seem to affect the analysis in a significant way. From this we may conclude that the Oedipus complex was not pathogenic, or that issues concerning the preservation of the self and self-preservation were so overwhelming that there was no opportunity for the Oedipus to emerge. I think that most experienced analysts would agree that more commonly the picture is mixed; even in the presence of severe narcissistic pathology, derivatives of the Oedipus are in evidence and contribute significantly to the character structure (Panel, in press).

It would be a simple matter if we could adopt a nosological solution for the model of the neuroses. If we could claim that the transference neurosis occurs in the classical case in which the Oedipus is still at the center, then we could call these narcissistic phenomena something else. But if you agree that most cases are mixed, this nosological solution will not work (see also Rangell, 1982). I do not believe that the disorders of the self have essentially displaced the Oedipus complex: what I am proposing is that we maintain a certain balance about this problem; that the Oedipus complex, on one hand, and the system of self-preservation, encompassing the self and the human environment, on the other, comprise two separate organizations or sectors within the personality.

Years of analytic work may be focused on issues concerned with the safety and preservation of the self to the relative exclusion of derivatives of the Oedipus complex, and if this work is successful there will be a definitive shift in the analytic process with the gradual emergence of a transference neurosis. The supposition of two separate sectors is further reinforced by the fact that the sequence of the analytic work is of considerable importance; issues of safety and entrustment of the self to the analytic process must take precedence over a focus upon the Oedipus complex; if the order of work is reversed the analysis may not succeed. This may be something that every experienced analyst knows, but the acknowledgment of a separate developmental sector encompassing the safety of the self provides a certain conceptual backing for our more intuitive therapeutic interventions.

If I understand Kohut correctly, he proposed that the Oedipus and the self not so much occupy separate developmental sectors or developmental lines but comprise separate psychologies. He has contrasted the conflict, drive, and structural psychology to which the Oedipus belongs with the psychology of the self (Kohut, 1977, 1982). In his last paper (Kohut, 1982), he proposes that the myth of kindly, protective Odysseus should replace the myth of Oedipus the father slayer; that parricide is the consequence of abnormal intergenerational relationships; that normally there is a joyous interrelationship. My own analytic experiences do not support these conclusions.

The centrality of the Oedipus complex and the earlier centrality of the erotogenic zones have had a lasting imprint upon the way we think about psychic development. The term "preoedipal" conveys the implication that the Oedipus is the point of reference, very much like the dating of our calendars from the birth of Christ. As the conflicts I have described concerning the autonomy and separateness of the self are traditionally identified as preoedipal, and the self and the Oedipus are seen as following separate developmental lines, we must modify our concept of the preoedipal. Erotogenic zones have points of closure; they are not unlike archaeological strata. The preoedipal phase has been thought of as such a stratum with closure at about the point where self/object differentiation is maintained (Mahler, 1967). From this point of view the appearance of problems of self/object differentiation and of the autonomy of the self bespeak something primitive, archaic, or at least regressed. Our experience with the analysis of the so-called narcissistic personality indicates that such problems, however, can persist well into adult life and do not necessarily have such a pathological implication. There is a different developmental timetable here that extends into adult life. On this point I am in full agreement with Kohut; I have described the continued need for transitional objects for a sense of safety in the world (Modell, 1968), and Kohut has similarly described our continued need for selfobjects. Self/object differentiation does not reach a point of closure in the preoedipal period, and consequently narcissism cannot be fitted into some hierarchical arrangement in regard to the Oedipus complex. There is a further question regarding the Oedipus itself. Is there a point of closure? Loewald (1980) suggests that the Oedipus complex is not put to rest, as Freud believed, but is something whose influence continues to be felt as a normal constituent of adult life.

Our traditional theory does not separate the Oedipus from the development of object relations but views them as a continuous, comingling series. For example, when Anna Freud (1965) wished to illustrate the concept of developmental lines in her book *Normality and Pathology in Childhood*, she described libidinal stages and stages in the development of object relations as follows: "Stage One" would be the biological unity between mother and infant; "Stage Two"—part object or need-fulfilling object; "Stage Three"—that of object constancy; "Stage Four"—the ambivalent relationship of the preoedipal and sadistic stage; "Stage Five"—the completely object-centered, phallic oedipal phase, and so forth.

You might reply to all of this that the preoedipal mother is a protective object and yet is in a relationship to both son and daughter that is unquestionably eroticized. How, then, can the protective object upon whom the child depends for survival be separated from the erotic? Freud (1905) may have offered a solution to this problem in his "Three Essays on Sexuality" where he discusses the relationship between self-preservation and the erotic development that culminates in the Oedipus. In his description of autoeroticism, sucking, and the erotogenic oral zone, Freud states, "To begin with, sexual activity *attaches* itself to functions serving the purpose of self preservation and does not become independent of them until later" (p. 16). Laplanche (1976) focused his attention on this particular passage and believes that a more accurate English translation would be that the sexual activity *props* itself against the functions serving the purpose of self preservation. To use the word "props" rather than "attaches" emphasizes the temporary nature of this relationship. One could say that the function of self-preservation leans upon or borrows something from the erotic; the eroticization of sucking, for example, may be in the service of self-preservation. The erotic provides a point of crossover in what otherwise are two separate psychic systems. But the point of crossover is temporary for, as Freud noted, self-preservation does in fact become independent of the erotic later on.

The organization of the personality concerned with self-preservation and the preservation of the self and the organization of the personality that is centered upon the Oedipus are, in Laplanche's words, "propped up against each other," but, like apartheid, have a separate and unequal development. To follow the analogy further, it is the erotic that provides the points of crossover. Self-preservation borrows from the erotic and is propped up by it; we see this in caricature in certain perversions where the wish to control and be controlled is literally acted out and eroticized. The complexity of the negative Oedipus complex may be due in part to the fact that the theme of self-preservation is condensed onto the Oedipus. In the negative Oedipus complex in the male, the eroticized passivity and idealization of the father reflect not only a defensive retreat in the face of castration anxiety but a positive wish-for protection.

I would like to illustrate this dualistic—and I hope balanced—view of those determinants of neuroses arising from the Oedipus complex and those determinants arising from conflicts in self/object differentiation, by referring to a common if not ubiquitous symptom, unconscious guilt. Some years ago, I described a form of guilt that was not derived from the Oedipus complex. At that time I mistakenly labeled it as preoedipal, not understanding that I was observing a different series. This is a form of guilt that has its origin not so much in the preservation of the individual as in the preservation of the nuclear family. I first described this in the paper "On Having the Right to a Life" (Modell, 1965). I understood this form of guilt as something that is experienced in the process of individuation: having the right to a separate existence is fraught with guilt. In this sense one can speak of separation guilt. Behind this may be the universal belief that in order to be born someone else must die. Of course I am referring to the guilt of the survivor. We have learned about this guilt in its most extreme forms from survivors of holocausts. But survival also takes on more subtle forms, and in this sense we may all be survivors. There is, I believe, in mental life an unconscious bookkeeping system that takes into account the current fate of other family members. Frequently, other members of the family do not survive; those who achieve upward mobility may do so at the expense of the guilt of leaving the other family members behind. The suffering that this form of guilt imposes is not insignificant. This form of guilt does, of course, coexist with the more familiar oedipal guilt of surpassing the achievements of the parent of the same sex. But here the sex linkage is not so apparent; a son may feel guilty because of separation from his mother, and as I have said the fate of the other siblings is significant.

In addition to individuation one can observe a related belief that there is a limited quantity of "good" available to the nuclear family. If someone has more the others invariably have less. Thus the mere possession of something good can evoke guilt. Since this of course includes the good that obtains from psychotherapy and psychoanalysis, this form of guilt may contribute to the negative therapeutic reaction. It will not have escaped you that there is a clear analogy between the belief in a quantity of "good" as a concrete substance and the idea of a limited supply of food upon which the survival of all depends. In addition to the fate of other family members, there is no doubt that this type of guilt will be affected by the intensity of one's envy and greed. Here the analogy of "good" to food is even more apparent.

What I have been describing are essentially parallel organizations within the personality: the Oedipus and the preservation of the self. Both foci obviously serve adaptive purposes. Oedipal guilt enforces, however imperfectly, the maintenance of the incest taboo. In this sense it is a biological given whose evolutionary function was suggested by the geneticist Darlington (1969) as follows: "The incest taboo has been the decisive agent in holding together not only each human tribe but also the whole human species" (p. 61). The guilt that ensues from having more may be the remnant of a similar, originally adaptive "primal fantasy." In many primitive societies there are unavoidable times of hardship during which the band is threatened by extinction through starvation. The prevalence of infanticide as a means of population control in primitive societies attests to the need to adapt to a limited food supply. Therefore the altruistic impulse to share food promotes the survival of the group. There are good biological reasons to inhibit greediness; the alternative would be the survival of a few stronger individuals, but as has been observed there is greater value in the survival of the group. I must add that these ideas were proposed some years before (Modell, 1971) the movement currently known as sociobiology made its appearance. The sociobiologists have popularized the survival value of altruism, but I wish to disassociate myself from their simplistic belief in the genetic origins of complex characterological and cultural phenomena.

In proposing that we separate an erotic series that culminates in the Oedipus complex from a series encompassing the self and its protective objects, it would seem that I am proposing a return to what Freud (1915), in "Instincts and Their Vicissitudes," called the ego or self-preservative instincts. This has been implicit in other conceptualizations of narcissism (Rangell, 1982). Freud, for a period of time, contrasted the sexual instincts with the instincts of self-preservation. This distinction was supported by August Weissman's separation of the somatic and the germ cells; so that the adaptation of the individual might have a separate fate in evolution from the preservation of the species.

Freud (1914) states in the paper "On Narcissism": "The individual himself regards sexuality as one of his own ends; whereas from another point of view he is an appendage to his germ-plasm, at whose disposal he puts his energies in return for a bonus of pleasure. He is the moral vehicle of a (possibly) immortal substance—like the inheritor of an entailed property, who is only the temporary holder of an estate which survives him. The separation of the sexual instincts from the ego-instincts would simply reflect this two-fold distinction of the individual" (p. 78).

In Bibring's (1969) closely reasoned description of the history of Freud's instinct theory he noted that self-preservation included not only the nutrient functions but also "impulses to control, and instincts of power and self assertion" (p. 297). We would now also include what the ethologists call attachment behavior, that is, the primary dependent relationship upon the protective caretaker.

Freud felt that he was on solid biological ground when he separated the instinct for self-preservation from the erotic; he was distinguishing between the transitory need of the individual for survival and the more lasting requirement of the preservation of the germ-plasm. Although he appeared to have abandoned this classification with his introduction of the death instinct he never quite gave up his earlier conceptions. In "An Outline of Psychoanalysis" Freud (1940) states: "Just as the id is directed exclusively to obtaining pleasure, so the ego is governed by considerations of safety. The ego has set itself up the task of self-preservation, which the id appears to neglect" (p. 199). Sandler (1960) has emphasized this point in the context of ego psychology with his felicitous concept, "The Background of Safety."

I have used the term "self-preservation" in a somewhat different context. I have referred to the dependency of the individual upon the protective parental objects who stand between the self and a potentially dangerous environment. I have described certain forms of narcissism as a response to the perceived failure of the parents to provide in Winnicott's terms a "good-enough" holding environment. A biological analogy to the holding environment can be found in what the ethologists call attachment behavior. Bowlby (1969) states: "There are three main reasons why it is wise to keep attachment behavior and sexual behavior conceptually distinct. The first is that activations of the two systems vary independently of one another. The second is that the class of objects towards which each is directed may be quite different. A third is that sensitive phases in the development of each are likely to occur at different ages" (p. 231).

Bibring (1969) also observed that Freud's motive for eventually abandoning the concept of ego instincts came from psychiatry—specifically from the studies of the narcissism of schizophrenia, where symptoms such as megalomania were understood as a libidinal cathexis of the ego. If the ego or the self (and here I do not imply that these terms are interchangeable) were libidinized the distinction between ego instincts and sexual instincts could not be maintained. We know that Freud resolved this problem by substituting a new duality, that of eros and thanatos, for the older duality of the sexual and self-preservative instincts. It may seem ironic that it is again the subject of narcissism that may lead to the rehabilitation of the instincts for self-preservation. In an earlier paper (Modell, 1975b) I suggested that the instincts subserving object relations are of a different order from those of the sexual instincts. However, I am not proposing a direct or simple return to Freud's 1915 theories of instinct. Such a path backward is made impossible by the advances in biology which have radically revised our thinking about instinct.

A review of the advances in biology that have made some of Freud's biological assumptions obsolete is beyond the aims of this paper. I wish only to mention that Freud himself assumed a totally ad hoc position regarding these biological questions, recognizing that they could not be derived from psychoanalysis itself. In this respect psychoanalysis was dependent upon contemporary biology for the classification of instincts and indeed for the concept of instinct itself. The biology of Freud's intellectually formative period did not appreciate the dynamic relationship that existed between the organism and its environment. (For a more extensive discussion see Modell, 1984b.) Freud understood instinct as a force arising from within the interior of the organism (an id relatively cut off from the external world). This is no longer the view of contemporary biologists (Freedman, 1982) who consider the interplay between the environment and biological units from the level of the cell to the organism. Further, the concept of an overarching process such as an instinct may seem to some biologists as antiquated; the term does not appear in many textbooks of ethology.

There is, then, a decided shift in our view of the role of the Oedipus complex in the structure of the neurosis. What I am describing are, of course, my own views; there is no uniformity of opinion within psychoanalysis. There are those who believe that nothing has changed—that the Oedipus is still at the center and that narcissistic character structure is but an epiphenomenon that does not require us to consider any fundamental change in our etiological assumptions. The self psychologists would have us believe that a complete revolution has occurred and that the Oedipus complex has, in effect, been replaced by disorders of the self. From what I have said earlier you will understand that I do not agree. The Oedipus complex shares the stage with other forces equal in power which also have their roots in our phylogenetic history.

I have been describing the narcissistic neuroses as in part a response to a relative failure in the parental holding environment, and I have also invoked two organizational foci—the Oedipus complex and the preservation of the self—both of which can be traced phylogenetically. This view may appear, on the surface at least, to be inconsistent with my earlier statement that neuroses are a barometer of social change (see also Modell, 1984a).

Although we do not know the pathways through which society impacts upon the personality, to acknowledge these social forces is not inconsistent with an equal acknowledgment of developmental trauma and a genetic predisposition to primal fantasies such as the Oedipus complex and other forms of unconscious guilt (Modell, 1965, 1971). For example, the *grande hystérie* of Victorian days may be in part a response to the extreme cultural hypocrisy regarding sexuality that existed in the Victorian era and the tension between what is known and what is concealed (see Gay, 1984). The hysterical symptom was both a defiant symbolic expression of a hidden sexual wish, as Freud described, and simultaneously the carrier within its structure of an element of punishment for what was forbidden.

Self-preservation and the preservation of the self, in a larger context, are part of one's adaptation to reality—which includes of course social reality (see also Samitca, 1981). If it is true that the increase of narcissism is in part secondary to cultural change, then how does culture influence development? There are two general hypotheses: first, that cultural change is transmitted through the personality of the parents. This could be described as indirect cultural transmission. A second hypothesis, and one to which I subscribe, is the belief that the individual experiences the impact of culture directly during adolescence and preadolescence, and this impact may accentuate already existent character traits. For it is generally recognized that there is a reorganization of the personality in adolescence, that adult neuroses are by no means a simple recapitulation of childhood or infantile neuroses. This second hypothesis can be termed a theory of direct cultural transmission. These two hypotheses are not, of course, incompatible.

To describe parents as increasingly emotionally unavailable to their children or unempathic and intrusive is to say essentially that they themselves are more narcissistic. (Kohut, 1977, in addressing this problem, spoke of the trend toward small families and the concurrent understimulation of the child.) If we are correct that there has been a marked increase in the incidence of narcissistic personalities in the last fifteen years, we are describing young adults who were adolescents in the late fifties and sixties, and infants and children in the years following World War II. Their parents, for the most part, would have been children in the middle twenties. Why, we must ask, would this group of parents have become increasingly narcissistic? The end of the twenties, of course, marked the beginning of the Great Depression, but the previous years were ones of relative stability compared to our own era.

An alternative hypothesis is the effect of the parent's neurosis has become magnified because of the loss of the extended family. This is a plausible hypothesis, but I personally find it less than fully convincing, as I believe that there is a more direct and profound relation between the failure of the human protective environment and narcissistic neuroses.

The critic Lionel Trilling (1971), in his celebrated essay, "Sincerity and Authenticity," has grappled with the same problem. As he was a critic and not a clinician, he examined literature and not patients. He believed that in the late sixteenth or early seventeenth century something like a mutation of human nature took place, with the formation of a new type of personality, a personality centered on the virtue of sincerity. Trilling defines sincerity as the degree of congruence between feeling and avowal. Sincerity is judged to be a virtue as it supports the workings of society. Social institutions require a measure of trust in order to function so that sincerity, the congruence between feeling and avowal, is in its turn a measure of truthfulness. Trilling further believed that this mutation of personality coincided with the emergence of the idea of society as we conceive it now; there was a time in which the concept of society did not exist. If Trilling defines sincerity as the congruence between feeling and avowal, the breakdown of sincerity corresponds to what I have described as states of nonrelatedness and noncommunication.

Our contemporary world confronts the adolescent with failures in the protective environment analogous to those experienced earlier in relation to the parental environment. This second disillusionment with our social institutions, a disillusionment that is far-reaching indeed, is in part supported by the fact that there is in public life a gradual and accelerating erosion of trust; there is no longer any congruence between what people believe and what people say. This second disillusionment of adolescence will reinvoke the same coping mechanisms the individual used earlier.

Sincerity was rightly considered to be a moral virtue since it supported the underpinnings of society itself. Any spurious or counterfeit communications by the leaders of our society will reinforce the responses that the individual learned earlier in coping with parental falseness. There is a reflexive reinforcement of the privacy and secrecy of the self which remains hidden behind a façade of compliance, that is, the façade of playing the game. The authenticity of the self remains private. To hide the self from others may be socially adaptive, but when the authenticity of the self is also hidden—that is, split off—from other sectors of the personality, psychopathology ensues. It is the tragedy of those who present themselves to us as patients that they are cut off from their inner authentic self—they have played the game too well.

In 1950 David Riesman and his collaborators, in a remarkably prescient book, *The Lonely Crowd*, described a change in American character—a shift from "inner directed" to "other directed"—a character change in the direction of complying, turning off, and playing the game. Social compliance is perhaps the paradigm of the normal narcissistic personality of our time.

There are additional analogies to be observed between our contemporary institutions and the early parental environment. Defensive narcissism is in part, as we have described earlier, a reaction to the perceived loss of the parental protecting environment. The child correctly perceives that the parent cannot in fact protect him/her from the dangers of the real world. The individual has always experienced a certain helplessness regarding his own fate. Human beings have always been at the mercy of uncontrolled social eruptions which can and do inalterably change their lives. Pasternak's Dr. Zhivago is perhaps the clearest example of this. But even after revolutions there is hope for the future. We all know that with the spread of atomic weapons there is a real possibility that civilization will be entirely destroyed—there is a possibility that there will be absolutely no hope. The response has been a search for hopefulness not in relationship to the world, but in relationship to the self (see also Morgenthau and Person, 1978). One cannot master one's fate, but perhaps one can at least master the self, or the body that stands as a proxy for the self. Today the options for self-determination appear to be limitless—one even has the option of changing one's sex. The current national preoccupation with what we eat and how much we weigh may support the illusion that we, in the face of helplessness vis-à-vis the larger world, can at least control the small world of our bodies.

We all have a need for privacy and secrecy. We need to keep a part of ourselves isolated, hidden, and unfound. It is ironic that the social revolution that has resulted from Freud's discoveries may have inadvertently contributed to an intrusion upon this privacy; today almost anyone can

ARNOLD H. MODELL 85

become an amateur psychoanalyst. Pity the unfortunate child whose psychoanalytically oriented parents interpret the unconscious meaning of his or her behavior. Public inauthenticity has combined with a certain intrusiveness to result in the narcissistic defense of noncommunication. The preservation of the self is truly a form of self-preservation.

## REFERENCES

Bibring, E. (1969), The development and problems of the theory of the instincts. *Internat. J. Psycho-Anal.*, 50:293–308.
Bowlby, J. (1969), *Attachment*. New York: Basic Books.
Darlington, C. (1969), *The Evolution of Man and Society*. New York: Simon and Schuster.
Durkheim, E. (1897), *Suicide*. New York: Free Press, 1968.
Freedman, D. (1982), Of instincts and instinctual drives: Some developmental considerations. *Psychoanal. Inquiry*, 1:153–167.
Freud, A. (1965), *Normality and Pathology in Childhood*. New York: International Universities Press.
——— Burlingham, D. (1944), *War and Children*. New York: International Universities Press.
Freud, S. (1905), Three essays on the theory of sexuality. *Standard Edition*, 7:125–248. London: Hogarth Press, 1953.
——— (1914), On narcissism. *Standard Edition*, 14:111–140. London: Hogarth Press, 1957.
——— (1915), Instincts and their vicissitudes. *Standard Edition*, 14:117–140. London: Hogarth Press, 1957.
——— (1920), Beyond the pleasure principle. *Standard Edition*, 18:3–66. London: Hogarth Press, 1955.
——— (1940), An outline of psychoanalysis. *Standard Edition*, 23:141–208. London: Hogarth Press, 1964.
Gay, P. (1984), *The Bourgeois Experience*. New York: Oxford University Press.
Graves, R. (1955), *The Greek Myths*. Baltimore: Md.: Penguin Books.
Green, A. (1975), The analyst, symbolization and absence in the analytic setting. *Internat. J. Psycho-Anal.*, 56:1–22.
Khan, M. (1963), The concept of cumulative trauma. In: *The Privacy of the Self*. New York: International Universities Press, pp. 42–58.
Kohut, H. (1977), *The Restoration of the Self*. New York: International Universities Press.
——— (1979), The two analyses of Mr. Z. *Internat. J. Psycho-Anal.*, 60:3–27.
——— (1982), Introspection, empathy, and the semi-circle of mental health. *Internat. J. Psycho-Anal.*, 63:395–407.
Laplanche, J. (1976), *Life and Death in Psycho-Analysis*. Baltimore: Johns Hopkins University Press.
Loewald, H. (1980), The waning of the Oedipus complex. In: *Papers on Psychoanalysis*. New Haven: Yale University Press, pp. 384–404.
Mahler, M. (1967), On human symbiosis and the vicissitudes of individuation. *J. Amer. Psychoanal. Assn.*, 15:740–763.
Modell, A. (1965), On having a right to a life: An aspect of the superego's development. *Internat. J. Psycho-Anal.*, 46:323–333.
——— (1968), *Object Love and Reality*. New York: International Universities Press.
——— (1971), The origin of certain forms of preoedipal guilt and the implications for a psychoanalytic theory of affects. *Internat. J. Psycho-Anal.*, 52:337–346.
——— (1975a), A narcissistic defense against affects and the illusion of self-sufficiency. *Internat. J. Psycho-Anal.*, 56:275–282.

—— (1975b), The ego and the id: Fifty years later. *Internat. J. Psycho-Anal.*, 56:57–68.
—— (1976), "The holding environment" and the therapeutic action of psychoanalysis. *J. Amer. Psychoanal. Assn.*, 24:285–307.
—— (1980), Affects and their non-communication. *Internat. J. Psycho-Anal.*, 61:259–267.
—— (1981), The narcissistic character and disturbances in the "holding environment." In: *The Course of Life*, vol. 3, ed. S. Greenspan & G. Pollock. Washington, D.C.: Department of Health and Human Services, pp. 367–379.
—— (1983), Comments on the rise of narcissism. In: *The Future of Psychoanalysis*, ed. A. Goldberg. New York: International Universities Press, pp. 111–121.
—— (1984a), Self psychology as a psychology of conflict: Comments on the psychoanalysis of the narcissistic personality. In: *Psychoanalysis: The Vital Issues*, vol. 2., ed. G. Pollock & J. Gedo. New York: International Universities Press, pp. 131–148.
—— (1984b), *Psychoanalysis in a New Context*. New York: International Universities Press.
Morgenthau, H. & Person, E. (1978), The roots of narcissism. *Partisan Rev.*, 45:337–347.
Orwell, G. (1968), Such were the joys. In: *In Front of Your Nose*. New York: Harcourt Brace Jovanovich.
Panel (in press), The Oedipus complex revisited, M. Sacks, reporter. *J. Amer. Psychoanal. Assn.*
Rangell, L. (1982), The self in psychoanalytic theory. *J. Amer. Psychoanal. Assn.*, 30:863–891.
Riesman, D., Glazer, N., & Denney, R. (1950), *The Lonely Crowd*. New York: Doubleday Anchor.
Samitca, D. (1981), L'influence des facteurs socio-culturels sur la demande en soins psychiatre. *Arch. Swisses de Neurologie, Neurochirurgie et de Psychiatre*, 130:158–177.
Sandler, J. (1960), The background of safety. *Internat. J. Psycho-Anal.*, 41:352–356.
Spence, D. (1982), *Narrative Truth and Historical Truth*. New York: Norton.
Sulloway, F. (1983), *Freud Biologist of the Mind*. New York: Basic Books.
Trilling, L. (1971), *Sincerity and Authenticity*. Cambridge, Mass.: Harvard University Press.
Winnicott, D. W. (1965), *The Maturational Processes and the Facilitating Environment*. New York: International Universities Press.

*February 1984*

# The Self and the Oedipus Complex

DAVID M. TERMAN, M.D. (Chicago)

## Introduction

Freud's monumental insights into the nature of inner experience and the genesis from and continuity with the vicissitudes of childhood life have provided the means to chart the new world of the psychoanalytic situation, which he also created and discovered.

The central feature of this terrain was the Oedipus complex, first formulated in his letter to Fliess in 1897. Though his systematic use of it began with "The Interpretation of Dreams" (1900), the first actual publication of the term (Oedipus complex) was in 1910.

Freud's conception of the Oedipus complex emphasized the importance of renouncing the infantile incestuous aims. In the topographic model, this resulted in freedom from neurotic symptoms, whereas conversely, the retention of oedipal aims caused neurotic symptoms. After Freud introduced the structural model, he conceptualized the important structural developments, i.e., the formation of the superego, as a consequence of the renunciation of the incestuous objects. Using the mechanism he had conceived in "Mourning and Melancholia," he postulated the internalization to be a consequence of the loss. For boys, the motivation for the incestuous renunciation was, of course, castration anxiety. This renunciation then *strengthened* the internalized prohibiting father by making available the aggression formerly directed to it.

Schafer (1968), in his erudite consideration of the problems of internalization, points to a number of ambiguities in this formulation. He poses a number of pertinent questions, one of which is stated as follows:

Considering that the Oedipal identifications entail major renunciations

87

and reorganizations, how can one account for the ego strength that must be necessary to effect these changes? [p. 185].

Schafer goes on to explain:

> Having stressed only the strength that *results from* these identifications (it is the *modified* ego that the id turns to), Freud's theory is incomplete and perhaps, as a consequence, inexact. His reference to borrowing strength from the father is too metaphorical to be an explanation . . . [p. 185].

But is it? For with the concepts of the vicissitudes of the development of the self and especially the function and essential role of the selfobject in that development, I think we may be able to create a valid construct from Freud's metaphor.

In this paper, I shall try to apply the model developed by Kohut (1966, 1971, 1977) to a description, and I hope an increased understanding, of the oedipal phase. Looking at the Oedipus complex as a phase of self development rather than in object-relations terms may seem like a paradox. Yet such a view may be likened, perhaps, to looking at the terrain from another perspective.

What I am proposing, then, is that we look at the Oedipus complex as a special case of *self* development. I propose that it be considered as (1) a stage in which the issues are not the fragmentation or cohesion of a whole, nuclear self, but the differentiation, the addition to the self, of important gender-related goals and delineations which may be subject to disintegration; (2) the phase of true emancipation from the obligatory need for massive parental selfobject function (Loewald [1962] has described the oedipal situation as "a resumption, on a new level, of boundary creating processes"); and (3) an important phase in which the still-plastic self is molded in the form of the selfobject templates.[1]

The implications of using this model to understand the vicissitudes of the oedipal period are numerous, but I would like to focus on two of them in this paper.

(1) *The parent has an important role as selfobject, and aspects of parental function have an impact on the formation of both subsequent structure and pathology.* Specifically, some of the content of the superego derives from important mirror functions: the content of the superego is, in part, the residue of mirror experiences at the oedipal level. In particular, I shall focus on the effects

---

[1] After this paper was first presented in 1975, Kohut suggested (1977) that oedipal problems might have their genesis in empathic failures of the oedipal period. Though I do not think that his concept of oedipal drives as breakdown products is felicitous, I do think that understanding of the oedipal phase is incomplete without the elucidation of the experience of parent-child transactions which this paper begins to spell out.

of disruption on the development of the miscarriage of parental narcissistic functions. The quality of badness of self may also be derived from the mirroring experience and hence may make a significant contribution to both the intensity and the conditions of the later production of guilt.

(2) *Abandonment of infantile aims depends on gratification of certain important self experiences as much as on the ultimate frustration of infantile phallic grandiosity.* Another way of stating that is to say that the grandiose ambitions embodied in the oedipal fantasy become transformed by virtue of the appropriate mirroring of the child's gender-determined displays, through which the child derives the confidence to pursue the means to become a true adult like the admired parent.

In making these suggestions, I realize that I am not quite the first to do so. Schafer, in particular, has raised some of these considerations. In his 1960 article on the "Loving and Beloved Superego," he carefully combed Freud's work on the structural theory. Schafer drew on Freud's suggestive statements to point to some potentially significant functions for the psychic economy. For example:

> ... normal courage, endurance and ability to withstand intense stimu-
> lation or deprivation all depend on the feeling of being recognized or
> attended to by the superego or destiny ... [p. 175].

In other words, some of the most important ego functions depend on benevolent superego functions. Schafer made the point that these later internal functions must be derived from the parental protective functions.

He emphasized the importance of the execution of those functions when he stated in another section of the paper that:

> If the parent's superego is immature, hostile and distant from his ego
> it will produce disruptions in crucial parent-child interactions, in partic-
> ular those interactions concerning the child's budding instinctual and
> ego expressions. It is under these conditions that we might expect the
> child to develop an Oedipus complex, both masculine and feminine, that
> is especially difficult to relinquish, and consequently, a severe superego
> [p. 184].

Again this implies that the Oedipus complex and its vicissitudes have some relationship to the parental response to their manifestations.[2]

I wish to present a case which I think highlights two aspects of this formulation. I think it is illustrative because I believe that the trauma was

---

[2] Kohut in 1977 raised the question whether the traumatic nature of the Oedipus complex may in fact, have arisen from "empathy failures from the side of the self object environment of the Oedipal phase" (p. 247). This echoes the question explored here and, in this case I believe, merits an affirmative answer.

(1) within the oedipal context—it occurred at the developmental level after the question of cohesion of the nuclear self had been established; and (2) a failure of the mother to function as a selfobject for the specific oedipal development of this patient.

## Clinical Example

The patient was a 26-year-old single, semiprofessional woman when she came for analysis. The precipitating circumstance was a holiday visit to the home of her older, married brother during which her parents were guests as well. She found herself becoming enraged at her mother as she had been as a child. Her awareness of something highly inappropriate about her rage was her most important conscious reason for seeking analysis. She also mentioned that she had a boyfriend who wanted to marry her; but although she was willing to live with him, she did not want to marry him—or anyone. She was somewhat uneasy about such a resolution, but nonetheless felt her life to be more in order if she kept it. She was working for a family personnel agency in which she held a responsible but ill-defined position. She got along well with the man who ran the shop, but disliked and was suspicious of his wife.

Miss N. was born and raised in a small New England town. Her brother was eighteen months older and her sister four years younger. Father owned a small business and was a quiet, rather contented man. Mother was irritable, dissatisfied with her marriage, and frequently told patient that she should "live" before she was married—though it was selfish just to enjoy and not marry at all. Mother was anxiously and intrusively involved with her children. She was very pleased with brother who tended to do what she said, but was angry with patient, who often opposed her. Brother, patient felt, was mother's boyfriend, while patient reached out to father who was passively accepting.

Patient's relationship with brother was worshipful and rivalrous. Her rivalry felt hopeless, however. She recalled many times an incident in which she was aggressively excluded from brother's play. She threatened to tell her mother. Brother replied that he would deny his exclusion and say patient was lying and that mother would believe him. Patient sadly and angrily swallowed her threat. She knew brother was correct about mother's attitudes.

Another frequently recalled incident of childhood centered around her sexual experimentation with a neighborhood boy. When she was discovered by her mother, she was reprimanded severely. She felt she had done something unmentionably awful, though she wasn't sure exactly what it was.

Later, she was accused a second time, and though this time she was innocent, her mother did not believe her. She decided that she would have to grow up herself—without being able to count on her mother.

Patient did decently in school. She was bright and felt she did not exert herself. She went away to a prestigious eastern school, then upon graduation came to work in Chicago for the firm in which she was still employed. She'd had several affairs of some duration—the first after she graduated from college. She did not want to marry any of the men.

## SUMMARY OF THE ANALYSIS

The first hours illustrate some of the problems macroscopically. The patient began the first several hours telling more of her history. In the course of the third hour she wanted to change one of the arrangements we had made around the analysis. She felt uncomfortable asking about this. She was concerned in the next hour that she was being too aggressive. I linked that concern with her requests—but my lack of response implied to her that the request was not understandable and reasonable. I held the question open to see what such a request meant to her, but did not acknowledge the reality of her need.

She then reported a dream in the following hour. It was the first dream of the analysis.

> Brother and sister and I were having breakfast together. Brother and sister were on one side of the table and I was on the other. Father was standing behind brother and sister. Mother was telling where things would be if she died. She gave a list and said, "We have two keys to the house; one for each of you and you know who you are." I [patient] said to father, "See what she did. She gave keys to brother and sister and none to me."

She clearly felt that my lack of acknowledgment amounted to a narcissistic injury which evoked the narcissistic injury of the past—mother's great favoritism toward brother and her attention to the subsequent child. She recalled the situation that precipitated the analysis, the visit to her brother in which, I then learned, her mother had reneged on the promised gift of a trip to Mexico. She felt she had become enraged with mother after that and felt a return of the feelings of childhood that her brother got everything and she was the inferior, no-good child.

In the following hour (the seventh), she related the incident of her childhood sexual explorations—though not mentioning the time when she was falsely accused—and emphasized both her enormous feeling of badness and her bewilderment over what she had actually done wrong.

My point in relating this material is to show how, in these first few hours, the outline of the problem had begun to take shape. Any mild hesitation on my part, or lack of awareness of her needs, became a narcissistic injury. The injury was related to someone else being chosen, and it was also somehow connected with sexual misdemeanors. There was a suggestion that she had brought on such injury because of her sexual badness.

Paradoxically, in spite of the feeling of badness about sexuality, her subsequent hours became more filled with blatant associations of conscious wishes to seduce me, finally culminating in a brief sexual affair with a casual acquaintance in which she felt elated. She became depressed when it shortly fizzled.

At this point in the analysis, I understood the vicissitudes of her analytic experience in terms of the vicissitudes of her object relations in the oedipal and the defenses against their mobilization in the transference to me. I saw the sexual activity as an acting out of the impulses rather than as directed to me in the analysis. I saw evidence of both guilt and fear in response to either her sexual experiences outside the analysis or the impulses mobilized inside. I interpreted such guilt or bad reactions to her feelings. She responded with rage, indifference, or humiliation. That she wanted to please me and have me like her was not accepted as a good thing in itself but was experienced as a humiliation. That is, when I commented that she had a fear of not pleasing me, or was feeling something from the past, etc., she felt put off or put down. She had a dream in the fortieth hour alluding to a secret note she had written in fourth grade saying, "I love Michael." She recalled how her teacher had found the note and humiliated her. This was how she felt in the transference.

It should be clear by now that the patient was suffering from a narcissistic character disorder and that my initial technique aggravated the narcissistic tensions. Yet the subsequent unfolding of this self in the analysis centered largely around the typical concerns of the oedipal child: the wish for a baby, the wish to be as big as mother, the wish to be important to father, the wish to take mother's place, the wish to be sexually responded to, etc. The *fears* associated with these wishes were also typical of the oedipal period—the fear that I would be angry, jealous, derisive—the feeling that she was bad or would be punished. She became phobic at night at times and had to sleep with her lights on. At other times she could not answer her phone. In short, she became, psychologically, an oedipal child, and what seemed central in this oedipal child was the wish for recognition of herself as a future woman, welcomed into the club, as it were, and the fear that I would punish her for it.

The interpretation of either the impulse or reactive fear or guilt over the impulses only made the situation worse, i.e., the impulse heightened or the rage with herself or me increased. In essence, she felt my activity amounted to a merciless exposure of her "I love Michael" note.

After a year of this approach and increasing despair in the patient, I reviewed my notes of the analysis over a vacation break. I realized that the interpretations I had been making had had the effect of humiliating her, and that the oedipal tensions—the wish to get a loving response from me of some kind—were in the service of an important self confirmation. So I told her at an appropriate point that she wanted to be able to give herself to me as she had to her father, who was quite accepting of her, and not have me push her aside with what amounted to judgments. She cried in response and said she wondered what she'd said that made me understand.

The material following this interpretation concerned wishes to be pregnant. These consisted of relivings, in part, of her feelings around the time mother was pregnant and delivered her younger sister. As I was more empathic to her feelings of inferiority vis-à-vis a mother who could do such wonderful things, she had dreams and associations which retraced her feelings and experiences around a tonsillectomy she underwent during her mother's pregnancy. It was all quite scary and bewildering, done by the local family doctor who was a frightening, paranoid-type man, whom mother ultimately refused to use a few years later. I said to her that perhaps the meaning of that experience to her was that mother had taken away her capacity to have children because she wanted a child. She could see that, but then, to my puzzlement, she began to be afraid of acting out the impulse to get pregnant. She became afraid of both her impulse and the judgment of badness such an action would provoke.

Later in the analysis the patient told me some of why she wanted to get pregnant: she really thought she was unable to do so, quite literally, and it was with the wish to show herself that she could that she wanted to try—like a boy reassuring himself of the presence of his penis. There was also an element of defiance of both the anxiety and the feeling of badness in carrying out the act.

She then had fantasies about being seduced by a dermatologist with whom she had an appointment. She didn't want to tell me these fantasies, and when he finally did *not* seduce her, she felt enraged with me as she told me. She calmed when I noted how humiliated she felt and assured her that we would have time to look into all this.

Here again it is important to note that what is focal is the humiliation of the frustration of the oedipal fantasy, thinly displaced from the analyst. In my transference reincarnation as mother, she felt inferior to me and humiliated that she could not really be the sexual adult.

The oedipal fantasy was not repressed. Indeed, it had never been held back for long. Fear of punishment and fear of me were very clear. She did not want to tell me of her fantasies—partly out of fear of what I, like a punishing parent, would do.

A few analytic hours later, she told about the prospect of becoming sexually involved with a man and became quite excited with reporting it. As she did, she again felt much more fearful of me. Her heart would beat fast, she hesitated to talk, etc. I interpreted her fear of me as being a revival of her fear of mother, which was, in turn, however, defensive against her fear of impregnation. What is more, she was afraid of her wish for pregnancy. Hence, I said, she saw mother as angry with her. That is, her perception of me as angry derived from her impulse to do what was forbidden. She became more and more enraged with me. Was this because she could not tolerate confrontation with her impulses? She would not relinquish the incestuous object? Yes, but also no.

I was bewildered by her rage at such interpretations, but less bewildered at this point in the analysis than I had been earlier. What I had learned—and learned again at this point—was that *linking mother's anger with her impulses implied to her that mother wasn't really angry with her*. I had to understand that mother really was angry with her for legitimate needs and wishes. I had to understand that mother really got angry at her competitive wishes, as though she really *were* a threat to her. I had to bear witness to mother's *inappropriate* anger at her in the past for presentations of her proud and feisty little-girl self.

When I did not, she became more afraid and slept with her light on over a weekend. When I said that she must feel hurt by me, she immediately thought of my interpretation that her feelings about her mother were projections. The real trauma was that she *was* punished for loving and competitive feelings and fantasies.

Let me underscore again that the sexual transference to me was displaced and the predominant mode of the mother transference was narcissistic. The gendered, sexual self was defiantly, fearfully, and uncertainly engaged. She was out to "prove" that a man could be interested in her and, in more regressed forms, that she could get pregnant. The need for me was to be a mirror to such affirmations; the fear was that I would be a dark, punishing mirror.

This mode of analysis continued for about two years. I was essentially the punishing and narcissistically wounding mother while she less desperately sought affirmation from occasional men and then entered into a longer, slightly more hopeful affair. The separations from the analysis were usually greeted with anger and fear that my response would be one of retaliation. She would also try to disavow any need for me which she feared would only make me angry and impatient with her. She began to report feeling better. She became more aware of liking me, but was afraid I would ask her to leave if she admitted such feelings to me. She recalled how irritable her mother became with professions of affection.

As she reexperienced these difficulties of maternal response with me, the picture of her childhood filled in with greater subtlety and detail. The tonsillectomy experience was paradigmatic for the difficulties, both real and perceived, in the relationship with mother. Of course, the real daily relationship was the determinant of the later pathology. It appeared with our reconstructions that things got difficult with mother when she became pregnant with the younger sister. Patient apparently became more assertive and wished to be able to do things herself. Mother was simply not able to tolerate such an assertive developmental step. She would become angry and/or withdraw. She took such movements as a rejection. On the other hand, patient's brother was very eager to please mother on her terms, as young oedipal boys are wont to do. And mother was extraordinarily delighted with his wish to be pleasing. Mother doted on the brother, while she was critical, irritable, and depreciating of patient and father.

Aggravating mother's obvious preference for brother was their unholy alliance against patient in her struggle with mother. When patient would complain about the unfairness of mother's critical attitudes toward her, brother would usually side with mother. Later, patient was able to realize that her defensiveness and assertiveness was cause for mother's anger. But her own insistence was stimulated by the unfair tilt of the childhood situation and mother's angry response in turn to patient's protest. Brother, who was in treatment in another city, related a portrait *he* had drawn of their childhood relationships. He and patient were holding mother on their shoulders, with a gun aimed at the patient. Periodically, the gun would discharge into patient. Patient had her arms out to father who was on the side, detached from the picture.

This picture of the childhood situation and mother's character assembled in memories was greatly reinforced by recounts of her present interactions. Often, undoing the patient's distortions resulted in even more vivid confirmation of her perception of her character. It was also clear, of course, that the patient brought out the worst in her mother. As she progressed in the analysis, her antagonism toward mother, and in turn mother's tense irritability, lessened.

The specific choice of the patient as one outlet for mother's own tensions was made more comprehensible by certain facts in mother's own childhood. She had been born of her mother's second marriage to a man whom grandmother despised. Intense quarreling ended in a long and bitter separation, marked by continued bickering. Grandmother, in her turn, grossly favored the children of the first marriage; she considered all children from the second marriage, and the husband as well, as poor in comparison. She liked the girls least of all. Hence, when the patient began to assert herself and rather implicitly protest her ill-favored status, mother could not tolerate her assertiveness—any more than she had been tolerated in her own.

The reliving of the relationship to father, a father transference, developed sporadically and slowly after considerable working through of the mother mirror transference. Her sexual affairs during this previous period of analysis were with brother-type men. She was reliving the triangle between her mother, brother, and herself. The collapse of a more long-standing affair and her increasing wish not to be involved in such things because of her increased self esteem led to mobilization of some father transferences in the analysis. They were accompanied by a displacement and an inhibition. She became interested in an older, married roué who had also achieved a great deal in their particular business area. He had previously gone with a younger girl for several years. He frequently called patient in a drunken state, making wild propositions. She felt genuine affection for the man and some ambivalence about his propositions. However, she never had an affair with him, and pulled away from any sexual relationships with men for about one and one-half years as she continued to work through her fear of my responses to sexual feelings or self-assertive stands. In the context of the father transference, she feared I would really expect her to be "grown up" sexually and not be satisfied with her childhood coquettishness, and the thought of such expectations terrified her. She worked through some of the father's overstimulating seductiveness in the context of early showers together and some insensitivity to the stimulation of her fantasies. She was fearful that I would become impatient with the process and that I would cut it off before she was truly finished. She realized that something had definitely changed and she was definitely "better," but she was concerned that I would be bored with the work to follow.

It became very important to her to go into detail about her life situation. She needed my understanding of her side of a potential conflict with her woman boss, a mirroring of either her ambitions or her wish for recognition of her work. The infantile roots of her inner responses to mother's narcissistic injuries were recalled, and she felt some easing of her external tensions. But the real working through in the transference consisted of her reaching through the distortions of my witnessing to the experience of my valid understanding. She began to feel freer with me, and less expectant of rage, disinterest, etc.

With these experiences, her self esteem rose and she began truly to take herself more seriously. She found real ways to realize her ambitions to exercise her initiative in her work. Ultimately, that meant leaving her employer and pursuing an independent, free-lance career.

But most centrally, she began to come to terms with serious aspirations for marriage and a family, though she could hardly bear to admit them for fear of their frustration. At the same time, a termination process began to unfold as she had a sense of the end of our work. She felt both that she could do it herself and that I was no longer as important. In the course of it she began a relationship with a man who was serious about marriage and with whom she had an intense and gratifying sexual relationship. He was quite frustrating also, for he was not able to adore automatically or consistently. Indeed, he was, at times, unpredictably hypersensitive. Patient discovered a pleasure in being able to feel decent about herself in spite of his irrascibility and still feel interested in him and not vindictive or withdrawn. She was very proud of herself as she realized that she could really feel that "being grown up doesn't mean that you live happily ever after." It meant not marrying the "right man," the prince who would make her happy, but rather the capacity to tolerate the frustration, even of erratic withdrawal.

She realized that she was identifying with me in being tolerant of his irritability and handling it so well. With her genuine capacity to do so, with considerable pain, she felt that the important aspect was, again, that I recognize the appropriateness of her wish to be like me, as she had wished to be like her mother. The central anxiety of the late termination was that I would not be empathic with her need and capacity to work out her life for herself. Most especially, she needed to feel she could work out her romantic life for herself. She had to feel the freedom to be herself in the relationship and to make mistakes. It was with that confidence that she left the analysis.

DISCUSSION

This case is an especially clear illustration of a failure in selfobject function at a relatively late stage of development and the structural sequelae of that failure. Hence, I think these difficulties can be separated from earlier challenges to self cohesion.

Two aspects of the case struck me vividly and suggested its formulation in self-oedipal terms: her intense need for my confirmation of her point of view—her competitive grandiose feelings toward other women or her sexual activity—and her clear expectation of my raging criticism, derision, etc., for either of the above. I realized clearly that these were internalized attitudes that were being projected onto me. It was also clear that these projected attitudes were related to the underlying impulses.

Yet interpretations of internalized reactions to such impulses only produced further disavowal and rage and enhanced the perception of me as critical and not understanding.

On the other hand, when I did become more understanding of the self-confirmatory functions of her impulses, she demonstrated considerable capacity to regulate them, and there was no further significant regression. The center of the analytic stage was dominated by the vicissitudes of this mirroring function.

This shows, I think, that the narcissistic manifestations of this case are central. If this were simply a classical oedipal neurosis, my interpretations of the impulses and defenses in conflict would have permitted their working through and amelioration with further unfolding. But that did not occur.

Several objections may be raised. From the side of those who would see this in classical terms the questions would be: "Did I not just foster a defense against her oedipal wishes? After all, did I not just go along with her projection of her guilt in agreeing to the reality of mother's damaging attitudes?" No, if that had truly been a defense against the underlying impulse, fostering the defense would have made the impulse stronger, and the need to blame someone would have become more rigid as well. The contrary occurred. As she worked through her feelings, she blamed everyone less—her mother in the past, people in her life, etc. Well, if she seemed less defensive, was it because I had allowed her to keep her incestuous ties? Had I seduced her to give up her rage by promising to fulfill her infantile wishes? I think the evidence again says, no. She terminated with a mourning process. Her relationship with a man whom she could truly love, who was reasonably available (though not without problems) was part of the resolution of the separation. The freedom and integration of her sexual feelings within the relationship and her experiencing herself as attractive argue for the integration and maturation rather than the repression of her infantile incestuous ties.

But if the narcissistic manifestations of the case are central, then the developmental level of the fixation must be questioned. Is this not, after all, a case of the sort Kohut has described in which the vulnerabilities of the nuclear body-mind self are the central issues? Is the intense apparent concern with oedipal-type conflicts only a defense against earlier fragmentation anxieties? Or, aren't the earlier fragmentation tendencies just telescoped into later concerns over oedipal issues?

Several clinical phenomena are inconsistent with these objections. The specific expectation of punishment and/or derision in the transference in response to the sexual or competitive self-assertive needs and wishes was the most conspicuous. In earlier fixations, the expected responses to the exhibition of the self may be coldness or indifference, not punishment. The regression in the self almost always includes hypochondriacal anxieties which are diffuse—cancer, heart disease, or shift from one body part to another. This patient was hypochondriacal about only one thing—her capacity to have children. Rather than depreciating the analyst in a haughty, arrogant way, she was much more urgently—and sometimes angrily—childlike. Her language and similes were vividly evocative of childhood experiences. She would speak of wanting to "play with" a friend, or she would ask "may I?" when she changed the stream of her associations. She complained of her inability to use "big words" to describe her feelings. Her dreams and images were full of whole people. There was no evidence of inhuman, cold, mechanical experiences.

Finally, her sexual activity was not exacerbated by separations. The sexual feelings were stimulated, and sometimes acted out during the week (though not, of course, invariably) in response to stimulations and understanding, or misunderstanding, in the transference as I have described. The separations were not marked by perverse preoccupations or addictive yearnings.

What we see here in rather pure culture, I think, is a grandiose oedipal self (or a self whose grandiosity has been confined to phallic oedipal claims)—and an idealized parent imago which is not yet a superego.

It was the phase-specific failure of the mother's empathy which produced the fixation that unfolded. The empathic failure occurred in several areas. (1) She failed to understand the narcissistic injury to her daughter of her real favoritism to her son; (2) she was, in fact, irritated with the patient's attempt to show proudly her own initiative or capacity in the competitive context of the oedipal situation; and, (3) she gratuitously attacked the patient's character with any increase in her own irritability from nonpatient-related sources.

In any event, the result of the failures of mother's empathy was patient's insistence on more grandiose claims for her self vis-à-vis her mother and brother in an oedipal rivalry. Her protest and need to right the wrong of blame were mostly directed to her mother. In any confrontation with either mother or brother, she was held to account. Any badness was automatically assumed to originate from her.

It was her willfulness, competitiveness, and teasing provocations which brought down mother's rage, not just for any specific act committed, but as representative of a character type that mother abhorred. Her mother also reacted negatively to her "healthy" self assertion.

Any understanding that the function of the sexual impulses she experienced in the transference was to elicit recognition of her, as in the past, as a "pretty girl," or "loving girl," as worthy of brother's attention as her mother, etc., enabled her to differentiate her perception of me from that of her mother in the past and brought the impulses into her autonomous control.

The exaggeration of her claims vis-à-vis other women, and her demanding, promiscuous sexual behavior as a woman, as well as her more regressive impulsive wish for pregnancy in the transference, arose from the defiance of the mother's rage over their derivatives in the past.

In addition to her fear of humiliation over the frustration of her grandiose claims, she also feared punishment and experienced herself as bad for her sexual impulses and acts.

Didn't this experience of badness stem from (1) her rage at her multiple narcissistic injuries, and (2) her possessive oedipal fantasies involving mainly her brother, but also her father, who was unattended by mother? Didn't her *impulses* cause her fear of punishment?

Yes, but also no. I think patient was correct. The burden of the experience of *intolerable* badness came not from her impulses, but from her mother's response to them. Further, the derivatives of those impulses were expressed not only for pleasure, but also for self expansion. In that context, mother's response of anger affectively warped the mirror of the self thus engaged. That warp was experienced as "bad self." Irritated or rageful responses to the phase-appropriate expressions of assertion, aggression, or attractiveness made those experiences punishable and wrong. It was necessary to understand the *self-confirmatory aspects of any impulse* in order to undo the experience of me as derisive and allow further unfolding of the vicissitudes of the impulses. The badness feeling had to be understood as the residue of these phase-appropriate self expressions which were greeted by rage or deflation. Then the patient could also see her own exaggerated claims and/or her own provocative anger in the past.

There was a clash between the more grandiose phallic oedipal self and the internalized judgments which were disavowed. The defiance of the internalized judgments set up an addiction to action which was to prove the self right and which, of course, failed with consequent feelings of badness. Hence there was an absence of effective superego regulation; indeed there was not yet a superego.

With the working through of the origins of this fixation in self development, she could both regulate her impulses and take her goals seriously.

## GENERAL DEVELOPMENTAL DISCUSSION

If we look at the oedipal period in terms of the psychology of the self, we see some of its vicissitudes in a different light. As Kohut has suggested, the self is a separate and cohesive structure at the time of oedipal development. Or rather, there are a cohesive grandiose self and idealized parental imagos. The parents are yet experienced in important selfobject terms. Kohut has delineated the process by which the idealized parental imagos are converted into the ego ideal and the superego structure: it is, of course, the gradual de-idealization of the idealized imagos by the bit-by-bit experience of parental limitation and failure.

However, there is a complementary process implicit in Kohut's description, the maturation of the so-called grandiose self. In this realm, too, the experience of the parents is in the selfobject mode. In order to achieve the gradual integration and transformation of its aims, the grandiose self requires phase-appropriate mirroring. The transformation of archaic aims into realizable ambitions is, indeed, an essential developmental step. And, of course, the oedipal crisis and resolution can be seen in just those terms. The male child changes from wanting his mother now—just the way the father has her (which means getting rid of the father)—to wanting a girl like the mother when he grows up. The jobs of learning to be smart, or strong, or dexterous, etc., become the mode of realizing the ambitions with their own gratification and becoming, in reality, adult like father.

In addition to its importance in transforming archaic to realizable aims, the process of mirroring also determines, in part, content and the relationship of the superego to the ego. The content of the superego can be conceived of as the residue of the mirroring experience. How one feels about oneself in the pursuit of goals or in the conduct of one's life is determined by the earlier parental response to the infantile precursor of the later adult activity.

Looking again at the oedipal period as an experience of grandiose self and mirroring parent, what do we see? We find a child excited by the discovery of his or her sexual apparatus. (I shall leave aside, for this discussion, the question of the vicissitudes of the differences between male and female experience.) There is, in any event, analogous admiration of the parent of the same sex for his or her genital capacity. In the boy, of course, this is much clearer. But there is, in addition, admiration of the parent for his or her bigness and capacities. The motivating wish, however, is not so much for genital pleasure—which is, in the final analysis, quite frustrating—as it is to be big and to be big instantly, magically, etc. And the heart of the trauma of the frustration of the oedipal fantasies is, indeed—as Freud maintained—narcissistic. One simply isn't big enough.

What is the mirroring task of the empathic parents, then? Intuitive parents will be pleased with their child's pride in his independence, and though perhaps often exasperated with his contrary and vacillating self assertion and perhaps limiting of it, they usually will not ragefully consider the child "bad" because of such behavior. The empathic parent perceives and enjoys the strengths of the child while letting the child perceive and integrate the parent's weaknesses.

Some parents do not tolerate this process well, and, in effect, insist on their own perfection while pointing out the child's defects. Sometimes this occurs in the guise of discipline. In such a context, the child is most often regarded as bad. I think this was precisely the situation of the patient I have described. To generalize just a bit further from that situation, we may say the following. Harsh, same-sex parental attitudes toward self display and bids for self confirmation during the oedipal phase may result in more strident expressions of the oedipal self. There may be a kind of hypertrophy of some of the sexually associated traits together with some rebellion at the social or interpersonal values that would limit such traits or use them for broader aims.[3] Most frequently one sees this kind of situation in men with fathers who are very harsh disciplinarians. "Machismo" might be an example.

Harsh parental attitudes increase the distance between the idealized parental imago and the grandiose self. The patient was a vivid example of that distance. Both formations were exaggerated in her development, and their separation made smooth control of the oedipal self impossible. The resolution of the distance between the idealized parent imago and the grandiose self is the complementary process of de-idealization and mirroring. Hence, the motivation for resolution of the Oedipus is based not on castration anxiety, but on the experience of beginning to close the distance.

It is for this reason that individuals with gentler parents have stronger superegos. They can close the distance and submit the self to the regulation of the mirroring memories. Moreover, they are more likely to enrich and proliferate their values as they experience the warmth of approval from maintaining them.

The residue of the mirroring experience becomes the skeleton of the superego. Some of the problems of the conceptualization of the process of internalization are simplified. The mirroring experience is internal, psychologically, at the outset. Hence, the problem of internalization of the

---

[3] Psychosocial considerations aside, for the society's values to be accepted, the individual must feel himself valued by the institutions of society. Justice must underlie order. Disruptions of justice create instability in the social milieu.

attitudes is bypassed. Rather, the question becomes one of understanding the way the internalizations become integrated and regulatory.

The affect of the mirroring parent determines the quality of the self experience engaged. Specifically, the anger of the parent in the selfobject position becomes the experience of "bad" for the child. Often the experience of bad is, indeed, associated with aggression or rage. For it is these childhood behaviors to which the parents are most likely to respond with rage. Hence, the experience of "bad" is, indeed, often associated with the feeling of anger or the wish to exert power. And it is often in the necessary course of limiting the child that badness, too, becomes part of the self experience. The necessary parental limitation of the overexpansive grandiose exuberance of the child may form some of the usual quotient of "bad self" which later becomes guilt. Even here, however, it might be possible to conceive of a degree of firm limitation which in the adult would develop into a calm, steadfast, internal regulation incapable of moral excess.

The experience of selfobject rage may have an important developmental line. The vicissitudes of self-directed rage may be understood not only as internally generated rage, but also as selfobject rage. I suspect that severe self hate—certainly that of psychotic proportions—cannot be generated from structural conflict and that it must arise, as Freud said, from fusion between the object and the self. Such states are, indeed, regressive and may have their nidus in early selfobject rage at the presentation of the self. In the patient discussed, I felt that such a regression was conceivable. If the grandiose oedipal self collapsed, the regression would have been to a merger with a raging idealized parent, which could only have meant self destruction.

Finally, with respect to technique, in patients with injury to the oedipal grandiose self, attention must be directed to the parental responses—as perceived by the patient—and their role in the genesis of the injury. Attributing the self-injurious attitudes to the strength of underlying impulses re-creates the original narcissistic injury. The errors in the analyst's empathy concerning the display of self are important to understand as such and should not be interpreted as defensive—guarding incestuous attachments.

## REFERENCES

Freud, S. (1887–1902), *The Origins of Psychoanalysis: Letters to Wilhelm Fleiss, Drafts and Notes.* New York: Basic Books, 1954.
—— (1900), The Interpretation of Dreams. *Standard Edition*, 4 & 5. London: Hogarth Press, 1953.

——— (1917), Mourning and melancholia. *Standard Edition*, 14:243–260. London: Hogarth Press, 1957.

Kohut, H. (1966), Forms of transformation of narcissism. *J. Amer. Psychoanal. Assn.*, 14:243–272.

——— (1971), *The Analysis of the Self.* New York: International Universities Press.

——— (1977), *The Restoration of the Self.* New York: International Universities Press.

Loewald, H. (1962), Internalization, separation, mourning and the superego. *Psychoanal. Quart.*, 31:483–504.

Schafer, R. (1960), Loving and beloved superego in Freud's structural theory. *The Psychoanalytic Study of the Child*, 15:163–188. New York: International Universities Press.

——— (1968), *Aspects of Internalization.* New York: International Universities Press.

*May 1984*

# Affects and Selfobjects

DAPHNE D. SOCARIDES, M.A. (Los Angeles)
and ROBERT D. STOLOROW, Ph.D. (Los Angeles)

Selfobject—the central, foundational construct in the psychoanalytic psychology of the self—can be defined phenomenologically as an object that a person experiences as incompletely separated from himself and that serves to maintain his sense of self (Kohut, 1971, 1977). We perceive this concept to be vulnerable to two maladies that can afflict important theoretical ideas in the early phases of their evolution. On the one hand, there is a tendency for the concept to remain unduly static and narrow, restricted to the particular idealizing and mirroring ties delineated by its originator. On the other hand, in the enthusiasm of theoretical expansion, there is the danger of the concept becoming overly general and imprecise, as when it is extended to encompass almost any caregiving activity that a child or developmentally arrested adult may require. Our intention in the present paper is to offer an expansion and refinement of the selfobject concept that we believe can skirt both the Scylla of theoretical encrustation and the Charybdis of overgeneralization. It is our contention that selfobject functions pertain fundamentally to the integration of *affect,* and that the need for selfobjects[1] pertains most centrally to the need for phase-appropriate responsiveness to affect states in all stages of the life cycle. To develop this claim we must first examine briefly the pivotal role of affect and affect integration in the structuralization of the self.

We conceive of the self as an *organization of experience,* referring specifically to the structure of a person's experience of himself (Atwood and Stolorow, 1984, chap. 1). The self, from this vantage point, is a psychological structure through which self-experience acquires cohesion and continuity,

---

[1] Here and elsewhere, when we use the term "selfobject" we refer to an object *experienced subjectively* as serving selfobject functions.

105

and by virtue of which self-experience assumes its characteristic shape and enduring organization. The fundamental role of affectivity in the organization of self-experience has been alluded to by generations of analytic investigators and has found considerable confirmation in recent studies of the patterning of early infant-caregiver interactions (see Lichtenberg, 1983, and Basch, 1984). Defining the self as a structure of experience, therefore, brings the central importance of affect integration in its evolution and consolidation into particularly bold relief.

Affects can be seen as organizers of self-experience throughout development, if met with the requisite affirming, accepting, differentiating, synthesizing, and containing responses from caregivers. An absence of steady, attuned responsiveness to the child's affect states leads to minute but significant derailments of optimal affect integration and to a propensity to dissociate or disavow affective reactions because they threaten the precarious structuralizations that have been achieved. The child, in other words, becomes vulnerable to *self-fragmentation* because his affect states have not been met with the requisite responsiveness from the caregiving surround and thus cannot become integrated into the organization of his self-experience. Defenses against affect then become necessary to preserve the integrity of a brittle self-structure.

It is the thesis of this paper that selfobject functions pertain fundamentally to the affective dimension of self-experience, and that the need for selfobjects pertains to the need for specific, requisite responsiveness to varying affect states throughout development. Kohut's (1971, 1977) conceptualizations of mirroring and idealized selfobjects can be viewed as very important special instances of this expanded concept of selfobject functions in terms of the integration of affect. His discovery of the developmental importance of phase-appropriate mirroring of grandiose-exhibitionistic experiences points, from our perspective, to the critical role of selfobject responsiveness in the integration of affect states involving pride, expansiveness, efficacy, and pleasurable excitement. As Kohut has shown, the integration of such affect states is crucial for the consolidation of self-esteem and self-confident ambition. The importance of early experiences of oneness with idealized sources of strength, security, and calm, on the other hand, indicates the central role of soothing, comforting responses from selfobjects in the integration of affect states involving anxiety, vulnerability, and distress. As also shown by Kohut, such integration is of great importance in the development of self-soothing capacities which, in turn, contribute vitally to one's anxiety tolerance and over-all sense of well-being.

Kohut (1977) seemed himself to be moving toward a broadened selfobject concept in his discussion of two ways in which parents can respond to the affect states characteristic of the oedipal phase:

The affectionate desire and the assertive-competitive rivalry of the oedipal child will be responded to by normally empathic parents in two
ways. The parents will react to the sexual desires and to the competitive
rivalry of the child by becoming sexually stimulated and counteraggres-
sive, and, at the same time, they will react with joy and pride to the child's
developmental achievement, to his vigor and assertiveness [p. 230].

Whether the oedipal period will be growth enhancing or pathogenic will
depend on the balance that the child experiences between these two modes
of parental response to his oedipal feelings:

If the little boy, for example, feels that his father looks upon him proudly
as a chip off the old block and allows him to merge with him and with
his adult greatness, then his oedipal phase will be a decisive step in self-
consolidation and self-pattern-firming, including the laying down of one
of the several variants of integrated maleness. . . . If, however, this aspect
of the parental echo is absent during the oedipal phase, the child's oedipal
conflicts will, even in the absence of grossly distorted parental responses
to the child's libidinal and aggressive strivings, take on a malignant quality. Distorted parental responses are, moreover, also likely to occur under
these circumstances. Parents who are not able to establish empathic contact with the developing self of the child will, in other words, tend to see
the constituents of the child's oedipal aspirations in isolation—they will
tend to see . . . alarming sexuality and alarming hostility in the child
instead of larger configurations of assertive affection and assertive competition—with the result that the child's oedipal conflicts will become
intensified [pp. 234–235].

In these quotations Kohut not only emphasizes the importance of parental
responsiveness to oedipal-phase affectionate and rivalrous feelings; in addition, by focusing on affectionate and rivalrous feelings he expands the
affective domain requiring responses from selfobjects considerably beyond
that which is implicit in his earlier, more delimited formulations of mirroring and idealizing selfobject ties.

Basch (1983), in a discussion of the earlier, sensorimotor phase, advances
an argument closely similar to ours by expanding Kohut's (1971) original
concept of mirror function as pertaining to archaic grandiosity to encompass broad areas of "affective mirroring." Drawing on the work of Stern
(1983), he writes:

Through affective attunement the mother is serving as the quintessential
selfobject for her baby, sharing the infant's experience, confirming it in
its activity, and building a sensorimotor model for what will become its
self concept. Affect attunement leads to a shared world; without affect
attunement one's activities are solitary, private and idiosyncratic. . . .

[I]f . . . affect attunement is not present or is ineffective during those early years, the lack of shared experience may well create a sense of isolation and a belief that one's affective needs generally are somehow unacceptable and shameful [pp. 5–6].

Basch views the defenses that appear in treatment as resistances against affect[2] originating in an absence of early affect attunement.

We now wish to extend the expanded concept of selfobject functions to certain other aspects of affect development that we believe are central to the structuralization of self-experience. These include: (1) affect differentiation and its relationship to self-boundary formation; (2) the synthesis of affectively discrepant experiences; (3) the development of affect tolerance and the capacity to use affects as self-signals; and (4) the desomatization and cognitive articulation of affect states.

## Affect Differentiation and Self-articulation

Krystal (1974), who has been most comprehensive in applying a psychoanalytic developmental perspective to affect theory, has pointed out that an important component in the developmental transformation of affects "involves their separation and differentiation from a common matrix" (p. 98). He has emphasized as well the critical importance of the mother's responsiveness in helping the child to perceive and differentiate his varying affect states. What we wish to emphasize here is that this early affect-differentiating attunement to the small child's inchoate feeling states contributes vitally to the progressive articulation of his self-experience. Such differentiating responsiveness to the child's affects, therefore, constitutes a central selfobject function of the caregiving surround, in establishing the earliest rudiments of self-definition and self-boundary formation.

The earliest processes of self-demarcation and individualization thus require the presence of a selfobject who, by virtue of a firmly structured sense of self and other, is able reliably to recognize, distinguish, and respond appropriately to the child's distinctive affect states. When a parent cannot discriminate and respond appropriately to feeling states of the child—for example, when those states conflict with a need for the child to serve the parent's own selfobject needs—then the child will experience severe derailments of his self-development. In particular, such situations will seriously obstruct the process of self-boundary formation, as the child feels compelled to "become" the selfobject that the parent requires (Miller, 1979)

[2] Basch notes that, as early as 1915, Freud, too, had expressed the belief that defense was always against affect.

and thus to subjugate or dissociate central affective qualities of his own that conflict with this requirement (see Atwood and Stolorow, 1984, chap. 3, for a detailed clinical illustration).

## The Synthesis of Affectively Discrepant Experiences

A second critical selfobject function of the early caregiving surround concerns the child's synthesis of contradictory affective experiences, a process vital to the establishment of an integrated sense of self. These early affect-synthesizing processes require the presence of a selfobject who, by virtue of firmly integrated perceptions, is able reliably to accept, tolerate, comprehend, and eventually render intelligible the child's intense, contradictory affect states as issuing from a unitary, continuous self. When a parent, in contrast, must perceive the child as "split"—for example, into one being whose "good" affects meet the selfobject needs of the parent and a second, alien being whose "bad" affects frustrate those needs—then the development of the child's affect-synthesizing capacity and the corresponding advance toward integrated selfhood will be severely obstructed, as affectively discrepant experiences become enduringly sequestered from one another in conformity with the parent's fragmentary perceptions (see Atwood and Stolorow, 1984, chap. 3, for a clinical illustration).

## Affect Tolerance and the Use of Affects as Self-signals

Closely related to the role of early selfobjects in the processes of affect differentiation and synthesis and the corresponding differentiations and syntheses of self-experience is the contribution of the early caregiving surround to the development of affect tolerance and the capacity to use affects as signals to oneself (Krystal, 1974, 1975). These developmental attainments, too, require the presence of a selfobject who can reliably distinguish, tolerate, and respond appropriately to the child's intense, shifting affective states. It is the caregiver's responsiveness that gradually makes possible the modulation, gradation, and containment of strong affect, a selfobject function alluded to in the concept of the parent as a "stimulus barrier" or "protective shield" against psychic trauma (Krystal, 1978), in Winnicott's (1965) notion of the "holding environment," and in Bion's (1977) evocative metaphor of the container and the contained. This modulation and containment of affects make possible their use as self-signals. Rather than traumatically rupturing the continuity of self-experience, affects can thereby become employed in the service of its preservation.

The primary caregiver, as selfobject, must assist the child in comprehending and interpreting his constantly shifting and evolving emotional
experiences. Through countless experiences throughout early development, the caregiver, by interpreting, accepting, and responding empathically to the child's unique and separate feeling states, is at the same time
enabling him to monitor, articulate, and understandingly respond to them
on his own. When the caregiver is able to perform this important selfobject
function by way of using her own affect-signaling capacity, a process of
internalization occurs, culminating in the child's ability to use his own
emotional reactions as self-signals (see Tolpin, 1971, and Krystal, 1974,
1975). When affects are perceived as signals of a changing self-state rather
than as indicators of impending psychological disorganization and fragmentation, the child is able to tolerate his emotional reactions without
experiencing them as traumatic. Thus some rudimentary capacity to use
affects as self-signals is an important component of the capacity to tolerate
disruptive feelings when they emerge. Without this self-signaling capacity,
affects tend to herald traumatic states (Krystal, 1978) and are thus disavowed, dissociated, repressed, or encapsulated through concrete behavioral enactments, self-protective efforts that literally cut off whole sectors
of the child's affective life. In such cases, the emergence of affect often
evokes painful experiences of shame and self-hatred, arising originally
from the absence of positive, affirming responsiveness to the child's feelings. Emotionality thereby becomes linked with a solitary and unacceptable
state that must somehow be eliminated. Trauma is viewed here not as an
event or series of events overwhelming an ill-equipped "psychic apparatus."
Rather, the tendency for affective experiences to create a disorganized (i.e.,
traumatic) self-state is seen to originate from early faulty selfobject attunement, with a lack of mutual sharing and acceptance of affect states,
leading to impaired affect tolerance and an inability to use affects as self-
signals.

## The Desomatization and Cognitive Articulation of Affect

Krystal (1974, 1975) has stressed that an important dimension of affect
development (and we would add, of self development) is the evolution of
affects from their early form as predominantly somatic states into experiences that can gradually be verbally articulated. He also emphasizes the
role of the caregiver's ability to identify correctly and verbalize the child's
early affects in contributing to this developmental process. In our view, the
importance of empathically attuned verbal articulation is not merely that
it helps the child put his feelings into words; more fundamentally, it grad-

ually facilitates the integration of affective states into *cognitive-affective sche-mata*—psychological structures that, in turn, contribute significantly to the organization and consolidation of the self. The caregiver's verbal articulations of the child's initially inchoate, somatically experienced affects thus serve a vital selfobject function in promoting the structuralization of self-experience.

The persistence of psychosomatic states and disorders in adults may be seen as remnants of arrests in this aspect of affective and self development. When there is an expectation that more advanced, cognitively elaborated organizations of affective experience will not be met with the requisite responsiveness, replicating the faulty affect attunement of the childhood surround, the person may revert to more archaic, somatic modes of affect expression in the unconscious hope of thereby evoking the needed responses from selfobjects. Such psychosomatic states thus represent an archaic, presymbolic pathway of affect expression through which the person unconsciously attempts to establish a tie to a selfobject required for affect containment and thus for the maintenance of self-integrity. In the psychoanalytic situation we regularly observe that when the analyst becomes established as an affect-articulating and containing selfobject, the psychosomatic symptoms tend to recede or disappear, only to recur or intensify when the selfobject tie becomes disrupted or when the patient's confidence in the analyst's receptivity to his affects becomes significantly shaken.

## Implications for Psychoanalytic Therapy

Two major therapeutic implications follow from our expanded concept of selfobject functions as pertaining to the integration of affect, and from our corresponding emphasis on the fundamental importance for the structuralization of the self of the responsiveness of the early caregiving surround to the child's emerging affect states. One implication concerns the analytic approach to defenses against affects when these emerge as resistances in the course of psychoanalytic treatment. As we have stressed, the need to disavow, dissociate, or otherwise defensively encapsulate affect arises originally in consequence of the failure of the early selfobject milieu to provide the requisite, phase-appropriate attunement and responsiveness to the child's emotional states. When such defenses against affect arise in treatment, they must be understood as being rooted in the patient's expectation or fear in the transference that his emerging feeling states will meet with the same faulty responsiveness that they received from the original caregivers. Furthermore, these resistances against affect cannot be interpreted as resulting solely from intrapsychic processes within the patient. Such resistances are most often evoked by events occurring within the analytic situation which for the patient signal a lack of receptivity on the analyst's part to the patient's emerging feeling states and which therefore herald a traumatic recurrence of early selfobject failure.

A second therapeutic implication of our thesis concerning affects and selfobjects is that once the transference resistances against affect based on the "dread to repeat" (Ornstein, 1974) the damaging childhood experiences have been sufficiently analyzed (in the context of "good-enough" affective attunement on the part of the analyst), the patient's arrested developmental need for the originally absent or faulty responsiveness to his emerging affect states will be revived with the analyst. The specific emotional states involved and the specific functions that the patient requires the analyst to serve in relation to these states will determine the particular features of the unfolding selfobject transference. The analyst's ability to comprehend and interpret these feeling states and corresponding selfobject functions as they enter the transference will be critical in facilitating the analytic process and the patient's growth toward an analytically expanded and enriched affective life.

It follows from this formulation that when remnants of early selfobject failure have become prominent in structuring the analytic relationship, the central curative element may be found in the selfobject transference bond itself and its pivotal role in the articulation, integration, and developmental transformation of the patient's affectivity. Thus the therapeutic importance of analyzing ruptures in the selfobject transference tie may not lie solely or even primarily in the "transmuting internalizations" that are believed to result from "optimal frustration" (Kohut, 1971). The therapeutic action of such analysis, in our view, lies principally in the mending of the broken selfobject tie which, *when intact*, provides a nexus of archaic relatedness in which the patient's derailed emotional growth and the corresponding structuralizations of the self can resume once again, in the medium of the analyst's attunement.

In order to exemplify our thesis concerning affects and selfobjects, we turn now to a consideration of the integration of depressive affect.

## The Integration of Depressive Affect

Depressive affect states, such as sadness, grief, remorse, disappointment, and disillusionment, have many origins, meanings, and functions. Our focus in the present section is on how and under what circumstances depressive affect is tolerated and integrated throughout development. Our assumption is that all affects, in this case depressive affect, undergo development in concert with the consolidation and structuralization of the self. Such affect integration has its earliest rudiments in the sensorimotor phase, in the specific selfobject responsiveness to the child's affect states that serves to facilitate full emotional growth and development.

Depressive affect is integrated into the structure of the self through consistent, reliable, empathic selfobject attunement. When such attunement is chronically absent or faulty, such affect may herald a breakup of the cohesion and stability of the self-organization. The capacity to identify and withstand depressive feelings without a corresponding loss of self, fear of self-dissolution, or tendency to somatize the affect has its origins in the early affect-relatedness between the child and primary caregiver. A process of mourning and grief following loss or separation can occur only if depressive affects can be identified, comprehended, and tolerated. The ability to integrate depressive affect is therefore related to early selfobject attunement, which, in turn, lends definition to the child's experience of himself, solidifying self-boundaries. Depressive *disorders* (as distinct from depressive affect states) are rooted in early selfobject failure, leading to an inability to integrate depressive feelings and a corresponding derailment of self-development.

Kohut (1971, 1977) has shown that the child's (or developmentally arrested patient's) phase-appropriate experiences of gradual disillusionment with idealized images of himself and his primary objects constitute critical milestones in the structuralization of the self. As an alternative to Kohut's concept of "optimal frustration," we are contending here that it is not solely or even primarily the "quantity" of the accompanying depressive affects that determines whether they will be experienced as traumatic and self-disintegrative or as tolerable and capable of being integrated into the evolving self-organization. We believe that what is crucial to the child's (or patient's) growing capacity to integrate his sadness and his painful disappointments in himself and others is the reliable presence of a calming, containing, empathic selfobject, irrespective of the "amount" or intensity of the affects involved.[3] When the caregiver is able to tolerate, absorb, and

---

[3] We are objecting here to the concept of "optimal frustration" because of its retention of economic and quantitative metaphors that are remnants of drive theory. For example, when Kohut (1971) describes an optimal frustration of the child's idealizing need as one in which "the child can experience disappointments with one idealized aspect or quality of the object after another" (p. 50) rather than with the total object, or one in which the shortcomings of the object "are of tolerable proportions" (p. 64), he places his emphasis on the "size" of the disappointment—and, by implication, the "amount" of the depressive affect—as the decisive factor that determines whether the disappointment will be pathogenic or growth-enhancing. In contrast, we are claiming that what is decisive is the responsiveness of the selfobject milieu to the child's depressive (and other) reactions. We are thus shifting the emphasis from "optimal frustration" to the centrality of affect attunement.

contain the child's depressive affect states, which presupposes that they do not threaten the organization of *her* sense of self, she then functions to "hold the situation" (Winnicott, 1965) so that it can be integrated. Optimally, if such responsiveness is consistently present, the caregiver's selfobject functions gradually become internalized in the form of a capacity for self-modulation of depressive affect and an ability to assume a comforting, soothing attitude toward oneself. Consequently, such affect will not entail irretrievable losses in the self. The expectation that restitution will follow disruption becomes structuralized, providing the basis for a sense of self-continuity and confident hope for the future.

When a parent cannot tolerate the child's depressive feelings—because they do not conform to her own affect states, self-organization requirements, or selfobject needs—then she will be unable to assist the child in the critical task of affect integration. When the child experiences such protracted derailments of affect attunement, he may, in order to safeguard the needed tie, blame his own depressive feelings for the selfobject failure, resulting in a pervasive, self-hating helplessness and hopelessness or—if he responds by defensively dissociating the "offending" affects—in lifelong states of emptiness. It is here, we believe, that one can find the origins of chronic depressive disorder. Such patients in analysis resist the emergence of their depressive feelings for fear that once again they will be met with the same faulty responsiveness experienced in early childhood.

## Clinical Illustration

Steven, an unusually intelligent 26-year-old man, sought treatment for insomnia, failing graduate-school grades, and a sense of being "exhausted from covering over depression" in response to his girl friend of three years unexpectedly breaking their engagement. He was initially quite agitated, spending numerous sessions detailing the exact dates and times of the traumatic events that had necessitated his first contact with a psychotherapist. The breakup with his girl friend had followed closely on the heels of his mother's emergency hospitalization—one of a series of such hospitalizations for a variety of physical and psychiatric conditions that she incurred throughout his development. Steven's obsessional style and lack of connection with his emotional life were the most salient aspects of these early sessions. He desperately wanted to communicate in detail an accurate account of what he had experienced, and he showed an acute sensitivity to whether or not he was being understood. The patient explained that fears of being found "incorrect" or "inaccurate" were at the root of his anxiety, but it soon became clear that he believed that his feeling states, to the extent that he experienced them at all, were unacceptable and would ultimately drive the therapist away from him and destroy the therapeutic relationship. The growing tie to the therapist was therefore continually in jeopardy.

He believed that the preservation of the tie depended upon his never making a "mistake," which was later understood to mean that he must not express any feelings that were not in line with what he perceived the therapist required and, more importantly, that might disturb her or make her feel inadequate. Thus he was very compliant with the therapist's interventions, but his responses were strikingly devoid of affect. He was terrified that any spontaneous feelings that might be disjunctive with the therapist's state of mind would both be rejected by her and have a disorganizing impact on him. When an intense emotional reaction was evoked, he would become confused and panicky, seemingly unaware that he was experiencing an emotional reaction and thus completely unable to recognize its significance as a self-signal. Additionally, he was convinced that while on the surface the therapist would appear to accept his feelings, nonetheless she would secretly feel hatred, disgust, and loathing for him—especially, he said, because "they represent my feelings toward women."

Steven's fears of his own depressive affects maintained a prominent place in the treatment for a long period of time. Initially, he was somewhat aware of his dread of depressive feelings, believing that once he "got in touch" with them they would ultimately destroy him. He feared that he would fall into a dark hole never to return again, forever empty, helpless, and hopeless about his future. He believed that once he allowed himself to feel the massive disappointment, sadness, and remorse that lay beneath the surface, he would "go crazy" and end up like his chronically and sometimes psychotically depressed mother. Thus his dread of feeling and acknowledging his depressive affects was based in part on his strong identification with, and incomplete differentiation from, his mother. In addition, the mother's own extreme vulnerability to depressive reactions rendered her unable to provide any sustained, attuned responsiveness to *his* depressive feelings. Any such reaction on Steven's part was met with ridicule and negation, with the mother scolding him and saying, "You must think of other people's feelings." His parents were able neither to understand nor to tolerate the patient's unhappiness, considering any such affect as a vicious attack on their self-esteem and efficacy as parents. At other times his despair and disappointment were met with what he perceived as superficial apologies that left him feeling not responded to, worthless, deflated, unacceptable, and empty.

During his many visits to his mother when she was in the hospital, Steven often felt extremely upset and frightened about losing her and being left alone. On such occasions, she could focus only on herself and how *she* was feeling, communicating to him quite clearly that what he was feeling was unimportant and unacceptable and that his affect state must somehow correspond to her needs. Nor could he at such times turn to his father, who always seemed too preoccupied with his own grandiose schemes and fantasies to respond to his son's distress. The emotional unavailability of his father compounded Steven's depressive feelings and intensified his enmeshment with his mother. No collateral pathway for affect integration was available. Steven thus came to believe that his depressive feelings were loathsome imperfections in himself. Since painful aspects of his subjective life could not be tolerated by his parents, he developed a firmly embedded conviction that painful affect must be "eliminated" and that "hurt must not be allowed."

Steven's very early memories, while sparse and unarticulated (a phenomenon consistent with massive early dissociation of affect), focused on the lack of attunement to his depressive affect states. Whenever he would dare to show such emotions his mother would accuse him of being too self-absorbed like his father and uncaring about the feelings of others, meaning principally her own. She always responded to his depressive feelings in terms of how they related to her own vulnerabilities and needs at the moment. She subtly communicated to him her own fear that his depressive feelings would lead to a psychotic regression as they had with her. Steven felt continuously alienated from his parents and peers alike. In treatment he eventually portrayed his childhood as lacking in any true, genuine feelings except pervasive emptiness and hopeless despair, coupled with a constant struggle to "survive just one more day."

Previous to the crisis situation that brought Steven to treatment he had been a most obedient son, especially in relation to his mother. When the mother found herself in intolerable social and professional situations she would rely on her "bright, creative, and compliant" only child to rescue her and "fix" what she had done wrong. Steven had become a very religious Catholic following his parents' divorce when he was eight, channeling all his energies—physical and emotional—into his religiosity. In this way he found an added source of structure for his increasingly chaotic inner world. His terrifying emotional reactions both to his parents' divorce and to his mother's hospitalizations were dissociated and repressed, solidifying his obsessional, cerebral character style. A state of pure, affectless intellectuality became his self-ideal of perfection, embodied in his intense idealization of the Star Trek character Mr. Spock, whose life seemed completely free of the "imperfections of emotions." His struggle to attain this affectless ideal became poignantly clear as the treatment began to bring forth hitherto disavowed aspects of his emotional life.

For Steven, depressive affects of all degrees of intensity had become embedded in specific, dangerous meaning-contexts and consequently had remained a source of powerful anxiety throughout his life. In reaction to his mother's last hospitalization and his being "dropped" by his girl friend, Steven was unable to maintain his defenses against affect. An understanding of the dangers involved in acknowledging and expressing his depressive feelings evolved gradually in the course of treatment, finally centering on two separate but interrelated dreaded outcomes. One was the expectation that his feelings would lead to further disorganization in his mother, completely precluding any accepting, affect-integrating responsiveness on her part. The other was his belief that, in the context of his merged relationship with her, he, too, would become psychologically disorganized, a hopelessly disintegrated self. Thus the emergence of depressive affect immediately triggered states of acute anxiety.

To summarize, Steven's inability to integrate depressive affect into his self-organization was seen to result from both profound selfobject failure in relation to his states of sadness, grief, and disappointment and his deeply embedded association of depressive affect with the specter of disintegration—of both the self and the maternal object.

Steven's transference relationship with the therapist quickly replicated with distinct clarity his tie with his mother. He was in constant fear that when he expressed any depressive feelings the therapist would see him as a fragile, disintegration-prone individual who was at the brink of psychosis. Additionally, he was frightened of any such moods in the therapist for fear that she, like his mother and himself, would "lose control" and become psychotic. As with his mother, he believed that the therapist's failures and mistakes were his own and felt her limitations as fatal flaws in himself. This incomplete self-object differentiation, in turn, made it all the more necessary for him to disavow any experiences of disappointment in the transference.

When depressive affects were evoked in the patient, along with the corresponding states of acute anxiety and panic, the therapist focused on the specific meaning-contexts and dreaded repetitions to which these feelings were linked. Through repeated analysis in the transference of the patient's resistances to depressive affect and the anticipated, extreme dangers that made them necessary, the therapist gradually became established for Steven as a selfobject who could comprehend, accept, tolerate, and aid him in integrating these feelings, regardless of their "quantity" or intensity. Two immediate consequences followed from this consolidation of the selfobject transference. The first was that the patient began to feel and express formerly dissociated feelings of deep, suicidal despair. Despite the painfulness of these feelings, the therapist was able to interpret them as a developmental achievement in affect integration.

A second consequence, following from the first, was the crystallization of his conviction that his emerging depressive feelings constituted a deadly threat to others—a remnant of countless early experiences in which he perceived that his sadness and disappointment were experienced by his mother as psychologically damaging. This theme was dramatically symbolized in dreams that followed immediately upon the disclosure of his suicidal feelings. In the imagery of these dreams he portrayed his emerging feeling states as uncontrollable destructive forces that, once unleashed, would engulf and annihilate everyone around him.

Not unexpectedly, Steven's belief that his depressive affects were dangerous and destructive to others began to dominate the transference, as he became frightened that his feelings would inflict psychological harm upon the therapist. As this fear was repeatedly analyzed in the transference its genetic roots in his mother's extreme vulnerabilities and consequent inability to tolerate and "hold" his depressive affects became clarified in increasingly bolder relief. This ongoing transference analysis, together with the patient's progressively solidifying new experience of the therapist's "good-enough" affect attunement and containment, made it possible for him not only to experience and express previously dissociated depressive feelings, but also to reunite with ever-widening spheres of his affectivity in general and, in turn, gradually to experience himself as an emotionally complex, differentiated, and integrated human being. The establishment of the therapist as an affect-integrating selfobject thus permitted Steven's stalled emotional growth and the corresponding structuralizations of his self-experience to resume once again.

## Conclusion

We have offered an expansion and refinement of the concept of selfobject functions, claiming that they pertain fundamentally to the integration of affect into the evolving organization of self-experience. This conceptualization brings into sharpened focus the critical developmental importance of reliable affect attunement from the caregiving surround in assisting the child in the tasks of differentiating, synthesizing, modulating, and cognitively articulating his emergent emotional states, affect-integrating functions which, in turn, contribute vitally to the structuralization of his sense of self. We exemplified this thesis by focusing on the necessary integrations of depressive affect throughout development and by presenting a clinical illustration of severe selfobject failure in this area. As our case example demonstrates, a focus on affect integration and its failures holds important implications for both the analytic approach to resistance and the understanding of the curative element in the selfobject transferences.

## REFERENCES

Atwood, G. & Stolorow, R. (1984), *Structures of Subjectivity: Explorations in Psychoanalytic Phenomenology.* Hillsdale, N.J.: Analytic Press.
Basch, M. (1983), Interpretation: Toward a developmental model. Presented to the Sixth Annual Conference on the Psychology of the Self, Los Angeles, Calif., October 7–9.
———— (1984), Selfobject and selfobject transference: Theoretical implications. In: *Kohut's Legacy: Contributions to Self Psychology,* ed. A. Goldberg & P. Stepansky. Hillsdale, N.J.: Analytic Press, in press.
Bion, W. (1977), *Seven Servants.* New York: Aronson.
Freud, S. (1915), The unconscious. *Standard Edition,* 14:159–204. London: Hogarth Press, 1957.
Kohut, H. (1971), *The Analysis of the Self.* New York: International Universities Press.
———— (1977), *The Restoration of the Self.* New York: International Universities Press.
Krystal, H. (1974), The genetic development of affects and affect regression. *This Annual,* 2:98–126. New York: International Universities Press.
———— (1975), Affect tolerance. *This Annual,* 3:179–219. New York: International Universities Press.
———— (1978), Trauma and affects. *The Psychoanalytic Study of the Child,* 33:81–116. New Haven: Yale University Press.
Lichtenberg, J. (1983), *Psychoanalysis and Infant Research.* Hillsdale, N.J.: Analytic Press.
Miller, A. (1979), *Prisoners of Childhood.* New York: Basic Books, 1981.
Ornstein, A. (1974), The dread to repeat and the new beginning: A contribution to the psychoanalysis of narcissistic personality disorders. *This Annual,* 2:231–248. New York: International Universities Press.
Stern, D. (1983), Affect Attunement. Presented to the World Association for Infant Psychiatry, Cannes, France, April.
Tolpin, M. (1971), On the beginnings of a cohesive self: An application of the concept of transmuting internalization to the study of the transitional object and signal anxiety. *The Psychoanalytic Study of the Child,* 26:316–352. New York: Quadrangle.
Winnicott, D. (1965), *The Maturational Processes and the Facilitating Environment.* New York: International Universities Press.

*January 1984*

# Translation between Psychoanalytic Theories

## ARNOLD GOLDBERG, M.D. (Chicago)

Translation is a part of every psychoanalyst's life. It begins of course with the translation of Sigmund Freud's words from German to English or any language (and the debate over the accuracy of that effort still engages many scholars [Bettelheim, 1982; Mahoney, 1982]). It extends to the daily work of translating the language of dreams and the unconscious to the common-sense terms of the analytic consulting room. It lives in the mind of every analyst who tries to explain an idea in a set of words and sentences that will be "understandable" to a patient or a colleague, and it struggles for life with all of those feelings and images that never or hardly ever seem to gain access to the ease of communication that translation hopes to achieve.

Anyone who translates knows that the simple exchange of word for word or word for image will never do. Good translation requires conceptual bridges that encompass whole sets of ideas and feelings, and bad translation can be dangerous as well as uninformative. To translate is to carry or convey and therefore to bear the burden of the weight of information moved from one locale to another. So very much has been written on translation (Steiner, 1975) that it might be well at the outset to acknowledge the fact that some people feel that translation is always inadequate or, in some cases, impossible (Quine, 1969). The intent of this essay is, however, to examine the exercise of translation between psychoanalytic theories. It assumes that people can and do succeed in conveying information to one another, do manage to feel understood and to operate as if they comprehended what was intended by another. The crucial question to be asked is whether our

Presented at the January 24, 1984, scientific meeting of the Chicago Psychoanalytic Society.

present sets of theories are easily or even with difficulty understood in terms of the others. Does a word or an idea mean approximately the same thing according to (say) Margaret Mahler as it does to Winnicott, or does a similar idea perhaps lie buried in an altered vocabulary and could a simple uncovering aid in translation? The basic premise of the inquiry is the assumption that theory in psychoanalysis is exchangeable. How much of analytic theory is a monolithic entity with numerous variations and branches? How much of it is a wilderness of unconnected paths?

The answers to these questions begin with a political and social set of positions. One school of theorists is characterized by the "one-big-happy-family" approach. It says that the fundamental tenets of psychoanalysis are firm and set and all theory extends from these tenets (the number of which is uncertain). Thus every new idea must be an offshoot or an elaboration of a basic tenet. An example of this might be the Hartmann (1964) addition of the ego's own energy, which is derived from the libido theory by way of additional views involving neutralization, etc. This builds upon the basic theory and in no way clashes with it, save for the opinion of some purists who may feel that it does depart from Freud's original intent. Nevertheless, this basic approach is an all-embracing one that wholeheartedly believes in a translation which serves to connect what may seem to be alienated. Thus adherents of the unitary approach will therefore expend time and effort explaining what Fairbairn or Adler or Winnicott "really mean" in terms of the given and acceptable theory.

It should be evident that everyone at some time is a member of this group since we all tend to approach new findings by exchanging them for old ones. Our private thoughts and public forums are filled with phrases like "that is no more than" or "that is just another way of saying" or "isn't that really the same as?" etc., etc. We delight in reducing things to the tried and true since this is a necessary part of weeding out what is an essentially trivial novelty. Our fallback position is the existence of a sort of basic program for psychoanalysis. This assumes that some findings or new positions may be included or integrated into the extant theory, some must be discarded as being clearly nonanalytic, and some must be held suspect until they can be integrated. This last immigrant group is the one that evokes the greatest controversy over "not being understood" or being distorted. Translation is strained mightily in this area.

A radical position which lies in sharp opposition to the one-big-happy-family group is a stance that encourages diversity and insists that translation is impossible among different theories. It states that the words and sentences of Winnicott, Kohut, Mahler, etc., are part of separate theoretical systems that share only common areas of interest and not common vocabularies. At its most extreme this position probably concedes that even single individuals have singular theoretical perspectives that may not easily be mapped upon one another. It is often the case in psychoanalysis that analysts from different training programs seem unable to agree upon what different terms stand for, and indeed the field of psychoanalysis is often ridiculed as being unable to agree upon the definition of the word "psychoanalysis." This position does not deny that persons share ideas and agreement but does say that essentially we deal in approximations of meanings with many of them being negotiated during discussion. It also seems to claim that theories in science are not clear-cut systems of logical structures but rather are clusters of propositions. In regard to this point we can recall that theories are usually thought of as hypothetical-deductive systems in which observations are tied to hypothesis by correspondence rules. Hypotheses are assumed but laws are generated and in turn are verifiable. Statements or facts can be predicted and follow from the general laws. Theories, therefore, are examples of deductive logic—or at least this has been the customary definition (Suppe, 1974).

The aforementioned contrasting position holds that a theory is but a cluster of accepted problem solutions (Barnes, 1982) and there is no basic logical structure behind the application of any theory. Scientific inference, therefore, is not deductive but is derived by analogy. This cluster theory of theories allows for a divergence of positions which need not share any common fundamental structure. It is an unhappy resolution for many scientists who dislike the laissez-faire and ad hoc application of theories and who feel such freedom of theory erodes the status of a science. Thus it is no surprise to note how a third or compromise position has emerged.

The compromise between diversity and unity has to do with carving out a family of connected and similar theories which overlap in some areas and separate in others. Therefore, for example, Mahler and Winnicott would fundamentally agree on a wide area of findings (i.e., observations and conclusions) but would diverge in others. The job for the integrationists would be to bring more of the divergents back into the family by way of translation. The task for the anarchists would be that of sharpening differences by emphasizing the failure of translation. The compromisers will usually hold out promise for the arrival of an umbrella theory which will be all-inclusive. It will provide a vocabulary that will allow for translation of what has heretofore been untranslatable. For example Hartmann's (1964) efforts to extend psychoanalysis into a general psychology had, as one goal, the inclusion of certain social phenomena into the over-all theory of psychoanalysis. It was a bigger, more expansive theory and thus gave new hope to the integrationists. It was also condemned by some as being nonanalytic, by others as changing the meaning of the words of psycho-analysis—such as ego—and thus essentially being another analytic theory entirely (Klein, 1968).

The implications of these positions are not insignificant since they direct attention to the activities of our scholarly contributors. If translation from one theory to another is feasible then one can profitably work in this area to aim for an integrated whole theory. Of course this may be achieved by contraction as well as by expansion, but it does require a standard of correctness for judgment, i.e., one judges whether, for example, words such as splitting, countertransference, self are being used legitimately or whether there is an idiosyncratic employment that goes beyond what is considered to be normal usage. So, too, does one decide whether parataxic distortion is "really" transference or countertransference or whether it falls outside the realm of reasonableness. If, however, such translation is not feasible then it might be well for the recognition of the fact and for the efforts in this direction to be understood as reflecting an entirely different sort of phenomenon, e.g., a social or political problem that will need a different kind of solution. An exercise is in order.

## An Exercise in Translation

Any comparison between terms and concepts in different theories will undoubtedly provoke controversy because some will immediately say that these are erroneous comparisons. Thus, when we examine and compare the *part object* of traditional Freudian theory with the *transitional object* of Winnicott with the *selfobject* of Kohut, we invite an early argument about these being of unequal and/or of incompatible significance and meaning. If, on the other hand, we chose the supposed exact same word for comparison, we might expect equal degrees of difficulty since many words are used differently within a given theory, and unless one proceeds to rather trivial words there will always be larger areas of fuzziness of definition. Inasmuch as some authors (Gedo and Goldberg, 1972, p. 62) seem to feel that these three terms are capable of translation it probably can serve as a reasonable exercise to test the feasibility of any translation. Thus we are not in this exercise aiming for accuracy but rather are attempting to stake out the possibility of reasonable translation.

1. Part object

The part object is defined (Laplanche and Pontalis, 1973) as follows:

A type of object toward which the component instincts are directed without this implying that a person as a whole is taken as the love-object.

In the main part-objects are parts of the body, real or phantasied (breast, feces, penis) and their symbolic equivalents. Even a person can identify himself or be identified with a part-object [p. 301].

From this we see that part objects have only partial qualities of whole persons; likewise this is a developmental perspective so that, for example, the object of the anal-sadistic stage is feces and at that time persons are treated in the same manner as feces.

Since objects for Freud are seen as tied to the instincts and their gratification, the progression of and elaboration of the concept of objects should retain this essential link. The term "part object" is said to have been introduced by Melanie Klein in its fullest sense since these partial objects became endowed with traits comparable to a person's (Laplanche and Pontalis, 1973).

No doubt the concept of part object is easily linked to that of need-satisfying object or archaic object since they all bear the sense of an infantile form of drive gratification which should be but a step toward a more mature object relationship involving whole objects (persons) dealt with in a constant manner not dependent upon the drive state of the self.

2. Transitional object

This term was introduced by D. W. Winnicott (1953) and is defined (Laplanche and Pontalis, 1973) as designating "A material object with a special value for the suckling and young child particularly when it is on the point of falling asleep (e.g., the corner of the blanket that is sucked)" (p. 464).

Reliance on such objects, according to Winnicott, is a normal phenomenon which allows the child to make the transition from the first oral relationship with the mother to the "true object relationship."

On first glance one might feel an immediate correlation with the part object (or need-satisfying object) in that they share the qualities of an infantile usage on the developmental road to appreciation of complete or true or whole objects. The link to instincts seems to be maintained although the transitional object is seemingly tied to the oral phase. Winnicott also made much of persistent transitional objects (and phenomena) as connected to certain forms of pathology and creativity. A certain enthusiasm was soon attached to this concept, and upon close scrutiny it seemed to be popularly seen in terms of its material constitution, i.e., a blanket or doll or even a poem or song. This is not quite the same as the clear intrapsychic usage of Freud for whom an instinctual drive cathects an intrapsychic image of an object. In fact much of Winnicott's work on the holding environment is presented as an interpersonal theory involving the interaction of mother and child. So, too, does his definition of transitional object maintain a shared relationship with another so that the transitional object lies neither inside nor outside of the self. To be sure, one can posit an inner picture or image or representation of a shared transitional object (see Gedo and Goldberg, 1972, p. 59), but essentially Winnicott's work concentrates on the environment and upon what the infant creates in the world outside. The transitional object is but a step into the world of relationships between the developing child and the caretakers that Winnicott proceeds to explore. His is not a theory of intrapsychic vicissitudes but rather one of the nature of the facilitating environment (Winnicott, 1965). Of course one can translate any term or idea or part of object-relations theory back into intrapsychic terms and concepts. This is usually strained and unsuccessful. As Klein and Tribeck (1981) put it in response to splitting, "it is spurious to equate Freudian splitting with that of the theorists of the object-relations approach, because in the former the origin, meaning and motivation of splitting is set within a different theoretical context than the latter approach" (p. 29).

The transitional object is a part of an over-all, albeit somewhat poorly articulated, theory which Winnicott developed and which was likewise joined by others such as Guntrip, Fairbairn, etc. It does not sit alone as a new term added to an existing theory, but rather it extends to a web of other theoretical ideas having to do with relations, and it joins a cluster of like-minded theoretical terms. If one attempts to tear it free from its own theoretical matrix then one runs the risk of minimizing its significance, reducing it, for example, to being but an oral precursor of the fetish. Seen in its full sense, however, it is an essential part of a new theoretical orientation.

3.  The selfobject

This term does not enjoy a place in the psychoanalytic dictionary of Laplanche and Pontalis. It is defined by Kohut (1971) as another person experienced as part of the self. Again one can position the concept as belonging to that early phase of development wherein other persons are utilized and/or exploited for needs that do not take into account the issue of mutuality. Persons are thus not seen as whole and are only partly appreciated. The move to maturation would then allow for the gradual increase in self and object differentiation and the ultimate recognition of another person as an entity in his or her own right. In this sense it seems to correlate with the part object as well as the transitional object in terms of both its infantile status as well as its characteristic lack of clear differentiation. Of course Kohut (1977) upset the neatness of this translation by insisting that selfobjects could be mature as well as infantile. He further strained the compatibility of the terms in his relative neglect of the drive aspect of object relations and his insistence on the structural or sustaining and supporting role of the selfobject. In this matter he seems closer to Winnicott, but he departs from that association in his emphasis on the introspective assessment of the object. Thus a selfobject is recognized not in terms of any environmental or material factor but rather entirely in terms of an empathic assessment. In this respect it is hardly equivalent to Winnicott's transitional objects save again for some sort of heroic effort to translate. For Kohut the selfobject sits in a sea of connected concepts that see psychological data in a manner distinct from both Freud and Winnicott as well as others. His theory is perhaps better articulated and therefore can be seen more clearly to be different. He attempts to incorporate much of classical psychoanalysis within his theory but more as a way of explaining how all analysis works than of retaining its terms and ideas. He aims for a unified theory.

If single words or terms are not easily translatable could it not be the case that whole concepts may instead be exchanged? Is it not possible that what Winnicott describes as the early mother-child relationship in toto is the same as that, say, of Kohut? Of course it is possible, but a return to the fundamental ideas of these theories can easily disabuse one of the likelihood. Each sees things differently but neither need be more right or more wrong. One concentrates on the growth of a self sustained and carried forward by selfobjects which are linked by empathic communicative ties. The other speaks of objects which aid in fostering independence and self-reliance. One stresses an open system that remains so; the other a semipermeable one that must separate off. To try to make them as one strips them of their richness.

What of the possibility that these supposed new theories are merely additions to or elaborations on the cluster that is the main body of psychoanalysis? If Heinz Hartmann could add to psychoanalytic psychology by way of ego psychology could not the same be said for self psychology and the theories of Winnicott and Mahler? Are these not mere additions to the existing corpus of knowledge? The answer to this is in two parts. The first, of course, is that a true addition to a theory is not translated or absorbed back into the theory but adds something that in no way need challenge the theory. The only translation that is needed is one to insure the continuity of ideas, and indeed this need is not often met. The crucial or second point has to do with the points of linkage or addition. It may be that what at first appears to be an addition turns out to be an incompatible concept. This, in truth, is to be hoped for since it allows one to define the limit of the previous theory and to embark on a new one. Probably Kohut's first presentation of narcissistic personality disorders was seen as an expansion of the theory, but soon thereafter it was recognized for the radical and therefore nontranslatable theory that it was. Additions or elaborations of known theories are either trivial in nature or soon turn out to be unhappy guests in an unwelcome house. To quote Toulmin (1974), "The integration of theoretical concepts . . . will not consist solely in the formal running together of different propositional systems; more typically it will require the development of a whole new pattern of theoretical interpretation" (p. 389).

We have seen that the three terms discussed seem to occupy significant roles in their respective theories as well as seemingly similar positions in the world of our psychological data. Such a familiar, inviting set is the natural impetus for the task of translation of terms. The failure in such an effort is due less to the inadequacy of the translator than to a mistaken idea about theories. It reflects the belief that theories sit outside of the field of investigation and are used to examine and explain the unknown. More powerful theories explain more and deeper; indeed we build upon a theory to make it grow and encompass more data. It seems rather to be the case that any given part of the world is capable of being understood by a variety of theories. No theory explains everything since theories are basically underdetermined, i.e., some explain some things and some others and some are better for some explanations than others (Gedo and Goldberg, 1972, p. 172; Hesse, 1978, p. 14).

Nature does not seem to care how we choose to view it, to categorize it, or to explain it. Whatever "it" may be, the world comes into being by our own vision of it and this vision is a product of our theory. Since observations are not distinct from theory any given chunk of the world will be seen in one way by one theory and in a somewhat different, or perhaps a radically different, way by another. In a given community of persons who share a common language and are trained to see things in a like way there will be a high consensus of agreement as to just what is out there. The first person who discovers something new or sees something heretofore unseen asks the others to look again with the kind of gestalt switch that Kuhn describes in his pictures that can yield two forms to the viewer. These gestalt switches need not change the vision of the entire world but rather direct attention to those areas that had been viewed and therefore agreed upon to be composed or constructed in a particular manner. The new theory must change that or else it is not a new theory but just a version of the old one. Progress in science demands new theories. They need not be radical ones that shake the foundations of the old but they do need to be different; and different enough to force a new perception of the investigated area of the world. If a new theory could be translated back into the old one then it, by definition, would be without merit. It must be untranslatable since a theory is a cluster or web of new percepts that force us to see things differently. Winnicott's transitional object would have no value to us if it were the same as the part object. Efforts to reduce the new to the tried and true are really stifling of scientific progress.

As Donald Spence says (1982):

> If truth is contingent and if we can only understand the meaning and significance of an interpretation against the full set of background assumptions that were operating in that particular analytic space, then we should not be surprised at the periodic appearance of theoretical disagreements. . . . these disagreements indicate . . . the less significant result of drawing conclusions from insufficient data. Supporters of one school . . . take into account only a certain subset of the clinical data. . . . Another school, arguing from another subset reaches different conclusions. Each group . . . [is] . . . less than completely informed [p. 277].

Unfortunately, however, Spence seems to think that this phenomenon is due to the lack of complete accessibility of all information or the failure to naturalize our data. He suggests that until that circumstance occurs, the fate of psychoanalysis is to live with tentative theory while the real facts remain elusive. He ignores the abundant evidence that every science is interpretive (Hesse, 1978), that every investigator brings a certain sort of "privileged competence" to his observations, and thus that every theory deals only with certain subsets of data. Psychoanalysis needs no further license to be more aesthetic than scientific; the contingency of truth is with us everywhere (Habermas, 1978).

If different theories see the world differently and if every theory is limited and necessarily insufficient, then how can psychoanalysis or any scientific enterprise determine what its domain of interest should be? The subject matter of psychoanalysis cannot be defined by the theory since in that case it would be locked in by a community of people speaking the same language and not allowing a change in perception or words. At times, sadly, some seem to encourage this (Moore, 1981). Kohut (1971) would have us define the field by our method whereas others would say that even that may inhibit our progress. Whatever the resolution of that question it is certainly naïve for anyone to declare what is or is not psychoanalysis except in a social and political declaration that exists for the time being.

When and how one adopts a changed theoretical outlook are vexing problems to scientists who may on occasion lay claim to revolutionary changes or else find such subtle evolutionary modifications that it is difficult to pinpoint the exact point of the perceptual switch. Not every new observation is a demand for a new theory, but contradictory ones do beg for reconciliation. One may live with them for variable periods of time, but, then again, as Quine (1969) has suggested, almost any theory can be modified to accommodate any and all anomalous findings. An example of theory accommodation is illustrated in a recent critical review of the work of John Bowlby (Gediman, 1982). Aside from the usual "what is good is old and what is new is bad" form of overview, the work of Bowlby is judged on the basis that either the data are nonanalytic, since they are derived from interviews outside of the consulting room, or the positions they take, such as those on environmental influences and object constancy, are already shared by a host of analysts. As we have seen, the first offense is hardly sustainable, but Bowlby is also evaluated by comparison to Margaret Mahler whose own work is rather outstandingly derived from other kinds of "nonanalytic" data. The definition of that peculiar data base is loaded with problems for the reviewer. The other criticism tends to say that analysts are not of one mind, that many of them consider the impact of the environment and the real needs of people for people outside of mere libidinal gratification. It is felt that Bowlby is constructing straw men to attack.

While not attending to the merits of the particular issues it does seem to be the case that contradictory ideas (i.e., the environment counts vs. the environment doesn't count, or people attach to others for libidinal gratification vs. people attach for supposed other needs) really do exist in analysis and therefore that Bowlby attempted to *explain* his position in a particular and different manner. Of course one may be of a mind to say that it is obvious that the environment counts. However, it is only by theory tinkering that one can get a theory that initially says it doesn't count to say later that it does. Such contradictory positions in a theory may live for quite a while, and sometimes an investigator like Bowlby declares a new theory and thus emphasizes the partition.

At other times we see the tinkering of theory to avoid a clash with other disciplines. For example, when Freud's ideas about psychic energy were shown by a host of investigators (Basch, 1975; Rosenblatt and Thickstun, 1977) to be incompatible with modern-day ideas about energy, the notion of psychic energy was modified: first to be unique to analysis and then gradually to denote something like psychological interest (Kohut, 1971) or even meaningfulness. For some the evolution of the definition was palatable, but for others it could not be digested (Rosenblatt and Thickstun, 1977). Over a period of time the accumulation of differences of opinion does allow for the kinds of basic shifts that warrant a claim for incompatibility: the claim that Bowlby makes. Such seems to be the case for the several theories in psychoanalysis.

Theories in psychoanalysis are not translatable nor should they be. Just as a given word in any language enjoys a cluster of meanings based upon its usage by the community of speakers, so, too, is a theory a cluster of connected solutions to problems. Psychoanalysis seems to have a number or at least several such clusters. They see the world differently, as indeed they should. Some seem to work better than others, and the dedicated and prolonged use of such theories is the single criterion of acceptability. Efforts to translate theories into one another are wasted and do a disservice to the theoreticians. To criticize a theory as being different or wrong is much like condemning a book for being readable: that's what it's supposed to be.

## A Unified Theory

At first glance one might look with envy at those sciences which seem to have a minimum of controversy about the facts of the field and therefore are able to pursue a variety of research programs without argument or rancor. Certainly, chemists are not openly disagreeing about what a compound is, and physicists do not part company on the nature of a simple thing like temperature. Or do they? Kuhn (1970, pp. 130–135) tells an interesting story of how the term "compound" changed in chemistry from the meaning attributed to it by a theory of "elective affinity" to that explained by Dalton's new theory of atoms. The history of the change was a reconstruction of the term "compound" to fit Dalton's theory. The pre- and post-Dalton conceptual fabrics were neither incompatible with experience nor inconsistent logically. Kuhn claims that they could not be compared using either experience or logic. And today the meaning of the word is different in even a different way.

Even the concept of temperature cannot be said always to mean or have meant the same thing. Philosophers may disagree as to whether there does exist some unyielding phenomenon that is indeed temperature (see Putnam, 1981, for the range of arguments here), but for some it is a tactile sensation, for others a point on a thermometer, and for still others a quality of molecular activity.

Given the changing meanings and evolving theories that are common to all science one might still protest that the newest and latest one does seem to unify or integrate everything that has gone before. Certainly, psychoanalysts are familiar with words having multiple meanings, but should we not aim for and reach a point where we can agree on what an object or an ego is? Why can we not bring together part object and transitional object and selfobject in a unifying theory? The answer to these questions is very qualified: maybe we can, and the possibility has to do with the historical moment in which psychoanalysis now finds itself.

Freud developed psychoanalytic theory to cover a particular area of study and data. Some followers of Freud attempted to apply and extend the theory with mixed results. Efforts, for example, to utilize the structural theory of the mind to explain psychoses stretch the theory beyond its limits and result in explanations such as "ego weakness" or the absence of certain structures (Arlow and Brenner, 1964). The struggle with a term and concept such as superego is an interesting one by which to follow the efforts of the faithful adherents of a theory to use it where it seems to have little value (Hartmann and Loewenstein, 1962). Those analysts who studied non-neurotic disorders and the psyche of the preoedipal child were hard-pressed to employ all the terms or concepts of the theory and, as did Winnicott, developed new terms and began to stake out a new theory. One such attempt at a theory is that of object relations. The spirited condemnation of it by Klein and Tribeck (1981) as not being faithful to Freud is, of course, entirely misplaced, just as is Calef and Weinshel's (1979) harsh critique of Kernberg. Whether or not one agrees with him, it is only to Kernberg's credit that he is different; those voices of blame for infidelity are simply unaware of how science progresses.

As a new theory of self psychology was formulated by Kohut a new wave of protest arose. Seeing perhaps more clearly that his theory was not one to be integrated with classical analysis, Kohut chose to absorb or subsume classical analysis into self psychology. Here is a beginning attempt at unification, and it remains to be seen as to whether it will be successful. Certainly the theory of classical analysis will not remain the same if it does succeed. It does not seem to be the case that the development of over-all theories is the way of all science, and many thrive in an atmosphere of pluralism. As Toulmin (1974) says about James Clerk Maxwell's integration of electricity, magnetism, and optics: "it remained possible after Maxwell's work as before, to distinguish between straightforwardly electrical, magnetic and optical phenomena on the empirical level; but on a more general, theoretical level such distinctions lost their earlier significance and it ceased to be necessary to keep the problems, methods and explanatory categories of the three earlier sciences separated" (p. 389). However, we cannot preserve the older meanings in the newer one because as Barnes (1982) says, "Terms connect to other terms differently and they connect to nature differently" (p. 67). The author, for example, who urges healthy dissent without generating a disruptive movement (Stevens, 1980) is confusing scientific progress with his own personal unhappiness at change since, to paraphrase Popper (1959), any change in science must, of necessity, be disruptive. But disruption should not be equated with personal animosity or discomfort. The counterclaim by others (e.g., Richards [1981]) that they seem to do well with the old theories, which therefore should be maintained in the interest of parsimony, is another mistaken personal opinion. It is an open question whether one or another theory is more parsimonious (and how would one decide that?), and it is no secret that a patient can be treated effectively with a variety of theories. The question is whether the new theory explains more to more people; and certainly if one person votes in the negative then he or she has the freedom to renounce it—but such dissent would not qualify for publication in most sciences since it again confuses scientific standards with personal familiarity and comfort.

The need is not for psychoanalysis to still the voices of dissent or discordance in the name of unity or familiarity or fidelity. We do not seem to lack for our cadre of orthodoxy. Rather, we need more, not less, bold and imaginative theories. Psychoanalysis suffers not from too much difference but rather from too little courage in staking out the unexplored for fear of being deposed and alienated. In some sort of effort of concentration we must now reject the routine connection to Freud just as we once insisted upon it.

## Discussion

There can probably be no correct translation of Freud. Every reader reads a different book. Each time one rereads Freud the text means something different. There is no hard and fast rule for words standing for certain things or for one word of one language definitively replacing another. In fact an author often is not completely aware of his meaning until it is written, and even then it may communicate more than one idea. Interpretation is a variable thing and is brought to bear on every text and in every discourse and thus yields variable meanings. We translate in arbitrary ways and use community consensus to determine issues of truth or accuracy. One may argue that one translation of Freud is more pleasing or more reliable or more telling than another, and certainly one may be more popular or readily acceptable than another. But to assert what a word really stands for or what Freud really meant is to wrap truth in a package that always comes undone.

The translation of theory is a severe case of the translation of words. It is made most unlikely in that we may be attending to different parts of the world, i.e., we are reading different books. Hesse (1978) says: "theories should be more or less plausibly coherent with facts, but they can be neither conclusively refuted nor uniquely derived from statements of fact alone, and hence no theory in a given domain is uniquely acceptable" (p. 1). The underdetermining of theory is no longer controversial. It is therefore vitally important for psychoanalysis to cease a preoccupation with the translation of theory and with a search for the true or correct theory. We need to embark upon an effort of maximum comprehension of different ways of explaining the data of our field. We must do so by a pragmatic consideration of the scope and yield of our interpretations and explanations, not by utilizing the test of orthodox compliance. However, "pragmatic" cannot be read as indicative of "anything goes" (see Rorty [1982], especially p. 168, for an explication of modern-day pragmatism) since every science has both a central content and peripheral expansions, and explanations should articulate with and support one another. The cluster of accepted propositions consists of mutually supported ones. They hold together both within the accumulated data of analysis and between it and other disciplines. We cannot consider allowing the incorrect to flourish as pragmatic since to be pragmatic is to have good reasons for adopting one standpoint rather than another, and we do so by a process of negotiation. Translation is a step in such negotiation; it is the way in which we come to understand one another, and such understanding is not to be translated as convincing the other of the truth of one's position.

## REFERENCES

Arlow, J. & Brenner, C. (1964), *Psychoanalytic Concepts and the Structural Theory.* New York: International Universities Press.

Barnes, B. (1982), *Kuhn and Social Science.* New York: Columbia University Press.

Basch, M. F. (1975), Toward a theory of depression. In: *Depression and Human Existence,* ed. E. J. Anthony & T. Benedek. Boston: Little, Brown, pp. 485–534.

Bettelheim, B. (1982), *Freud and Man's Soul.* New York: Knopf.

Calef, V. & Weinshel, E. (1979), The new psychoanalysis and psychoanalytic revisionism. *Psychoanal. Quart.,* 48:470–491.

Gediman, H. K. (1982), Review of *Loss, Sadness, and Depression,* by J. Bowlby. *Psychoanal. Rev.,* 69:391–399.

Gedo, J. & Goldberg, A. (1972), *Models of the Mind.* Chicago: University of Chicago Press.

Habermas, J. (1978), *The Critical Theory of Jurgen Habermas,* ed. T. McCarthy. Cambridge, Mass.: MIT Press.

Hartmann, H. (1964), *Essays on Ego Psychology.* New York: International Universities Press.

────── Loewenstein, R. M. (1962), Notes on the superego. In: *Papers on Psychoanalytic Psychology Psychological Issues,* Monogr. 14. New York: International Universities Press, pp. 144–181.

Hesse, M. (1978), Theory and value in the social sciences. In: *Action and Interpretation,* ed. C. Hookeway & P. Petit. Cambridge, Eng.: Cambridge University Press, pp. 1–16.

Klein, G. (1968), Psychoanalysis: Ego psychology. In: *International Encyclopedia of the Social Sciences.* New York: Macmillan & Free Press, pp. 11–31.

Klein, M. & Tribeck, D. (1981), Kernberg's object-relation theory: A critical evaluation. *Internat. J. Psycho-Anal.,* 62:27–40.

Kohut, H. (1971), *The Analysis of the Self.* New York: International Universities Press.

────── (1977), *The Restoration of the Self.* New York: International Universities Press.

Kuhn, T. S. (1970), *The Structure of Scientific Revolution.* Chicago: University of Chicago Press.

Laplanche, J. & Pontalis, J. B. (1973), *The Language of Psychoanalysis,* trans. D. Necolson-Smith. London: Hogarth Press; New York: Norton.

Mahoney, P. (1982), *Freud as a Writer*. New York: International Universities Press.
Moore, B. (1981), Review of *The Psychology of the Self: A Casebook. J. Amer. Psychoanal. Assn.*, 29:249–252.
Popper, K. (1959), *The Logic of Scientific Discovery*. London: Hutchinson.
Putnam, H. (1981), *Reason, Truth and History*. Cambridge, Eng.: Cambridge University Press.
Quine, W. V. (1969), *Ontological Relativity and Other Essays*. New York: Columbia University Press.
Richards, A. (1981), Self theory, conflict theory, and the problem of hypochondriasis. *The Psychoanalytic Study of the Child*, 36:319–338. New Haven: Yale University Press.
Rorty, R. (1982), *Philosophy: The Mirror of Nature*. Princeton, N.J.: Princeton University Press.
Rosenblatt, A. & Thickstun, J. (1977), Modern Psychoanalytic Concepts in a General Psychology. *Psychological Issues*, Monogr. 42/43. New York: International Universities Press.
Spence, D. P. (1982), *Narrative Truth and Historical Truth*. New York: Norton.
Steiner, G. (1975), *After Babel*. London & New York: Oxford University Press.
Stevens, J. (1980), Review of *Advances in Self Psychology. J. Phila. Psychoanal. Assn.*, 7:208–212.
Suppe, F. (1974), *The Structure of Scientific Theories*. Urbana: University of Illinois Press.
Toulmin, S. (1974), Philosophy of science. *Encyclopedia Britannica, Macropedia*, 16:375–393.
Winnicott, D. W. (1953), Transitional objects and transitional phenomena. *Internat. J. Psycho-Anal.*, 34:89–97.
——— (1965), *The Maturational Processes and the Facilitating Environment*. New York: International Universities Press.

*September 1983*

# The Concept of Structure in Psychoanalysis

## MARK LEVEY, M.D. (Chicago)

In recent years there has been much heated debate about clinical questions which are couched in terms of psychic structure. Some theorists have written that analysis requires intact structure as a prerequisite (Eissler, 1953). Other have argued that analysis can build structure (Kohut, 1971). Some analysands are described as having structured personalities, others as suffering from structural deficits. There are arguments about whether the latter group is analyzable. Often the distinguishing characteristic of analytic change is said to be structural change, as distinct from changes occurring in other types of psychotherapy.

I think it is useful to step back and clarify what we are referring to when we speak of "psychic structure." In this paper I will examine the way "structure" is used in psychoanalytic discourse. In particular, I will highlight the relationship between the meaning of "structure" and developmental theory in psychoanalysis. I believe that the developmental view adds an important perspective to the current clinical controversies.

## Review of the Literature

"Structure" has been used to refer to two groups of phenomena. David Rapaport characterized these groups of phenomena as "relatively stable characteristic configurations that can be abstracted from behavior observed" (Rapaport, 1957, p. 701) and "enduring underlying determiners of behavior" (Rapaport, 1959, p. 53). The first group includes such stable behavioral patterns as symptoms, character traits, transferences, and defenses. The second group consists of more theoretical entities which are understood as determining these behaviors. Although most of the clinical arguments involve structure in this second sense, the two meanings are related.

Psychoanalysis was originally developed during Freud's study of several particular types of behavior: neurotic symptoms, dreams, parapraxes, and jokes. He created the topographic model of the mind to explain them. In that model these behaviors were understood as manifestations of compromise formations between the unconscious push of drives for discharge and the preconscious restraining structure which was called ego.

What "structure" means in this model was most clearly articulated by Rapaport. He described structure as a clinical concept based on two clinical observations: (1) drives alone do not determine behavior; and (2) the factors that conflict with drives and codetermine behavior have a slower rate of change. These abiding codeterminers of behavior are the basis for the concept of structure. However, Rapaport said, the concept of structure might alternatively have been based on the fact that drive energy can only be conceived of in well-defined systems with definite thresholds of discharge. These thresholds could have been the initial conceptualization of structure. The givens of memory, motility, and perception were a third possible basis of the concept of structure. Structure, in Rapaport's view, referred to all three; factors which conflicted with drives, thresholds of discharge, and ego.

Although Freud originally believed that all behavior might be determined by drives and defenses in the same way as the particular behaviors he studied, he later revised this view. By 1923 Freud's clinical interest had shifted to the effects of unconscious resistance and unconscious guilt on the analytic process. These behavioral configurations (structures) were not readily explained by the topographic model. Freud proposed the tripartite model to explain them, introducing the superego and ego ideal as psychic structures. The most obvious result of the new model was a more complex view of the sources of conflict which determined behavior. Now both the ego and superego were codeterminers, with drives, of behavior. Superego motives were a potential source of conflict which could not be reduced to ego or id motives.

However, the change in our understanding of the determiners of behavior which followed the introduction of the tripartite model went well beyond the simple addition of superego motives. To begin with, both the unconscious (now the id) and the "ego" had different meanings in the new model. Whereas the unconscious had been a unitary motivational structure in the topographic model, where all instincts were stimuli pressing for discharge, the tripartite model included the dual instinct theory. Superficially, the aggressive drive was simply an additional instinctual motive, but in other respects it represented determiners of behavior which had not been previously conceptualized. Freud (1920) saw the aggressive drive as the basis for the repetition compulsion which acted in the service of the death instinct. For Melanie Klein and her followers the death instinct became a crucial determiner of behavior. Even for analysts who reject the idea of the death instinct, the repetition compulsion has continued to be invoked as an explanation for behaviors which do not appear to be subjectively motivated in accord with the pleasure principle. More recently, other biological determiners of behavior have been proposed. For example, George Klein (1976) described a hierarchy of basic pleasures. Gedo (1979) recognized a biological principle of self definition, and Basch (1977) has proposed that the propensity to order stimuli is a nonsubjectively motivated, "instinctual" underpinning of behavior. What is important for this discussion is the recognition that the dual instinct theory opened the way for a conceptualization of biological determiners of behavior above and beyond the press of instincts for discharge.

"Ego" also had a new and more complex meaning in the tripartite model. The ego was no longer precisely equivalent to the preconscious. Now the ego was defined as a collection of functions, some of which were preconscious, and others unconscious. The ego was no longer precisely equivalent to defense. Now the ego was a cohesive organization whose function was to synthesize the demands of the id, superego, and reality. The ego was responsible for the coordinated and organized character of behavior, including, but not confined to, drive-discharge actions and defense. Furthermore, as analytic interest shifted from id to ego, it also shifted from conflict per se to problems in adaptation, and from the development of defense per se to the development of behavioral controls and regulations (Klein, 1976). These new interests led to the realization that drive conflict could not be the only source of ego motives. In his discussion of signal anxiety and the synthetic function of the ego, Freud paved the way for the conceptualization of ego motives not originating from drives and for the understanding of ego as a purposive agent: a supraordinate regulating agency (Freud, 1926).

This was more explicitly stated by Hartmann, who found that conflict resolution alone could not account for adaptive behavior. To account for such behavior, he postulated two additional developmental principles: primary autonomy and secondary autonomy (Hartmann, 1939). He argued that certain ego capacities such as memory, perception, and thought develop as parts of the ego, but do not arise from conflict. He called these capacities "apparatuses of primary autonomy" (p. 22). They are biological givens and form one root of the ego, where the ego is seen as an organ of adaptation. They are nonmotivated capacities which can partly determine behavior when the behavior is motivated by a wish to adapt.

Secondary autonomy, functional change, was used by Hartmann to account for the development of ego motives other than defense. An attitude which was originally a defense could undergo a change of function and become an independent structure serving other ego functions. It could change from a means to an end in its own right, and become an irreducible basis of behavior. Thus there was now a range of "ego structures." These were classified by Rapaport as defense structures (motives), means structures (apparatuses), and control structures (ego motives other than defense).

Hartmann also postulated an initial undifferentiated id-ego matrix. This allowed for the direct effects of biology and experience in ego development. This postulate creates the potential for primary ego motives, as well as primarily autonomous ego capacities. In Hartmann's view both the wish to adapt and the wish to synthesize experience are primary ego motives. The idea of an undifferentiated matrix also enables psychoanalytic theory to include the enduring results of learning as determiners in their own right. Later, Erikson (1950), in his cross-cultural studies, added the resolution of developmental incompatibilities as still another source of enduring ego motives. These motives arise from developmental conflict resolution, but not drive conflict.

The tripartite model also opened the way for a more complex view of how environmental interactions, especially with important people, can determine behavior. Freud explicitly added identification as a developmental principle in "The Ego and the Id." He stated that the character of the ego was the precipitate of abandoned object cathexes, and that the superego resulted from the identifications with the parents which accompanied the resolution of the oedipal ties. He also said that identification can occur without object loss and that the ego is formed in part by immediate identification with the father. The concept of identification underlined the importance of early relationships in molding development.

Like the focus on adaptation, the focus on the effects of relationships has added another dimension to our understanding of the sources of motivation and behavior. When Freud spoke of immediate identifications he was alluding to a biological basis for identificatory behavior. More recently, Bowlby (1969) has postulated attachment behavior as a biological imperative. The study of relationships and their effect on development has also brought to light additional motives. Separation and individuation have been described by Mahler as biologically based motives in their own right. The use of objects for the maintenance of self cohesion has been cited by Kohut (1971) as an irreducible basis of behavior.

To summarize, since Freud proposed the tripartite model, the range of phenomena which analysts have considered as "structures," in the sense of enduring determiners of behavior, has broadened considerably. Behavior can be motivated or nonmotivated. Nonmotivated behavior can be determined by biological principles (e.g., repetition compulsion, attachment, withdrawal from overstimulation). It can also be determined in part by nonmotivated capacities (e.g., memory, perception, reality testing) in the service of a given aim such as adaptation. The most important determiners of behavior, from an analytic standpoint, are motives. But motives themselves are no longer viewed as derived from, at bottom, the need to discharge stimuli. They are now recognized as having a broad range of derivations. They can be the result of drive conflicts, either as defenses or as motives of secondary autonomy. They can be the result of other conflicts, such as developmental incompatibilities. There are also ego motives, such as synthesis and adaptation, which are not the outcomes of conflict. Motives can result from relationships and also from learning. Moreover, the hierarchy of motives, their organization, has itself come to be viewed as a determiner of behavior.

It has been demonstrated that these different "structures" cannot be easily related to each other in a consistent way. Rapaport (1957) discussed some of the inconsistencies resulting from the attempts to integrate the different meanings of "structure." He noted that defenses, identifications, and the inner world (the representational world) all result from internalization. All are structures, so all must bind cathexes. But the realization that identification itself is both a defense and a structure-creating mechanism led Rapaport to ask a whole series of questions. Do defenses and identifications (some of which are also defenses) arise by the same mechanism? Is bound cathexis the same in defense and in identification? What is the relationship of identification and defenses? What motivates identification? How do identifications and defenses relate to learning? Is it not contradictory that the ego is formed by identification with abandoned object cathexes, but develops prior to object choice? If identification occurs very early, even before self-object differentiation, how can it be explained by cathectic shifts? How can processes which create the inner world and thus exert a regulatory effect on behavior not alter the structure of the ego at the same time?

These questions reflect the continuing ambiguity about the relationship between internal representations and psychic systems. More recently, Schafer (1968) noted that if representations are structures, then, in this model, they have cathexis. Since each representation has its own influence (energy), representations are doing the same conceptual work as id, ego, and superego.

Some analysts have advocated limiting the term "structure" to a particular meaning in order to resolve the ambiguity. Gill (1963) suggested separating function, a process, from structure, a mode of organization. Lustman (1966) advocated using structure descriptively for the stability of a function. Spitz (1965) used it to mean a number of functions brought into a coherent unit. Holt (1965) suggested using structure to mean the ordering of patterns of stimuli in the service of adaptation, the widening of the tolerable range of stimulus input. Beres (1965) wanted to limit the meaning of structure to that of enduring function in the tripartite model, and not use it for phenomena like memory; for him, using it to mean organization of function or relative stability was tautological. Apfelbaum (1966) felt that the theoretical need for structure came from drive theory and the necessity of denying the existence of ego motivations. He said that the structures of the tripartite model should be acknowledged as really being aim-organizations: motivations. Others have advocated using structure exclusively to denote the supraordinate regulation of behavior. Guttman (1973) has written that the essence of structure is not its elements, but their interrelation. This use of the concept corresponds to that of Piaget and other structuralists. Here, the organization, form, or pattern of phenomena is structure. Meaning comes from the patterned relationship of elements, and it is the isolated elements or words which are the abstractions. In this view structures are identical with functions. Schafer (1975) calls this Freud's cosmogonic view. In this view structure refers to more complex organization. Nagera (1967) and Gedo and Goldberg (1973) also use it the same way.

## A Developmental View

Although it is certainly possible, logical, and perhaps desirable to choose one meaning for structure, the more basic ambiguity about the interrelationship of the different behavioral determiners still needs to be addressed. I think the essence of the ambiguity can best be appreciated in the framework of psychoanalytic developmental theory.

Freud's basic view of psychological development was an economic view, most clearly stated in "The Project for a Scientific Psychology" (Freud, 1895). All development was understood as a result of the need for the central nervous system to discharge tension effectively. This need was complicated by the fact that endogenous, recurrent instinctual tensions arose, and reality often blocked immediate discharge, since gratification during infancy required the presence of an external object. This inevitable frustration led to the development of reality testing, which was necessary in order to know if the external object was present. It also led to the development of the capacity to inhibit drive discharge until the object was present. This inhibition of discharge was accomplished by the binding and neutralization of drive energy. The result of these developmental processes was ego, which was synonymous with psychic structure.

The crucial assumption upon which this model rests is that the nervous system works by trying to rid itself of energy—stimuli. At bottom that is the basis of all human motivation. The two important corollaries which follow from this are, first, that all ego development is reactive—there are no primary ego motives and no spontaneous ego development—and, second, that the ego develops by the single process of limiting drive discharge. The only developmental principles are binding, neutralization of energy (cathexis) and frustration (by the environment). It is only in the context of this view of development that Rapaport's equation of all the structural determiners of behavior (factors that conflict with drives, thresholds of discharge, and the givens of memory, motility, and perception) is valid. The factors which conflict with drives are the same as all other ego functions and all other bases for behavior in that they all have a common origin in the unitary process of controlling drive discharge.

It is in this context that ego and structure have complementary meanings from the topographic, economic, and dynamic points of view. In its topographic aspect, ego is the preconscious, the secondary process, speech presentations, and memory. In its economic aspect, it is bound cathexes, neutralized cathexes, and anticathexes. In its dynamic aspect, it is defense. So, in this model, psychic structure = ego = preconscious = secondary process = speech presentations = memory = bound cathexes = neutralized cathexes = anticathexes = defense.

Using this understanding of development, Freud devised the topographic model of the mind which he then used to explain the role of structural determiners in the formation of neurotic symptoms, dreams, parapraxes, and jokes. The success of the topographic model in understanding these behaviors seemed to validate the assumptions of the underlying model of development. The introduction of the structural model was an acknowledgment that important behavioral configurations could not be understood by using the topographic model. This limitation of the topographic model implied that the general model of development, which had been confirmed by its role in constructing the topographic model, and thereby explaining dreams and neurotic symptoms, was not a comprehensive model of behavioral development. In fact, as we have seen, Freud added identification as a developmental factor in its own right, and later added primary ego developmental factors as well.

Once we recognize innate ego development, we are no longer thinking of ego development as a unitary process, and the metapsychological points of view no longer must have a complementary relationship to each other. Enduring determiners do not necessarily bind energy, limit discharge, or serve as defenses. The theoretical ambiguity in the concept of structure arises from our failure to realize this. By maintaining the assumption that the metapsychological points of view had their old complementary relationship in regard to behaviors which could not be adequately described by the topographic model, we felt that the products of identification and learning had to be describable in terms of energy, topography, and dynamics.

In discussing the relationship between observations and theory, Gedo and Goldberg (1973) write: "Conclusions derived from a particular set of observations have been formulated as clinical theories, and these have led to metapsychological abstractions. The latter have been reapplied by certain authors to a different set of observational data without examination of the pertinence of these constructs to this new area. In logic, this fallacy is called generalization—the treatment of separate populations with some shared characteristics as if they were the same population" (p. 170). This is what has happened as the ideas and assumptions about development have continued to be applied to a range of behaviors to which they are not pertinent. The ambiguities which Rapaport and Schafer have detailed indicate that this new range of behaviors cannot be effectively ordered this way. The old relationships among structural determiners of behavior no longer hold. So, when "structure" is used to refer to all enduring behavioral determiners (e.g., learning, relationships, control of discharge, defense, etc.), it has different meanings which are not systematically related to each other as they were in the simpler model of development.

Thus the meaning of structure now depends upon the particular theoretical viewpoint regarding the behavior in question. In the economic view, where behavior is determined by the need to discharge psychic energy, structure is limitation of discharge, neutralization of energy, bound cathexes, and countercathexes. In the dynamic drive-defense model of behavior, structure is defense. In the more complex dynamic conflict model, the tripartite model, the structures (id, ego, and superego) are enduring motivations. From the adaptational point of view, where behavior is motivated by the need to adapt, structures are enduring functions (nonmotivational capacities) in the service of that aim. These would include secondary process, ego apparatuses, cognitive schemata (including the inner world), linguistic tools, and the ego itself (as a collection of functions). From the object-relations point of view, where the lasting effects on behavior of early relationship are explored, structure refers to the products of identifications, as well as to enduring self and object representations (the inner world) and to enduring motives in relationships. In the learning-theory view, where the effect of learning in determining behavior is in focus, structure is learned behavior patterns. These include habits, automatisms, and schemata in Piaget's sense (an adaptively successful integration of need, perception, and action).

The relationship between these different points of view is complex and not clearly understood. The viewpoints overlap with each other. They are not reducible to each other, but neither are they mutually exclusive. The same character trait can often be understood in terms of its derivation from early relationships, its current dynamic function, or its adaptive value. But each viewpoint would represent the structure underlying the character trait differently. In addition, many behaviors and character traits cannot be well described from every point of view. For example, purposive behavior, the active structuring of goals and values, is not understandable in terms of limitation of discharge. So how can we conceptualize the relationship of these different viewpoints?

Eventually, these viewpoints, and no doubt others as well, may be incorporated in a new comprehensive model of development. Such a model would clarify the interrelationship of learning, cognitive maturation, neurological maturation, relationships, drive and defense, language, and culturally determined experiences, all of which have a role in the development of the motives and capacities which underlie behavior. Our current knowledge of development does not yet enable us to understand the interactions of these factors. There are some clinical questions which cannot be answered effectively until we have such a model of development. Specifically, answering questions about how change occurs in analysis requires such a model. (Although a full discussion of this point is beyond the scope of this paper, the limitations of our current theoretical understanding of change—as described by Strachey [1934], Freud [1937], Loewald [1960], and Meissner [1981]—are discussed by Feffer [1982] and Schafer [1976].)

Another way of ordering these different points of view developmentally, which does not require a comprehensive understanding of the complexity of the developmental process, is the hierarchical model proposed by Gedo and Goldberg (1973). They identified specific behavioral configurations which could be best understood by each model of the mind, and then related the different models in a discontinuous, hierarchical developmental series. Each model implies a particular meaning of structure, and thus the prime structural determiner of behavior in succeeding developmental periods can be identified.

For behaviors characteristic of the reflex-arc model, phase I, structure is limitation of discharge. During phase II, structure is the actual selfobject relationship. In all of the last three models, which occur after the consolidation of the self as a purposive agent, structure refers to different groups of enduring motives. For behavior characteristic of the third phase, the need for a cohesion-maintaining relationship is the prime motive (structure) determining behavior. In phase IV, the tripartite model, the motives grouped as id, ego, and superego are the determining structures. For behaviors characteristic of phase V, a nonconflicted hierarchy of motives is the determining structure.

The Gedo and Goldberg model does not attempt to clarify the interrelationships of the different sources of the prime structural determiners of behavior at each stage or the processes by which they succeed each other. It simply states that they do so in a particular sequence. The main assumption of the model is that each developmental stage can be characterized by a single major determiner of behavior. This is certainly a simplification, but the important point is that it is useful in addressing particular clinical questions.

Although it is not a model which can shed much light on the process of change, for example, it is a very good model for presenting a psychoanalytic developmental nosology, as the authors point out. An important strength of the model in this regard is that the meaning of structure changes as development proceeds. Since each determiner can also account for behaviors at a later stage than its time of dominance, particular structural problems can be related to specific stages of development. This model also illustrates a general principle about the clinical usage of "structure": that is, that many clinical questions imply a particular point of view, which in turn implies a specific notion of structure. In the final section I will explore the relevance of this to several clinical questions.

## Clinical Implications

The three related controversies which I will consider in this section relate to the form the transference should assume in analysis, the analyzability of patients with structural deficits, and the structure-building potential of psychoanalysis.

### Transference

The shift from an interest in neurotic symptoms to an interest in character pathology was the clinical change which led to our more complex view of how behavior is determined. Schafer (1979) defines character, phenomenologically, as patterns of action with properties of continuity, coherence, and consistency. It is a dynamic concept and a predictive one; it tells us what someone may ordinarily be expected to do. It reflects the complex rules and set priorities people follow. Analytic understanding of what determines these rules and priorities, of which character is the reflection, includes all the various viewpoints about what determines both ego and structure. Character is no longer seen as simply the result of instinctual conflict and defense. It is also built from solutions to adaptive crises, and from the patterns of environmental response to primary ego needs. Character also reflects the way in which early relationships are experienced. The results of perceptions, patterns of meaning, and the characteristic hierarchical ways in which they are organized, which are products of learning, constitute character. Character reflects, as well, the self-interpretation of one's own history (Ballas, 1974).

During analysis a patient's character is reflected in the transferences to the analyst. What we call the transference is actually a particular viewpoint about the meaning of behaviors in analysis. Transference is understanding current attitudes, wishes, needs, and expectations of the analyst as a reflection of their origin in past formative experiences and relationships. As such, our understanding of the basis of transference reactions has inevitably changed as part of the change in our understanding of the basis of all current behaviors.

Originally, the wishes and fears which motivated patients in their creation of symptoms and in their relationship with the analyst were felt to derive exclusively from childhood libidinal wishes and inhibitions. In the context of the original developmental model, transference was the manifestation of the desire that the analyst gratify reactivated childhood wishes. This was equivalent to the shift of cathexis of psychic energy across a repression barrier and to the emergence of the unconscious sexual and aggressive longings. Defense, the attempts to ward off the anxieties associated with these wishes, was equivalent to ego and superego prohibitions, and to the damming up of libidinal and aggressive energy.

With our broader understanding of human motivation this is no longer the only way to understand symptoms, character traits, and therefore transferences. As with structure, this broader range of possibilities means that the earlier complementary relationship between dynamic and economic aspects of transference is not universally valid. How the transference is understood and interpreted depends upon the theoretical set. When the transference is understood as arising from libidinal conflict, then the sexual and aggressive feelings, as well as the unconscious ego resistances and superego reactions (the transference neurosis), become the focus of interpretation. When it is viewed as the result of past relationships, the unconscious self and object representations and their relationships are interpreted. When it is seen as a reflection of an enfeebled self, the unconscious use of the analyst as a selfobject is interpreted. When it is felt to be the result of faulty cognitive learning, perceptual and conceptual distortions are interpreted.

As indicated earlier, these different viewpoints are the results of our recognition of the complexity of the determiners of behavior and pathology. They are different ways of understanding the motives and unconscious meanings of behavior. They are neither mutually exclusive nor interchangeable. They are all needed to describe the variety of causes of different aspects of character and pathology. Arguments from one point of view about what form the transference should take disregard the complexity of human motivation.

## STRUCTURE VS. DEFICIT

The meaning of "structure," and therefore the meaning of deficit (lack of structure), depends upon the context. In looking at questions about whether patients with "structural deficits" can be analyzed and whether analysis can "build structure" we should be clear about the frame of reference in which these questions are raised. As the frame of reference changes, so do the meanings of structure and deficit.

The question about analyzability is essentially an adaptational question: can the patient effectively adapt to the analytic situation? It is a question posed from an external observer's point of view, and the patient is evaluated in terms of his possession of relevant adaptive behavioral capacities. These include the capacity to delay, to identify, and to tolerate affective pain. They also include the capacity for reality testing, frustration tolerance, conceptual thinking, insight, basic trust, and object constancy. If these behavioral configurations are to be grouped together and called ego functions, or ego strengths, or psychic structure, it must be kept in mind that ego here means an organ of adaptation to analysis, and structure is the availability of particular behavioral capacities in the context of a wish (motivation) to adapt to analysis.

A different frame of reference is used in descriptions of the analytic process and in clinical questions about the need for analysis. These are essentially dynamic questions about motives: what is the meaning of a person's behavior, and what wishes, fears, and expectations motivate it? The need for analysis arises when the person is having difficulties in living which result from meanings of and motives for behavior of which he is not aware. Structure, in this dynamic context, refers to enduring motivations and their hierarchical arrangements including, but not limited to, the sets of motives which we call id, ego, and superego.

Thus the meaning of structure depends on its context; dynamically, as in questions about the need for analysis, it refers to enduring meanings and motives, whereas adaptively, as in questions about analyzability, it refers to the presence of particular behavioral capacities. Keeping this in mind we can look again at the clinical questions: Does analysis require intact structure or can it build structure? Can only structured personalities be analyzed, or can personalities with structural deficits be analyzed as well?

Those who say that intact structure is required are referring to the presence of particular behavioral configurations. These are the adaptive capacities mentioned earlier as criteria for analyzability. The self psychologists and others who speak of analysis building structure are referring to different behavioral configurations. The structures being "built" are the more effective organization of motivations (ambitions, goals, and values) to regulate behavior better.

This distinction is not always clearly stated in Kohut's writing. In trying to differentiate the patients whom he calls narcissistic personality disorders from those who develop a more classical transference neurosis, he speaks of the former as lacking in structure. He says that the analysis of a transference neurosis leads to a better arrangement of functions, whereas in a narcissistic personality disorder new structures and functions are built (Kohut, 1971). He is referring to the superego and the ego ideal, which in narcissistic personalities are insufficiently idealized. It sounds as if he is talking about a lack of adaptive capacity, not of motivation.

However, he very clearly states that he is speaking about structures from the empathic-introspective point of view, not that of the outside observer of objective behavioral capacities. He is also well aware that the successful analysis of any patient will result in new adaptive capacities. Thus it cannot be a lack of structure as adaptive capacity that distinguishes narcissistic personality disorders from neurotic disorders. The "structural deficit" Kohut writes of is the relative ineffectiveness of the ego ideal as a group of regulatory motives which are needed in the service not of adaptation, but of self-actualization. The "deficit" is not the lack of the adaptive behavioral configurations referred to in questions of analyzability. He is, rather, describing the need for analysis of a group of people who have always been considered "structured" in the sense of having the capacities required for analysis. There is no difference of opinion here about the behavioral capacities needed for analysis, regardless of whether the patient is said to exhibit a "structural deficit." (There are other analysts, such as Kernberg and Fromm-Reichman, who do differ in their view of which behavioral capacities are actually necessary. There can be valid empirical debate about this. My point here is that couching the argument in terms of the presence or absence of ego or structure will only cloud the issue. It will either, as in the case above, lead to an argument where none need exist, or serve to obscure which specific capacities really are or are not needed.)

The second question, whether we can analyze people with structural deficits, as well as those who have structured personalities, is phrased as if it were also a question of analyzability. However, structure here refers to behavioral configurations seen in the transference. A structured personality in this context is a patient who experiences the analyst as either a loved or a hated person, or as the external embodiment of one set of internally conflicting motives, usually the projection of the patient's superego. To the analyst, this transference means that an internal conflict between motives (id, ego, and superego) is responsible for the maladaptive behaviors and psychic distress which led the patient to seek and to need analysis. "Structural deficit" is used to describe a patient who experiences the analyst as a part of the patient's self, performing a mirroring or idealizing regulatory function. To the analyst, this transference means that the unconscious need to use other people in this capacity is responsible for the maladaptive behaviors and psychic distress which led the patient to seek and need analysis. Why should a difference in the need for analysis be discussed as if it were a question of analyzability?

One reason for this confusion is the failure to distinguish between the different meanings of "structured personality." Hartmann, Kris, and Loewenstein (1946), in their paper on the formation of psychic structure, used "structure" to describe the inner cohesion of the forces which can repeatedly be observed to oppose each other in conflict: the ego, id, and superego. Each of these is a source of motivation. Thus, when they go on to say that a structured personality is one where ego and id are sharply demarcated, that there is a fixed functional relationship of id, ego, and superego, and that "structure" is no longer formed after age five or six, they are referring to only one meaning of structure: the existence of a particular group of enduring, potentially conflicting motives in the personality. However, when "structured personality" is also used to refer to a person with an effectively organized behavioral regulatory capacity (a cohesive hierarchy of aims and motivations, the converse of a structural deficit), as well as to one who has the behavioral capacities necessary for analyzability, there is the implicit assumption that all three of these sets of characteristics will invariably be present in the same people. The *clinical* meaning of Kohut's notion of two lines of development, however controversial it is as theory, is the recognition that these aspects of personality do not always develop together. Someone may have id, ego, and superego clearly defined in his personality, yet lack a well-functioning regulatory capacity, and vice versa. These problems may be different results of faulty development, and neither invariably implies the lack or the presence of the capacities needed to benefit from analysis.

A second reason for the current debate about who is really analyzable is that many analysts use the development of a transference neurosis as a criterion of analyzability. Here, however, analyzability has a different meaning from that in my previous discussion. The earlier question about analyzability concerned the clarification of who could tolerate the analytic procedure and benefit from it. Here what is being asked is when is an analysis really an *analysis*?

As indicated earlier, to answer this on the basis of the nature of the transference that develops is to disregard what we have learned about the complexity of human motivation. A more productive way to approach this question would be to try to clarify precisely how analysis exerts its therapeutic effects on all patients. This question is hard to address without a comprehensive understanding of how different factors interact in development to give us the "structure" we attempt to change. I think at the moment it must be considered an open question. It is possible that patients with pathology from different stages of development utilize different aspects of the analytic relationship. Gedo and Goldberg have suggested this. It may also be that the combination of interpretations, affective reliving, and identification with the analyst which characterizes the analytic experience may constitute a particular kind of learning which can be differentiated, both theoretically and functionally, from other kinds of learning. This is an empirical question, and one that poses a challenge and an opportunity for us to refine and re-evaluate our understanding of both development and change.

## Summary

In this paper I explore the uses of the concept of "structure" in clinical theory. It is used to refer both to stable characteristic configurations that can be abstracted from behavior and to enduring underlying determiners of behavior. As the range of behaviors we have examined analytically has expanded from neurotic symptoms, dreams, parapraxes, and jokes to the study of guilt, adaptation, character, and behavioral regulation, our understanding of what determines behavior has expanded greatly.

Originally, all behavior was felt to be determined, at bottom, by the need of the nervous system to rid itself of stimuli. Here binding and neutralization of drive energy were the only developmental principles. But as the range of behaviors being explained was expanded, identification, primary and secondary autonomy, and spontaneous ego development were added as determiners. How these different determiners were related to each other became a theoretical problem.

By retracing the assumption of the developmental models of psychoanalysis, it becomes clear that some confusion was created by assuming that the dynamic, topographic, and economic points of view had to be complementary aspects of all behaviors. This is only the case in Freud's original model of development, where all ego development was a reaction to the need to limit the discharge of drive energy. Clarifying the interrelationship of the different determiners of behavior, which we call "structures," is an important task for the future. It is particularly relevant for a better understanding of how change occurs. However, our current understanding of development is useful in resolving some current clinical debates. These are explained in the last section of the paper.

## REFERENCES

Apfelbaum, B. (1966), On ego psychology: A critique of the structural approach to psychoanalytic theory. *Internat. J. Psycho-Anal.*, 47:451–475.
Ballas, C. (1974), Character: The language of the self. *Internat. J. Psycho-Anal. Psychother.*, 3:397–418.
Basch, M. F. (1977), Development theory and explanatory theory in psychoanalysis. *This Annual*, 5:229–263. New York: International Universities Press.
Beres, D. (1965), Structure and function in psychoanalysis. *Internat. J. Psycho-Anal.*, 46:53–63.
Bowlby, J. (1969), *Attachment*. New York: Basic Books.
Eissler, K. R. (1953), The effect of the structure of the ego on psychoanalytic technique. *J. Amer. Psychoanal. Assn.*, 1:104–143.
Erikson, E. (1950), *Childhood and Society*. New York: Norton.
Feffer, M. (1982), *The Structure of Freudian Thought*. New York: International Universities Press.
Freud, S. (1895), Project for a scientific psychology. *Standard Edition*, 1:295–391. London: Hogarth Press, 1966.
——— (1920), Beyond the pleasure principle. *Standard Edition*, 18:3–67. London: Hogarth Press, 1955.
——— (1923), The ego and the id. *Standard Edition*, 19:3–66. London: Hogarth Press, 1961.
——— (1926), Inhibitions, symptoms, and anxiety. *Standard Edition*, 20:77–179. London: Hogarth Press, 1959.
——— (1937), Analysis terminable and interminable. *Standard Edition*, 23:211–253. London: Hogarth Press, 1964.
Gedo, J. (1979), *Beyond Interpretation: Toward a Revised Theory for Psychoanalysis*. New York: International Universities Press.
——— Goldberg, A. (1973), *Models of the Mind: A Psychoanalytic Theory*. Chicago: University of Chicago Press.

Gill, M. M. (1963), Topography and Systems in Psychoanalytic Theory. *Psychological Issues*, Monogr. 10. New York: International Universities Press.

Guttman, S. (1973), Psychoanalysis and science: The concept of structure. *This Annual*, 1:73–81. New York: Quadrangle/New York Times.

Hartmann, H. (1939), *Ego Psychology and the Problem of Adaptation*. New York: International Universities Press.

——— Kris, E., & Loewenstein, R. (1946), Comments on the formation of psychic structure. *The Psychoanalytic Study of the Child*, 2:11–38. New York: International Universities Press.

Holt, R. R. (1965), Ego autonomy re-evaluated. *Internat. J. Psycho-Anal.*, 46:151–167.

Klein, G. (1976), *Psychoanalytic Theory: An Exploration of Essentials*. New York: International Universities Press.

Kohut, H. (1971), *The Analysis of the Self*. New York: International Universities Press.

Loewald, H. (1960), On the therapeutic action of psychoanalysis. *Internat. J. Psycho-Anal.*, 41:16–33.

Lustman, S. L. (1966), Impulse control, structure, and the synthetic function. In: *Psychoanalysis—A General Psychology: Essays in Honor of Heinz Hartmann*, ed. R. M. Loewenstein, L. M. Newman, M. Schur, & A. J. Solnit. New York: International Universities Press, pp. 190–221.

Meissner, W. W. (1981), Internalization in Psychoanalysis. *Psychological Issues*, Monogr. 50. New York: International Universities Press.

Nagera, H. (1967), The concepts of structure and structuralization: Psychoanalytic usage and implications for a theory of learning and creativity. *The Psychoanalytic Study of the Child*, 22:77–102. New York: International Universities Press.

Rapaport, D. (1957), A theoretical analysis of the superego concept. In: *The Collected Papers of David Rapaport*, ed. M. Gill. New York: Basic Books, pp. 685–709.

——— (1959), The Structure of Psychoanalytic Theory: A Systematizing Attempt. *Psychological Issues*, Monogr. 6. New York: International Universities Press.

Schafer, R. (1968), *Aspects of Internalization*. New York: International Universities Press.

——— (1975), Psychoanalysis without psychodynamics. *Internat. J. Psycho-Anal.*, 56:41–55.

——— (1976), *A New Language for Psychoanalysis*. New Haven: Yale University Press.

——— (1979), Character, ego-syntonicity, and character change. *J. Amer. Psychoanal. Assn.*, 27:867–891.

Spitz, R. (1965), *The First Year of Life*. New York: International Universities Press.

Strachey, J. (1934), The Nature of the therapeutic action of psychoanalysis. *Internat. J. Psycho-Anal.*, 15:127–159.

*January 1984*

# Toward a Psychoanalytic Theory of the Charismatic Relationship

JEROME A. WINER, M.D. (Chicago)
THOMAS JOBE, M.D. (Chicago)
and CARLTON FERRONO (Chicago)

What is charisma? What is a charismatic leader? How do charismatic leaders have the effect they do? How do they inspire such devotion from their followers? Do their followers share certain psychological traits? How do the leaders acquire their followers? But, most importantly, what intrapsychic processes enable charismatic leaders to produce and disseminate new values and institutions or reshape old ones to the great benefit of or great harm to their societies? These questions stand in need of intrapsychic and group-psychological explanation. A comprehensive depth-psychological theory of charismatic leadership, though badly needed, has not yet been developed despite beginnings by psychoanalytic, psychohistorical, social-psychological, and sociological theorists. This paper will examine the concept of charisma with particular emphasis on some of the unexplored psychological issues, in an attempt to understand the charismatic relationship from a psychoanalytic viewpoint.

Psychoanalytic theorists have tended to see charismatic leadership as a problem for social psychology, sociology, and political science rather than for depth psychology. This is understandable because of Max Weber's brilliant development of the concept earlier in this century in a series of works which remained totally within the sociological realm (Weber, 1968). Yet, when Weber introduced the concept of the force of the charismatic

Portions of this paper were presented at the Oedipus Revisited conference cosponsored by the Chicago Institute for Psychoanalysis and the Psychoanalytic Association of Greece, October 15, 1983, in Patras, Greece.

personality to address the problem of how new values and institutions were introduced and propagated within a society, he was describing a power that had impact on the inner life of people. Weber described charisma as "a certain quality of an individual personality by virtue of which he is set apart from ordinary men and treated as endowed with supernatural, superhuman, or at least specifically exceptional qualities" (quoted in Eisenstadt, 1968, p. xviii). Weber took the appeal of the charismatic leader for granted, however. Eisenstadt (1968) collected Weber's writing on charisma and institution building and found that Weber says nothing explicit about the source of charismatic power. Because Weber did state that "charisma may involve a subjective or internal reorientation born out of suffering, conflicts or enthusiasm" which may occur "in times of psychic, physical, economic, ethical, religious, political distress" (quoted in Eisenstadt, 1968, p. xxiii), he could be read as being in agreement with later writers who claim that it is the disturbed, the disoriented, and the alienated who chiefly respond to charismatic appeal. Shils (1965) has taken the position, however, that the charismatic bond is not necessarily abnormal. Shils includes scientific discovery, ethical promulgation, artistic creativity, and all forms of genius as instances of things charismatic.

Instead of focusing upon these positive features, or upon the origin of values and institutions, most psychologically oriented writers have construed charismatic leadership in exclusively psychopathological terms with respect to both the leaders and the followers (Galanter, 1982). Erikson (1958, 1969) has given a more balanced view, showing that a leader's personal conflict and resolution, when it is in resonance with societal conflict, can provide a new ordering force. Recent popular usage of the term has associated charismatic leadership with cults, particularly of adolescents and young adults, or with the long-distance sensationalism exhibited by certain types of "rock" and movie personalities. In fact, however, there is a continuum of charismatic leadership stemming from the highly pathological leader and the sick follower to the innovative, creative, ameliorative leader and the follower who utilizes the relationship to become the fullest possible affirmation of his own potentialities.

## The Concept of Charisma in Homer's *Iliad*

The Greek word χαρισμα conveyed the sense of special gifts bestowed on an individual by the gods (Dematrakou, 1950; Brown, 1982). These gifts could take either a material or a spiritual form. In the *Iliad* Homer, although he never used the word, provided us with one of the most vivid descriptions of the charismatic leader and his effect on others, a description which foreshadowed several aspects of charismatic authority later depicted by modern social scientists.

There can be little doubt that Achilleus, who represented charismatic authority on the Greek side, may be viewed as a prototype of the modern charismatic leader. Achilleus, until Patroklos's death, withheld himself from battle, in petulant, almost adolescent anger at Agamemnon. News of his beloved comrade's death stirred Achilleus. He entered a period of mourning and isolation, as the Greek forces stood in disarray, having been routed by the Trojans in battle. His anger at the defilement of Patroklos's body was equaled only by his sense of impotence, since he no longer had his magnificent armor with which to do battle. Patroklos had worn it and it had been stripped from his body. In this condition, Achilleus is visited by the gods. First comes his mother, Thetis, who promises a new set of armor to be forged by the lame god, Hephaistos. She next pleads his case before Zeus. When Thetis then brings the gifts to Achilleus, he alone among the company of Greeks dares to gaze at it.

> None had the courage to look straight at it. They were afraid of it. Only Achilleus looked, and as he looked the anger came harder upon him and his eyes glittered terribly under his lids, like sunflare. He was glad, holding in his hands the shining gifts of Hephaistos [Homer, *Iliad*, bk. 19, ll. 14–18, p. 392].

Further, his mother drove "the strength of great courage into him . . ." (l. 37, p. 393), and the goddess Athene came to him, to drop ambrosia and nectar into his breast, "so no sad weakness of hunger would come on his knees . . ." (l. 354, p. 401). In fact, Achilleus is so protected and aided by the gods that no Trojan has a chance against him. Through these *charismata*, Achilleus underwent a complete transformation, from a sulking, withdrawn, moody adolescent, to an inspired, potent, and persuasive leader, who rallied men to battle. At dawn, as he put on the armor, the transformation was complete.

> A clash went from the grinding of his teeth, and his eyes glowed as if they were the stare of a fire, and the heart inside him was entered with sorrow beyond endurance. Raging at the Trojans he put on the gifts of the god, that Hephaistos wrought him with much toil [ll. 365–368, pp. 401–402].

Although he knew his death was fated, Achilleus had finally found the cause for which he would fight and die.

In summary, there are several stages of charismatic leadership portrayed in Homer's description of Achilleus: first, the potential leader must undergo a personal crisis in which he is rendered helpless (death of Pa-

troklos, loss of armor); second, the leader must become the living embodiment, the human representation of a specific, passively endured situation
reversed by divine intervention (gift of armor, decision to enter battle,
redirected anger); third, by virtue of these newly acquired personal attributes (courage, capacity to arouse awe, will to fight), the charismatic leader
emerges during times of distress and crisis (imminent death and defeat of
the Greeks) as a figure around whom others who are in a similar, passively
endured traumatic circumstance coalesce into a unified group and form
a potent, active movement. In this early conceptualization of charisma it
is the gifts of the gods that make possible the reversal in the leader which
paves the way out of helplessness. We shall propose the substitution of a
psychological mechanism for this external agency, for divine gifts. We shall
claim that a paradigmatic reversal from passivity to activity by the charismatic figure resonates with an unconscious fantasy of passivity in the follower. The reversal is elaborated by the leader into a mission or message
much as a primal fantasy can be elaborated in a poem or play. Potential
followers have similar unconscious fantasies with similar passively endured
experience. The effect of the follower's unconscious recognition of the
matching patterns is the attribution of special powers to the leader—the
attribution of charisma.

Perhaps the best way to begin our psychoanalytic study of the continuum
of charismatic relationships is to examine the concept of charisma historically.

## The Concept of Charisma in the New Testament and Its Interpreters

Although employed earlier, charisma acquired a special prominence in the
New Testament, largely because of Paul's extension of the concept. Here
also it denoted a gift of God; more specifically, however, it conveyed a
sense of spiritual gifts, encompassing several extraordinary attributes of
personality. Thus charisma was embodied in the receipt of the "gifts of
grace" conveyed by the Holy Spirit (Shils, 1965):

> For to one is given by the Spirit the word of wisdom; to another the word
> of knowledge by the same spirit; to another faith by the same Spirit; to
> another the gifts of healing by the same Spirit; to another the working
> of miracles; to another prophecy; to another discerning of spirits; to
> another divers kinds of tongues, to another the interpretation of tongues;
> but in all these worketh that one and the self-same Spirit, dividing to
> every man severally as he will [Corinthians, 12:8–11].

The division of these charismatic gifts was not equal but apportioned on the basis of proximity to the figure of Christ; the greater part was shared by the apostles and the prophets. Such charismatic gifts were not meant for personal gain or sanctification. They were to be used for the common good following the example of God the Father, whose free gift of his son's life gave eternal life to all Christians.

Wilhelm (1908) has traced the later history of the concept. The notion of charisma remained important throughout the subsequent history of the Catholic church, undergoing manifold elaboration on the basis of the New Testament texts. Little significant change in the concept occurred until the nineteenth century, when theological debate over charisma experienced a renaissance in Germany. The debate centered on a dichotomy between two basic types of *charismata*: (1) those which furthered the inner workings and development of the Church, through its offices and dignitaries; (2) those which furthered the outer growth of the Church, by strengthening the faith of believers and bringing in nonbelievers. This dichotomy appeared to have been part of a long-standing historical conflict over the role of charismatic powers in Christianity. Does charisma lie in the Church as an institution or primarily in certain chosen individuals? It was this concern with the distinction between institutional authority and personal authority which caught the attention of Max Weber, the German sociologist of the early twentieth century. His analysis of charisma has become the model on which the modern secular usage of the concept is based.

## The Sociological Concept of Charisma

Even in Weber's conceptualization, "charisma" retained the connotation of "divine intervention" and "religious inspiration," in binary opposition to the "everyday routine" (*Alltäglichkeit*) of economic life. Several commentators have noted its similarity to Rudolph Otto's (1917) "Idea of the Holy" and Durkheim's (1912) distinction between the "sacred" and "profane" spheres. Weber himself felt that his contribution lay not in the introduction of a new sociological term, but in the elucidation, elaboration, and application of an already accepted concept to a wider context.

Weber's principal concern was to distinguish different forms of legitimate order (*Ordnung*) and authority (*Herrschaft*) within the corporate group (*Verband*). He delineated three basic "ideal types" of such groups and the form of authority on which they were founded: traditional (patriarchal), rational (bureaucratic), and charismatic. Despite the wide divergences between traditional and rational authority, these two forms, according to Weber (1968), "have in common a most important peculiarity: permanence. In this respect they are both institutions of daily routine" (p. 18). On the

other hand, the third type of group order based on charismatic authority
had an entirely different basis, materially and psychologically. Thus, Weber
concluded:

> ... "natural" leaders—in times of psychic, physical, economic, ethical,
> religious, political distress—have been neither office-holders nor incum-
> bents of an "occupation" ... that is, men who have acquired expert
> knowledge and who serve for remuneration. The natural leaders in dis-
> tress have been holders of specific gifts of the body and spirit; and these
> gifts have been believed to be supernatural, not accessible to everybody
> [pp. 18–19].

To Weber charismatic authority emerged at times of genuine crisis and
distress in the larger society. Moreover, this authority rested on a single
individual and the qualities of his personality by which "he is set apart from
ordinary men and treated as endowed with either supernatural, superhuman, or at least specifically exceptional powers ... on the basis of them
the individual concerned is treated as a leader" (p. 48). Tucker (1968) has
pointed out, in elaboration of Weber's ideas, that the charismatic leader is
idolized not only because of his extraordinary personal qualities but also
because he uses these qualities in the process of summoning people to join
in a movement for change and in leading such a movement. Tucker concluded that "To speak of charismatic leaders, then, is to speak of charismatic
movements; the two phenomena are inseparable" (p. 738).

Unlike traditional and rational (bureaucratic) forms of authority, which
gained and maintained their power through *institutional means*, charismatic
authority obtained its legitimacy through the *personal attributes* of the leader
as well as through "the normative patterns of order revealed or ordained
by him" (Weber, 1968, p. 46). Whether or not an individual becomes a
charismatic leader depends on his capacity to influence others. His ability
to attract followers, to convince others of the correctness of his ideas, and
his capacity to lead become decisive. Weber did allude to the linkage of
these factors to intrapsychic processes when he claimed that

> Charisma knows only inner determination and inner restraint. The
> holder of charisma seizes the task that is adequate for him and demands
> obedience and a following by virtue of his mission. His success determines
> whether he finds them. His charismatic claim breaks down if his mission
> is not recognized by those to whom he feels he has been sent. If they
> recognize him, he is their master—so long as he knows how to maintain
> recognition through "proving" himself. But he does not derive his "right"
> from their will, in the manner of election. Rather, the reverse holds: It
> is the *duty* of those to whom he addresses his mission to recognize him
> as their charismatically qualified leader [Weber, quoted in Gerth and
> Mills, 1958, pp. 246–247].

## A Psychological Theory

What was most needed at this point in Weber's analysis was a psychological theory, one that would illuminate both the inner experience of the leader and his followers and the bond between them. Although several partial contributions have appeared, none has been totally satisfactory. Kohut (1976) offers an attractive nucleus of a theory, particularly so because he describes the leader's attributes in depth-psychological terms. Kohut sees evidence of the pathology of the self system in both charismatic leaders and their followers, although acknowledging that what he calls charismatic and messianic personalities come in all shades and degrees including mixtures of the two. Such leaders are totally devoid of empathy except where even subtle reactions in others are related to their own narcissistic requirements. They appeal to individuals with an enfeebled self because "they display an apparently unshakable self confidence and voice their opinions with absolute certainty" (p. 825). To a greater or lesser extent the messianic figure's self and the ideals of his superego have become one; the charismatic leader's self has largely become the carrier of the grandiose self. Messianic personalities tend to be idealized; charismatic personalities become the nonidealized target for identification with an omnipotent object. In crisis, an enfeebled nation may turn to such a figure much as an individual with an enfeebled self does. Kohut believes that such messianic characters suffered a traumatic withdrawal on the part of the mirroring selfobject of early childhood and the charismatic figures have suffered analogous disappointments from the archaic idealized object. He does not explain what other elements are necessary for such common developmental traumas to eventuate in these two particular types of personalities. Kohut leaves the question of how these personalities "dovetail" with the widespread yearning for omnipotent figures for future research (p. 834). He then goes on to posit the nuclear group self (the group's central ambitions and ideals) as a concept that will have explanatory power with respect to the continuity, cohesion, and important actions of the group. Gehrie (1980), Strozier (1980, 1983), and Zonis and Offer (in press) have elaborated Kohut's ideas.

Although Kohut's constructs about the charismatic relationship have broad explanatory power, he stated explicitly that they were beginning notions that he was leaving for the next generation to develop. They lack specificity with respect to the match between the needs of the followers and the particular offerings of the leaders. Kohut does not explain in depth the particular nature of the charismatic relationship so as to distinguish it from most other self-selfobject relationships.

LaBarre (1972), a psychoanalytically oriented anthropologist, claimed that a man has charisma if he has a "praeternatural and awe-inspiring quality" (p. 359). LaBarre found the source of the awe in the first *mana* a child knows, which is part of his parents. An animistic concept that originated among the Melanesians, *mana* is the spirit responsible for all good and evil in the universe, the spirit which pervades all things. "The unregenerate child who would still command the *mana*-laden spirits becomes a shaman; the one who would domesticate God, manage, cajole or placate Him, the priest; and the one who would identify with the artificer-creator, the 'maker' poiesis, the 'shaper' scope, becomes the culture hero" (p. 359). All have charisma. LaBarre believes the culture hero's fascination is initially his narcissistic fascination with himself which stems in turn from his mother's fascination with him. He is a narcissistic character who embodies what others only dream of being and often possesses a prescient sense of the people's needs. LaBarre is vague on the power of the leader's message, claiming it is "not new information of the structure of the world, but only of new inner emotional structuring in people's culture-personality" (p. 360). By this he means that charismatic leaders arise in response to crisis situations in a people's culture, with culture construed as a set of defense mechanisms protecting the people from anxiety and stress. The leader's message, often elaborated out of a dream or vision, is adopted as an emergency defensive measure, sometimes with catastrophic results. According to LaBarre, each religion has its origin in such a phenomenon.

Zaleznik (1974) contrasts charismatic leaders with those who lead by consensus, claiming that the former have "a highly developed and well-populated inner life as a result of introjecting early objects and later identifying with objects, symbols, and ideals which have some connection to the introjects. The imagoes, or internal audience [especially the mother], exert a powerful influence on the leader and form the basis for the ties he establishes with the masses" (p. 225). Consensus leaders lack stable, benevolent, and well-integrated introjects because of disruption in object ties, usually in the form of separation from mother or birth of siblings. Once again Zaleznik's ideas seem to fit many who are neither charismatic nor leaders. Zaleznik's theory does point to the charismatic leader's special capacity to wait passively until the time he can act assertively, a trait worth emphasizing.

Arlow (Panel, 1979) discusses the prophet as a type of charismatic leader who can discern the unconscious fantasies reality has evoked in a group. He then acts as a catalyst by shaping the emerging morality or ideology as a derivative of the group unconscious fantasy. Mazlish (1976) sees the revolutionary ascetic leader as someone not subject to countertransference or suggestion. He is masterful and independent because he has displaced his libidinal impulses onto a beloved abstraction. Lewy (1979) claims that myths about the hero, such as those described by Rank (1914), demonstrate intuitive knowledge of the psychological factors necessary for the development of a charismatic leader-hero, knowledge which makes use of symbolism and other primary-process mechanisms. Such myths universally portray a sequence characterized by an ordeal—exile, exposure, destruction, and humiliation—and succeeded by greatness. At the core, he finds a special oedipal solution which is characteristic of such leaders.

The most elaborated and elegant psychoanalytic explanation of the phenomena of charisma is surprisingly to be found in the sociological literature (Camic, 1980). Camic draws on two undeveloped ideas of Weber. The first of these nascent concepts is to be found in Weber's own statement, made sometime after having read Freud, that the sources of charisma were "altogether unconscious and seldom fully conscious" (p. 6). The second of these ideas is Weber's early hint, largely neglected in his later work, that the preconditions for charisma are extraordinary human needs. Camic, using Freud's structural theory of the mind, argues that these extraordinary human needs can be of four types leading to four varieties of charisma. In each, the followers unquestionably obey the commands of those to whom they attribute specialness or extraordinary power.

Camic begins by citing Weber's early notion that it is because of extraordinary needs that primitives impute magical power to stones or persons. Similarly, prophets were considered charismatic because of their being perceived as able to meet the pressing need for meanings through which discrepant aspects of the world could be understood. Camic then engages in a systematic analysis of the extraordinary human needs which serve as preconditions for charisma. Following Schafer (1968), he understands the id, ego, and superego to be categories designating groups of functionally related motives or needs. Id needs involve the full satisfaction of sexual and aggressive wishes and other less infantile wishes rejected by the superego and ego as too dangerous to act on or even acknowledge. Superego needs fulfill the moral standards of a given society which have been internalized as a consequence of identification with parents and significant others. For Camic ego needs are of two types: (1) dependency needs for protection, certainty, physical security, and meaning; (2) needs for achievement and attainment, consistent with prevailing cultural standards, mastery, and self-regard (called ego-ideal needs). All such id, dependency, ego-ideal, and superego needs "when extraordinary, are the basis for attributions of specialness to need-gratifying persons or objects . . . a certain type of need is the precondition for a particular variety of charisma, while other types of needs are preconditions for different varieties" (p. 12).

Camic introduces the Ego (capitalized) in contrast to the narrow usage above (dependency needs) to denote the "supraordinate decision making, reality testing, regulatory agency (and its controls and apparatuses) of the personality system" (p. 12). When the Ego is passive—i.e., overwhelmed, helpless, no longer in control—ordinary needs become extraordinary needs. Camic cites Rapaport's (1957) observation that when the Ego is passive and consequently in extreme needfulness, potential objects of gratification are endowed "with a power the effect of which amounts to slavery and surrender" (p. 731). Camic's reading of ego-psychology theorists (Hartmann, 1939; Hartmann, Kris, and Loewenstein, 1946; Brenner, 1974) leads to his belief that Ego passivity comes about either because of certain complex patterns of sociocultural experience and learning (Rapaport, 1957, 1961) or because of object loss (Pollock, 1961). On the group or societal level, the former takes place in highly ordered settings and is consistent with the sociological position that claims that charisma emerges in such settings. The alternative sociological position that charisma emerges in periods of social change is consistent with the object-loss view for loss of leaders, institutions, and roles accompanies historical upheaval.

Camic goes on to demonstrate how Freud's structural theory, coupled with some of his other concepts, allows one to separate the vast array of charismatic leaders into four broad categories. First Camic takes up extraordinary dependency needs and applies Freud's (1913, 1927) concept of the attribution of *omnipotence* to leaders who appear capable of gratifying such needs. Next Camic notes that when Freud (1914, 1921) talks specifically of those who meet ego-ideal needs he uses the term *excellence.* Such charismatic individuals usually offer vicarious gratification, but on occasion relationships are struck in which "excellent" individuals gratify the needs of others directly by recognizing and promoting their success and attainment. The third type of attributed specialness has extraordinary superego needs as the precondition, and Freud (1939) designates this attribute as *sacredness.* Fourth, Camic employs Freud's (1919) term *uncanny* for those who achieve id aims by virtue of special powers. Here, for example, are the charismatic film stars and entertainers noted for their misbehavior, sexual promiscuity, and rebellion.

Camic concludes with remarks on the consequences of charisma. As Weber noted, first there is the establishment of a relationship in which the needy individual responds to the need-gratifying figure with attitudes of awe, devotion, and reverence. Second, the needy individual totally accepts the leader's commands as binding and dutifully obeys them. Camic employs Freud's concept of positive transference to explain the awe, devotion, and reverence, yet he is mindful that the extent to which such attitudes obtain is always a function of the social interaction between leader and follower. As for the dutiful obeisance, Camic says that often individuals internalize the leader's values and dictates in a way that radically changes their own superego (Freud, 1921) but notes this is not the typical response. The social matrix in which the charismatic relationship develops is the ultimate determinant, but Camic speculates that those figures deemed sacred are less likely to revolt against the moral standards of an order than those considered uncanny.

Rangell (1982) has recently discussed charisma in outline form with views quite similar to those of Camic. Rangell believes that the charismatic leader appeals to one or another of the components within the psychic organization of the unconscious, and often to different components at different times. In Anna Freud's (1936) concept of identification with the aggressor Rangell sees, for example, an acquisition to the id. Or, in the case of Nixon and Watergate, Rangell sees identification with a leader who symbolized the brushing aside of superego restraints. Rangell believes that the freedom from pain promised by certain mystical leaders probably involves gain to all three psychic systems and causes a shift in their interrelationships. In short, Rangell provides empirical support for several of Camic's formulations.

Although Camic provides us with an elaborate and scholarly psychoanalytic view of charisma his position has three inadequacies. First, he, too, tells us little about the specific attributes of the charismatic leader that qualify him for the position as apparent gratifier of unmet extraordinary needs. What are the needs of the leader that either propel him or, at minimum, permit him to become a charismatic figure? This question remains unanswered. Second, positive transference, which in his view is the source of the charismatic leader's power, is too simple an explanation. There must be a day residue (Freud, 1900) that allows for the transference, and it must be an aspect of the leader's actual person and unconscious fantasy life. Although Camic acknowledges that the extent to which specialness is attributed to a need-gratifying figure is contingent upon the interaction between leader and followers, his discussion of transference does not take into consideration the important contributions made by regression, the level of individual psychic development, and the particular constellation of the interaction. Third, Camic does not really separate the leader from the led. His theory is a unitary theory of charisma. A true psychoanalytic theory of charisma must look at two (and more) independent mental apparatuses in a social field but with separate unconscious, preconscious, and conscious foci, separate structures, and separate selves.

## The Role of Psychic Structure

Camic and Rangell utilize Freud's structural theory which assumes that the mind is a well-developed psychic apparatus. The tripartite model and the structural theory of the mind presume that considerable prior development has occurred in "an average expectable environment" (Hartmann, 1939) with "good-enough mothering" (Winnicott, 1953), sufficient parental empathy (Kohut, 1971), and maternal support of the child's separation and individuation (Mahler, Pine, and Bergman, 1975). These later psychoanalysts have identified preoedipal patterns of environmental failure that seem to eventuate in severe narcissistic, borderline, and some types of psychotic pathologies which often lend themselves to a charismatic followership. We shall call this and other predispositions toward charismatic followership "charismatic susceptibility." Freud knew as early as his "Group Psychology" (1921) that "In many individuals the separation between the ego and the ego ideal is not very advanced; the two still coincide readily" (p. 129), by which he meant that because of insufficient structuralization of the superego, wholesale identifications with impressive figures could take place easily and moral standards could crumble. We might add that in other cases personality development has been so compromised that where ego should be, id still is.

Thus, in addition to the four established agencies of the mind that Camic described, a fifth extraordinary need for firmly established and well-separated mental structures exists in the "charismatically susceptible" individual. This structuralization involves ego, superego, and ego-ideal development beyond rudimentary forms and in some cases even includes development of the id. *In these severe cases, the charismatic leader supplements or replaces poorly developed psychic agencies as a kind of mental exoskeleton.* At the worst extreme the charismatic leader stimulates extraordinary id, ego, and superego needs and then becomes the source of gratification of those needs himself. In some *cults* an unscrupulous leader may himself provide libidinal and aggressive stimulation (need enhancement) by seductiveness and bellicosity and then have sex or fight with the followers. He may create the need for protection and then protect. He may obscure reality and then provide his own brand of reality testing. He may stimulate the need for standards, ideals, and prohibitions and then actually proscribe or punish. Common parlance describes this type of charismatic susceptibility with the expression that the follower has "no mind of his own." The leader provides the various mental structures in prefabricated form, stimulates them to a state of need, and then offers the gratifying object—sometimes himself. He teaches the followers to desire in accordance with *his* wishes; to regulate, integrate, and synthesize in accordance with *his* central organization; to experience guilt in accordance with *his* prohibitions; and to strive to live up to ideals of *his* promulgation. At the positive end of the spectrum of this type of charismatic relationship is the therapeutic community leader whose id, ego, and superego are emulated by the drug abuser, the adolescent schizophrenic, or criminal patient-followers. Almond (1974) has called this "healing charisma."

To those people with the type of charismatic susceptibility we are calling the "insufficiently structuralized mind," the leader represents the chance for reversal of a kind of helplessness of everyday life. Because of his special sensitivity to the tensions of those with poorly developed psychic apparatuses, the leader knows how to exploit their needs. That he, himself, had once been in an earlier, but analogous passive need state which he reversed will be taken up subsequently.

## The Role of Regression

What propels better-developed personalities to follow a charismatic leader? Common misfortune often draws people together. In times of social unrest, economic dissatisfaction, national disgrace, persecution, excessive corruption, military threat, or defeat, people gather in groups and crowds. Freud (1921) discussed the well-documented observation that even highly developed personalities regress when placed in such large, unstructured group situations. A brief review of Freud's *Group Psychology and the Analysis of the Ego* (1921) is important to the understanding of this regression and the subsequent attraction of the leader. Freud had noted that a group needs continuity, definition, interaction with other groups, traditions, and customs to fend off the lowering of intellectual ability, decline of conscience, and intensification of affect found in "crowds" or primitive groups, i.e., to fend off the regression inherent in group formation (Scheidlinger, 1980). Freud felt that such "organization" was only procuring for the group the higher characteristics of individuals which are extinguished by group formation, restoring the barriers against unconscious wishes and intense narcissism. Rejecting suggestion as an explanation of the leader's power, he offered the concept of libido, "the energy, regarded as a quantitative magnitude (though not at present actually measurable), of those instincts which have to do with all that may be comprised under the word 'love' " (Freud, 1921, p. 90). If an individual allows a group to influence him by suggestion he does it *"ihnen zu Liebe"*—for love of them (Freud, 1921, p. 92). It is libidinal ties to the leader and among the members that counter the narcissistic pull.

Freud used the Catholic church and the army as prototypes of highly organized, lasting groups. Christ and the commander-in-chief share the center of the same illusion—that the leader loves all the members equally. In these and other groups, the love for the leader overcomes the narcissistic intolerance of others, and the essence of a group formation consists in new kinds of libidinal ties among the group members, i.e., identifications. Identification, according to Freud (1921), is the "earliest expression of an emotional tie with another person" (p. 105). Freud distinguishes identification from object love using the father as an example. In identification, the earlier phenomenon, one wants to be like the father. In object love, one loves the father.

Freud continues the explanation of how regression in groups is counteracted by libidinal ties to the father-leader by examining idealization. In extreme cases of idealization in love, the functions of the ego ideal cease to operate: "Everything that the object does and asks for is right and blameless. Conscience has no application to anything that is done for the sake of the object . . . *The object has been put in place of the ego ideal*" (p. 113; Freud's emphasis). Freud carries the argument to the group, saying there are a number of individuals who have put the same loved object in place of their own ego ideals and consequently identified themselves with one another in their egos (selves) (p. 116). The love for the same leader causes the followers to identify similarly.

Saravay (1975) takes up the regressive dedifferentiation of the ego and the superego, the reappearance of such primitive mechanisms as suggestion and imitation, and the reappearance of identification in place of object love. He notes that several later writers have claimed that such a group wishes to merge with the leader as mother rather than relate to him as father, as in Freud's conception. With the regressive loosening of superego controls there is also an unexplained externalization of previously internalized self and object representations (Kaplan, 1967). Saravay states (1975) that ". . . the leader becomes the object around whom these previously internalized object representations are projected and toward whom the associated instinctual wishes are redirected. He occupies the same position to them as did the parent prior to the development of a stable ego and superego" (p. 86).

We can easily see, then, how adverse disruptive social circumstances which draw people together and the ensuing regression brought about by primitive group formation make these individuals somewhat similar to the previously discussed "charismatically susceptible." A charismatic leader offering an apparent solution to the calamitous disorganization finds willing recruits among those regressed by natural primitive group formation. His

power stems from the compelling attraction of an idealized infantile identificatory figure. The regressed or primitive person must follow the charismatic leader just as the infant must identify. We are studying a
phenomenon at the very beginning of human interaction. To ask why the
follower does as the charismatic leader does or wills is to ask why a toddler
puts his father's hat upon his own head or tries to walk in his mother's
shoes.

## The Role of the Leader's Reversal of Passivity into Activity

Taking a different tack from Camic we would argue that it is the radical
reorientation which first occurred within the individual who later becomes
the charismatic leader that is the area from which a psychoanalytic theory
must grow. As in the case of Achilleus, it is out of the leader's personal
suffering and conflicts that the charismatic movement begins. Moreover,
we would argue that it is through his active reversal of the helpless situation
that he not only repairs himself but gains the capacity to transform others
as an identificatory object. Achilleus was helpless without armor. The
Greeks were helpless without Achilleus and in risk of having their ships
burned by the Trojans. By means of the gift of the gods Achilleus gains
active mastery and the Greeks are able to identify with this strength.

In addition, we contend that a potential charismatic leader must have a
very significant unconscious element in his self representation where he
is passive, powerless, and "acted upon" by the object. We would further
argue that a "charismatically susceptible individual" has a matching passive,
powerless, and "acted-upon" unconscious element to his self representation,
a specific matching unconscious fantasy of traumatization. Indeed, it is the
similarity in specific unconscious object relationships of both leader and
follower that makes the charismatic situation a particular case of the far
more general phenomenon of reversal of passivity into activity which Freud
described.[1] Furthermore, a current crisis situation which resembles the
unconscious fantasy brings about personal suffering in the potential leader.
He then achieves active mastery over it and goes on to become the inflicter
rather than the victim, or the liberator rather than the enslaved—the "doer"
rather than "the done to." He is driven to elaborate this accomplishment

[1] "It can easily be observed that in every field of mental experience, not merely that of
sexuality, when a child receives a passive impression it has a tendency to produce an active
reaction. It tries to do itself what has just been done to it. This is part of the work imposed
on it of mastering the external world and can even lead to its endeavoring to repeat an
impression which it would have reason to avoid on account of its distressing content" (Freud,
1931, p. 236).

into a mission, and he does so much as the creative artist produces a work. He repetitively and compulsively re-enacts this paradigm because his unconscious fantasy is inaccessible to modification by his life experience. In the unconscious fantasy he remains passive and helpless despite success after success, just as the "Don Juan" neurotic fails to find satisfaction despite "success" with woman after woman. The leader seeks followers in order to immerse himself repeatedly in the traumatic situation and repeatedly reverse it both for himself and, vicariously, for others. He also seeks followers to enhance his sense of activity vis-à-vis the passive other. At times, he may go so far as to re-create the particular unconscious object relationship with himself as the active participant and the follower as the passive one. The follower, on the other hand, is "charismatically susceptible" because of his own disposition toward reversal of his unconscious passivity and his vulnerability to an identificatory object who will serve that purpose. A current social, personal, or intellectual crisis catalyzes the recruitment of the potential follower.

Freud (1920) described the basic human tendency to re-create, either in action or in fantasy, *in an active mode*, an unpleasant, passively experienced event. Klein (1976) called this "the principle of self-initiated active reversal of passive experience" (p. 259). "What I have experienced as being done to me, I must make happen," either by, at minimum, having the power to summon it up myself or, going further, by doing to someone else what someone did to me. Rejecting Freud's death drive as an explanation of the compulsion to repeat, Klein felt that repetitiveness was "the inevitable consequence of activated (cognitive) schemata that are in a state of repression" (p. 264), i.e., that unconscious fantasies program the self's efforts at reversal of imposed passivity into activity. Klein goes on to state that "Self-initiated repetition brings a feeling of having 'made sense of'; alienation turns to familiarity, accompanied by experiences of controlling through knowledge" (pp. 270–271). "It controls me" has become "I control it." Gedo (1979) notes that early passive experiences encoded as cognitive schemata serve as motives for future active behavior and that such building blocks of motivation can be thought of as "nuclei of the self" (Gedo and Goldberg, 1973). It is the charismatic follower's unconscious recognition of the leader's active role in the same prototypical repressed situation in which the follower has endured a passive role that is consciously experienced as the charismatic leader's possession of special or extraordinary power. His power seems magical because he represents the unconscious controlling object. LaBarre (1972) has employed Freud's (1919) concept of the uncanny to explain the attribution of magical power to the shaman. "The uncanny appositeness of his communication (congruence with each unconscious) is proof enough of his charisma or 'supernatural' charm" (p. 208). A similar but more individually meaningful uncanny recognition of an unconscious object relationship is at work in our view of the charismatic relationship.

Shils (1965) believes that the charisma of an individual lies in "his connection with (including possession by or embodiment of) some *very central* feature of man's existence" (p. 201). We believe this centrality is a derivative of the two-layered nature of the charismatic leader's appeal. He is an identificatory model for activity where there is passivity in the present, and more importantly he is a model for activity where there is passivity in the unconscious fantasy. It is this connection to the unconscious fantasy, we claim, that is experienced as the unknown, "very central" feature of man's existence, or what Shils calls elsewhere (1968) the "ultimate," "the powers which guide and determine human life" (p. 387). Because a repressed passive experience is the central organizing fantasy of any charismatically susceptible follower, a charismatic leader who seems to offer a reversal of that elementary object relationship is experienced as someone in contact with "the ultimate."

Weber (1968, p. 20) noted that the charismatic figure must be able to demonstrate his specialness from time to time to keep his position. Any failure would be viewed as a loss of his power, and his position as a leader would crumble. Because the prototypical conflict remains unconscious in the followers and is usually not worked through by membership in the charismatic movement, the need for repeated demonstration obtains. To use the analogy of psychotherapy and analysis, let us say that the leader's goal is supportive intervention rather than insight.

Why does the leader require followers? As each follower becomes like him, the leader repeats the reversal of passivity into activity. Again, because the driving force is his unconscious fantasy, no action is sufficient to call a halt to the reversals, so long as the fantasy remains unconscious. What is more, in the very acts of recruitment and leadership the charismatic figure often inflicts upon the naïve follower exactly what the leader endured in the original situation. He does unto others as was done unto him. For example, charismatic leaders who have been revolutionarily innovative in a sterile atmosphere often inculcate a sterile atmosphere which stultifies creativity among their followers.

How does the charismatic leader elaborate his reversal of passivity into activity so that it becomes a mission that has understandable appeal? Freud's (1908) understanding of the creative process is illuminating in this regard. Speaking of unacceptable wishes, Freud saw the creative work as representing them as fulfilled but in a manner sufficiently disguised that their personal source is not revealed. Nor are they so disguised as to escape transmission. Kris and Kaplan (1948) have described the creative process as necessitating shifts in "psychic level," i.e., "when regression goes too far, the symbols become private, perhaps unintelligible even to the reflective self; when at the other extreme control is preponderant the result is described as cold, mechanical and uninspired" (p. 254). Similarly, an essential attribute of the charismatic leader is the power to elaborate his mission in such a way as to disguise the unconscious fantasy yet reveal enough so that those individuals who carry within their own selves a repressed matching pattern will follow him.[2]

The unconscious passive element in the follower's self representation explains why he follows the charismatic leader whereas others in equally bad straits in the same reality crisis do not. When the social circumstances thrust passivity upon an individual, he is more vulnerable to "rescue" by the charismatic leader if a matching unconscious dystonic cognitive schema is activated. Consideration of the unconscious passivity factor also illuminates why some individuals who are in no acute distress drop their successful lives, possessions, or families to follow the charismatic figure wherever he might lead.

On occasion, as in the case of certain "false messiahs," unwise actions by the charismatic leader may increase the helplessness of his followers. Some followers become disaffected, but others only increase their devotion and blind adherence, precisely because the new reality crisis has put them in even greater need for the reversal of helplessness. Membership in the movement has led to the atrophy of their personal resourcefulness and has cut them off from potential help from outsiders. Like the compulsive gambler (Winer and Pollock, 1980) unconsciously determined drivenness in charismatic leaders of this type pushes them beyond their capacity for success. His repressed fantasy of helplessness causes the leader to escalate his acts of mastery. Never being satisfied with one success he is spurred on to more and more until he overcommits himself and creates a "do-or-die" crisis situation. This "do-or-die" situation increases the follower's sense of entrapment and inescapability until even the "faint hearts" or "cool heads" among those who remain give way to absolute devotion and commitment to the leader. The leader and followers find themselves in the very same psychological situation that both leader and followers share in the unconscious fantasy. The follower's acceptance of the leader's solution has eventuated in greater enslavement to the leader's will. On the other hand the charismatic leader who effects positive societal change and accomplishes

---

[2] Charisma differs from aesthetics, however. The leader's appeal does not lie in his capacity to entice the follower by means of offering him the fulfillment of forbidden wishes in a disguised way. The reversal of passivity into activity emphasizes an unconscious object relationship rather than a drive satisfaction. Drive satisfaction is, of course, often attained.

amelioration in the lives of his followers has a sufficiently accessible unconscious so that active reality successes modify his primordial self representation and weaken its propelling force.

The dynamic considerations are necessary elements but not sufficient to explain the entirety of the charismatic relationship.[3] Certain character traits of the leader must also be present, such as an uncommon supply of physical energy often accompanied by copious libido and aggression in less than fully neutralized form. Possessing a gift of dramatization, the charismatic leader kindles hope in those who follow him. His physical appearance is often striking. Many written and visual representations highlight the eyes as being "spellbinding," or the smile as particularly engaging. A successful charismatic leader must be adroit at obtaining and using power. The leader must have a special capacity to identify the actions necessary to the accomplishment of his goals. He must have extraordinary powers of communication, usually oratorical as well as written. His certainty about his convictions comforts the doubts among followers. In the Homeric prototype of Achilleus such gifts are accompanied by physical might and swiftness.[4]

To reiterate, then, the charismatic relationship lies in the leader's missionary elaboration of an unconscious fantasy in which he has reversed a passively induced trauma into a situation of activity, at times to the point of inflicting the same type of trauma upon another. He remains unaware of the origins of his visionary message and is therefore driven repetitively to re-enact the reversal by means of his movement. Individuals who have become charismatically susceptible either because of inadequate personality or regression brought on by crisis and/or group formation follow the leader as an identificatory model in the wished-for reversal of a parallel unconscious object relationship. So long as the leader can present himself as if this were happening he retains power among them. What was attributed by the ancients to a gift of the gods is in fact a quality stemming from matching unconscious fantasies in leader and followers. With sufficient organization of the movement lasting societal changes may come about often in the direction of considerable betterment.[5]

## REFERENCES

Almond, R. (1974), *The Healing Community: Dynamics of the Therapeutic Milieu*. New York: Aronson.

[3] We are indebted to George H. Pollock for stimulating this area of the discussion.

[4] Samson, on the other hand, had no followers despite his God-given strength because he represented the opposite transformation, the transformation of strength into weakness, of power into helplessness even before he was blinded.

[5] We are presently engaged in a systematic study of charismatic leaders in their historical contexts in order to provide empirical support for our views.

Brenner, C. (1974), *An Elementary Textbook of Psychoanalysis*. 2d. New York: International Universities Press.

Brown, C. (ed.) (1982), *The New International Dictionary of New Testament Theology*, vol. 2. Anonymous article entitled Grace Xaris. Grand Rapids, Mich.: Zondervan.

Camic, C. (1980), Charisma: Its varieties, preconditions, and consequences. *Sociological Inquiry*, 50:5–23.

Dematrakou, D. (1950), *Mega Lexicon Tes Ellenikesglosses*. Athens: Plateia Suntagmatos.

Durkheim, E. (1912), *The Elementary Forms of Religious Life*. New York: Free Press, 1965.

Eisenstadt, S. N. (1968), Charisma and institution building: Max Weber and modern sociology. In: Weber, M., *On Charisma and Institution Building*, ed. S. N. Eisenstadt. Chicago: University of Chicago Press, pp. ix–lvi.

Erikson, E. H. (1958), *Young Man Luther*. New York: Norton.

—— (1969), *Gandhi's Truth: On the Origins of Militant Nonviolence*. New York: Norton.

Freud, A. (1936), *The Ego and the Mechanisms of Defense*. New York: International Universities Press, 1966.

Freud, S. (1900), The Interpretation of Dreams. *Standard Edition*, 4 & 5. London: Hogarth Press, 1953.

—— (1908), Creative writers and daydreaming. *Standard Edition*, 9:141–153. London: Hogarth Press, 1959.

—— (1913), Totem and taboo. *Standard Edition*, 13:1–162. London: Hogarth Press, 1953.

—— (1914), On narcissism. *Standard Edition*, 14:67–102. London: Hogarth Press, 1957.

—— (1919), The uncanny. *Standard Edition*, 17:217–256. London: Hogarth Press, 1955.

—— (1920), Beyond the pleasure principle. *Standard Edition*, 18:1–64. London: Hogarth Press, 1955.

—— (1921), Group psychology and the analysis of the ego. *Standard Edition*, 18:67–143. London: Hogarth Press, 1955.

—— (1927), The future of an illusion. *Standard Edition*, 21:5–56. London: Hogarth Press, 1961.

—— (1931), Female sexuality. *Standard Edition*, 21:221–243. London: Hogarth Press, 1961.

—— (1939), Moses and monotheism. *Standard Edition*, 23:1–208. London: Hogarth Press, 1964.

Galanter, M. (1982), Charismatic religious sects and psychiatry: An overview. *Amer. J. Psychiat.*, 139:1539–1548.

Gedo, J. (1979), *Beyond Interpretation: Toward a Revised Theory for Psychoanalysis*. New York: International Universities Press.

—— Goldberg, A. (1973), *Models of the Mind: A Psychoanalytic Theory*. Chicago: University of Chicago Press.

Gehrie, M. J. (1980), The self and the group: A tentative exploration in applied self psychology. In: *Advances in Self Psychology*, ed. A. Goldberg. New York: International Universities Press, pp. 367–382.

Gerth, H. H. & Mills, C. W. (eds.) (1958), *From Max Weber: Essays in Sociology*. New York: Oxford University Press.

Hartmann, H. (1939), *Ego Psychology and the Problem of Adaptation*, trans. D. Rapaport. New York: International Universities Press, 1958.

—— Kris, E., Loewenstein, R. (1946), Comments on the formation of psychic structure. *The Psychoanalytic Study of the Child*, 2:11–38. New York: International Universities Press.

Homer, *The Iliad*, trans. R. Lattimore. Chicago: University of Chicago Press, 1951.

Kaplan, S. (1967), Therapy groups and training groups: Similarities and differences. *Internat. J. Group Psychother.*, 17:473–504.

Klein, G. (1976), The principle of self-initiated active reversal of passive experience. In: *Psychoanalytic Theory: An Exploration of Essentials*, ed. M. M. Gill & L. Goldberger. New York: International Universities Press, pp. 259–279.

Kohut, H. (1971), *The Analysis of the Self*. New York: International Universities Press.

—— (1976), Creativeness, charisma, group psychology: Reflections on the self-analysis of

Freud. In: *The Search for the Self*, ed. P. H. Ornstein. New York: International Universities Press, 1978, pp. 793–843.

Kris, E. & Kaplan, A. (1948), Aesthetic ambiguity. In: *Psychoanalytic Explorations in Art*, ed. E. Kris. New York: Schocken, 1952, pp. 243–264.

LaBarre, W. (1972), *The Ghost Dance: Origins of Religion*. New York: Delta.

Lewy, E. (1979), Historical charismatic leaders and mythical heroes. *J. Psychohistory*, 6:377–392.

Mahler, M. S., Pine, F., & Bergman, A. (1975), *The Psychological Birth of the Human Infant: Symbiosis and Individuation*. New York: Basic Books.

Mazlish, B. (1976), *The Revolutionary Ascetic*. New York: Basic Books.

Otto, R. (1917), *The Idea of the Holy*, trans. J. W. Harvey. New York: Oxford University Press, 1958.

Panel (1979), Psychoanalytic knowledge of group processes, K. T. Calder, reporter. *J. Amer. Psychoanal. Assn.*, 27:145–156.

Pollock, G. H. (1961), Mourning and adaptation. *Internat. J. Psycho-Anal.*, 42:341–360.

Rangell, L. (1982), The self in psychoanalytic theory. *J. Amer. Psychoanal. Assn.*, 30:863–891.

Rank, O. (1914), *The Myth of the Birth of the Hero and Other Essays*, ed. P. Freund. New York: Vintage Books, 1959.

Rapaport, D. (1957), The theory of ego autonomy. In: *The Collected Papers of David Rapaport*, ed. M. M. Gill. New York: Basic, 1967, pp. 722–744.

——— (1961), Some metapsychological considerations concerning activity and passivity. In: *The Collected Papers of David Rapaport*, ed. M. M. Gill. New York: Basic Books, pp. 530–568.

Saravay, S. (1975), Group psychology and the structural theory: a revised psychoanalytic model of group psychology. *J. Amer. Psychoanal. Assn.*, 23:69–89.

Schafer, R. (1968), *Aspects of Internalization*. New York: International Universities Press.

Scheidlinger, S. (1980), Freud's group psychology. In: *Psychoanalytic Group Dynamics: Basic Readings*, ed. S. Scheidlinger. New York: International Universities Press, pp. 5–13.

Shils, E. (1965), Charisma, order, and status. *Amer. Sociological Rev.*, 30:199–213.

——— (1968), Charisma. In: *International Encyclopedia of the Social Sciences*, ed. D. Sills. New York: MacMillan, 1968, 2:386–390.

Strozier, C. B. (1980), Heinz Kohut and the historical imagination. In: *Advances in Self Psychology*, ed. A. Goldberg. New York: International Universities Press, pp. 397–406.

——— (1983), Fantasy, self psychology and the inner logic of cults. In: *The Future of Psychoanalysis: Essays in Honor of Heinz Kohut*, ed. A. Goldberg. New York: International Universities Press, pp. 477–493.

Tucker, R. C. (1968), The theory of charismatic leadership. *Daedalus*, 97:731–756.

Weber, M. (1968), *On Charisma and Institution Building*, ed. S. N. Eisenstadt. Chicago: University of Chicago Press.

Wilhelm, J. (1908), Charismata. In: *The Catholic Encyclopedia*. New York: Robert Appleton Co., 3:588–591.

Winer, J. A. & Pollock, G. H. (1980), Disorders of impulse control. In: *Comprehensive Textbook of Psychiatry*, 3d ed., ed. H. L. Kaplan, A. M. Freedman, & B. J. Sadock. Baltimore: Williams and Wilkins, pp. 1817–1829.

Winnicott, D. W. (1953), Transitional objects and transitional phenomena. *Internat. J. Psycho-Anal.*, 34:89–97.

Zaleznik, A. (1974), Charismatic and consensus leaders: A psychological comparison. *Bull. Menninger Clin.*, 38:222–38.

Zonis, M. & Offer, D. (in press), Leaders and the Arab-Israeli conflict: A psychoanalytic interpretation. In: *Psychoanalytic Study of Leadership*, ed. C. B. Strozier & D. Offer. New York: Plenum.

*January 1984*

# Deceived and Betrayed

## MEYER S. GUNTHER, M.D. (Chicago)

### I

INTRODUCTION

In this presentation I shall describe a character type revolving around recurrent crises of deception and betrayal. Patients who fall within this category appear to be so paranoidlike in their outrages, so excessively demanding of perfection, and so puritanically moral in their expectations of others, that they are frequently regarded as totally insufferable. Among a few good friends, they may be humorously labeled "the local anarchist," "the local malcontent," or "the local narcissist." At first view their behavior seems to alternate between two extremes: (1) a state of vigorous, competent, single-minded devotion to the goals of an institution, the high moral purpose of a cause, or the personal well-being of a friend, as if their entire selves were merged with such aims; (2) a reaction of indescribably intense, all-encompassing outrage and disappointment which extends far beyond mere verbal expression or ordinary discharge of affect. In this reaction they feel grievously wounded and grossly betrayed by the occurrence of an ostensibly trivial but unexpected event, an event unimportant in others' terms, but vital to them. For instance, a friend may say "no" to a request, a colleague may disagree with a feature of a plan, a fortuitous minor stress may interfere with a planned project, or a spouse may make a modest but unusual request. What is of critical importance is that the event is felt to be wholly unexpected, utterly incompatible with previous experience. Its

I am grateful to Dr. John E. Gedo, whose steady encouragement and thoughtful criticism accompanied the preparation of this paper, and whose creative ideas have enriched the development of many concepts contained therein.

177

over-all effect is selective disruption in many areas of ego-monitored behavior—affective, volitional, cognitive, etc. The immediate consequences are surprise, disappointment, disbelief, and resentment culminating in the onset of a state of temporary cognitive disorganization and personality fragmentation. Rather quickly this state gives way to the massive conviction of having been betrayed, but also to the suspicion of having been totally deceived throughout the past relationship, that is, of having been taken in. There follows a monumental expression of outrage at, and hostile intent toward, the perpetrator, often in the form of a histrionic dramatization of rage which overawes observers as well as the instigator. This dramatization, in turn, becomes the leading edge for a series of idiosyncratic, complex, but ultimately reintegrative psychological steps.

If these individuals are seen by an analyst in the midst of an episode of rage and disorganization, the analyst will not unexpectedly ponder the diagnosis. He will ask himself whether he is dealing with an intense narcissistic-rage episode (Kohut, 1972), behavior heralding a true manic episode or a chronic paranoid reaction, the onset of a megalomaniacal psychosis, or perhaps an atypical temporal-lobe seizure. Careful long-term analytic evaluation discloses an array of diagnostic elements which form a complex logical pattern, point to an unusual adaptive style, and make for a less ominous diagnosis. What eventually emerges from behind this adaptive persona is a constellation of developmental factors organized around the unusual childhood role bestowed on these individuals by their mothers.

Many aspects of their behavior and character, though diagnostically specific, appear paradoxical. In their capacity for active, devoted investment in intellectual, professional, or social aims, their behavior may be truly impressive. These people are regarded by friends as ethical, morally trustworthy, deeply responsive, and reliable. In particular, the men are regarded by their women friends (not their lovers) as sensitive, compassionate, and deeply understanding. They will often focus their ministrations on a single individual as a special or "best" friend, as if to ask in a tenuous way for reassurance about some uncomfortable, deeply concealed aspect of their behavior. In so doing, they indicate that they are subject to secret suffering regarding the worthiness of their motives and the ultimate reliability of their intentions. In their early adolescent histories, they often appear good-natured, modest, and inhibited regarding their own abilities, as well as very proper socially. But toward the end of adolescence and the beginning of adulthood, with new responsibilities, real achievements, and separation from home, a pattern of alternating productivity and disintegrative episodes of disappointment, rage, and depression begins to assert itself. To this degree, they appear, superficially, to suffer from a success neurosis

(Alexander, 1930). In the face of their recurrent distress and inconsistent patterns of achievement, they reveal the extent of their underlying defensive grandiosity and the vulnerability, fragility, or deficiency of their self-esteem that fuels it.

Beyond their considerable energy, these people are frequently talented, creative, intellectual, athletic, and endowed with an unusual ability to perform before others in some particular area. Cognitively, they are often good abstract thinkers with quick intuitive abilities to grasp hidden relationships about the essential meaning of things, often with minimal information or incomplete data. A noteworthy exception to this high-level cognitive capability, however, is their utter incapacity to think logically about problems connected with their overvalued and misunderstood bodies or with their own developmental histories. In these areas their thinking processes remain magical, even bizarre. They are compulsively organized in many ways, but before analysis their talents are unpredictable, inhibited, and basically distrusted. It is for this reason that they are such inconsistent achievers.

At a deeper level these individuals betray strong, depressive-masochistic trends which make them especially vulnerable to disorganization—not just disappointment—when confronted by the unexpected (Panel, 1981). Any unpredictable change is viewed as a potential loss, as something too traumatically disorganizing to be handled by the usual incremental working-over, working-through, mourninglike process. Their reaction to the unexpected reminds one of Pollock's (1961) description of the first or "shock" phase of mourning. They have an exaggerated, conservativelike difficulty in giving up anything that is part of the (fantasied) stability and predictability of existing life patterns. This is especially true with respect to their chronic, obsessive immersion in memories of their own childhood past; they often come to grief in their continuing efforts to find or rediscover something out of the actual infantile past. Their truly significant difficulty is not in rediscovering that past, but in giving up its endless re-enactment. They have limited ability to shift emotional investments from old objects to new experiences; they thereby forgo the creation of new relationships and, by implication, the formation of new intrapsychic structure. Because the process of change is both painful and distrusted, these character types often have prolonged, interrupted, and, for the analyst, maximally trying analyses.

The most dramatic characteristic of all is the nuclear significance of ethics in the organization of their lives, their personalities, their very existence. This cannot be overemphasized. It is not merely part of the surface or defensive layers of the personality; despite endless ambivalence, it arises from the very core of their being, and pervades every layer and area of their character structure. It constitutes the raison d'être for the organization of all solutions to underlying conflicts and deficits. They share an un-bounded universal contempt bordering on maniacal outrage for hypocrisy, immorality, or the failure of friends or idealized others to attempt (as they themselves attempt) to live consistently by the highest ethical standards. It is the passion of others' dedication which counts in this connection, not the nobility of others' underlying values or even the degree to which others meet their own standards. The issue is how courageously, consistently, and honorably the other tries to live by his own best standards. It is simply unthinkable to be guided perpetually by anything less than the highest moral principle one adopts, to display less than one's maximal efforts, or to be less than absolutely loyal to one's friends and one's ideals. In this sense, these character types may represent *the last of the old-fashioned moral purists.*

EXAMPLES

*Case A*

A young business executive entered analysis because of his massive re-current tendencies to disrupt contractual enterprises in which he was in-volved, and thereby threatening his meager equity. One day, emerging from a cab in front of my office and late as usual for his appointment, he brushed up against the doorframe of the cab. A thread of the sleeve of his suit caught on an irregularity in the doorframe. He demanded that the cab driver notify his supervisor in order to get proper instruction in facilitating a damage claim. The driver, assuming he was dealing with a kook, indig-nantly refused to comply and demanded his metered fare. After further argument he indicated that he would forget about the fee if the patient, becoming increasingly belligerent, would simply get out of his cab. At this point the patient reached over the front seat, turned off the ignition, and threatened to punch the driver in the nose. A passing police car was hailed. The patient was now in a full-blown uncontrollable rage at the driver for his recalcitrance, at the cab company for the irresponsible way it maintained its equipment, and at the policeman for his slowness in comprehending the injustice of the situation. The policeman suggested that instead of ushering both parties to the station, the whole matter might be settled if the patient would only agree to pay his metered fee and withdraw his threat to sign an assault-and-battery complaint against the company. When the patient finally realized that the policeman was becoming increasingly intolerant of his continued claims of moral aggrievance, it dawned on him that he might end up spending the night in a police lockup. After further angry denunciations, he calmed to the point of recognizing that an exchange of money would ease the situation. Finally, one hour later, he walked away from the situation with a barely detectable flaw in his suit coat and $250 less in his pocket. He met me as I was emerging from my building. While the experienced analyst may tend to see this episode of outrage as a conventional transference displacement, the example illustrates the manner in which these unique rage episodes operate, especially the moral absoluteness which seems to underlie them.

*Case B*

After finishing graduate school a young man undertook an analysis because he was phobically restricted to his parents' home and unable to work. After several years of analysis he was able to confront the enormously complex attachment to his mother, the root of his phobia. He progressed to the point where he could leave the house and work, first in the family business and then as an independent entrepreneur. Still, he found it necessary to live at home. When he had become fully self-supporting I raised his modest fee. When I announced this at the beginning of one session, he indicated he had not understood me. I repeated my statement with an appropriate explanation, but with some incipient feeling of discomfort. At the end of the explanation he sat up, looked at me in bewilderment, and then slowly underwent a dramatic change. In a way that I had not seen before, an expression of shocked bewilderment passed over his face; he became excited, florid, and shook with rage. Although virtually incoherent, he managed to convey to me his conviction that I had betrayed him throughout the past years of our work; I was not in the business of helping people, but only in the business of making a living. Obviously, I did not understand now, and perhaps had never understood, the vital importance of morality and ethics in his life. He and those select others in whom he had placed his trust must let their behavior be guided only by selfless moral principles, as his parents had always done with respect to him and his siblings. He began to pace, saying that he had better leave the hour lest he punch me in the nose, and then abruptly ran out. He returned the next hour, somewhat calmer, and we spent much of the remaining portion of his analysis probing, and arriving at an understanding of, this incident.

*Case C*

A promising young physician who had undergone two incomplete intervals of treatment, one of them an analysis, began to suspect that his promise of being a superstar might never be realized. He was an extraordinarily talented researcher in genetic oncology, not only as a laboratory researcher, but also in his capacity to win the responsive devotion and compliant behavior of patients, families, and staff. He entered analysis with me following a strikingly dramatic episode. As part of his current research, he had undertaken clinical responsibility for a group of very seriously ill children. Complex medical procedures and measurements were required in order to systematize treatment effects. One Sunday morning he discovered that part of his treatment protocol had been violated. The senior nurse on duty was a reliable person, and he was dismayed. Unable to obtain a satisfactory explanation from her, but still able to control his mounting outrage, he determined to wait until Monday to confront the head nurse on the unit whom he knew well, and with whom he had worked on previous projects on terms of mutual respect. But by Monday he was totally out of control. In self-defense, the head nurse indicated that although the omission of part of his protocol was technically an error on the staff's part, it was clinically quite inconsequential. Furthermore, she felt that the exquisite precision with which he demanded that certain readings be taken was unnecessarily burdensome, and she wondered if it might not perhaps be a matter of competitive pride on his part, his way of saying, "Follow these guidelines for me, but not for the other researchers." They were unable to come to any agreement, and he continued to feel massively betrayed, as if his reliability and value as a person were in question. His rage escalated for days. He complained to the research chief and then to the director of the hospital. Eventually, in an effort to affect a compromise, a committee of the administration and research chiefs of the hospital staff was established to negotiate a reasonable solution. His response was to hand in his resignation after launching into a screaming tirade in front of the joint committee. Subsequently, he set about carrying his outrage and condemnation of the calumny of the hospital to national carcinoma-research circles with predictably dire results on his future efforts to obtain funding.

How shall we explain the genetic origin and dynamic meaning of the kind of adult adaptation described above? The concept of "empathic failure" (Kohut, 1977; Goldberg, 1978, 1980; Ornstein, 1979) may be applied to the expectation by all patients of the analyst's capacity for understanding and responsiveness. It may be argued that it is a legitimate expectation of both patient and analyst for the latter to be consistently oriented toward achieving an optimal empathic stance (Schwaber, 1981; Lichtenberg, 1981; Basch, 1982), that is, to expect the analyst to be immersed selectively, sensitively, and selflessly in the subjective experience of the patient as the orienting framework of his understanding. But it is hardly an expectation that one ordinarily has with regard to other human beings in everyday personal, professional, or business relationships. Moreover, the exquisite disappointment of children who believe they have been deceived by their parents and caretakers hardly represents a new psychoanalytic discovery (Freud, 1896, 1900, 1905). What preoedipal child has not come to experience with bitterness the frustration of his infantile omnipotence, especially the assumption of the magical power of his gestures or thoughts to influence the behavior of other people in his world in order to gratify his needs (Ferenczi, 1913)? What oedipal-aged child has not felt grievously disappointed, if not overtly deceived, by the realization that he or she is not the singularly unique, all-absorbing focus of dyadic interest on the part of the parent of the opposite sex (Kohut, 1977)? How terrible a betrayal if that parent were to have a multiplicity of relationships, including one of greater importance than she or he had with that child! Furthermore, sensitivity to the seductive misuse of the child is reflected in the contemporary dialogues about the actual role of pathological parental environment in the formation of defects and distortions of psychic structure (Basch, 1977, 1981; Tolpin, 1978; Gedo, 1979, 1981; Goldberg, 1980; Rothstein, 1980; Arlow, 1981; Treurniet, 1983).

Yet, despite such "normal" developmental experiences, few people become like the patients described here. The crucial issue for these patients is not simply some quantitatively excessive sensitivity to, or specially intense experience with, parental betrayal. The underlying basis for this personality configuration is a defensively determined predisposition for self-deception and disavowal arising directly from a unique mother-child relationship. The adults described here had been assigned an especially intense but partly disavowed role in their mothers' lives: to preserve the order and stability of their mothers' internal psychic milieu. The specific need they were to fulfill, the age of assignment, and their method of responding to that assignment (especially the fantasy meaning attributed to that experience) collectively determined the kinds of distortion to which the process of personality formation and integration were subjected. Common to all the adaptations was a denial or disavowal of the mother's pathology along with the real nature of the role assignments foisted on them. What was substituted as a replacement was an unintegrated series of personality configurations built upon a nuclear belief in the supremely controlling effect of moral forces in determining their own well-being. An implacable belief in the universal superiority of moral motivation as the ultimate determinant of all behavior would endow them, they believed, with the capacity for predicting, if not controlling, the vicissitudes of their mothers' intentions toward them. It was this firm conviction of the necessity to build their personalities around such a moral core, combined with the specific content of the mother's attitudes, vulnerabilities, and bizarre needs, which account for unique distortions at *all* developmental levels of the self-organization (Gedo, 1979). This may be illustrated by offering brief developmental histories of the three aforementioned patients, with emphasis on the past as reconstructed from direct verbal reports and through the transference as well.

*Case A*

This is the young business executive with the "torn sleeve." Early in his life as an only child, he was led to believe that his mother was a "tough old bird" who had become that way to survive a complicated marriage to an idiosyncratic, money-making husband. She regularly preached the necessity of self-reliance which, in reality, signified a quasi-suspicious, self-protective hustling in order to survive in a hostile Gentile world. Her oft-repeated goal was that her son should acquire competence to take care of himself in the world, no matter what kind of disappointment or exploitive assaults he encountered. She regularly enforced this ideology via painful physical, social, and emotional retaliations, not for failures, but, paradoxically, for behaviors which expressed the very assertive autonomy she held forth as her ideal! Her attitudes were presumed to have originated in family history, but this history may well have been mythical.

Both parents were Eastern European immigrants from the chaotic period at the end of World War I. During those pogrom-ridden, revolutionary days when Jewish survival was often unpredictable, the mother, then in latency, had been pushed by the family into rescue missions, such as finding lost relatives, transmitting messages, and transporting secret funds. Consequently, she had come to believe herself to be specially protected from harm, and especially gifted in her ability to make decisions about other people's well-being. In this respect she resembled those "exceptional" children described by Jacobson (1959). Perhaps predictably, the patient excused her scathing assaults and retributions, her endless erratic changes of mind, her illogical and often contradictory expectations of him, by assuming that they were designed to prepare him to survive in the hard world he would face as he grew up. Only after years of analysis was he willing to entertain the suspicion that his mother had been a pathologically greedy, omnipotently messianic woman engaged in a lifelong combative relationship with her husband over the management of their various economic enterprises.

It was similarly difficult for him to recognize that she was forever keeping a host of less fortunate friends and relatives attached to her, but "off balance" by her unpredictable paradoxical demands, her seductive gifts and bribes, and her unexpected, devastating rejections. Her assaultive behavior with respect to her son might well have represented, in part, a capricious displacement from her chronic, ambivalent combat with his father. Unwilling to accept this acquisitive, destructive, yet symbiotic expectation of him, the father would totally retreat from any involvement with her from time to time. On those rare occasions when he would take an appropriate stand, she would turn venomously upon the son. In so doing, she undertook to prove to herself that she was entirely capable of managing her (= our?) universe without assistance from anyone, simultaneously to prove that the patient was totally incapable of effectively acting for himself. One is reminded here of the extrusion of the "bad self" in Kleinian theory (Segal, 1964). Her son, my patient, had learned this aspect of his mother's teaching only too well. Without her, he believed that he could not survive in the outside world, and was therefore doomed to be worthless as well as ineffective. Yet he retained an enormously positive attachment to this woman.

In his early preschool days, when his upbringing was in the hands of a tough, kindly British nanny, his mother endlessly intruded upon that relationship. By latency, his mother was actively directing all aspects of his social development. His resentment notwithstanding, he desperately wanted to be her good son, the proper little gentleman. His unconsciously motivated solution for survival was already evident in school—his good-natured negativism was clearly apparent with respect to scholarly performance. He was a bright but erratic scholar. There would be angry, arrogant intercessions by mother, often concluding with a new round of tutors or a school transfer. By puberty he was assigned household tasks to learn the value of work—gardening, scrubbing windows, etc.—even though the family were millionaires with a retinue of servants. At adolescence he was sent during summers to a country residence to learn the economics of farming, only to discover that he was there as a day laborer to clean animal stalls. When a chronic serious psychosomatic illness emerged early in adolescence, an endless round of consultations at medical centers ensued, with mother deciding imperiously that any proposed course of therapy was not worth completing because, like teachers and other experts, doctors were untrustworthy and unintelligent Gentiles. This was irrevocably confirmed when one of the physicians had the temerity to suggest psychotherapy—not for the patient but for her.

During mid-adolescence when the patient was attending a private day school and father and mother were engaged in one of the frequent bouts of combat which ended in separation, the mother responded by elevating the patient to the status of a substitute for the missing father. Placing him at the head of the table, she utilized the dinner-time situation to ask his advice on major decisions concerning the family's economic enterprises, issues with servants, and the like.

During adolescence the patient found a secret source of respite by developing a disguised idealizing attachment to the family chauffeur, who taught him such vital adolescent skills as poker playing, driving, and drinking. Occasionally, uncles assumed the role of the good older brother or involved father he did not have. After being sent off to college, he was abruptly brought home before completing the first year for no apparent reason since he was consistently making better-than-average grades. This was the first of several short-circuited efforts at obtaining a college degree, with mother pointing to his allegedly poor performance and wasting of family funds as the ostensible reasons for interrupting his education. At the insistent intercession of an aunt, mother placed him in one of the family businesses, but here, too, his passive-aggressive behavior led to his undoing: he proceeded to live out her prophecy that he would lose money and eventually destroy the business. Desperate, he left home and, through the aid of the good aunt, obtained a job in a distant city. There he began treatment, only to have mother sabotage that enterprise, as if she had to have him back under her jurisdiction. Finally, approaching the age of thirty and suspecting that he would never realize his creative potential as a writer, let alone become truly self-supporting, he began living with an unusually competent, accepting woman, who helped him to establish a small business of his own and supported him emotionally through the early years of financial difficulty. Despite mother's sabotaging his first efforts at marrying his lover, he eventually succeeded and was able to become modestly successful though subject to mother's continuing destructive intrusions. With a modicum of financial success finally assured, the pattern of overt outrage at endless deceptions intensified.

*Case B*

This is the young man with the dramatic reaction to having his fee raised. Early in the analysis, he stated his unequivocal conviction that his parents were exemplary, selfless individuals who never placed their interests, especially their pleasure aims, ahead of the well-being of their children. Not only had his parents' transactions with the children been guided by true altruism, but this same value guided him in all his transactions. He was convinced that his siblings and he always came first in their developmental needs. However, some evidence existed that his mother had suffered well-disguised postpartum depressions after the birth of each child. Indeed, the patient was aware quite early that beneath the "one-big-happy-family" façade each parent had formed a particularly intense alliance with one of the two sons, that his two sisters had been left out, and that the parents had serious marital problems. Yet he consistently disavowed an awareness of the meaning of these facts, thereby facilitating a special attachment to his "saintly" mother who "always knew best." There were countless private and special moments together throughout latency and puberty, which included lying on her bed with her while she was resting or before she had arisen for the day's activities.

By the time he was twelve the family had accepted him as her confidant and consultant, and he remained so throughout the rest of her life. His conviction of the greatness that he was to achieve was the result of her special interest in his future. An example of the intensity of that special attachment occurred when he was five and the family was spending a summer in a European city. He and his older brother were placed in an American day-care nursery two miles from their apartment. The second day, after mid-morning nap, the patient was missing. Hours of frantic searching ended when he walked into their apartment building, having made his way home by himself through this strange city because he did not want to be separated from his mommy. He felt that he was perfectly capable of finding his way back alone, a striking event in the light of his subsequent phobia.

By adolescence, all four children believed themselves to be talented, socially outgoing, charming, though perhaps a bit priggish. After all, hadn't they had the advantages of upper-class upbringing, all the enrichments associated with culture, and perfect, selfless, loving parenting? They were prepared to face the world as conquering heroes. Yet by the time they were finishing college they were aware that beneath their very proper, pompous, superstar façade, they felt seriously impaired in their capacity to struggle independently and effectively with the tasks of life. The mother, of course, simply "knew" that if they just tried harder they would be successful. Eventually all four children entered treatment, but the youngest sister—the sickest—only as the result of heroic rescue behavior on the patient's part.

Following the dramatic blowup in response to my fee raise, the patient revealed that this experience had been disorganizing to him because for the first time it made him seriously question the pillars of his belief system. He had unconsciously transferred to me the same set of sublimely altruistic expectations which he believed characterized his parents' relationship with him. Until that point he had no reason to wonder from whence the need to believe in the universality of altruism arose. The experience with me shattered his absolute confidence in his ability to judge accurately the intentions of other people toward him. Finally, the coexistence of unworthy or contradictory aims in a person he had come to respect was utterly unthinkable. Eventually he was able to recall several forgotten experiences in high school and college in which he had encountered bitter disappointment in an idealized teacher who revealed selfish interests in the patient's intellectual development or the performance-oriented deployment of his academic talents. When these experiences were explored, it became apparent that his outrage at the instructors was matched by a strange sense of surprise and disappointment in himself.

Early in adolescence he had repressed his chronic underlying rage, partly through the use of acting-out behavior. He was able to confess a recent but uncomfortable insight about the origin of this behavior. At puberty he had become afraid that there might really be something wrong with his persistent closeness to his mother. "Coincidentally" he began stealing items of modest value from stores, feeling a vague erotic excitement when he was able to get away with it. His system of puritanical ideals as the sole motives of his behavior seemed to have an unexplained flaw. His experience of an analogous flaw in my morality may have stimulated an unconscious fear of a counterpart in his mother's intense, seemingly altruistic investment in him.

In the termination period of his first analysis he was able to acknowledge three highly relevant insights. Behind his contempt for his father, whom he thought of as a good-natured, passive fool, there existed a great deal of fear and guilt which he had been chronically unable to face and which had limited his periodic efforts to become closer to the father. Similarly, he avoided facing his problems of aggression with me throughout the analysis.

Although his mother was viewed by the world as a charismatic, vigorous, saintly person, he recognized that she had actually sustained herself through the bitter periods of marital incompatibility by recourse to an overtly eroticized intimacy with the patient in a desperate effort to slow down her ultimate descent into chronic alcoholism. It was not simply that his mother, in her ambitiousness, was trying desperately to live through him in the usual phallic manipulative manner. Rather, it was necessary for her to thwart his autonomous ambitions lest his departure doom her to the continuation of the progressive disorganization and depression that had begun early in her marriage, after her mother died and her husband drifted away. At the end of his analysis with me, when the patient became engaged to a woman who apparently had his mother's approval (a vigorous type, aware of her own goals and untroubled by self-doubt), the mother's depression became openly manifest, and her drinking increased dramatically so that it could no longer be hidden. During her long, ultimately fatal illness, he resumed his role as her sustaining, intimate companion, again supplanting his father in that role. He was able to ease her terminal days, facilitating her ability to maintain a considerable degree of personality integration until just before her death.

*Case C*

The research physician, oldest of two children, grew up convinced that his chronic troubles with his mother were all his fault. Being a demanding, unnaturally selfish youngster from birth, perhaps the victim of a congenital predisposition, he had unwittingly contributed to her inability to mother him. Both parents had colluded in this diagnosis, and his first analyst had also agreed. According to other relatives, he really had been unresponsive to her efforts to cuddle and soothe him. He grew up believing that his mother had been a good, self-sacrificing woman of modest endowment who tried hard in the face of burdens, especially the desertion of her husband when the patient was four. However, prior to this time, the father had participated equally in his elemental physical care.

The father's desertion, occurring during the oedipal period, complicated this youngster's guilt-ridden, ambivalent attachment to his mother. Her helpless entreaties and his guilt and resentment set up a cyclically reinforcing, mutually stimulating, and mutually rejecting relationship, the eroticized content of which was not the only source of his difficulty. The underlying dynamic basis for their relationship was actually a role reversal, although this knowledge was completely repressed. He was expected to comfort, direct, and nurture her, as if he were the parent and she were the child—but this was never acknowledged. In addition to repression of the conscious knowledge of her pathology, he managed to repress well into his adult years his overpowering anger and resentment from childhood. In part, displacement of negative affect onto the complex relationship with the father facilitated this repression. In analysis, it emerged that mother was a fragile personality prone to fall apart, and not only because of her own pervasive preoccupation with the death of her own mother from cancer (!) and the subsequent depression which set in. The patient's parents divorced at the beginning of his adolescence, after which time his father deteriorated into a frightened, marginally employed technician, devastated by his multiple failures. But in the resulting situation of renewed potential closeness to his mother, the patient learned to keep her at some distance, perhaps by displacement and a new acting-out behavior—unprovoked, but disguised physical attacks on his female schoolmates.

In high school he became a first-rate scholar and athlete of considerable promise, winning an athletic scholarship to a prestigious university. He was recognized early as potentially a person of great promise, but erratically inhibited in social and team activities despite his efforts to be cooperative. His academic and athletic competencies were encumbered by occasional angry, uncontrollable disputations with school authorities. The truly shattering experience, however, came during his first (surgical) residency when he had a sensational row with an important attending physician whom he felt had deceived him regarding a cooperative research project. At this time he suffered a significant clinical depression and left the residency. In his next residency, he was still so subject to periodic rages and self-destructive confrontations that he was able to complete few of the promising enterprises in which he became engaged. However, in his social relations he was good-natured, pleasant company and highly valued by his friends.

A first analysis initially provided great improvement, yet ended in failure along with a marriage undertaken in the middle of analysis. Both events were probably affected by his mother's death in the midst of these struggles. Despite his grudging appreciation of his father's efforts to help him at the time, he was not able to see father as a deeply hurt, beaten person. It was as if he could never forgive father for not having been able to effect a significant restoration of their early loving relationship or a rescue from his burden of responsibility for the mother's well-being.

In the analysis with me, he began to realize that mother had been able to split herself, assigning her "bad self" to the patient, while lavishing her affection and the best of her personality on a new husband and her infant daughter. She continued to do what she had probably done during the desertion of the patient's father—preserve her integrity and her own resources at the expense of a symbiotically destructive misuse of her son, a use which persisted despite her remarriage. In the transference, the patient effected a chronically unmanageable criminalization of me, as he had done with his former analyst and at least one psychotherapist, paralleling his criminalization of his father. This suggested an intense ambivalence about being cured of his attachments to his maternal introject, as if he still required that attachment to preserve his structural stability, and not simply for libidinal gratification.

PRELIMINARY INFERENCES

From these vignettes several things stand out. These men had intense, complex, persistent attachments to their mothers, with a strong implication of some special meaning and role beyond those usually ascribed to oedipal wishes, including, on occasion, actual libidinal gratification. Second, they appeared to have developed implicitly depressive personalities consisting of layered, incompatible, incomplete, and isolated self-organizations, similar to the "self-nuclei" described by Gedo and Goldberg (1973) and Gedo (1979). Their unintegrated personalities involved such "islands" as identification with the aggressor, special dramatizations of the family romance, complex splits and disavowals, partial selves, exaggerated grandiose fantasies, and combinations and recombinations of parental introjects. Third, by early adulthood all had a tendency to suffer breakdown in their capacity to cope with adult responsibilities, and this at a time when normal developmental demands required them to become more self-sustaining and autonomous in their functioning. It was as if an obligatory relationship to an imagined maternal omnipotence was either no longer available or acceptable or (in the masochistically perverted way it had formerly been utilized) no longer protectively effective. Fourth, in the place of this relationship arose an awesomely developed moral sense, implacable and peremptory, an organizing center for the entire personality which, nonetheless, seemed to lack any clear origin via identifications with their parental backgrounds. Its central importance to all functions of ego and character is without question. Fifth, a defensive characterological orientation, with considerable emphasis on external sources of gratification, the outward expression of energies, and the predominant authority of the outside world proved adaptively ineffective in enabling them to preserve their inner equilibrium. Sixth, each of these men preserved a selective capacity for introspective curiosity, but it led only to painful self-doubt and self-condemnation rather than to deeper levels of understanding. Their limited insights, never shared with anyone, led to a series of questions about which they ruminated continually without being able to arrive at satisfactory answers: "How flawed am I? How defective am I? How evil am I?" Thus they all retained at the core a fundamentally autoplastic personality despite the apparently reversed organization of their defenses and their manifest behavior.

In fact, these young men all grew up fearing at bottom that they *did* carry a flaw, and that the flaw was responsible for the primary difficulties with their parents as well as all manner of unhappiness as they grew up. Ultimately, they all insisted on the pragmatic utility of a solution based on the Golden Rule: if only they could become "good-enough" persons, they would have an island of moral safety to which they could cling behaviorally until the security of a fully stable adult personality arrived. When this happened, they would be freed from the recurrent episodes of self-deception, betrayal, and disappointment that had led to a life of endless suffering.

In an imaginary conversation with the world, these men seemed to be saying the following:

(1) "There is something wrong with the way I understand people's behavior and motives. My basic uncertainty of the meaning of others' intentions predisposes me to the self-deception which makes me so vulnerable to crises of disorganization that I experience as betrayal, disappointment, and outrage. Thus, when I experience chronically recurrent interpersonal traumas, they threaten to confirm my worst anxieties about my thinking."

(2) "However, if I act honorably and morally, this will guarantee an honorable and moral response from the world. The more ethical my own behavior, the greater will be the predictability of the spontaneous behavior of the outside world. In addition, such ethical behavior will guarantee the worthiness of my intentions as well as the reliability of my own competencies."

(3) "An honorable response from the world would prove that I have become what my mother wanted me to be. She would say that if only I could become an ethical person the world would respond better, and I would never need to experience ineptness or helplessness, disappointment or failure. Thus a reliable response would signify that I have finally mastered my own flawed and unreliable nature. Once and for all I would have wiped out the terrible fear that I have no ability to monitor the subjective qualities and cognitive meanings of others' interpersonal intentions. I would have finally grown up. I would no longer need to rely upon her judgment, guidance, and presence to take care of myself in the world."

But the wish to predict the behavior of others and thereby control one's world in an effort to avoid being traumatized by it, like all forms of disguised infantile omnipotence, is inevitably doomed by reality. Like any compact with the Devil [= mother] it must ultimately fail as a life plan despite its adaptive motivation. Sooner or later, someone takes advantage of one's good nature. Someone with less sensitivity or lower standards fails to demonstrate an anticipated piece of understanding. Someone is revealed to have conflicted, false, or selfish motives. Someone criticizes unexpectedly or accuses one of acting like a selfish child. This disappointment precipitates an attack of unbelievably intense, all-encompassing rage. The underlying immaturity of the patient's psychological organization, the Repressed with all its primitive introjects, dreadful fears, childish fixations, and organizational incoherence—those aspects of the unconscious overwhelm the rational "good-self" core and seize control of the executive apparatus of the ego. Fresh vertical splits (Kohut, 1971) develop, the constituents of the "good self" are isolated or rendered totally inoperative, massive regression occurs, and a bewildering episode of total rage ensues.

It is as if the patient says:

(1) "I did not anticipate the demand or failure of the other, I don't

deserve it, and I don't really understand it; it's not part of the 'moral compact.' It makes me feel helpless and disorganized, and I am ashamed that this is happening without being able to influence it. It is too threatening to be curious about myself. Therefore, I focus exclusively upon the other. I am led to wonder whether an honorable, reliable, understandable relationship ever existed between myself and the other. How could I have been so wrong?"

(2) "Could it be that my own reality testing was inadequate in this situation? No, I must have been deceived from the very beginning by forces beyond my knowledge or control—forces emanating from the outside. It is intolerable even to imagine that I have some subjective motives for participating in the deception."

(3) "All this cannot be due to me. All of this must really be due to the intentionally wretched behavior and corrupt morality of the false other. *He* must be the depraved, worthless individual, contemptible and evil in his own right. Because his behavior was deliberately designed to make me suffer, no form of retaliation can be too great. He should be obliterated from the face of the earth. A simple admission of error and guilt, actual compensation or symbolic restitution, will never be sufficient."

In summary, the experienced venality of the *other's* motivation becomes infinitely more important than the substance of the reality issue. It outweighs the modest tendency toward introspective curiosity regarding the nature of the deception which occasionally breaks through. Any hint of awareness of complicity, especially through projection, is immediately dismissed. The overriding conviction is of the other's monumental moral betrayal and ethical falseness as the origin of the emotional trauma. The vengeful lengths which the patient fantasies about, and to which he may actually go, not only suggest a willingness to ignore all reality considerations, but also signal the extent of the potentially severe, unmanageable disruption of psychological equilibrium and adaptive ego functioning which had been set in motion by the traumatic betrayal.

The linchpin of this unique variant of narcissistic rage (Kohut, 1972) is the failure of an adaptive structure organized around morality. *Behind the insistently adaptive self or proper moral intent and moral expectations of these patients, there lies in wait the ever-present, but temporarily sequestered, depressed core of the self that represents the relationship with the parents as it had actually been experienced.* This aspect of the self, containing horrid oral-anal-sadistic elements, now threatens to engulf the entire personality. For the betrayal sequence to have begun, this part of the self must be restimulated and reawakened—and projected. Initially, the rage outpouring is especially frightening, not only for its traumatic and surprising intensity, but also because it constitutes paradoxical evidence validating the patient's worst fantasies: his implacable moral compact really is inadequate to prevent a sadistic assault by the bad part of the patient's self (projected onto and joined with the venal individual in the outside world) on another part of the patient's self, that is, the truly moral good self.

Some rebalancing and restabilizing continues as the rage gradually becomes more orderly and attenuated. Not only is subsequent tension-regulation made possible through lowering of this rage via discharge or fantasy, but the experience of the residual and eventually signal rage constitutes, in its own right, a means of reorganizing and reintegrating the personality. The offending other and the offending self merged with this other now become the subject of an active retaliatory attack mounted by some residual portion of the healthy self. This is analogous, in reverse, to the primitive assault the patient believed he had experienced at the hands of the omnipotent mother at those times when he failed in some assigned function. The difference in these re-enactments is that they constitute a pseudo-victory in which the patient believes that by mounting such a vigorous counterattack he can undo the dreadful fear of being permanently doomed to a state of disorganization and helplessness. Thus these patients regularly report a constructive feeling of wholeness in the sheer fantasy of hitting somebody. Sometimes this is not limited just to fantasy. Furthermore, the construction of a protoparanoid fantasy to explain the long-standing deception additionally helps in the task of self-reorganization since such ideation involves recathecting then utilizing complex ego functions (Meissner, 1978).

Even after some balance has been restored, and the bad self has been temporarily extruded or sequestered, even after the re-enacted passive assault has been transformed into an active attack so that victory can occur, the ultimate tragedy of these disorganizing symptomatic episodes is that the restored self remains as fragile and incomplete and inchoate as ever. Nothing has been learned or gained despite the seeming psychological-mindedness of these patients. No new structural rearrangements, no new insights, no new identifications. There are inadequate intrapsychic resources for the evolution of a capacity to stand back from the recent crisis and ask the crucial question, "What do *I* have to do with the fact that I experience people deceiving and failing me so regularly?" These complex fantasy re-enactments thereby constitute the fruitless, cyclical, regressive acting out of a profound fantasy anchored in structurally based pathology. Without effective analysis these people remain utterly unable to begin to explore the complexity of meanings that their behavior has been designed to deal with, let alone face the profound distortion, incoherence, and instability that typifies the self-organization at multiple levels.

## DEVELOPMENTAL SPECULATIONS

What is the origin of a personality core of quasi-isolated self-nuclei (Gedo and Goldberg, 1973; Gedo, 1979, 1981)? Lying sequestered at the nucleus of the personalities of these patients are unconscious memories of special experiences with an omnipotent, but flawed and sadistic mother. It is the impact of these memories which perpetually destabilizes the patient's frantic efforts to rebuild his personality even through compensatory adaptations, let alone to harmonize effectively the host of disparate self elements which coexist with the maternal introject at the core of the personality.

The mothers' lifelong, *persistently inconsistent* presentation of intense libidinal, aggressive, and narcissistic demands and special role expectations (together with responses) directed toward their sons constituted an environmental determinant of an unusual sort. The resulting dilemmas imparted a special cast to the relationship with their sons, unusual in its intensity, in its dyadic exclusiveness, and in its recurrent intrusiveness throughout all developmental phases. This special relationship resulted in the development of a cognitively distorted personality core, but one which retained a morally flavored grandiosity as the compromised focus around which a nuclear self was partially organized. A sound and stable hierarchical arrangement of personality elements was prevented by the dangerous and unpredictable behavior of their first and continuing love object—mother. This relationship, in turn, set the pattern for their perceived expectations of behavior by crucial love objects in all developmental phases. The outcome of this development was a personality core consisting of several incomplete or incompatible islands or self-nuclei (Gedo and Goldberg, 1973; Gedo, 1979, 1981), each separated, if not isolated, from the other, albeit not at a borderline personality level. This polycentric core, infused with an idealizing moral sense and protected by an outwardly facing false self, was highly vulnerable. As late adolescence and young-adult experience confronted them with the inadequacy or unavailability of the fantasy-ridden attachment to their "powerful" mothers, and with a pragmatic awareness of their poorly integrated ego tools, regression to the adaptive crisis of "Outrage-Deception-Betrayal" became inevitable. Each crisis served to stimulate, only to lead to the immediate rerepression of, an intolerable question: "Could this terrible experience have anything to do with my relationship with my mother?"

The relationships between these patients and their mothers were much more than ordinarily dependent and symbiotic (Robbins, 1982). They were extraordinarily important to their mothers in terms of the special needs they served, and *the mothers never gave them up in these respects.* There is evidence that all three women had significant personality flaws, best conceptualized as high-level thought disorders, together with a tendency to lose the ability to regulate tension. All three women were, to varying degrees, grandiose, omnipotent, or messianic; their sons were utilized in recurrent attempts to maintain or restore such a privileged status when they feared that they were undergoing serious personality disorganization. All three mothers looked to external circumstances, i.e., relied on projection and externalization, to explain their difficulties in life, particularly their inability to gratify their grandiose ambitions. All three turned to their sons very early for a special "something." This "something" subserved their attempts to maintain a fragile integration by splitting off and then projecting their bad self onto the child, i.e., their own feelings of being ineffective, devalued, or in danger of disorganization. By these maneuvers they hoped to maintain a more effective and comfortable level of functioning, best construed in terms of Freud's (1911) purified pleasure ego.

These projective maneuvers alternated with efforts to manipulate the phallic potential of their sons to bolster their own flawed feelings of power and effectiveness, either by controlling the sons' activities overtly, by inhibiting these activities totally, or by merging symbiotically. In the oedipal period there was a major effort at seducing the sons into some version of a gratifying oedipal victory by exploiting the phase-appropriate libidinal intensification of their previously established ties to them. In effect, the sons were led to believe something tantamount to the following fantasy: "If you renounce your independently directed aims or normally arising developmental interests and agree to become totally subject to my choice, and never to leave me, I will present you with the Golden Apple. You will be more important to me than your father. Like an invisible cloak, my eroticized omnipotence, restored by this latest merger with your phallic potency, will provide you with magical protection and power forever."

This demand confronted the young sons with a series of impossible paradoxes: "If I am so special that I am automatically entitled to all of her power and privileges, why aren't they available to me whenever I want them? Why don't I feel that they have finally become mine? Where is the payoff? And, if there is no payoff, this is a deception, and the real truth is that my behavior proves just the opposite: that I am really so inept, so rotten, and so defective that only by maintaining a relationship to her special powers will I be able to survive in the world. But if only I could learn to be morally perfect in my behavior, like she wishes me to be, then perhaps I would be entitled to all her power and protection and privileges forever."

It is understandable, then, that these men functioned with some degree of effectiveness only when under the aegis of feminine power. Intuitively knowing as much, they chose vigorous women as their wives. Implicitly, they viewed power and phallic effectiveness as fundamentally feminine in nature; this made it exceedingly difficult to leave mother or the women to whom they had become attached, even as they resented, albeit unconsciously, that attachment. To leave was to face the danger of being inept and helpless. Thus sensitivity to women, a capacity for closeness to women, and an ambivalent dependence on women become explainable as derivatives of the complex relationship with the mother.

It was the need to know the true intent of the other, originally the mother, which became paramount. What were the current aims of the mother, and what were they going to be two minutes from now? This imperative need to know accounts for their tendency to simplify contradictions and paradoxes in interpersonal relationships, as if it were unbearable to face the risk of not fully understanding the complexities attendant to these relationships. Better to disavow that part of reality which was too complex, or too threatening, if this disavowal would facilitate a feeling of certainty. This propensity to simplify further explains the supreme importance they attached to moral attitudes and their absolute intolerance of ethical deception: only by attempting to structure a life of flawless behavior could they reassure themselves of the reliability of one set of their self functions, while simultaneously disavowing another feared set that connected to the apparently grandiose maternal introject. Similarly, their defensive identification with the aggressor (A. Freud, 1936), combined with disavowal and projection, seems to be modeled on their mothers' basic defenses. These patients were remarkably adept at submitting to the "bad" maternal introject and then proceeding to persecute the offending or frustrating object in the outside world upon whom their own "bad self" had been extruded (Segal, 1964). Following some degree of discharge leading to a diminution of their mobilized aggression, a series of rebuilding steps could occur. Thus their rageful demonstrations, their tendency to act toward the world as their persecutory mothers had acted toward them, could ultimately subserve their underlying conviction that if one proceeded morally, one's efforts *ought to* influence reliably the behavior of the world toward oneself. It was only via the preservation of this innermost belief that their chronically traumatized personalities (Khan, 1963) could provide the basis for maturely integrated adult functioning.

These men developed a defensive self bearing some relationship to Winnicott's (1963) concept of the "false self." This self enabled them to confront the world with an apparently reliable adaptation in the face of the burden of their mothers' paradoxical psychological pressures. It was based in part on a distorted belief in the overriding effectiveness of ethics and moral elements in determining their own behavior and facilitating their influence on the world. Despite the ultimate authenticity and nuclear significance of their core value system, its adaptive use was doomed to failure because it was a defensive construct modeled in response to their mothers' distorted thinking and actual corruption. It was a maladaptive compromise because it contained elements of the maternal introject that had been taken in and retained as part of a desperate effort to survive. Ultimately, it proved maladaptive for the very reason that it was based on an unending series of splits, disavowals, reaction formations, projections, and other incompatible defenses. It was also a deadly solution because it involved the renunciation of parts of their own reality testing and the substitution of magical thinking, as well as the contamination of those aspects of cognition responsible for judging the intentions of others' attitudes and aims toward them.

In the literature, there are several interesting suggestions which highlight aspects of the personalities of these mothers. Martin Wangh, in his paper, "Evocation of a Proxy" (1962), describes the designation of a proxy person utilized by certain women to maintain ego integration when endangered by the threatened loss of another crucial object relationship, usually their husbands. They achieve a measure of internal consistency by fusion with a designated proxy, usually another family member (typically a child), thereby maintaining control over their unbearably ambivalent feelings toward the deserting spouse. Predictably, the proxy becomes disorganized, anxious, and regressed. In an article entitled "Gaslighting," Calef and Weinshel (1981) describe the process by which certain individuals attempt to drive someone else crazy as a means of externalizing certain "bad" parts of their own personalities, thereby maintaining control over their own disorganizing tendencies. These efforts frequently miscarry. If the person who has been "gaslighted," i.e., treated so as to convince him that he is really the crazy one, removes himself from the clutches of his persecutor, the gaslighting perpetrator often undergoes a flagrant regression into a totally disabling depression or a paranoid psychosis. The mothers of my patients, like the subjects of Calef and Weinshel's study, all suffered from very early pregenital distortions and integrative failures which, despite their manifest grandiosity, made them prone to disorganization. All three mothers evidenced behavior bearing certain resemblances to the two character types described in these articles.

What was the role of the fathers in the genesis of these problems? Two of them were chronically uninvolved or uninterested in their sons. One was deeply involved initially, but absent during later crucial developmental periods. All three were targets of their wives' underlying ambivalence, disappointment, or resentment, and it was this attitude with which their young sons identified. But even this generalization must be qualified. While all three patients had significant difficulties establishing positive relationships with their fathers, two of them eventually did effect such relationships in adulthood following some disengagement from the involvement with the mother. In place of the absent father of childhood, all three had by puberty evolved fleeting but significant relationships with substituted male figures, such as an idealized servant, a teacher, or an uncle.

What led to the problems with the fathers? The quantitative intensity of the earliest relationships with the mothers might have blocked early or idealizing attachments to them. In addition, the pseudo-oedipal victory added a factor of significant guilt, often disguised as angry disappointment based on pre-existing deficiencies in the relationship. Thirdly, the paternal ideal system may have been significantly less available, not only because the mothers blocked its expression, but also because the fathers themselves were basically inhibited personalities. All three experienced recurring fears of retaliation and loss heightened by deeply rooted castration anxieties; these anxieties focused on their bodies, their possessions, their activities, and their love objects. The desire to relate to the fathers as persons of value and to acquire something of meaning from that experience came only after significant inner conflict, if at all, and regularly succumbed to the risk of the mother's displeasure. Even if the child did acquire something of value from the father, moreover, it only intensified the isolation and layering of his contradictory aims and attitudes.

Two intriguing etiological questions remain to be addressed: (1) What is the mechanism by which the implacable morality became established as the organizing focus of the nuclear self? How—and why—did these children "create" a morality so different from that of either parent? (2) What is the nature of the vulnerability which made them so prone to feeling deceived? What are we dealing with, dynamically and structurally? Is the susceptibility to deception the product of a secondary defense, i.e., a need to idealize falsely all important objects in order to compensate for parental deficiency?

Psychoanalytic thinking about superego formation (Freud, 1926; Hartmann, Kris, and Loewenstein, 1964; Arlow, 1982) relies on mechanisms of imitation, introjection, identification, idealization, renunciation, or transformation. But all of these mechanisms begin with an assumption of an available person, if not a reliable parental superego. For these patients, such explanations are incomplete since the contents and qualities of their superegos appear to be dramatically different from those of their parents. There appear to be only two or three logical answers to the simple question,

"Where does the morality arise from?" (a) The superego of these men was created afresh as an imaginative, intellectual act based on minuscule stimuli from the experience of other relationships. (b) These men may have had an intensely significant libidinal and idealized relationship with some other important childhood figure during or just after the oedipal period, an ancillary oedipal-teaching object whose influence was subsequently forgotten or repressed. (c) These men may have been able to discern and make contact with totally unconscious, reliable ideals present somewhere in the maternal parent, despite the threatening relationship with that parent. Let us examine each of the three examples with these possibilities in mind.

### Case A—The man in the cab

This man had two sources of elemental influence in his formative years. For a few preschool years, he was raised by a very proper English nanny, whom mother permitted to manage the child according to her own rules, at least at times. He had a disinterested, isolated father, but one who possessed a vaguely liberal social philosophy involving sympathy with the underdog, especially Jewish immigrants from Eastern Europe and World War II refugees. Transference evidence suggests that much of this patient's personality development was fueled by good-natured negativism that permitted him to resist strong maternal influence. It was imperative that he be able to oppose at some level the values of his mother. Thus his moral core might well have been a creative, intellectual act arising out of the stimulus of minuscule cues from the nurse and his father.

### Case B—The man with the phobia

The data here are less clear. He seemed to have imitated some of his mother's views, especially her pseudo-selflessness and pseudo-saintliness in human relationships. His adult contempt for, and distance from, his father make it difficult to estimate the latter's influence during early childhood. In no sense did his moral self seem to develop by opposition. Instead, it seems to have evolved by creative elaboration from within. Aside from the speculative possibility of more genuine values derived from the mother, evidence is lacking regarding other sources of his superego development.

### Case C—The unrealized superstar

Although details of his early upbringing, beyond those already given, are unknown, his mother had the assistance of an adolescent farm girl with whom to share the parenting tasks for a very brief period just prior to the father's absence. In this case, too, one would have to conclude that his implacable morality arose largely through his own devices, as some sort of creative act assisted only by minuscule stimulation from the maid and from some fragile element of moral certainty present in the father during the patient's early years.

The second intriguing question concerns the nature of the vulnerability which predisposes these patients to be deceived. There is no question of their need to distort, omit, or disavow reality percepts, and to deny one set of self-functions meaningful access to the perceptions and meanings belonging to some other self-nucleus. One might argue that this distortion of high-level cognitive processes is in the nature of a hysterical wish-fulfillment, i.e., that it is fantasy motivated. But that still does not account for either the origins or the mechanism by which structural elements in the personality facilitate such distortions in the everyday working of cognitive processes. There is an alternative explanation. Perhaps these men were so busy guarding themselves from the complexities of mother's unpredictable, paradoxical demands and responses that they had neither the time nor the developmental context (including a positive reward system) to evolve more complex capacities for learning the nuances of mother's complex behavioral assaults. In other words, they never acquired any competence in discerning and feeling comfortable with minimal signals and the logical complexities of others' intentions. They learned only to recognize those intentions which were accompanied by overt and unmistakably dramatic action equivalents—especially painful ones. Added to this may have been the predisposition for disguised mutual seductiveness which characterized their relationships.

Thus we may be dealing with a double set of motives: the lack of a reliable opportunity for incremental learning experience with ambivalent, contradictory, or unclear motives, plus the enormous wish to believe that if they were "good" in their own behavior, their mothers would love them. The result of betrayal experiences would serve to discredit and discourage their own attempts to discern ambivalent, paradoxical, subtle, or multilayered motives in the behavior of others. In a literal sense, they had failed to learn how to do this in childhood; worse yet, they would be unable to learn from experiences of failure what it was that they were unable to do! Metaphorically, they may be viewed as suffering from a self-perpetuating, high-level "learning disability" regarding the subtleties of human intentionality.

## THE DIAGNOSTIC DILEMMA

Are not these patients "just" variants of the nosological category of borderline personality syndrome or narcissistic personality disorder? Alternatively, do they fall within the rubric of masochistic-depressive character; or perhaps paranoid personalities? After all, these men had features de scribable as masochistic, depressive, perverse, protoparanoid, and ever borderline, as well as unquestionably narcissistic. The diagnosis of self system pathology is certainly the leading one. These patients meet the criteria posited by Kohut (1971, 1972, 1977), Kohut and Wolf (1978), anc most of Kohut's followers (e.g., Goldberg and colleagues, 1978; Goldberg 1980, 1984). They also meet the criteria of Gedo (1979, 1981) and Stolorow and Lachmann (1980). However, these three patients constitute a more select group within the self-pathology classification, with respect to the presenting symptomatology, adaptive character style, and the unique role of morality as the organizing center of their personalities.

Are these men borderline personalities? If we utilize the criteria of Kern- berg (1975) and Gunderson and Singer (1975), they do not clearly qualify in terms of genetic history, current symptomatology, or actual functioning. They lack the over-all severe difficulty in the management of strong affects, with the exception of aggression. Their problems in tension regulation and affect management are confined to more restricted areas and specific fan- tasy-organized relationships. They lack the blatant "cognitive slippage" problems that characterize borderline personalities. Their adult relation- ships are more stable, more give-and-take, more reliable, and feel more authentic than those of most borderline personalities. With the exception of the severe depression suffered by Patient C, the persistent depressive features, while significant, do not become uncontrolled and dominant. Their introjects do not seem to be as primitive as those of borderlines (Adler, 1980). The problems with self-cohesion are major, but there is a reasonably reliable nuclear self buried somewhere in these men, however archaic in nature. Thus their structural splits are less severe and more selective than those of borderlines.

Are they paranoid characters? Certainly, there is no argument that they use projective defenses and have paranoid ideas. At times of the betrayal crises, moreover, they organize their rationalizations in a way that is prim- itive and magical to the point of being quasi-delusional. Yet they use pro- jective identification only selectively, and there is no stable systemization of their paranoid thinking. Furthermore, their organization of affect does not resemble the cold, haughty, and implacable destructive rage at the world that characterizes most paranoid personalities (Segal, 1964; Kohut, 1971; Meissner, 1978).

Are they primarily depressive personalities? Again, the depressive core is clear and its influence often pervasive. Patient C did suffer severe de- pressive episodes related to narcissistic disappointment. However, there is

neither the profound sense of guilt one finds in well-structured personalities nor the profound apathy and lack of energetic endowment or "drain-
ng out" that characterize the chronic depressive problems in patients with
major self-system pathology (Goldberg, 1978, 1984; Tolpin, 1980). Between
critical episodes these people have considerable energy with which to work
oward and accomplish their goals, despite their very limited capacity to
derive gratification from such activities. It is this inability to experience
meaningful gratification, combined with the fact that gratification experiences do not alter their basic sense of self, which points to the persistence
of a depressive core.

What about masochistic character structure? Here the evidence is more
suggestive. Several of the analyses summarized by Cooper (Panel, 1981)
involved analysands who bear a significant resemblance to the patients in
his communication. In some of these cases regulation of self-esteem and
the development of function of a reliable, well-structured, cohesive self
system were intimately connected to parental-developmental distortions
and failures. This led inevitably to the development of a masochistically
flavored attachment to the faulty, omnipotent, and threatening parent.
Cooper observed:

> These patients share the sense of a deadened capacity to feel muted
> pleasure, a hypersensitive self-esteem alternating between grandiosity
> and humiliation, an inability to sustain or derive satisfaction from their
> relationships or their work, a constant sense of envy, an unshakable
> conviction of being wronged and deprived by those who are supposed
> to take care of them, and an infinite capacity for provocation [p. 677].

How one classifies these patients diagnostically depends on one's view
of how personality development is organized along an epigenetic continuum of phases and stages, as described by Gedo (1979, 1981). But the
etiological-diagnostic question hinges on what it is about early
parent/childhood relationships—with the associated differentiating, indi-
vidualizing, internalizing, and integrating processes—that becomes the
structural basis for developmental pathology. A detailed exploration of
these matters must await a subsequent communication.

## CONCLUSION

What saved these three young men from a still more pathological outcome—from disabling borderline pathology or grossly perverse organization of their personalities? All were bright, well-endowed, reasonably
creative individuals with a particularly good perceptual sensitivity. All had,
from early life, utilized their perceptual capabilities selectively in the service

of knowing in order to survive—to survive by relating "somehow." Thi intellectual effort culminated in a distorted defensive adaptive device tha enabled them—at times—to anticipate which set of mother's intrinsicall unpredictable, but implacably deployed attitudes would be turned towar them at any one time. All three learned how to deceive themselves abou which products of their perception were reality-based and which wer fantasied distortions—and they learned to do so with respect to each paren To allow themselves full validation of what they knew would have interfere with the development of the vitally necessary, outwardly facing adaptiv self; it would also have provided them with much more knowledge of wha *they* were really like than they could tolerate at the time.

The same circumstances that necessitated this distorted adaptation re quired conspiratorial compliance with the bizarreness of the mother's men tation throughout all childhood developmental phases. Whether thi distorted self was compliant and passive, pseudo-stupid, priggish an proper, ambivalently assertive, or aggressively vigorous, it directed thes boys, at some level, to comply meekly with mother's view of herself, o father, and of themselves. Above all, this adaptive self facilitated their abilit to serve the mother as some form of selfobject (Kohut, 1971), an assigne role which continued throughout their lives. This protracted selfobje status, interfering with their own autonomous development, defined th price which had to be paid in exchange for a modicum of integration a the level of the nuclear self. The ability to create an effective defensive adaptive self and the secondary supports necessary to sustain it were vita not only to developmental survival, but also to their episodic and selectiv effectiveness as adults.

The adaptive self had other protective aspects. It permitted them t maintain a secret part of themselves apart from their mothers wherei something of meaning and value could be nurtured and shielded, howeve fragile or tenuous it might be. This secret self, an idea of just how virtuou they might be "inside," what their life might have been like under differen circumstances, and what it might be like in the future, was especially pre cious and important as an imaginary world in which all of them secretl played. This enclave permitted them to assign a secret space to authenti aims which at some time in the future might become realized. Although that part of themselves, with its feelings, aims, attitudes, and values, migh never be realized in overt experience, it was one way of sustaining a feeling of being real and worthy without having to fall back on somatic forms o self-stimulation.

The common organizing ingredient was the exaggerated role assigne to moral and ethical values as human motivators. At the innermost core of their secret selves, such things as moral virtue, faithfulness to one's ideals and one's friends, and, above all, the role of helpfulness were accorded absolute and authentic dominance. Because these values were contaminated and distorted by their defensive use, these patients were in constant danger not merely of being disappointed, deceived, and betrayed by the world, but of discovering that they might not really be like the secret self which they cherished, nurtured, and protected. *The overriding fear was that at the innermost core they might really be like the introjected parent of childhood, an array of assaultive, greedy, and impulsive motives; of contradictory, selfish, and corrupt principles; of fuzzy, magical, and contaminated thought processes; and, above all, of disorganized, incompatible pieces.* No wonder that the experience of betrayal carried with it the sense that something fundamental to the entire organization of the personality was being challenged. This "something" was the elaborate defensive-adaptive organization that shielded these men from an intolerable yet dimly sensed possibility: that *the ultimate "cause" of their pain at the hands of the world might be projection of parts of their own flawed self-organization.*

# II

I have to this point explored the dynamic and genetic aspects of an unusual, lifelong personality adaptation originating in an extremely intense, special relationship to a pathological mother. I now wish to make some technical observations about the analytic treatment of such individuals. After offering some preliminary generalizations, I shall draw more extensively on one particular analysis in order to exemplify the technical problems and process issues at stake. These matters will be treated at the level of clinical theory rather than metapsychology.

## THE ANALYSES

In analysis these individuals are penetrating and demanding, although not so much primarily for perfect understanding and perfectly tuned interpretations. Rather, it is the analyst's absolute devotion and absolute personal honesty based on maximal self-knowledge and ethical reliability that are crucial. These expectations are defended against for long periods of time. Catching the analyst in an attempt to excuse or deny a weakness, or in an attempt to intrude a subjective need of his own toward the patient, may cause the analysis to founder. It is the analyst's efforts to conceal the need or the flaw, however, and not the mere fact of its existence, which are the essence of the trap. Although these issues appear to constitute the pathology-specific basis for repetitive empathic failures (Schwaber, 1981), they actually have a more significant meaning than that. On thoughtful inspection it becomes apparent that these transactions represent the patient's "innocent" efforts at bringing into the analysis, in the form of a classical archaic transference crisis (Gunther, 1984), elements of the nuclear issue: the unpredictability of others' intentions and the disruptive consequences which follow.

In contrast to other narcissistic types, these patients do not lie in wait for evidence of error or ordinary human frailty on the analyst's part. On the contrary, they are frequently quite tolerant of his errors as long as they are assumed to arise from unwitting ignorance. They will temporarily forgive and wait for the analyst to learn—though not forever. A typical comment might be, "How can anybody as smart as you be as dumb as you were during the last hour?" or "After ten years are you growing tired of the burdens that I place on you? If you are, at least you could recognize it." The unconscious hope informing the analysis is for the silent evolution of a longed-for experience with the good parent of early childhood who never was—idealization of the analyst as the selfless and loving purveyor of predictable, protective, holding and other growth-promoting functions (Winnicott, 1949; Kohut, 1971; Modell, 1976). Above all, the analytic learning environment must carry no surprises suggestive of idiosyncratic or impulsive self-pathology on the part of the analyst in which, similar to the behavior of the real parent, he attempts to utilize the patient to manage and/or satisfy needs of his own.

Much of the analytic work involves a series of central transference issues which oscillate endlessly around a pair of predictable transference configurations. The first is a good, powerful, and protective mother, juxtaposed to an absent, inept, or threatening father. The second is an omnipotent, sadistic, narcissistically monstrous mother, juxtaposed to a competitively superior and protective father who defeats this mother. These deeply buried configurations shift continuously during the course of the analysis (even in the course of an hour) instead of unfolding in a neat, linear manner. The transference is complicated by other dynamic elements: (1) These patients conceal their intense wishes for a reliable holding environment behind a series of "one-party re-enactments" in which they live out one or another of their major self-nuclei. Typical configurations will include the contemptible monster/child, the devouring mother, the omnipotent magician/rescuer, the helpful Boy Scout. The analyst must not only decode, in an ongoing way, the hidden wishes which are being simultaneously conveyed and concealed; he must also understand the relationship of these wishes to the particular "self" (among many) that is being presented at the moment. (2) The re-enactment of incomplete self-nuclei configurations is preliminary to the ·patient's revelation of the nuclear self which shall be utilized as the (moral) basis for reintegrating disparate self-nuclei. Thus the experience of differentiation by negation can be understood as a necessary transference enactment of the part selves which the patient *rejects* as the basis around which an integrated cohesive self will be established. (3) Complex transference configurations are frequently presented by burying them in "real-life" problems. This presentation of a reality problem as the "real issue" is not simply motivated by the wish to evade; it must be understood as the unique way in which these persons have learned to know themselves—through dramatized merger with, or immersion in, the seething reality relationships (i.e., with mother) with which their lives are filled.

The following six issues arising in these transferences are typical of the tasks confronting the analyst:

(1) He must help the patient learn to organize, anticipate, and manage his bizarre disintegrative reactions to unanticipated events by assisting him in the process of introspective curiosity about his predisposition to deception. Along these lines, he must help the patient think about the complex relationships subserving this subjective predisposition, the actual reality events precipitating his disintegrative reactions, and the poorly monitored disorganization that is the sequel to such reactions. This group of issues involves some straightforward teaching (Gedo, 1979).

(2) The patient requires help with the painful task of working through his reactions to the analyst's periodic failures to anticipate and protect him from such difficulties. This process hinges on the recruitment of the patient's own observing and analyzing ego as an ally. This ally can seldom be mobilized simply by interpreting resistance; it must arise from the patient's own struggles, constructively guided and appropriately validated by the analyst. It will be the sequel to optimal empathic failures, clarified, acknowledged, and endlessly reworked in detail by both patient and analyst (Kohut, 1977; Schwaber, 1981).

(3) The resistance to the recognition of the "good-father" transference must be interpreted repeatedly since it is deeply buried, reflects the depressive core, and is defended against by helplessness, hopelessness, disavowal, and angry acting out. The adaptive confusion and cognitive distortion imposed by the patient's false evaluation of early events conceals a strong passive dependent wish; this wish can be understood in the context of obligatory maternal introjects reinforced by the developmentally spontaneous longing for father.

(4) Potentially dangerous and destructive as it might be, that repressed part of the personality in which the mother was at one time realistically

perceived as bad and crazy must be validated and even highlighted. Those adaptations which sustained the pathological disavowal must be explored, together with the pathological content of the introjects. Only then may underlying competencies be brought into active relationship with the healthy core of the self. Invariably, the needed merger with maternal omnipotence turns out to have been not nearly so life sustaining as these patients had been led to believe. The analyst's firm, interpretive "holding" is necessary in the exploration of these issues.

(5) The seemingly endless analytic task is that of separating out, filling in, and integrating a more cohesive and unified self while developing new solutions to the dangers attendant to giving up the pathological introject and its accompanying distortions. This task quickens as these patients become able to idealize and authenticate their true personal aims, including their recent analytic achievements (Gedo, 1981).

In combination, these issues propel the analysis toward a new stability for the patient. To achieve this therapeutic goal, even in part, the analyst must demonstrate maximal *flexibility*, sensitivity, and patience. His guiding technical objective must be facilitation of the patient's use of him *as a new object* (Newman, 1984). His technical process requirement must be alertness to hidden and new meanings. Without such an orientation, these analyses flounder.

## An Illustrative Analysis

I return to the 45-year-old real-estate entrepreneur who had been in analysis for ten years. At the outset, several striking features of his personality were immediately apparent. To say that he had a histrionic trend is an understatement; he re-enacted and relived events rather than describing them. After two diagnostic appointments he cancelled his third hour and showed up late for his first appointment on the couch. When he came in, his left leg was taped and he was using a crutch, having sprained his ankle while running gleefully down a flight of stairs to keep his appointment. This inauspicious start notwithstanding, he was, as best I could determine, genuinely pleased to be starting analysis.

He also betrayed an underlying element of good-natured negativism, the most overt manifestation being a continuing problem with time. In the first three years of the analysis he was present for approximately 150 to 200 minutes out of a scheduled 850 minutes per month. An unbelievably creative array of excuses was presented, each accompanied by genuine contrition and good humor, as if he, too, did not believe them fully. Several times during the first year of our work I wondered aloud if he might be re-enacting some compromise originating in the way he grew up. Perhaps he was repeating in the new relationship what he had done with his mother in a milder form, i.e., individuation by negation? In any event, I was often kept off base and uncertain about our work by his life-and-death, problem-oriented presentations which fragmented the continuity of our work and shifted our themes. While I was perhaps "partly castrated," I was never rendered completely unable to function in an analytic role in contrast to the way he had been rendered totally inept in his adolescence.

These difficulties aside, the patient showed a winning, adolescentlike, ingenuous desire to please, to be approved of, to be found capable of doing "real" analytic work. This was his third attempt at serious treatment, an earlier psychotherapy and analysis having been broken off due to mother's intercession. He maintained a perpetual enthusiasm for the work, and a genuine effort to try to figure out things about himself, no matter how desperate his life circumstances seemed in terms of current financial problems or how bleak he felt about my periodic incapacity to understand him. Reciprocally, I always found him good-natured, likable, and pleasant; I never felt intolerably upset, helpless, angry, or beset by the usual reaction formation to those affects—namely, the desire to rescue him.

His analytic behavior had a good deal of latencylike "show and tell" in it. Most hours during the early years of his analysis were introduced by his relating, through re-enactment, the day's events in regard to business activities, his physical problems with his body, and his difficulties with his relatives (especially mother) or various governmental or institutional authorities. This litany culminated in his promise to try to do better than he had been able to do recently. My initial attempts to interpret this plea as mixed resistance along the lines of a premature pseudo-idealization of me as a mother figure who had to be placated led to a rather routine impasse of empathic failure: the patient would become bewildered, painfully angry, and then miss even more hours than he normally did. When he returned, it would be with some degree of sadness and hopelessness, accompanied by a propensity to recite his failures more rigidly still. Eventually, he mustered enough courage to express his hope that I would learn to understand the true significance of his "show-and-tell" behavior (i.e., the need for validation), and not simply impress upon him my shallow imputations of meaning; such judgments, he informed me, were utterly useless to him.

My most useful interpretations during those early years conveyed my sense that he must desperately want to test whether I could recognize that beneath the chaotic surface, the obsessive recitations of problems, the vague fearfulness, the monumentally creative disorganization in his life, he really did have an urgent need to find someone who would stick with him as his wife had. Specifically, he sought to determine whether I had the staying power to discern, without premature or conventional analytic judgments, what lay beneath the surface of this crazy behavior. After two years, in reference to his tardiness and chronic episodic absences, I asked him why he did not wear a watch. He walked over to the briefcase which he always carried, took out an expensive, nonfunctioning watch which had been his father's, and indicated to me that it had stopped functioning shortly after the latter's death. He had been carrying it around for the last three and a half years, trying to find a moment when he could take time out from his busy schedule to take it in for repair! He laughed and indicated that perhaps now he was ready to face something, that is, the process of un- raveling the many layers of meaning of the death of his father, which had precipitated this current analytic effort. Within a month he was wearing the watch in good repair, and subsequently acquired several more which he continues to wear from time to time. He has improved his compliance with standard analytic expectations by reducing his tardiness to perhaps ten minutes per hour. Rarely now, twelve years after starting, will he come in for the last five minutes of an hour. Much like his behavior in school, his attitude had been one of good intentions, inept passive-aggressive test- ing, and opposition, but not carried to destructive ends. As the work of the analysis permitted him to become more stable in his ability to tolerate the unexpected, my occasional errors and misunderstandings interfered less and less with his sense of newfound stability. He would always be there next time, and he no longer required my calling him up after several missed hours in a row.

In the fifth year, when he had begun to trust my reliability, and his serious psychosomatic disorder had begun to abate, his dreams revealed the existence of painful, passive masochistic fantasies that involved sub- mission to various eroticized tortures at the hands of powerful women. It was at this time, moreover, that he began regular efforts at sexual inter- course with his wife. His severe anxiety about body damage at both genital and pregenital levels thereupon came more clearly into focus. After a year of working over of this material, he began to detach himself from his mother, although these efforts were confounded by his lifelong reluctance to believe in the actuality of her ongoing greed, megalomania, and infinitely pathological effects on his personal stability. It was only after innumerable transactions in which she blackmailed him into turning over significant portions of his hard-earned equity that he began to believe I might be correct. With this partial emancipation, however, he developed an obesity problem matching his mother's own chronic corpulence.

As involvement with the mother diminished, there emerged a more complex picture of the father as a person whose distance from his wife and child was partly explained by his anxiety about intimacy and mutuality. In addition, he had been preoccupied both with the need to protect himself from his wife and with the serious illness which eventually proved fatal. With poignant feelings the patient recalled his adolescent efforts to become closer to his father, especially after the parents' divorce. He sought to be close not simply to learn from his father, but to provide him with a degree of comfort. A variant of this behavior occurred in the transference. It took the form of assuring himself that I was comfortable and untroubled about those aspects of my life of which he was aware. With respect to inquiries along these lines, he would become angry with my interpretive efforts, especially at those junctures when his "helpfulness" had become quite intrusive.

He recognized the morally based grandiosity that had led father to undertake a series of unwise business transactions toward the end of his life. These initiatives had involved confronting the local power structure of the community in order to expose the venality of their operations to the general public. Predictably, that power structure destroyed the father's wealth; moreover, humiliation to which he was subjected hastened his decline into early senility and death. The patient wondered how much he identified with this part of his father, thinking particularly of his morally implacable insistence on assaulting corruption in governmental regulatory bodies. Was he setting out to right the wrongs done his father only to end up repeating his father's defeats?

The specificity and uniqueness of empathic failures in the management of this man's transference can be illustrated by an incident six years into the analysis. I suggested I saw evidence in a dream of his beginning preparations for termination. In the dream he transcended certain long-standing anxieties attendant to his sexual relationships; more specifically, he was able to face more assertively the retaliatory threat he imputed to women. He disagreed with my interpretation of the dream, offering that it had something to do with transference. He then missed the next several hours, during which time he managed to lose approximately one-third of his amassed wealth. He quickly re-established his equilibrium, returned to analysis without my calling him, and joined me in searching for an understanding of my mistake. He decided that despite our years of work I still lacked enough of the "right sort" of experience with him to understand his concrete need to test and retest my reliability. Furthermore, he suggested that I perhaps did not recognize just how tired I had grown of the constant burden of using my best analytic capabilities to understand his chronic complaining and endless confrontations with reality problems.

Implicit in his explanation of my countertransference failure was the notion that my best analytic capabilities had not consistently been good enough. Coincidentally, this explanation of my failure mirrored a question I had earlier put to him to highlight the grave disparity between his increasing capacity to understand himself and his inability to value that understanding as a rational basis for future behavior. Concrete experience or intuitive, magiclike hunches had continued to have absolute priority in his ordering of the sources of self-knowledge. I asked him: "When are you going to feel self-confident enough to take the time necessary to mobilize your 30 extra I.Q. points and use them in an understanding, sophisticated, and planful way?" Buried within his parallel explanation of my countertransference failure was the issue of my ultimate capacity to tolerate his gradually increasing competitive competence; such competence pertained not simply to the accumulation of wealth (where there was no competition whatsoever!), but, more focally, to the utilization of rationally organized, secondary-process thinking on behalf of more constructive and mature efforts to influence his world.

During the seventh year, as he began to experience me more as the good father capable of standing up to the bad mother, he recalled his relationship with a good family servant during adolescence. He wondered about his serious difficulties in distancing himself from his intensely conflictful business transactions in order to observe more reflectively his own maladaptive behavior. Despite his anxiety at the thought of such elemental introspection, he was now struggling to value his intellect enough to protect himself from failure, even in my absence during vacation periods. In addition to spontaneous recognition of his method of "individuation by negation," he came to recognize serious interpersonal impediments to self-reflective efforts deriving from magical thinking based on identification with his mother. Intrusive, impulsive grandiosity abetted by physical size, screaming, and dreadful physical threats of harm were the essential ingredients needed to create an impression of competence and effectiveness in his world, and hence to guarantee compliance on the part of his objects. More ominously, screaming *was* competence; i.e., yelling automatically altered the course of events.

During this period (the eighth and ninth years) it became possible for him to note the kinds of problem-solving situations in which he preferred to ignore obvious evidence because of the complexity of factors involved, especially the presence of disparate elements which had to be evaluated, ordered, and harmonized in order to arrive at an appropriate decision. The parallel to what he experienced as his chronic state of protodisorganization was striking: better permanent opposition than permanent chaos.

Typically, he had spared himself such chaotic distress by ignoring those aspects of situations that simply seemed too paradoxical, contradictory, or unclear. Instead, he characteristically limited himself to a few large, obvious, and central evidential pieces in an interpersonal configuration, as if identification of them could reduce an entire transactional field to manageable proportions. He preferred to arrange things in simplified linear sequences wherein the gross, obvious pieces of a transaction became perceptually available to him at a concrete level. Yet, in so doing, he now recognized he was imitating his mother's constant charge to him: "You are a simpleminded fool, you cannot think logically." And, as a last desperate alternative, he would fall back on his own species of magical thinking in order to reach a decision.

It was the ultimate recourse to magical decision-making criteria that made him strikingly resistant to what he experienced as the intrusive counsel of others, including me, even when it paralleled what one part of his intellect was telling him. The implication was that the self-defining negativism around which he achieved integration and protected himself must have begun very early, probably preverbally, as a permanent organizing residue of the anal phase. This is a developmental period when normal childhood thinking is beset by persistent primary-process elements, utilized, together with negativism, in the service of establishing autonomy, achieving control, and formulating authentic aims.

Of this patient, we might modify Freud's famous remark in "The Interpretation of Dreams" (1900, p. 567) to the effect that "nothing but problems can set our mental apparatus at work." Yet, if he were to think and act realistically and effectively, it was crucial that he choose the situations that invited such secondary-process functioning, rather than have them imposed on him by unwelcome needs or outside agencies. Thus his performance in situations where the needs of others were at issue could be exemplary, provided that he volunteered for the situation, that his efforts were totally accepted, and that he could see in a "hands-on" way that his work was going to obviate an impending disaster. If the problem he was addressing was sufficiently outside of himself to preclude magical ideation, yet still resonated with one of his good-self nuclei to the point of mobilizing his values of helpfulness and responsibility, then his efforts could be ordered in an effective and logical way. Given these circumstances, this man's capacity for persistent personal efforts on behalf of others could be truly awesome. Among his relatives, friends, and professional colleagues, he was considered a "first-rate rescuer."

A fortuitous illness in the ninth year, typical of his recurrent attitudes toward his body, provided an opportunity to learn something of his difficulties in thinking about himself. The patient developed unclear pain somewhere in the region of his lower chest and right-upper abdomen which at first appeared to be gallbladder disease. His initial reaction alternated between denial and obsessive concern. As this ineffective defense faded in the face of persistent symptomatology, he became extremely anxious and disorganized and changed doctors impulsively and erratically. He continued to be unable to relate to his experts in a way that would enable him to organize their recommendations into meaningful choices; he could not get them to formulate a plan that he could understand and utilize.

A series of consultations at several major-medical centers ensued, but he could not deal effectively with any of the resulting recommendations. I suggested that his dilemma might have something to do with his mother's original inability to respond to him realistically: he was now relating to his physicians in a way that elicited a set of incompatible recommendations from them. The physicians seemed to present him with confusing feedback that the disorganized, crazy, infantile part of him secretly wished to hear, but which the sensible, adult part of him reacted to with anger, thereby making his rejection of them and their ideas doubly sure. He really did control his object's response to him in the same negative way he had controlled his mother's response: he acted like an enraged child who needed to be placated by an ambivalently controlling, but ultimately ineffective parent. Despite much resistance to this explanation, in which he identified with yet another version of his mother, he eventually accepted it to the point of being able to take medically appropriate steps. This progressive step, in turn, led to a fundamental reorganization of the now counterindicated indulgent activities which characterized his adult life.

The roots of his infantile omnipotence, his obsessive "problem orientation," his good-natured negativism as well as his lifelong fears of helplessness, body damage, and the uncertainty of the unknown became clearer to him during the several months we worked over aspects of this set of medical transactions. In the course of this analytic work, the major threat of logical disorganization and helplessness recurrently frightened him to the extent that he would lose what little capacity he had to think about his body in logically consistent and holistic terms. Omnipotent, pseudo-magical, and regressive processes would contaminate his thinking; that is, he would fall back on the maternal introject. It was in this context that he shame-facedly confessed as an absolutely firm conviction what he now knew to be pure fantasy: that weight loss was a state of mind, not so much dependent on how much one ate as on how much one exercised and how much one thought "correctly" about losing weight!

He then revealed another basic belief: my interpretations, his wife's concerns, and his mother's "solutions" were, in their respective spheres, more fundamentally reliable than his own—even though they were alien to him. He felt incapable of maintaining the continuity of his own thinking. Endlessly willing to dramatize his behaviors and feelings, he was not willing to assume responsibility for observing and describing in words the continuity of consciously available psychological events which led to those end-product behaviors and emotions. When pressed, he insisted that many of these emotions and behaviors, as deleterious as they might seem, were really in the nature of "conditioned responses." I told him that, while true, this was a defensive rationale. After nine years of analysis, he still feared the uncertainty of attending to conscious aspects of his own mental processing. Even more, he was fearful of what such self-observation would reveal. He wondered if the fear related to his realization of the implacable childhood need to embrace his mother's distorted view of reality. If he really observed his own conscious mental processes, he might learn that much of his thinking really was like hers: bizarre and magical. He suggested that, in the analytic relationship, he must have similar fears about overcoming the major impediment to the work of analyzing—i.e., his profound reliance on his magical thinking. If he gave it up, would he have to adopt the *analyst's* mode of logical thinking? Laughingly, he suggested that we had only been at work for nine years, and that I must not expect him to progress at the rate of other people. By the time another nine years had gone by, he mused, he might be carrying the work of the analysis in his own authentic way, without fear of intrusion, and requiring only occasional input from me!

Precisely at the time when he had begun to recognize how influential his projections were in determining his fate, a new crisis arose in his life. Based on a false estimation of the technical competence of a trusted associate, a series of errors went undetected in his business. When they came to light, a major financial crisis ensued, threatening the stability of all his enterprises. On this occasion, his anger was newly modulated, and was actually surpassed by his feelings of personal responsibility, guilt, and even some sadness. At one point he said,

> How could I have overlooked what was so obvious? How could I, once again, have re-enacted the *enfant terrible* self in such a "self-fulfilling-prophecy" manner. I must have unconsciously conveyed to this man that I expected him to act as if he really knew what he was doing, when, underneath, both of us really knew that he was incompetent for the task to which I had assigned him. But in a magical way, if I wanted him to be something that he wasn't, then "somehow" it would be so!

As he went about taking corrective action, a significant incremental shift occurred in the transference. He wondered spontaneously whether he had actually "set me up" along with himself, so that I could not possibly know what he was really doing, even though he expected me to. Once again, I was to be the failed father-rescuer. At the same time, he recognized that he had become very insistent that, since our work was more advanced, I *stop* treating him like an inept adolescent and desist from inquiring about the reliability of various judgments and his actions. In his words, as he observed,

> The real issue is my conflict about taking responsibility to observe consistently what I am doing. It is almost as if a part of me keeps insisting that since what I am doing is always reliable and perfect, I don't have to stand aside and observe myself. And I now realize that I don't really know how to do this! So instead I just retreat into an obsessive/omnipotent screaming binge—and then I'm really lost!

He began to disagree with me concerning aspects of the way he worked. In this context, he learned to distinguish his vulnerable childish behaviors from the reality of his actual adult resources and attributes. This opened the door to consideration of the existence of a nascent set of hierarchically organized adult aims of his own (Gedo, 1979). His capacity to anticipate flaws in his imperfectly predictable environment increased to the point where he could contain his periodic rage attacks, now humorously referred to as small earthquakes. As he expressed it in his own imagery, "When a calamity does occur the essential contours of the landscape remain intact despite the partial disruption of some of the surface features."

Concurrent with these changes of the past two years, his dreams began to alter. He reported them more regularly and worked with them more independently. Manifest content shifted away from situations, journeys, and nebulous interpersonal transactions (his typical metaphor) in which he tended to be the passive onlooker or victim of unclear forces. Transactions became better structured and more purposeful, individuals became more clearly defined and recognizable, and his own role shifted to that of initiator of action or principal participant. In one dream indicative of this evolution, his father took him to look at a building the father was preparing to buy. Father proudly displayed the building to his son, but the latter was troubled at evidence of subtle damage and argued with father. Associations had to do with the patient's ambivalence about confronting men he respected (or feared)—especially in the past—when it was clear he was privy to information or opinions contrary to their ideas. Eventually, this ambivalence was related to his disappointment with my delay in recognizing his efforts to warn me about a threat he was facing in one particular area of his life—and even more, his fear that I was about to "sell" him a distorted view of his improved status.

His basic tools, his more consciously accessible values, and his increasingly logical, reliable sense of himself all came to the fore during the most severe crisis he faced, the recently occurring fatal illness of his mother. Although she attempted to influence his behavior even after her death by the malevolently ambivalent plans that she fastened upon him via her will, he managed to maintain adequate equilibrium. Her loss led to a complex, lengthy, but reasonably well-managed period of disorganization. The sequel was a better working through of his now consciously recognized feelings about her fantasied strength and protectiveness, which he believed had sustained him over the years. The partial resolution that followed involved confronting the real, positive ties between the two of them. With this achievement his feelings of autonomy and personal peace increased. The analytic work continues, focusing on the need to make his analytic tools (especially cognitive processes uncontaminated by magic) more consistently available and authentic, and on further consolidation of the disparate elements of his new self.

## CONCLUSION: A DEVELOPMENTAL METAPHOR

The pathology underlying crises of deception and betrayal deserves to be considered among the more difficult amenable to psychoanalytic treatment. I have undertaken to explore this pathology genetically, dynamically, and structurally, suggesting that it is the earmark of a discrete character type, but may alternatively be viewed as a variant of one or more categories of character disorder current in the literature. In closing, I would highlight once more the developmental circumstances that seem to impart phenomenological specificity to this maladaptive life style. Developmentally, it is the mother who, during the presymbolic phase of development, serves as the primary interpreter of the child's world of reality, of self versus nonself, of the nature of self-boundaries, of the qualities that distinguish the world of reality from the world of imagination, and of the logical relations of cause and effect (Rocah, 1984). Insofar as the mother constantly deceives the child regarding aspects of reality, presenting him with logically impossible contradictions and rationalizations about herself, insofar as she prevents the child from organizing the world in a way that is at least partially authentic, individualized, and sensible, and insofar as she prevents the child from demonstrating to himself the reliability of his reality-testing tools—to this extent she in effect says to that child, "You must grow up as I grew up, not only with a fundamental flaw in your thinking about the relationship between women and penises, but with an equivalent flaw in your capacity to distinguish between (and yet harmonize) the inner world of the self with its subjective wishes and thoughts on the one hand, and the outer world of the nonself with its objective realities on the other." It was these mothers who became responsible for their sons' ominous inability to harmonize and integrate an unending series of splits in themselves, in their experience of objects, and in their capacity to know the world without the regulative presence of the mothers or their surrogates. Even with the assistance of a nuclear self organized around a sense of implacable morality, their capacity to cope with life's exigencies remained uncertain and restricted. Analysis was able to help considerably, but only within limits.

## REFERENCES

Adler, G. (1980), Transference, real relationship and alliance. *Internat. J. Psycho-Anal.*, 61:547–558.

Alexander, F. (1930), The neurotic character. *Internat. J. Psycho-Anal.*, 11:292–311.

Arlow, J. A. (1981), Theories of pathogenesis. *J. Amer. Psychoanal. Assn.*, 50:488–514.

——— (1982), Problems of the super-ego concept. *The Psychoanalytic Study of the Child*, 37:229–244. New Haven: Yale University Press.

Basch, M. A. (1977), Developmental psychology and explanatory theory in psychoanalysis. *This Annual*, 5:229–263. New York: International Universities Press.

——— (1981), Selfobject disorders and psychoanalytic theory: An historical perspective. *J. Amer. Psychoanal. Assn.*, 29:337–351.

——— (1982), Empathic understanding: Review of the concept and some theoretical considerations. *J. Amer. Psychoanal. Assn.*, 30:101–126.

Calef, V. & Weinshel, M. (1981), Some clinical consequences of introjection: Gaslighting. *Psychoanal. Quart.*, 50:44–66.

Ferenczi, S. (1913), Stages in the development of a sense of reality. In: *Sex in Psychoanalysis*. New York: Basic Books, 1950, pp. 213–239.

Freud, A. (1936), *The Ego and the Mechanisms of Defence*. New York: International Universities Press, 1946.

Freud, S. (1896), Further remarks on the neuro-psychoses of defence. *Standard Edition*, 3:159–185. London: Hogarth Press, 1962.

——— (1900), The interpretation of dreams. *Standard Edition*, 5:339–630. London: Hogarth Press, 1953.

——— (1905), Three essays on the theory of sexuality. *Standard Edition*, 7:125–145. London: Hogarth Press, 1953.

——— (1911), Formulations on the two principles of mental functioning. *Standard Edition*, 12:215–226. London: Hogarth Press, 1958.

——— (1926), Inhibitions, symptoms and anxiety. *Standard Edition*, 20:77–175. London: Hogarth Press, 1959.

Gedo, J. E. (1979), *Beyond Interpretation*. New York: International Universities Press.

——— (1981), *Advances in Clinical Psychoanalysis*. New York: International Universities Press.

——— & Goldberg, A. (1973), *Models of the Mind: A Psychoanalytic Theory*. Chicago: University of Chicago Press.

Goldberg, A. (ed.) (1978), *The Psychology of the Self: A Casebook*. New York: International Universities Press.

——— (1980), *Advances in Self Psychology*. New York: International Universities Press.

——— (1984), *The Future of Psychoanalysis*. New York: International Universities Press.

Gunderson, J. G. & Singer, M. I. (1975), Defining border-line patients: An overview. *Amer. J. Psychiat.*, 132:1–10.

Gunther, M. S. (1984), The prototypic archaic transference crisis. In press.
Hartmann, H., Kris, E., & Loewenstein, R. (1946), Comments on the formation on psychic structure. In: *Papers on Psychoanalytic Psychology Psychological Issues*, Monogr. 14. New York: International Universities Press, pp. 27–55, 1964.
Jacobson, E. (1959), The "exceptions"—an elaboration of Freud's character study. *The Psychoanalytic Study of the Child*, 14:135–159. New York: International Universities Press.
Kernberg, O. (1975), *Borderline Conditions and Pathological Narcissism*. New York: Aronson.
Khan, M. M. R. (1963), The concept of cumulative trauma. In: *The Privacy of the Self*. New York: International Universities Press, 1979, pp. 42–58.
Kohut, H. (1971), *The Analysis of the Self*. New York: International Universities Press.
——— (1972), Thoughts on narcissism and narcissistic rage. *The Psychoanalytic Study of the Child*, 27:360–400. New Haven: Yale University Press.
——— (1977), *The Restoration of the Self*. New York: International Universities Press.
——— Wolf, E. S. (1978), The disorders of the self and their treatment: An outline. *Internat. J. Psycho-Anal.*, 59:413–425.
Lichtenberg, J. D. (1981), The empathic mode of perception and alternative vantage points for psychoanalytic work. *Psychoanal. Inquiry*, 1:329–355.
Meissner, W. W. (1978), *The Paranoid Process*. New York: Aronson.
Modell, A. H. (1976), The "holding environment" and the therapeutic action of psychoanalysis. *J. Amer. Psychoanal. Assn.*, 24:285–307.
Newman, K. (1984), The capacity to use the object. In: *Psychoanalysis The Vital Issues vol II.* ed. G. H. Pollock & J. E. Gedo.New York: International Universities Press, pp. 149–176.
Ornstein, P. H. (1979), Remarks on the central position of empathy in psychoanalysis. *Bull. Assn. for Psychoanal. Med.*, 18:95–108.
Panel (1981), Masochism: Current concepts, N. Fischer, reporter. *J. Amer. Psychoanal. Assn.*, 29:673–688.
Pollock, G. H. (1961), Mourning and adaptation. *Internat. J. Psycho-Anal.*, 43:341–361.
Robbins, M. (1982), Narcissistic personality disorders as a symbiotic character disorder. *Internat. J. Psycho-Anal.*, 63:457–473.
Rocah, B. S. (1984), The origins of motivation. In: *Psychoanalysis The Vital Issues vol I.* ed. J. E. Gedo & G. H. Pollock. New York: International Universities Press, pp. 3–16.
Rothstein, A. (1980), Psychoanalytic paradigms and their narcissistic investment. *J. Amer. Psychoanal Assn.*, 28:385–395.
Schwaber, E. (1981), Empathy: A mode of analytic listening. *Psychoanal. Inquiry*, 1:357–392.
Segal, H. (1964), *Introduction to the Work of Melanie Klein*. New York: Basic Books.
Stolorow, R. & Lachmann, F. M. (1980), *Psychoanalysis of Developmental Arrests*. New York: International Universities Press.
Tolpin, M. (1978), Self-objects and oedipal objects: A crucial developmental distinction. *The Psychoanalytic Study of the Child*, 33:167–186. New Haven: Yale University Press.
Tolpin, P. (1980), The borderline personality: Its make up and analyzability. In: *Advances in Self Psychology*, ed. A. Goldberg. New York: International Universities Press, pp. 299–316.
Treurniet, N. (1983), Psychoanalysis and self-psychology, a metapsychological essay with a clinical illustration. *J. Amer. Psychoanal. Assn.*, 31:59–100.
Wangh, M. (1962), The "evocation of a proxy." *The Psychoanalytic Study of the Child*, 17:451–469. New York: International Universities Press.
Winnicott, D. (1949), Mind and its relation to the psyche-soma. In: *Collected Papers*. London: Tavistock Publications, 1958, pp. 243–252.
——— (1963), Psychiatric disorders in terms of infantile developmental process. In: *The Maturational Process and the Facilitating Environment*. New York: International Universities Press, 1965, pp. 230–241.

*August 1983*

# Loving Hate

## CHRISTOPHER BOLLAS, Ph.D. (London)

In Freud's early theory of the instincts love and hate were first conceived of as nonidentical twins. Love was that instinct that aimed to acquire pleasure and pleasurable objects, and hate was a counterinstinct: the drive to expel the unpleasurable into the outside world. "The ego hates, abhors and pursues with intent to destroy all objects which are a source of unpleasurable feeling for it," wrote Freud (1915, p. 138), equating hate with destruction. After a partial reworking of his instinct theory in "Beyond the Pleasure Principle" (1920) Freud incorporated love into the life instincts and placed hate in the service of the death instinct. At this point, therefore, hate had two potential functions; it could serve a mnemic purpose—*"to restore an earlier state of things"* (p. 36)—if considered a part of the death instinct, or, it could fulfill a purely expulsive-destructive function if conceived of according to the earlier instinct theory.

Psychoanalytic theory is not shy of references to destructive hate. Indeed, these days if we consider hate in object-relations theory, we assume a complex process whereby an internal object is damaged or destroyed and the ego is faced with the exceedingly daunting task of renegotiating internal reality in the wake of such hate. An internal object that is damaged by hate may lead to phobic withdrawal from the external representations of the object; it may lead to an addictively depressive state that amounts to a compromise formation between the wish to damage the object further and the dread of being attacked from within for such destructiveness. If the internal object is psychologically destroyed it may be expelled into fragmented objects that assume a bizarre quality (Bion, 1962).

When a person hates is it always true to say that he wishes *to destroy*? I am sure that most clinicians can find an exception to destructive hate in their clinical work, and in the spirit of what we find in our daily work,

221

rather than in the mainstream of our theory, I would like to examine certain forms of hate in a different light. It is my view that in some cases a person hates an object *not* in order to destroy it, but to do precisely the opposite: to *conserve* the object. Such hate is fundamentally nondestructive in intent, and, although it may have destructive consequences—in a larger sense it can be considered destructive—the aim of such hate may be to act out an unconscious form of love. I am inclined to term this "loving hate," by which I mean a situation where an individual preserves a relationship by sustaining a passionate negative cathexis of it. If the person cannot do so by hating the object he may accomplish this passionate cathexis by being hateable and inspiring the other to hate him. A state of reciprocal hate may prevail, but in the persons whom I shall describe such hate is singular: it is not genuinely mutual. The subject finds that only through hating or being hateable can he compel an object into passionate relating; thus, although two people in such circumstances may seem to have accomplished a reciprocity of hate, it is illusory, as the object is never assumed to be capable of genuine mutuality: even a mutuality of hate.

Viewed this way, hate is not the opposite of love, but a substitute. A person who hates with loving passion does not dread retaliation by the object; on the contrary, he welcomes it. What he does live in fear of is *indifference,* of not being noticed or seen by the other, and inspired hate or passionate hate is generated as an alternative to love which is assumed to be unavailable.

If we look at hate in this way, it should be clear that we are doing so within a context different from that of instinct theory. As this paper is written in memory of Heinz Kohut it will not come as a surprise that I am asking that hate be reconsidered within the framework of a psychoanalysis that uses the concept of the self as an organizing scheme. We need not be "self psychologists" to appreciate the extraordinary service Kohut has accomplished for psychoanalysis, because, like some of the bold theoreticians before him (Klein, Hartmann, Bion, Winnicott, and Lacan) he has inspired us toward new insights and different ways of viewing the same phenomenon. I do not think psychoanalysts will be surprised by anything I say in this paper; indeed, I rather expect many to say that hate of the kind that I write about is well-known to them in their clinical work. But our ability to say what we know to be true is often conditioned on a particular ambience, and in the case of my own clinical work, although I am in disagreement with some of the views of a Kohut or a Winnicott, I feel indebted to them for creating a new climate within the psychoanalytic movement.

The literature on the *positive* function of hate, or fundamentally nondestructive hate, is sparse. In Europe Winnicott was one of the first analysts to emphasize its positive functions. In an early paper on aggression (1936) he argues that "aggression is part of the primitive expression of love" (p. 205), and he further stresses that in the course of his ruthlessness an infant "does not appreciate the fact that what he destroys when excited is the same as that which he values in quiet intervals between excitements. His excited love includes an imaginative attack on the mother's body. Here is aggression as a part of love" (p. 206). Winnicott always saw aggression as a positive factor in human growth, frequently equating it with motility, and he would never have made it equivalent to hate. But in his work on the transitional object he makes it possible for us to imagine a form of hate which is positive; that intensely concentrated, aggressive use of a transitional object which is founded on the infant's knowledge and gratitude that the object will survive. The infant needs the object of his hate to survive attacks against it, and this object that is itself the trace of the mother's capacity to survive the infant's attack is carefully and jealously guarded by the infant against true destruction (against loss or actual change of state). Winnicott realized that each child *needs* to hate a safe object, since in so doing he can see the total experience of a certain kind of hate through to its completion. In attacking the object, the infant brings to bear, in reality, a self state that has been up to that point primarily internal, and as the object allows for this misuse of it, its capacity to survive is appreciated by the infant, who needs to externalize and to actualize his hate.

In 1940 Fairbairn wrote a profoundly insightful paper about the schizoid individual, who, because of his early experiences as an infant in relation to a particular kind of mother, regarded his love as destructive. Some schizoid defenses, therefore, aimed to isolate the individual from the other; more significantly, they were developed to prevent the schizoid person from either loving or being loved. Such an individual "may quarrel with people, be objectionable, be rude. In so doing, he not only substitutes hate for love in his relationships with his objects, but also induces them to hate, instead of loving him" (p. 26). By using hate in this manner the schizoid acts in a curiously "moral" manner. According to Fairbairn, "the moral motive is determined by the consideration that, if loving involves destroying, it is better to destroy by hate, which is overtly destructive and bad, than to destroy by love, which is by rights creative and good" (p. 27).

Balint (1951) regarded hate as a defense against primitive object love and archaic dependence, and Searles (1956) argued that vengefulness was both a defense against repressed grief and a covert means to maintaining an object tie. Pao (1965) said that one of the "ego syntonic uses of hatred" is that it allows the person to feel something, so that eventually "hatred may become an essential element from which one derives a sense of selfsameness and upon which one formulates one's identity" (p. 260). Stolorow (1972) added that there are certain patients who use hate as a defense against the "possibility of forgiveness" (p. 220) because to forgive would be to destabilize the person's evolved object world, one presumably constructed through hate.

There are other analysts who indicate in their work a sophisticated understanding of the ways in which hate serves specific functions of the self along potentially positive lines. But I am not attempting to view the literature, I am only suggesting in the above the outline of a tradition of looking at hate in something of a different way: associating hate more closely to love than to its radical opposite.

It is my view that different family environments bias a child's experience of and use of hate; thus, strictly speaking, there is no one particular family idiom that sponsors a loving hate. I intend to discuss different pathological family situations that I have reconstructed through analysis, but by no means do I claim these to be the only pathways to loving hate: I am sure there are many. Furthermore, it is worth bearing in mind that a discussion of pathology often precludes consideration of more "ordinary" forms of a phenomena. I am quite certain that in the natural course of affairs children hate their parents with a passion, lasting a few minutes or even hours, and that this hate aims to conserve the parental object, not to destroy it, so that the child can have the full course of pleasure in hating. There is an ordinary *need* to hate the loved object, one essential to the child's cumulative expression of self states that further enables him to feel a sense of personal reality in his lived life. That said, however, in the following clinical vignettes I will illustrate how loving hate emerged in the course of the history of different persons, and I intend to show what pathological purpose it served. It bears repeating that when I use the word "loving" I mean to suggest a passionate cathexis of an object, a "falling" into hate that constitutes a profoundly intense experience, in which the subject feels thereby merged with the object, and attempts to maintain an object relation through the terms of this fusion.

## "Well, He's a Pain in the Neck, But We Do Love Him."

We are all aware of that person who fashions for himself a rather unique aesthetic in his character by being an irritant, one whom we can predict will almost always prove to be difficult in a social situation, and one whom we are quite content to hate for a brief moment. And yet it would be untrue to say that we continue to hate this person; paradoxically, we may feel quite an affection for him. I can think, for example, of a friend who in many respects is a pain in the neck. If my wife and I invite him to dinner he will almost inevitably try to irritate at least one of us. After a journey to an exotic country where he basked in tropical luxury and returned to our English world with a magnificent tan he said to my wife: "The problem with men who have been living in England for a long time is that they no longer know how to be attractive to women. And look at *his* shape. He's fat and he doesn't stand like a man." Now, this comment most of the time would not bother me—that is, coming from him—but it just so happened that for the two weeks prior to seeing my friend, I had been trying to lose weight and I had been taking some exercise. This I had to do on an exercise bicycle which I could "ride" between patients. Ten minutes is not much, but it's better than nothing. Still, I recall during these rather pathetic "journeys" on my bike feeling a bit ridiculous and depressed that at mid-life things should have to come to this. I had, nonetheless, tried valiantly to convince myself that the results—being fit and trim—would compensate me for a newly acquired sense of the absurd. As it was, however, when I saw my friend, I was feeling rather handsome. This was not the moment when I wanted to hear about how I had degenerated, even if the jab was put in his ridiculous manner, but I am convinced that one of his talents is knowing when people feel vulnerable, and at that moment wading in and saying something that makes one want to kill him. And yet, in the moments that follow such an irritating encounter, it is possible to feel something like affection for him, a sort of "well, he sure has proved to be in good form!" Further, he does know something about oneself that borders on intimacy, and, since he tends to express affection through negative charm, one often knows his irksomeness for what it is. To be sure, now and then I do find myself asking why I keep seeing him, as he really can be maddeningly abrasive. (At the last dinner party he "ruined" a convivial discussion by informing us that we were all bourgeois dilettantes incapable of a genuine discussion of the very topics that we ourselves had raised. Of course, at *that* moment he was accurate, and we could have killed him!)

So it was with some additional interest that I discovered Paula, one of my patients, to be just such a person. She had a reputation among her friends for being outrageous, and in fact she was capable of setting one friend against another and of gossiping in a way that was moderately scandalous. I knew this about her from her accounts of her life, but for the first years of her analysis no meaningful aspect of this emerged within the clinical space. Looking back, I can see that her somewhat gigglish barks ("Ohhhhhh! You've got it *all* wrong! Oh, forget it. I'm just being bitchy. You are right, and I don't like the fact that you know so much about me") were designed to move me toward a more combative relation to her, and expressed a need on her part to be allowed unreasonable and troublesome behavior in the sessions.

She found it frustratingly difficult to be a troublemaker in the sessions because she was an analyzable person, was genuinely motivated to understand herself, and so, in an odd sort of way, being understood mitigated a full expression of a segment of herself. I understood her rather too well, or prematurely, and thereby denied her sufficient room in which to become a "bad character." But in the third year of her analysis she went through a series of personal crises in her private life that made her really quite dependent on me. Up until then she had always kept an almost exact emotional distance from me, and I was aware that she was keeping quite a bit of her internal life to herself. Now, as she became more dependent on me, she also became argumentative, loud, combative, and "unanalyzable." I was never in any doubt, however, that her bad behavior was an expression of loving hate. It became clear that as she began to fall in love with the other she felt herself in considerable danger and protected herself against this anxiety by developing her love along the lines of a negative intimacy. "Oh, you, you *would* say that"; "Oh, that's typical of *you*"; "On the way here, I was telling you about myself, but then, of course, *you* said to me . . ."; "What did you mean last week when you said . . . ? I suppose you meant the same thing you told me last year, which is just what you *would* say, isn't it! Why are you like this?": all of these "protests" revealed an intense preoccupation with me, a positive transference only partly, and ineffectively, negated by her use of hate.

Both of Paula's parents were greedy in needing to give to their child a certain kind of love. As a child she feared the intensity of parental affection, praise, and facilitative eagerness. Eventually, it seemed to us both that her difficult character was a defense against the fear of being consumed by her parents' love. So long as she was irascible—"Oh, you are a wretchedly uncooperative child!"—she could mitigate the intense need of her parents to have a wonderfully lovable offspring. To be difficult within the context of her family was a great relief. It was reassuring to find that she could be hateable, and she very carefully insured that she would develop into something of an eccentric, taking respite in her mother's warnings to friends—"Oh, don't expect Paula to warm to you, she's a rather *nasty* sort of little girl, aren't you, Paula?"—because she was insured against the parental need to extol her virtues and draw her into the depersonalized space of their idealized daughter. We can see how being hateful, if only in this modest, "pain-in-the-neck" way, may be a defense against the destructive valences of certain forms of love. Being hateful allowed Paula to conserve a sense of self, whereas being lovable would have jeopardized the integrity of her own identity.

It is also possible to see how in the transference Paula spoke to me rather like her mother spoke to her. It is not without irony that this seemingly rejecting mother was the safer object, while the all-embracing mother was worrying. In being the hateable object Paula identified with the rejecting element in the mother's character, a part of the mother that she could actually use and rely upon: the mother who does accept and cognize rejection and has some capacity for differentiated living. By being a difficult child Paula brought out certain latent features in the mother's personality, in particular mother's narcissistic anger: "Oh, the hell with you, if you don't want me, then just *be* difficult." It is *this* mother that Paula *can* love. It is this mother with whom Paula can identify, so that we can see how her eccentric character, in which she cultivates being a pain in the neck to her friends, is both a reflection of what she brought out in the mother and that part of the mother with which she was able to identify. This is a positive use of hate, if we take into consideration the peculiar circumstances of this family's idiom. It allows in this instance for a child to enjoy qualified love of the partly differentiated mother.

## "Oh, Thank God We Hate Each Other. I Feel So Free."

From Jane I have learned of another form of loving hate. Not content to be a pain in the neck, she has sought out a partner who will reciprocate her passion for destructive activity. She and Charles typically enjoy a few days of quite intense affection for one another. He brings her flowers, she cooks him wonderful meals, they have a lazy Sunday reading through the day's newspapers, they go to the movies and enjoy discussing the film, and they make love with considerable passion. Then after a few days of this each of them seems to feel slightly uncomfortable with the way things are going. "Too good to be true" shifts imperceptively into "it's not true to be so good." Jane feels a sense of oppression after a spell of getting on well with Charles. She has a sense of reliving that destiny set for her in her childhood when she was the family's "nice" girl, who would, according to her mother's oft-verbalized dream, "marry a nice man." For a substantial period of her childhood she was oppressed by her own premature ego development (James, 1960) which evolved into a false-self disorder by latency. As a model child she cannot recall ever having been a problem to either parent, and in adolescence she most certainly would either have become suddenly delinquent or had a breakdown were it not for the fact that both parents (as we shall see) acted this out for her.

Jane was never in doubt about why she needed to hate Charles. If everything was too good to be true from her point of view, then she would undo the sense of impending doom by becoming outrageously contentious and inspiring an almighty row with her partner. By hating Charles with a passion and by being hateable in turn, Jane felt more fully established as a person *and* more fully exhibited. It was as if she were saying: "Here I am, mother: look at me! *Look!*" And watching the externalization of hate was a significant feature of Jane and Charles's festivals of black passion. Standing in the kitchen, Charles would watch as she would pick up a dish and with careful and deliberate aim throw it at him. She would watch as he, in turn, would fill a cup full of water and with equally measured accuracy pitch it at her. Sometimes crying, sometimes screaming, and often laughing, in a short period of time they would almost destroy their flat. Exhausted, they would collapse on the bed or on the floor, leave each other alone for a period of time (it varied from a few minutes to a few hours), and then make up.

When she first reported these incidents to me Jane did so with considerable embarrassment. She expected that I would disapprove. Instead I said on first hearing about this, "It seems that you enjoy these fights"; and, in great relief, she said: "I do. I don't know what I would do if he couldn't hate me the way he does. It's such a relief! And he is so sweet. Even when he throws things at me I love him. But I love hating him too. I need to do it. I couldn't stand it otherwise."

Jane came from a family which prided itself on its calm and rational approach to life. Each member of this rather large family was quite an apparent extrovert, and as a group they threw themselves into shared interests, hobbies, and adventures (such as moving from one country to the next). Their ostensible individual strength and their collective heartiness were sufficient for quite some time to conceal an underlying inability to achieve intimacy. If any member of the family was in distress or trouble, the difficulty would be known only through the reports of persons outside the group. Jane can remember feeling terribly oppressed by the family's nature, and one day, or week, or month, when the entire system collapsed she experienced the family breakdown with mixed feelings. When the parents had a ferocious row and the children felt a collective paralysis, as they heard accusations being thrown back and forth between mother and father, Jane can recall feeling both terrified *and* relieved. A sense of "my God, what is happening, and how are we going to survive this?" was countered with another feeling: "Thank God, I am not the only one who feels this whole system stinks. They do, too!"

In a very brief period of time the marriage was over, the father left, married a person totally different from his previous wife, and Jane's mother changed from being an energetic and outgoing woman to a frenzied and

vengeful person who was determined to get even with "that son of a bitch."
In some ways both parents acted out and expelled a family false-self system,
but Jane could not participate in this primitive actualization of other parts
of the self, as she was then absorbed in looking after her mother, who
continuously asserted, "You children, God bless you, are all that I have in
this world."

At her parental home, Jane is still a model person. She cannot get angry
with her mother or father, and she fails to establish any of her own privately
developed interests if they meet with parental opposition. It is only in her
relation to Charles, and in the clinical space, that she can express the
primitive parts of herself.

Her need occasionally to love Charles with passionate hate amounts to
an unsuccessful but partial attempt to fuse love and hate, and to bring
unintegrated areas of the self into greater proximity to "one" another.
What she dreads is being captured into becoming that false self of her
childhood to which she reverts when she is with her family of origin.
Passionately expressed hate reassures her that she isn't capitulating into a
compliant self, and Charles's participation in loving hate insures the rights
of the infant self to be heard or expressed within the adult world. It hardly
needs saying that this solution is pathological, but I am intentionally avoiding further elaboration of the other aspects of this case in order to focus
on how loving hate can both conserve the integrity of the self and keep
object relating alive and true.

## "At Least I Can Hate You—You're All I've Got."

George's hate is comprised of an intensely nourished feeling that he is
neglected by people. He records each moment of slight with meticulous
care and takes considerable pleasure in storing such evidence to use against
the offending object in some imagined eventual confrontation. At the same
time, his microscopic observation of the other's disposition toward him does
give him a *certain* knowledge of the other's personality, and, at times, he
is aware of the nonmalignant, even good, portions of the other's being.
Such recognitions are distressing to him, and he often attempts to rid
himself of such perceptions.

George desires to hate the other because in so doing he experiences a
particular sensation in his own being that is the oldest feeling he knows
and the internal experience that has been most prevalent during the course
of his lifetime. In loving to hate someone he feels a sense of place; it is
always where he has lived, and he has told me that it also provides him
with specific erotic feelings. When he is "hating" someone he feels a very

particular sensation, a tension between his scrotum and his anus. I believe this registers that period of his childhood, specifically the transition between anal sadism and phallic narcissism, when he felt intensely impotent in his relation to his mother. The patient is, in fact, manic-depressive, and has had several psychotic episodes and one serious breakdown. During his manic phases he feels an increase in loving hate, as if he were empowered with the destiny of millions, and he feels the source of the power, on occasion, to be that sensation between the anus and the scrotum—the place of his developmental arrest. The grandiosity that seems to emerge when he feels a sensation in that area of his body is, in my view, a compensatory regressive denial of a sense of impotence.

In the course of his analysis it became clear that his intimate knowing of a hated other, often giving rise to feelings of déjà vu, was, of course, composed of his own projections. This other *has* to be made up of split-off parts of the self, because in George's case, the mother's absence in his early life did not give him sufficient sense of the other to facilitate generative introjections. A generative introjection is one in which the infant takes in a part of the mother, so that when it is linked up internally with a drive, and when the infant reprojects the introject, it matches up with the intrinsic characteristics of the mother, thus enabling the child to feel in some form of harmony with the outside world. George had to construct the mother out of a vacuum—rather than introject that which was there—and as her absences were so frequent, that which George tended to project into the mental space of "mother" were those moods in himself that were created by her absences. We can say that if a mother is an insufficient selfobject—and in George's case the mother was a withdrawn and depressed woman who avoided maternal care by immersing herself in her professional life—then the child must form some kind of alternate selfobject that is most likely to be composed of projected self states, such as isolation, despair, helplessness, frustration, and rage. In forming an object that contains these affects (Bion, 1962) the child constructs an object through loving hate. He dreads desertion, and although he may feel intense hate for the mother, he also treasures her, as she is all he has.

In that loving hate that characterizes George's contemporary object relations, he aims to make the object indebted to him forever. He looks forward to that day when the other acknowledges wrongdoing. The wish is not for justice. The wish is for a confession that gives the subject unconditional license to regress into dependency upon the other. As I have suggested, the ultimate aim of this form of hate, therefore, is a kind of loving merger with the object. This is why the hated object must not be destroyed—indeed, why it must be protected against true harm. George was, in fact, a staunch defender and protector of his mother, and for the first year of his analysis he rarely talked about her except in glowing terms. But these positive feelings suddenly collapsed quite dramatically, revealing a very private and secretive hateful relation to her. He really knew very little about her but insisted upon maintaining a sense of intimacy through detailed observations of her which filled him with private loathing. Not a courtly love. A courtly hate.

## The Negative Selfobject

In addition to the examples I have given above it is possible to talk about one other, exceedingly common, expression of loving hate in the clinical setting. I will not give a case example, but instead I will discuss the intent of that person who seeks to be an irritant to the analyst—to get under the analyst's skin—in order to compel the analyst to hate him. An example of this is unnecessary, as anyone who has been practicing for any length of time will know this situation only too well. For there are certain persons who feel that until the analyst can hate them, and until they can see evidence of such hate, there is a risk that they will never have been known. It is through hate, evoked in the analyst, that this kind of person seeks to achieve his sort of intimacy with the clinician. It is when the clinician's steady state of mind and even temper break down under the weight of the patient's negativity that the analysand takes hope; for it is *there*, in that moment when he sees the analyst's hesitation, or senses his frustration, that he feels himself in rapport with the analyst. In that state there is a sense of merger with the analyst, whose even-mindedness until then—even when he is being empathic and sympathetic—has felt like a refusal, a rebuff.

This person wants to convert the analyst into a negative object. He aims to find his double in the analyst's confusion and anger. If he can match his frame of mind with the analyst's frame of mind, then he has constructed a negative selfobject, an object not differentiated from himself, but carrying his projections and identifications. Although as far as I know Kohut intended his term "selfobject" to be used for those psychic situations in which no differentiation exists between self and object, the sort of person I am describing does recognize difference. It is more accurate to say, perhaps, that these people seek to convert a differentiated object into a nondifferentiated one, and this is accomplished through loving hate. Each of the objects is in fact split according to corresponding splits in the ego: one part of the individual recognizes the object's independence, while another part of the ego assumes self and object to be fused. It is only when negative selfobjects are formed that they feel in rapport with the other. A differentiated object is in some ways a lost object or a nonobject.

Such people are object seekers, even if that which they find or create is a negative selfobject. It is my view that the concept of the death instinct, insofar as hate is concerned, should be reserved for those individuals who seek to destroy objects in order to live in an objectless world. I do think there is a form of hate that can be identified as in the service of a death instinct, and I am of the view that certain forms of autism in children reflect this wish to annihilate the object world in order to be returned to the preobject world.

Some families are fundamentally cold and unloving. For varying reasons the parents find it next to impossible either to love their children, or more to the point, to demonstrate their love and also their lovableness. A child who is raised in a milieu of this kind discovers that his loving impulses and gestures are not mirrored in a positive way by the parent. The child's ordinary positive aggression and love are not validated by the parent. Instead such parents may interpret the child's aggressive libidinal cathexis of themselves as an insult or as an indication of a moral defect. These people may be exceedingly rigid, or very religious, or particularly sour in their being. Whatever the reason for the nature of their own family style, such parents refuse to celebrate their children and instead are constantly finding fault with them and in some cases seem drawn to conflict. Gradually, the child loses his belief in love and in loving. Instead, ordinary hate establishes itself as the fundamental truth of life. The child experiences the parents' refusal of love and their constant aloofness or harshness as hate, and he or she in turn finds his or her most intense private cathexis of the parents to be imbued with hate.

To some extent such children sense a need to hate in the parent. Disinclined, perhaps, to tamper with such a system, and curiously reassured by being the object of such intense cathexis, such children may become consistently hateful. To be cathected by a parent, even to the point of becoming a reliable negative selfobject for him or her, is a primary aim for such children, as their true dread is that of being unnoticed and left for dead.

When a person's hate is destructive of his internal objects, we know that the emptiness he feels is more than often due to his destructive activity. With his internal objects mangled or useless, there is nothing of value left, and he will feel only the deadness of the annihilated objects or the emptiness of an evacuated space. The precise opposite is true, however, of those persons I am discussing. Children who are reared by cold and unloving parents find that hate is a form of object relation, and they hate the object in order not to destroy it, but to preserve and maintain it. Hate emerges not as a result of the destruction of internal objects, but as a defense against emptiness. Indeed, it represents an effort to emerge from this vacuum into object relating.

Such children may suffer from a kind of *vacuum anxiety*, a state created by intense isolation. Affective life is so meager that objects are only dimly cathected. Such a person has a sense of losing the remnants of psychic life, of fearing the termination of affective existence altogether. Although this anxiety may have different causes and may evolve in different ways according to varying ego defenses, such an individual finds that by annoying someone or by inspiring hate in the other he has been provisionally guaranteed a psychic life.

## Retrospective Mirroring

There is another form of family idiom that sponsors a particular kind of hate. Some families are emotionally shallow. The parents may be unusually concerned with creating a "happy family." A certain kind of superficial support is provided, but core emotional issues are avoided and channeled through a kind of pseudo sublimation. In the last few years I have had the opportunity to supervise cases in three countries: England, Italy, and the United States, in Orange County, California. This is not the place to explore the differences in patient populations, but I mention these locales because psychotherapists working in Orange County face an unusual and startling kind of clinical situation. They receive in their consulting rooms people who have been reared by parents who have performed a kind of cliché-ridden, transformational-object function. If a child is acting out some distress, a parent might typically say, "That's not done here," or "Cut it out right now." Since there is no effort to investigate why the child is misbehaving, the behavior is never allowed a symbolic elaboration, as in an explanation to the mother. Instead the families rely upon stereotypical speech patterns to control the children. As such, these patients report family clichés as if they were life-defining categories, and in their own relation to themselves as objects of perception and interest, they are unusually impoverished. They *cannot elaborate* an internal experience. If asked how they feel they are surprisingly inarticulate and will resort to a cluster of clichés, such as, "Uh, I dunno, I'm kind of down," or "I've had it, you know, I'm going to be number one now." Although the clinicians know what the person means, or at least can make a fairly good guess, language does not serve to communicate, but instead to discharge the self of tension. Thus an effort to inquire about why someone doesn't feel himself to be "number one" anymore yields only further substitutive clichés.

Instead such people resort to fairly catastrophic actions. If angered by a friend they may "write him off." If a love relation goes wrong they can find another partner with comparative ease, and they can do so amid a culture that supports the replacement of an old part(ner) with a new one. Beneath the surface of an affluent culture (and I should say that the clinical problem these patients pose is all the more startling as they are often materially wealthy and have almost all they desire) there is a seething rage. Although they can be almost compulsively friendly, bidding one another multiple "have a nice day"(s), they can suddenly break out of this extraordinary friendliness into violent rage. One does not get the impression that they have the ego ability to cope with their own aggression and with narcissistic injury, and certainly even the cultural group therapy they provide for one another in the form of encouraging words—i.e., "take care, now,"—is insufficient to cure them of breakdown.

True love was never a real possibility for such people given the nature of their family life and the ethos of the culture. In subtle ways the parents did not provide enough characterological presence for the child to settle his loving feelings. Provided with almost any material object they could hope for, and utilizing the open air of Southern California, as children they are channeled into contact with the nonhuman object world. They become outdoor people, and even when they exist indoors they are often found to be gazing at the TV, which is another form of looking outside. As curiosity about oneself or the other is not encouraged, the children become deficient in techniques of ordinary insight and self-reflectiveness.

It is curious, then, that parental anger and the sudden emergence of hate may be the only deep experiences in which parent and child are mutually engaged. They rarely take place during childhood, but are exceedingly commonplace in adolescence, when conflict with a parent can create an atmosphere of fear and violence. Typically, the family atmosphere, which has previously been superficially harmonious, breaks down. An early adolescent discovers that his mother has become furious with him. An overly normal mother or exceptionally composed father might all of a sudden, when angry, say things otherwise deleted from the family vocabulary and the family's sense of its own being. In order to feel increased contact with the parent, the child may cultivate hate. For in doing so, he discovers that the parents will give signals about their private and often confused experience of their offspring.

In one case, for example, an eleven-year-old girl angered her mother by not minding. This led the mother to call her a selfish little bitch, an outburst which surprised the girl, but which also excited her. In this instance she had caught mother out of her ordinary self. She knew that to push mother more would yield both more of mother and more of mother's experience of herself as daughter. Using the veil of innocence by appearing oblivious to mother's reason for being cross, the child inspired the mother to recall many previous occasions when the child had annoyed her. Again the child experienced this interchange with mixed feelings. The mother's response was rather frightening, but it was also exciting, and beyond that it was interesting. For in mother's enumeration of all the times when she felt internally critical of her daughter, her child found images of herself within the mother. This recollection of the child is a form of *retrospective mirroring*. Retrospective mirroring is an ordinary form of object relation. Reflecting with a child on his or her past (selves) gives a child a chance to see how he was and to keep in touch with this phenomenon we call "self." But retrospective mirroring may be the only form of feedback that a child gets from a parent about his specific nature; when a parent lists observations about the child, a child has the sense of having been seen by the parent, which is an unusual, and gratifying, experience in itself. This need to feel seen may be so compelling that a child can continue to exacerbate parental hate just to have negative intimacy and retrospective mirroring.

Erikson's concept of "negative identity" (1968) is not unrelated to the formation of a negative selfobject and the abuse of retrospective mirroring. He claims that negative identity is "perversely based on all those identifications and roles which, at critical states of development, had been presented to them as most undesirable or dangerous and yet also most real" (p. 174). It is not difficult to see how a late adolescent may assume a negative identity in order to be what his parents have dissociated from human life, and he may compel the parent to act out aspects of his own negative identity. In so doing, he urges the parent to become a negative selfobject, one in which there is little psychological differentiation between the teenager's hate and the parent's hate. In such an interaction the teenager may feel strangely closer to his parent than ever before, and the parent may wish to rid himself of the adolescent not because he cannot bear his behavior, but because he cannot bear the intimacy of the relationship and refuses the claim being made by the child for such closeness.

## Loving Hate: A Perversion?

Certainly, those persons who are drawn toward being hateable and who cultivate the passion of hate alert us to the possibility of a perverse object relation. Stoller (1976) has argued convincingly that perversion is the erotic form of hate and in assessing whether an object relation is perverse or not one must ascertain whether or not the subject desires to harm the other. Is this the aim of loving hate: to harm the other? It certainly looks to be the case. We can add that as loving hate appears to be a singular mode of cathecting the object the range of affects is impoverished, thus alerting us to another feature typical of the perversions. Finally, we can point to the stereotypical and repetitive nature of loving hate; it seems that the person aims to create an object relation through an affect rather than to find an object and develop affective life in harmony with graduated intimacy. Does this not suggest a dehumanization of the object, a point which Khan (1964) stresses in his definition of perversion as a drive to alienate the object from true contact with one's inner life?

In my view we are once more called upon to ask whether the outcome of a psychic activity necessarily defines the intent. For it is true to say that the forms of hate I have discussed and term "loving hate" *may* harm the other or alienate the other. But Stoller and Khan are careful to define the perverse as the *intention* to harm or to distance the object, and it is my view that the primary aim of loving hate is to get closer to the object. Further, we know that in the perversions the subject uses an unconscious or derived scenario to close down the possibility of surrender to affective life, while in loving hate the person is surrendering to affect, even if this giving in is to the passion of hate.

## Conclusion

I have endeavored to explore a particular kind of hate that is primarily characterized by the wish to conserve rather than to destroy the object, and by the drive to involve another in a passionate form of relating, even if such desire is fulfilled through the cultivation of negative experiences. It is my view that we have given insufficient attention to this form of hate, although analysts are increasingly examining the countertransferences occasioned by working with such individuals (Feiner, 1979; Symington, 1983; Coltart, 1983; Bollas, 1983).

## REFERENCES

Balint, M. (1951), On love and hate. In: *Primary Love and Psychoanalytic Technique*. London: Tavistock Publications, pp. 121–135.
Bion, W. (1962), Learning from experience. In: *Seven Servants*. New York: Aronson, pp. 1–111.
Bollas, C. (1983), Expressive uses of the countertransference. *Contemp. Psycho-Anal.*, 19:1–34.
Coltart, N. (1983), "Slouching towards Bethlehem": Thinking the unthinkable in psychoanalysis. Unpublished ms.
Erikson, E. H. (1968), *Identity*. London: Faber & Faber.

Fairbairn, W.R.D. (1940), Schizoid factors in the personality. In: *Psychoanalytic Studies of the Personality*. London: Routledge and Kegan Paul, 1952, pp. 3–27.

Feiner, A. H. (1979), Countertransference and the anxiety of influence. In: *Countertransference*, ed. L. Epstein & A. H. Feiner. New York: Aronson, pp. 105–128.

Freud, S. (1915), Instincts and their vicissitudes. *Standard Edition*, 14:111–140. London: Hogarth Press, 1957.

—— (1920), Beyond the pleasure principle. *Standard Edition*, 18:3–64. London: Hogarth Press, 1955.

James, M. (1960), Premature ego development. *Internat. J. Psycho-Anal.*, 41:288–294.

Khan, M.M.R. (1964), Intimacy, complicity and mutuality in perversions. In: *Alienation in Perversions*. London: Hogarth Press, 1979, pp. 18–30.

Pao, P.-N. (1965), The role of hatred in the ego. *Psychoanal. Quart.*, 34:257–264.

Searles, H. (1956), The psychodynamics of vengefulness. In: *Collected Papers on Schizophrenia and Related Subjects*. New York: International Universities Press, pp. 177–191.

Stoller, R. J. (1976), *Perversion*. London: Harvester Press.

Stolorow, R. D. (1972), On the phenomenology of anger and hate. *Amer. J. Psychoanal.*, 32:218–220.

Symington, N. (1983), The analysts act of freedom as agent of therapeutic change. *Internat. Rev. Psycho-Anal.*, 10:283–291.

Winnicott, D. W. (1936), Appetite and emotional disorder. In: *Through Pediatrics to Psychoanalysis*. London: Hogarth Press, 1975, pp. 33–51.

*January 1984*

# Behind the Mask of the Persecutor: The Idealized Selfobject

JOHN M. HALL, M.D. (Cincinnati)

> The force that through the green fuse
> drives the flower
> Drives my green age; that blasts the roots
> of trees
> Is my destroyer
> —Dylan Thomas

## Introduction

The patient whose case will be discussed below once said: "I remember an old college professor telling us that love and hate are very close. Well, I know for sure that love can turn to hate. But I don't think, I don't know, if hate can turn to love." In its essence, this paper is about just such a transformation.

Kohut (1971) suggested that it would be valuable to general theoretical understanding to compare and contrast "the relatively healthy elaboration of a narcissistically cathected omnipotent and omniscient, admired and idealized, emotionally sustaining parent imago in the transferences formed by patients with narcissistic personality disturbances with the all-powerful persecutor and manipulator of the self in the psychoses: the influencing machine whose omnipotence and omniscience have become cold, unempathic, and non-humanly evil" (p. 8). What follows is a much more limited, though related endeavor: to explore one particular, central, vivid experience of a patient that appears to demonstrate the rather sudden transformation of a fantasized persecutor into the sharply focused image of an

239

idealized parental figure. In this rapid shift of psychic reality there occurred a concomitant breakthrough of a sense of well-being and revitalization.

To set the stage for this exploration, the case will be briefly reviewed and discussed. Then a careful examination of this acute transformation in the patient's self-experience, set in the context of an emerging idealizing transference, will follow. This is the pivotal point of the essay because it is on the basis of such an examination of the patient's "central" experience (brief as it was) that a unique, complementary, and, perhaps, generalizable relationship between the idealized selfobject and the persecutor can be formulated. Furthermore, it will also be suggested that, without evoking the ubiquitous, and at times, experientially distant projection and introjection defense mechanisms, it is quite possible to construct a mechanism of paranoia based primarily on the principles of self psychology. Finally, the clinical understanding and usefulness resulting from these efforts will be examined.

## Case Material

Mr. Drew, a blond, balding, athletic man, married and in his mid-thirties, started once-a-week psychotherapy after being convicted of embezzlement and placed on probation. He was an intense, angry man with low self-esteem since early adolescence and a sense of aimlessness and restlessness about his life and what to do with it. He also had an all-pervasive, consuming, and particular preoccupation with his father and his father's anger and power. Mr. Drew's chronic depression lifted somewhat after he had embezzled his company's funds, only to become intensified once again when he was arrested and prosecuted. For him, his stealing was an act of justified revenge against the company's owner who, he felt, had used him and treated him unfairly. Yet, despite this justification, he saw the theft as a stupid, shameful act that hurt his family, his wife, his children, and himself; he was deeply confused and puzzled by his behavior.

Mr. Drew was born and grew up in a New England city where his father had been a well-known police official. He had one sibling, a brother four years younger. After his father's death some years ago, Mr. Drew moved to the Midwest hoping for a fresh start. In the early phases of treatment Mr. Drew's memories of his father seemed to cluster around two periods in his life. As a young boy (ages four to five), Mr. Drew recalled looking up to his father and being proud of him. He would wait by the front door for hours, or so it seemed, ready to greet his father in his father's much-admired policeman's uniform. It is not too surprising that during these early years he wanted to be a policeman when he grew up. However, throughout his later childhood and adolescence, Mr. Drew saw his father in quite a different light. He described him as an "unyielding disciplinarian" who rarely spared the ruthless use of the rod. One particular beating stood out in Mr. Drew's mind. It happened in his early adolescence; he could not recall his "crime" but added, "The usual crime was not being perfect enough for my dad." After his father beat him black and blue and then beat him some more for crying, his parents left for the evening. Mr. Drew was all alone. With much embarrassment in the telling, he described retrieving his father's belt, lying down on the cold bathroom floor, and relentlessly giving himself another severe beating. Despite all the additional welts, he felt "strangely" soothed by doing this.

After Mr. Drew had a severe bout of hepatitis, his father repeatedly complained that this disease would stunt his son's growth. When Mr. Drew started wearing glasses, his father made him take them off whenever he was around him, particularly in public. After his father saw Mr. Drew limping off the field in a high-school football game, he left the stands in a hurry. Later he told his son: "You were disgusting with your little hurt knee. I have known guys that played with broken legs." With the recall of these memories, plus many more of the same ilk, Mr. Drew's hurt and rage explicitly centered on his father. However, implicit in the telling of these memories was an ever-present dread that he could repeat these painful feelings in his experiences with the therapist. He said very little about his mother; she seemed like a distant, almost nonexistent figure. He also hardly spoke of his brother who apparently was much more successful in his ability to please their father than the patient was. For Mr. Drew, the specter of his father always seemed to rise above everyone else in the family.

Mr. Drew described being painfully self-conscious most of his life; he made repeated unsuccessful attempts to complete college and was unsuccessful in many work situations as well. These endeavors, which he could not sustain, were always connected with the wish that his father would "finally" give him some recognition. However, only rarely did he get even a modicum of gruff praise from his father. In the face of his realistic failures and his internal turmoil, he began soothing himself with fantasies of great wealth. He imagined finding bountiful treasures and then would elaborate in his mind, in great detail, how he would use these fortunes. He would surround himself with rare works of art and would surely be admired by great men. He once commented: "I've always been possessed by others' possessions. Wealth gives people such importance." These fantasies were often coupled with fantasies of revenge. If he were wealthy, those who had slighted him would have to respect him, look up to him. Like a latter-day Monte Cristo, he imagined stealing the wealth of individuals who had hurt him or else wrecking their lives with the clever use of his money. In fact, many of Mr. Drew's elaborate fantasies, as well as his belief—with self-righteous overtones—that stealing was justified revenge, all seem to fit the "Monte Cristo" complex as described by Castelnuovo-Tedesco (1974).

At times of great turmoil and confusion, and particularly after experiencing empathic failures on the part of his therapist, Mr. Drew felt compelled to go to pornographic bookstores and look at pictures of naked, powerful, well-endowed men; he described such experiences as sexually exciting and—at the same time—settling. On occasion, and again often after "disappointing" therapy sessions, the patient would steal expensive bottles of wine by covering the price stickers on these bottles with the price stickers from cheap ones. He felt a thrill in getting away with something of value. He also jogged and swam vigorously, but almost always in a very driven, joyless way. Mr. Drew felt that without exercise he wouldn't get enough oxygen to his brain or be able properly to "cleanse" his body. Preoccupied by similar hypochondriacal concerns, he took large doses of various vitamins that would supposedly facilitate thinking, potency, and calmness, etc.

As. Mr. Drew's therapy progressed, there were more and more manifestations of transference reactions indicative of idealizing yearnings and the resistances to such yearnings. Concomitant with this, the patient noted an increasing sense of well-being and a waning of hypochondriacal thoughts. It was during this pivotal phase of therapy leading up to the "central" experience that Mr. Drew recalled with some surprise how he had had a particularly good week since the previous session. He then immediately presented two dreams. In the first dream he is talking to a fatherly psychiatrist in the "eleventh hour" who gives him some advice that burrows into his soul. The scene changes, and Mr. Drew finds himself talking with ease to people who usually "made him" tense and uncomfortable. In the second dream, he at first feels trapped and dizzy. The scene changes again, and suddenly he feels calm, "down to earth," while talking to his psychiatrist who appears as a holy man dressed in priestly garb.

These two dreams can be considered as self-state dreams reflecting the mobilization and effective engagement of an idealizing transference. In the first dream, the presence of the idealized selfobject-therapist allows Mr. Drew to feel good about himself. The "eleventh hour" signifies his hope that it's still not too late, that there is a belated chance to experience something important in his therapy that he had missed in his development. The number eleven also referred to the date of the previous treatment hour. In the second dream, narcissistic equilibrium is achieved in connection with the selfobject. Perhaps the "holiness" here reflects not only his idealization of the therapist but also his own aspiration to feel like a "whole" man. For it was during this very session that Mr. Drew noted a change in an almost daily preoccupation. In the past he would often imagine his father looking down from heaven, berating him and shaming him. He *now* felt that his father was perhaps, once in a while, looking down from heaven and feeling proud of him. The patient added, "When I think of that, I feel whole and good."

Mr. Drew cancelled the next week's session, ostensibly because it was the only time he could close a big sale with a very important, wealthy client. During the next regular session he presented the following dream:

He is walking with an old police sergeant (in actuality, a friend of his father's who paid special attention to Mr. Drew as a child). They are holding hands, and Mr. Drew is at peace. Soon this idyllic scene changes, and the two of them are being chased by bad guys and working very hard to stay ahead of them. He and the sergeant board a train, but the bad guys manage to do the same. In the next scene they are sitting in a compartment, and the bad men are approaching. The patient is frightened, but he can't wake the sergeant who has fallen into a deep sleep. Maybe he is even dead. When the bad guys arrive on the scene, the patient demands money from these men. At this point there is some confusion. It's not clear whether Mr. Drew is stealing the money ($51,000) or recovering stolen money. Nevertheless, the men give him the cash and then pursue him in deadly earnest with the intent to hurt him. Mr. Drew calls for the police, but they are far, far away. As the bad guys close in, the money suddenly dissolves into himself, into his body by osmosis! Mr. Drew woke from the dream with a severe headache.

Obviously, only those aspects of the dream that are directly germane to the thesis of this paper can be addressed here. To begin with, Mr. Drew and the sergeant "working hard to stay ahead of" the bad guys seem to reflect Mr. Drew's anxiety that he can't "hold onto" the selfobject transference, that he will be retraumatized. And indeed, in the dream, that seems to be the case. The good sergeant appears to die, and Mr. Drew is left alone to deal with his persecutors. Not surprisingly, given what brought him to treatment, he steals (or recovers?) what he feels is rightfully his. The police are far, far away and of no help, an aspect of the dream that again reflects, in part, his grievance against his father. Perhaps, however, what is at the heart of this dream, and certainly at the heart of this patient's urges to steal, is the vivid portrayal of the money being absorbed into himself by osmosis. This seems to concretize Mr. Drew's attempt to compensate for defects in himself by his intense wishes for great wealth with all the trappings. The dream was further motivated by his regretting his choice to cancel the previous session. It seems that not only had the deal fallen through, but he had felt belittled by his client. Consequently, Mr. Drew was enraged at this person and longed all the more to have been with his therapist. Thus his experience of this course of events provided him with another sleeping sergeant—his therapist—and another persecutor to contend with—his client. Overall, the patient's severe headache, his stealing in the dream, and his sense of being persecuted are manifestations of his narcissistic rage at the loss of the selfobject-therapist. After the therapist commented that in the dream Mr. Drew seemed to try to compensate for his sudden loss of the sergeant, this "good father," by absorbing the money, the patient became suddenly tearful and described another train ride a long time ago. Or, rather, one he didn't get to take. His father was traveling by train to Maine to see family. Mr. Drew wanted desperately to go, and his father refused him. Curiously, the year of that train ride was 1951, and the money stolen on the train in the dream was $51,000.

In the next session, the central point of this clinical vignette is reached. However, before focusing on it, I would like to address one more essential aspect of this case. Throughout this period, in the first year of treatment, the patient had experienced certain feelings of persecution that had waxed and waned but persisted. Specifically, he thought policemen were following him, talking about him, laughing at him, and observing his every move. However, on the way to the session on this particular day, something else happened. Mr. Drew reported the unusual event which he felt was very important and indeed "amazing and central" to his sense of himself:

He was looking suspiciously at this cop, this stranger, who he thought was following him, and he suddenly imagined this policeman was vividly transformed into his father wearing his old familiar policeman's uniform. The experience was intense. The patient felt unbelievably good and safe and invigorated. The image reminded him of a fuzzy picture of his father that he had always liked despite the poor quality of the photo. However, in contrast to this, the image in his mind, at this particular point in time, was sharp and clear and not at all fuzzy.

The experience of this transformation will be explored in depth later. However, one aspect of this experience that can be immediately addressed is that this transformation of a persecutor into an idealized father seems to be the reverse of the action in the previous dream which starts out with Mr. Drew blissfully holding onto the sergeant's hand and ends with him being pursued by the persecuting bad guys. Furthermore, given the timing of this "unusual" experience (on the way to the session), the transference implications are also apparent.

In the next session, and the last one in this vignette that will be discussed,

Mr. Drew seems to elaborate further on the same theme. As he comes to the medical school where his therapist's office is located, he imagines he is a doctor and feels valued by himself and others. He then imagines that the people in the lobby know what he has been thinking and are laughing to themselves about this absurd idea. His mood abruptly changes, and once again he feels persecuted and begins to conjure up fantasies of revenge. Once more, as he attempts to hold onto the idealized selfobject, form a union with it, the selfobject becomes a persecutor, or, to use the patient's metaphor and to carry it further: the clear, crisp image once again becomes the fuzzy photo and then evidently goes completely out of focus. In another sense, it becomes the "negative."

## DISCUSSION OF THE CASE

The case report, as abbreviated as it is, does readily demonstrate the patient's significant and diffuse narcissistic vulnerability. Very little, however, can be said about Mr. Drew's earliest stages of development and experiences with his mother. On the other hand, a lot can be said about his thwarted developmental needs to idealize his father and merge with him. Mr. Drew's earliest memories indicate that he turned with intense longing toward his policeman father. Yet he saw his father as belittling him for never being good enough. That is, the patient experienced his father as if he demanded perfection as the bill to pay before he would willingly provide a father's selfobject functions as an admiring, merger-permitting, idealized parental imago. Therefore growth vis-à-vis the gradual, and more or less optimal, deidealization of the selfobject with the concomitant internalization of selfobject functions could not take place. Indeed, Mr. Drew had little sense of himself as an independent individual with healthy self-assertiveness and sustaining ideals. Furthermore, what was most vividly being reawakened in his psychotherapeutic experience was the old yearning for the idealized father imago. The three dreams presented above graphically portray this reawakening.

Mr. Drew's shame at his voyeuristic experiences centered not so much on his apparent sexual feelings as on how settled and soothed they made him feel. Therefore his looking at pictures of powerful, naked, well-endowed men (which also brings to mind his admiring the *fuzzy* photo of his father) can be considered a sexualized attempt to admire visually or take in, to possess, the idealized selfobject. Yet this driven and desperate attempt to make up for his narcissistic vulnerability, and the structural defect that that implies, was obviously doomed to failure. Similarly, his beating himself in the bathroom after his father had just beaten him reflects a sadomasochistic attempt to identify defensively with and/or sexually merge with the brutally rejecting aspects of the omnipotent parental imago. Again, this activity seems to represent another futile attempt to "fill in" defects in the self. In a similar context, Kohut (1977) explained that when "a child's healthy merger wishes with the idealized selfobject have remained unresponded to, the idealized imago breaks into fragments, and the merger needs are sexualized and directed towards these fragments" (p. 127).

It seems that the urge for revenge, the impulse to steal, and the wish for wealth are intimately connected with each other. Often, but not always, Mr. Drew's fantasies of revenge involved stealing the wealth of a person who had hurt him, wealth that he equated with greatness. The patient's intense fantasies of material wealth, his wishes to surround himself with great works of art and other treasures, seem to represent a desperate longing for the enhancement of the self. This is vividly portrayed in the "train" dream when the stolen/recovered money is literally absorbed into his body. Mr. Drew's symptomatic acts and fantasies of stealing were always accompanied by a feeling of vengeful righteousness and a deep sense of entitlement. He himself felt robbed! He repeatedly felt compelled to steal the price of admission into his father's arena where he could then, and only then, bask in glory with him. In his fantasies of great wealth he could finally walk tall, admire, and be admired by great men. In the scenario of his stealing, he was able finally to humble, harm, and control the enemies who had slighted him. Kohut (1972) states: "The enemy is a recalcitrant part of an expanded self over which the narcissistically vulnerable person had expected to exercise full control" (p. 644). Thus revenge is ultimately an attempt to recapture the aberrant selfobject, to make it finally submit. On the surface, the wish is for the enemy to be brutally humiliated and tortured and to rave in fear. But beneath the surface there is another element—the hope that the enemy sees the error of his ways and just raves, admires, even loves, and forever submits to the greatness of the avenger—that is, in a very distorted way, to do what the selfobject was supposed to do in the first place.

On the basis of the above clinical material a tentative reconstruction can be made that Mr. Drew reached a stage in the narcissistic line of development where much of the archaic omnipotence of a "transitional" selfobject was integrated into the total structure of a cohesive idealized parental imago. However, here is where his development faltered. There was no transmuting internalization of the selfobject functions; rather, in the face of an aggressive, demeaning selfobject, the structure of the idealized imago broke down. Specifically, the patient's perverse activity, his self-beating experience, his daydreams of wealth, his yearning for revenge, and his acts and fantasies of stealing generally point in the same direction: a striving, distorted and fragmented as it may be, for merger with an idealized self-object. Could not his paranoid fantasies, especially given his "central and amazing" experience, also fit into the same constellation of symptoms and point toward the same basic striving?

## DISCUSSION OF THE "CENTRAL" EXPERIENCE

As a preamble to this discussion, one aspect of the case should be briefly addressed. Mr. Drew's fantasy (intense as it was at times) that policemen were persecuting him was not a fixed delusion, and the rationale for exploring such a delusion is just that: it is "movable" and in flux, shifting with the degree of narcissistic needs and yearnings mobilized by the therapy. Therefore this very mobility over time seems to provide an opportunity for exploration and study beyond that of either a fixed delusion or a transient paranoid regression. Generalizations derived from such a study, of course, must be quite tentative, but they are not without some value in pursuing. And what follows is such a pursuit.

One way to begin, then, is to view the patient's experience of the transformation of his persecutor into his idealized father as a clinical puzzle. What has exactly transpired? How and why? The clinical material surrounding this event indicates there had been a deepening regression and a concomitant mobilization of an idealizing transference. As mentioned previously, both the dream he reported in the session prior to the "central" experience and the fantasy in the medical-school lobby on the way to the subsequent session also reflect this transformation, but in the reverse direction. Therefore there appears to be something very unstable and very tentative about Mr. Drew's mobilized wish to merge with the idealized parental imago. The patient's attempt to embrace the selfobject emotionally brings to mind a light with a poor connection. It flickers but won't stay on. This resistance against the transference appears to be a fear of repeating, of risking being traumatized once again by the punishing, belittling, omnipotent, parental imago. Yet the hope for a "new beginning" is evident as well (Balint, 1968): the light does flicker. One other fact in the case should be noted. Both in the clinical puzzle itself and in the year-long unfolding of the therapeutic process, the fantasized persecutor was on the scene first. The idealized selfobject is the latecomer.

Thus, from a psychoeconomic point of view, the investment of narcissistic yearnings seems to transform the persecutor into an idealized selfobject, and the withdrawal of such yearnings brings about the reverse. Though such an interpretation is somewhat misleading and certainly simplified, it is as if the fantasized persecutor is a psychological ghost cell that can be filled with idealizing "love" and emptied of the same. And then there is another, rather familiar (though reversed) way to express all of this (Freud, 1911). Mr. Drew seems to be saying: "He hates me; He loves me; I love me"; or more parsimoniously, but perhaps more to the point given a self-psychological point of view: "He hates me; I-he loves me." Thus at this juncture, reflecting on these ideas that the clinical puzzle brings to mind, we see three "possible" avenues that might be worth exploring further. First, is there some inherent relationship, some descriptive parallel, between the fantasized persecutor and the idealized parental imago? Second, can the psychoeconomic point of view shed some further light on this particular clinical puzzle and paranoid mechanisms in general and the reason why this transformation took place at all? Finally, would it be useful to compare Mr. Drew's experience with Freud's early descriptions of the mechanisms in paranoia to ascertain "how" this transformation could have worked?

It seems that one would not think offhand to compare and contrast an idealized selfobject with the persecutor that springs from a delusion or fantasy. And if one did think of it, one would argue against the idea, given the somewhat different conceptual levels involved. Yet approaching this comparison in an introspective and empathic manner significantly over-rides the objection concerning the two conceptual levels. Whether or not such an exercise is productive remains to be seen.

The persecutor is experienced as a hated, intrusive, destructive stranger, outside the realm of the self, who is more or less omnipotent and omnis-cient, who ridicules and deprives the person persecuted of self-esteem or a sense of volition, or the ability to accomplish what he would without such interference. Furthermore, the persecutor is felt to be potentially and un-avoidably omnipresent, and the persecuted person feels he would be "just fine" if the persecutor would only go away.

On the other hand, the idealized selfobject is experienced within the realm of the self and is that part of the self where all bliss and power reside. The selfobject is unself-consciously beloved and admired and emotionally sustaining: a "fountainhead" of vigor and self-esteem. Without union with the idealized parental imago when needed, there is a sense of emptiness and powerlessness. At such times there is a longing for the selfobject to be omnipresent and a sense that everything would be "just fine" if the self-object would only return.

At this point it might be worthwhile to sift through some of these com-parisons. Both the idealized selfobject and the persecutor are experienced as having certain clear qualities of omnipotence, omniscience, and om-nipresence. The persecutor in sundry ways is painfully experienced as self-depleting while the idealized selfobject in sundry ways is, unreflectively, experienced as self-enhancing. Simply put, the former is disturbingly felt as a negative destructive force, and the latter is obliviously felt as a positive constructive force. However, there is one critical consideration that prevents this contrast from simply being reduced to a "Dr. Jekyll and Mr. Hyde" comparison: the quality of awareness, the sense of presence, differs in the experiencing of these two psychic entities.

To state the obvious, in the realm of his psychic reality the persecuted individual is only aware of the persecutor when the persecutor is "present" in one form or another or potentially present. If he is unaware of the persecutor, the persecutor is simply nonexistent, absent. On the other hand, there is very little awareness of the selfobject unless union with it is disrupted. How can one be aware of that with which one coincides? Therefore, in a certain sense, if there is no awareness of the selfobject, the selfobject *is* "present" or else not needed.

In short, one is only aware of a persecutor in its presence and only fully aware of the selfobject in its loss or absence. To make this point is not an empty exercise in semantics but, as shall be shown below, offers a meaningful connection between these two entities.

This qualitative difference in the sense of presence stems from the following considerations: The persecutor is always painfully experienced, of course, as someone other than the self, whereas the functioning idealized selfobject is obliviously experienced in a oneness with the self. Only with the selfobject's loss is there a belated awareness of that which *was* within the realm of the self.

In this particular regard, Kohut (1971) states, "The expected control over such (selfobject) others is then closer to the concept or the control which a grown-up expects to have over his own body and mind than the concept or control which he expects to have over others" (pp. 26–27).

Therefore, when there is a traumatic experience of loss or catastrophic disappointment in the idealized selfobject and the self-selfobject union is lost, the selfobject is then, and only then, prematurely and painfully experienced as "other." This "other" is both intimate and strange and no longer a seemingly controllable extension of self-experience. From this bewildering *new* self-experience it is but a small step to feeling controlled and persecuted by this now intimate stranger. In essence, then, there is a potential for traumatic transformation in which merger-seeking, wide-eyed admiration can become wide-eyed paranoia. In such circumstances it would be as if the persecutor were the malignant ghost of the selfobject that has gone away, gone awry, and returned to do its haunting, a haunting that for the paranoid person in fact lessens the ultimate threat of total disintegration panic (Blum, 1981). To this same point Kohut (1977) suggests that such a paranoid stance with its intense preoccupation with hateful omnipresent enemies provides some slight control over "diffuse and nameless archaic stimuli" that threaten further disillusion of the self (p. 108). That is, the secondary attachment of these stimuli to paranoid ideational content gives some organization, tragic as that may be, to the internal chaotic feeling state, thus limiting the fragmentation process. Could this very "function of the persecutor" be nothing less than the distortion beyond recognition of the original function of the idealized selfobject? If this is so, the absent selfobject has become the present persecutor, and paranoia is not so much a matter of projection as one of transformation. Paranoia is, then, not a way of dealing with unacceptable impulses but rather a way of dealing with an unacceptable loss of part of the self-selfobject world.

Perhaps this exercise of comparison, and the speculations derived from it, has been carried as far as it can be. As one of the concluding statements to his theoretical understanding of sexuality, Freud (1905) once said, *"Neuroses, are so to say, the negative of perversions"* (p. 165). Thus, paraphrasing Freud, it can be said that fantasized persecutors are, so to speak, the negative of idealized selfobjects. Yet this is still a beginning statement, not a concluding one, and it needs to be further elucidated.

From a psychoeconomic point of view, there is a hypothesis of Tausk's (1934) about the paranoid mechanism that is worth investigating. Tausk described his interaction with an acquaintance, Mr. B., a poet and writer and, in fact, a great admirer of Ibsen. Tausk and B. had met in the studio of a mutual friend to continue a conversation they had started the previous evening. The studio, very well-known to Mr. B., was filled with works of art. As Tausk and Mr. B. talked, B. walked back and forth in the room. He suddenly stopped in front of a life-size bust of Ibsen. He seemed tense, anxious, puzzled. After a bit he asked: "Who is this man? He seems so familiar" (Tausk, 1934, p. 137). Tausk replied that the man was the druggist. With that B. realized with some discomfort the bust was Ibsen. Tausk, knowing something about Mr. B.'s personal life and recalling the conversation from the previous night, had in effect given Mr. B. a rather cryptic interpretation.

It seems that the Norwegian playwright had come up in their earlier conversation. B. had forgotten that Ibsen had been a druggist, but Tausk reminded him. Later Tausk realized to himself that B.'s forgetting this well-known fact had to do with B.'s involvement with another druggist. He had had a love affair with the wife of a pharmacist. The husband discovered it and threatened B. Mr. B., growing tired of the affair anyway, used the threat as an excuse to end the relationship. Nevertheless, he felt ashamed and humiliated by this incident and wanted to forget it all together, and thus he wanted to forget all druggists, a wish that led to his forgetting Ibsen had been one. Finally, after Tausk had reminded him of that fact, B. forgot Ibsen as well. Going beyond the immediate dynamic considerations, Tausk (1934) concludes:

> Why did B. have to halt precisely before Ibsen's bust since there was nothing unusual about it to attract his attention? Now, actually there was something unusual about the bust. It had become strange to him, and therefore could not but attract his attention in this studio, in which every object had long been familiar to him. The repressed Ibsen returned in this form—as a messenger from the repressed pharmacist. An aspect of the paranoid mechanism is clearly revealed here. Persons from whom the paranoic has withdrawn his libido re-appear to him as *strangers* [p. 141].

In a footnote, Tausk goes on to say, "B.'s relation to Ibsen, that of a creative individual to the master who represents his ideals, is patterned after the father complex and is cathected with great quantities of libido" (p. 141).

It is curious and certainly original of Tausk to come up with this idea about the paranoid mechanism from a discussion of a case which, in actuality, has little, if anything, to do with paranoia. But evidently what intrigued Tausk was not the "run-of-the-mill" dynamics of the case but rather the withdrawal of libido. Mr. B. withdrew his conscious awareness of Ibsen because recognition of Ibsen came to represent a trauma, an affront to his self-esteem, an awareness of shame and humiliation. Thus it seems implicit in "Ibsen and the Druggist" and certainly explicit in "On the Origins of the 'Influencing Machine' in Schizophrenia" (1919) that Tausk, in examining paranoid mechanisms, emphasized the psychoeconomics, the ebb and flow of libidinal cathexes, over the dynamic/structural point of view. In this way, in the case of Mr. B., he saw the paranoid mechanisms in terms of something (libido) being withdrawn rather than something being added (projection). In reference to Tausk, Kohut (1957) states: "To him, the structural content of the delusion was a secondary expression of the awareness of a deeper primary libido regression" (p. 259). Simply put, this seems to be like the well-known comparison between the battle and the war.

Now, if we return to Mr. Ibsen's "central" experience, it seems strikingly similar to Mr. B.'s—the only difference is that they are reversed! In terms of the psychic-energy model, one is the ebb and one is the flow. Specifically, Mr. Drew had long felt persecuted by the cops. Recently in his therapeutic experience there had been a mobilization of an idealizing transference. On the way to the therapist's office, Mr. Drew cathected the persecutor/cop with narcissistic libido, and thus the cop came to represent the idealized parental imago, and Mr. Drew felt wonderful and soothed in his presence.

It seems that whatever else might come of this exploration, the comparison of Mr. B.'s experience with Mr. Drew's at least helps confirm Tausk's hypothesis about this particular paranoid mechanism. The fact that the direction of the experiences is reversed can only add weight to the confirmation. That is, the converse of Tausk's hypothesis, allowing for some modification given Mr. Drew's emerging transference reactions, seems to hold as well. To paraphrase Tausk, it can be said that a persecuting stranger who is invested with narcissistic libido reappears as a loving, idealized figure. Perhaps, however, there is still more that could be done with the material.

Tausk himself wondered why B. stopped before Ibsen's bust to begin with. He explains this behavior by saying that what was unusual for B. about the bust was its strangeness. Tausk then goes on to evoke "the return of the repressed" as the ultimate reason. This explanation perhaps sheds light on *how* B. was puzzled but not necessarily on *why* he chose to stop in front of the bust and be puzzled in the first place. Earlier Tausk hinted at another reason. For B. to lose Ibsen, "a master who represented his ideals," would be a grave intellectual loss. Thus, could not B. have been restlessly pacing back and forth in the room, in fact, in actuality, searching to find his lost "Ibsen" again? As he peered at the bust, this wish was balanced with the risk of feeling shame and humiliation because of the recent dynamic connection. The return of the repressed? Yes, but not without his first searching and longing for the lost object. Furthermore, there seems to be additional evidence for this plausible explanation of B.'s behavior. In looking more closely at the previous evening's conversation, it seems B. opposed the view Tausk (1934) was offering, that a "playwright should have a good head for science" (p. 138). B. gave Ibsen as the prime example of a great dramatist who certainly didn't concern himself at all with such things. At this point, Tausk reminded him that Ibsen was a druggist. Given B.'s recent unsavory business with another druggist, it seems that he was already loudly denying that his idealized Ibsen would have had this odious flaw of having a "head for science." Tausk's reminder could have only intensified B.'s disappointment in his "idealized selfobject," thus necessitating the further withdrawal of narcissistic libido. Ibsen being a druggist is nothing less than a significant shortcoming, the empathic failure of a much idealized figure. With this speculation, the parallel with Mr. Drew draws even closer, and the case of Mr. B. may have a little something to do with paranoia after all.

Mr. Drew, too, was restless. On the way to the therapist's office, he felt a sense of badness, emptiness, and powerlessness. As he scanned his surroundings with his usual "paranoid vigilance," as he searched the face of the stranger, the persecutor/cop, was he not searching all along for just what he finally found in his "central" experience, on this rare occasion—the idealized parental imago looking back at him? In other words, the transformation itself was what had always been sought, and what, at the deepest level, was driving his paranoid scanning was the hope of refinding the lost selfobject. Then that particular sense of being potentially omnipresent that is so often attached to the persecutor takes on an additional meaning, for it is nothing less than the disguised, distorted merger wish of wanting the selfobject to be constantly present.

In describing the paranoid's vigilant searching of his surrounds, Shapiro (1965) called this mode of attention "rigidly intentional." Meissner (1978), in addressing "the intensity of attention that paranoids bring to perceptual activity," concludes: "In part the paranoid is actively scanning his environment to pick up bits of information or data which will lend credence to his inner system" (p. 114). What is now suggested is that, in part, the hyperalert paranoid is doing more than buttressing his paranoid defense or finding "evidence" for the countercathexis and denial of his homosexual impulses. In his struggle with his persecutor there is also the ultimate longing (contaminated as it may be by the dread of disillusionment) to recover what was lost: the merger with an idealized selfobject. Though coming from a different conceptual framework, Searles (1965) feels that the paranoid position *denies and masks* frightening, primitive, loving feelings and intense dependency needs (and one could add the risk of retraumatization) if these feelings are experienced. Thus Mr. Drew's *unmasking* of his persecutor to find his loving father, despite the associated soothing feelings, is very tentative. On the way to the very next session he imagines he is an important doctor and then suddenly feels persecuted and revengeful. Ultimately, to feel like "a chip off the old block" entails a risk that he will again be found defective and belittled by the very figure he hopes to emulate. In effect, he will be once more traumatically disillusioned about both himself and the idealized parental imago. To the same point, Meissner (1978) remarks:

> The adult fixation on the object as bad is both a reaction to the unresolved disillusioning traumata in the past and an unconscious defense against positive feelings and a threat of disillusionment in the present. The paranoid's struggles with his persecutors are in effect struggles with the unmanageably painful and therefore repressed disappointments and disillusionments he has suffered from them. Or, as Freud indicated in his discussion of Shreber, the person who is hated and feared as a persecutor was once loved and honored [p. 131].

It seems very feasible, then, that for a number of patients suffering from chronic paranoid fantasies or delusions, there is an ultimate wish to reconcile with the persecutor and be "loved." And yet the "unmanageably painful, and therefore repressed, feelings of disillusionment with the persecutor" prevent that (Searles, 1965, p. 608).

Nevertheless, in the vigilant paranoid scanning, the search goes on for the perfect, wholly good parental imago before the fall of disillusionment. But over and over again "the beloved returns from a shadow world with changed appearance; from the familiar and beloved object, he is turned into a stranger. Strangeness in the unconscious is close to hostility" (Waelder, 1951, p. 174). Thus what seems remarkable about Mr. Drew's "amazing and central" experience (these are his words) is that it seems to be the exception to the above "rule of paranoia" and allows for a closer examination of just what kinds of "loving feelings" are involved, at least in some paranoid mechanisms.

Freud (1911) noted the prominence of humiliation in the causation of paranoia. Yet he went on to state that beneath these kinds of injuries lies the homosexual component which is the core conflict in cases of paranoia among men. However, since Freud's formulation about the mechanisms of paranoia, the centrality of the sexual conflict has considerably lessened and the relationship of paranoid defenses to depression and low self-worth has been given more emphasis (Meissner, 1978). One would have to deduce that this shift is related to clinical relevancy and the concomitant expansion of theory. Nevertheless, it is almost always useful to review Freud's work, to ponder and play with his rich ideas, thought models, and theories, and to do so especially when considering new conceptualizations or possibilities.

It was in the spirit of this approach that Mr. Drew's "central" experience was earlier formulated along the lines of Freud's well-known workings of the single proposition: "I [a man] love him [a man]." Specifically in delusions of persecution, the homosexual love is first denied: "I do not love him—I hate him." Then by projection the proposition "I hate him" becomes "He hates [persecutes] me." This last contradiction reaches consciousness and justifies hating the persecutor. Again, Freud (1911) concludes: "Observation leaves room for no doubt that the persecutor is someone who was once loved" (p. 63).

Now, in the case of Mr. Drew, the initial proposition is "He hates me [so I hate him]." Then, due to the breakthrough of idealizing yearnings mobilized in his therapeutic experience, the proposition is rapidly but very tentatively transformed into "He loves me [so I love me]," or more consistent with the emerging selfobject transference: "I-he loves me." Observation leaves room for little doubt that in the case of Mr. Drew the persecutor is someone who loved once, and it is hoped *will* relent and love again.

To begin with, in comparing Freud's formulations with those derived in the case of Mr. Drew, it is obvious that the word "love" means two entirely different things. Love has a tendency to have "many splendored" meanings anyway. Be that as it may, at least in the above two situations what is meant by the word "love" is quite clear. The driving force in Freud's formulation of a delusion of persecution is homosexual love that is defended against. That is, passionate hate replaces passionate love; the impelling unconscious feeling makes its conscious appearance as its opposite. The negative valence is the mark of repression. In the case of Mr. Drew, the driving force behind the shifting transformation of feelings in the "central" experience is narcissistic love or, more specifically, the narcissistic need for merger with an idealized selfobject and the intense resistance to such a need. Likewise, the hatred exhibited is more akin to narcissistic rage at a failing selfobject than to true object hatred. It is as if Mr. Drew is saying, "I hate my persecutor because he won't 'love' me." Thus, in the one case the delusion of persecution is motivated by a narcissistic regression leading to *forbidden* love and in the other case by a narcissistic fixation and its concomitant sense of *failed* love. A certain kind of love is at the core of both cases, but otherwise these two formulations lead in entirely different directions.

In Freud's formulation, given the starting point of the single-axis theory of narcissism, narcissism can only be conceptualized as a catastrophic regression, and, in turn, the therapeutic correction can only be conceptualized as overcoming this regression. The breakdown in homosexual sublimation follows from this intrapsychic catastrophe. The paranoid delusion itself is, then, both a defense against homosexual love as well as an attempt to rebuild the subjective world, a restitution after the onset of the illness itself (Freud, 1911). The connection between these two aspects of the paranoid mechanism is not clear.

In the formulation of Mr. Drew's experience, given the theoretical framework of a separate line of development for narcissism, and therefore the recognition of the narcissistic transferences, narcissism can be seen as a struggling, driving developmental force that has gone awry. This is a different order of things! The paranoid construction in such circumstances is thus not a defense against homosexual wishful fantasies, or not primarily that, but rather an attempted recovery, a searching need for an idealized selfobject that is defended against lest there again be disillusionment or retraumatization. Or, to put it more succinctly, the paranoid process in question is simultaneously both an attempt at restitution and a massive distortion and defense against such a restitution. Thus both the defensive nature and the restitutive nature of a paranoid construction come to be related in a rather intimate and therapeutically useful way.

The paranoid mechanism has long been considered to have such a dual nature (Freud, 1911, 1924; Fenichel, 1945; Jaffe, 1968; Meissner, 1978). Yet these two processes (defense and restitution) do not seem to be of the same order or level of conceptualization. From a dynamic, structural point of view the paranoid mechanism has been seen as a defensive way of handling unacceptable impulses or superego pressures. From a psycho-economic point of view, the same mechanism has been seen as an attempt to rebuild the world after its loss through withdrawal of libido. *"The delusional formation, which we take to be pathological product, is in reality an attempt at recovery, a process of reconstruction"* (Freud, 1911, p. 71; Freud's emphasis). What is suggested by the exploration of Mr. Drew's central experience is that the attempt at recovery is *simultaneously* distorted by the dread of repetition. That is, the paranoid mechanism in such cases can no longer be considered as sometimes a defense and sometimes an attempted resti-tution and sometimes both. It is specifically an attempt at recovery that, because of the fear and dread to repeat, is itself always defended against. The paranoid mechanism is indeed a twofold process, but each part of the process is inseparable from the other. In Mr. Drew's case, when he finally cathected his persecutor with narcissistic libido, he felt soothed in the presence of the image of his idealized father, and the paranoid mechanism broke down. What remained, at least briefly, at that moment was the truly undistorted attempt at recovery, the wish for merger with the idealized selfobject—the actual core of the then-defunct paranoid fantasy. The transference implications are clear. When there has been a major mobilization of an idealizing transference, following the gradual working through of resistances to such a transference, the paranoid position is abandoned and remains so until the transference is disrupted.

## THE PROBLEM WITH PROJECTION

There is perhaps one other issue that can be grappled with by continuing this comparison of Freud's formulation of a delusion of persecution with the situation in the case of Mr. Drew. It should not be lost sight of that Freud's main objective in working out the various permutations of the above proposition was to demonstrate the mechanism of projection. Having vividly done so, he comments that this mechanism is the most striking characteristic of symptom formation in paranoia. He adds, however, that projection is not universal in all forms of paranoia and therefore cannot be considered pathognomonic. Secondly, it is essentially a ubiquitous phe-nomenon anyway. He then postponed the further in-depth investigation of the nature of projection and in all the rest of his known writings essentially never returned to it. But now, to return to the question at hand, did Mr. Drew in his central experience likewise use the mechanism of projection? At first glance it seems obvious that he did. And therein lies one of the problems with the concept of projection; it is too easily and glibly used. Waelder (1951) wondered if projection isn't perhaps too convenient a psychoanalytic term that is applied in cases where a closer examination may have led to other conclusions.

In its essence, projection is a simplistic, unconditional concept in a relativistic world. It is primarily useful in an experientially distant mode of observation and becomes less so and more confusing to use as the subject allegedly projecting is more closely approached in an experientially near-empathic mode. Indeed, maintaining the focus on the "projection" and not temporarily letting go of it during trial empathic attempts may interfere with the empathic mode itself. To return to the case of Mr. Drew, it seems clear he was attributing feelings and motivations to the policeman that the policeman did not have. From that point of view, he was simply projecting. Yet given his self pathology, his genetics, his experience of his policeman father, the timing of the central experience, and the emerging idealizing transference, the happenstance policeman (before the "transformation") is by his mere presence, and his mere presence alone, a significant disturbance to the patient's narcissistic equilibrium and represents an empathic failure of his selfobject world, a flaw in a narcissistically perceived reality. Mr. Drew reacts initially with simmering narcissistic rage to this unempathic intrusion. He feels persecuted because his precarious narcissistic homeostasis was disrupted by the policeman's arrival on the scene, an event he cannot control. Thus in essence the policeman by his inadvertent presence does indeed become Mr. Drew's persecutor. Often what is projection on one level is the psychological truth on the other. Projection is not an absolute construct. Like beauty, projection is in the eyes of the beholder and more a reflection of the self experience of the beholder than an in-depth recognition of the self experience of the one who is beheld. To wit, it is a judgment call made by the observer from the vantage point of his own psychic reality and may have very little to do with the psychic reality of the observed.

There is still another problem with projection. It is not, it cannot be, a single mechanism. To say that a person attributed a feeling or impulse to some "other" says very little. It is equivalent to observing a magician materialize a rabbit in a hat and concluding that he did just that without realizing that the magician "projected" the rabbit into the hat by a series of necessary, intricate maneuvers. Psychological projection consists of subtle intrapsychic maneuvers. Likewise, psychological projection consists of subtle intrapsychic maneuvers that an observer can grasp only by applying the empathic, introspective mode over time. To see projection as a *basic* indivisible intrapsychic mechanism short-circuits the empathic process as discussed above and leads to the illogical conclusion, among others, that what a person faultily attributes to another he himself must own in an exact, "eye-for-an-eye" correlation. Thus it seems that all too often in the psychoanalytic literature projection is given more than its due as a basic explanation of intrapsychic processes when it, of and by itself, explains very little and indeed stands out as something to be explained carefully and understood in its own right. Along somewhat similar lines, Schafer (1972) concludes: "Consequently, the theory of introjects has always had the same spooky quality as the subjective experience it refers to; it has remained more a repetition or continuation of the problem than a clarification or explanation of it" (p. 423). Though Schafer is specifically talking about introjects, his comments can just as surely be applied to any theory of "projects." Furthermore, to speak of reintrojection, reprojection of introjections, etc., can only compound the problem.

## Conclusions

The question was raised earlier whether Mr. Drew's paranoid symptoms, like so many of his other symptoms and symptomatic acts, could be a distorted attempt at restitution of the self. Given the exploration of the "central" experience the answer seems to be yes. Descriptively, the persecutor is essentially an idealized selfobject masked by a negative valence and a sense of otherness. How does this strange transformation come about? To apply a somewhat revised version of Tausk's hypotheses, the traumatic withdrawal of narcissistic cathexis changes the selfobject into a "stranger," and, in the process, there is a premature awareness of the selfobject as *other*. With such repeated traumas, the striving for the developmentally needed merger with an idealized selfobject would also become dreaded; the negative valence would be the full measure of such a fear of retraumatization and the necessary defense against further potential activation of infantile rage experiences. Yet, ultimately, the driving force behind the persistent persecutory fantasies is the search for the idealized selfobject who will finally relent and love again.

Apropos of the paranoid's dilemma, there is a rather diabolical monster in Hindu legend—a version of the rakshasa. It appears to its victims as the one individual the victim most trusts or loves in life. But when the unfortunate victim gets close enough, the monster transforms back into the hideous thing that it is and destroys him. The paranoid individual, too, has had a number of close calls with just such a monster, knows him on an early, intimate level, and can no longer risk idealizing, merger-wishing love. This is paranoia from the paranoid's point of view. He is frightened and angry. In avoiding the greater trauma and greater disillusionment, he is chronically disillusioned and chronically traumatized. The negative valence that masks, the still- (and forever) needed idealized selfobject comes to have a persistent protective purpose. To use an analogy, there are some vaccinations that can potentially cause a sickness that is almost as bad as that which they are meant to prevent. Paranoid delusions are in some cases like such vaccinations. The paranoid person protects himself with his delusions, with his ideas of omnipresent persecutors. Such painful and tragic organization prevents further dissolution of the self and the further fragmentation which is the feared outcome of the risky union with a "flawed" idealized figure. In a sense this union can be forever attempted and forever blocked. Perhaps Winnicott's (1960) concepts of False Self and True Self are somewhat analogous to these constructs. Just as the False Self protects and hides the fragile True Self, so, too, the persecutor's mask hides the "unyielding" idealized selfobject and prevents the catastrophic union.

To look at it another way, the paranoid person is faced with the proverbial Catch 22. The more he feels narcissistically vulnerable, the more he strives for an idealized selfobject. The more he strives for an idealized selfobject, the more he fears the risk of retraumatization. The more he fears retraumatization, the more he hates and fears his persecutor. The more he hates and fears his persecutor, the more he feels narcissistically vulnerable, and so on and so on. This is the paranoid's narcissistically experienced view of the world in all its perpetual intrapsychic "motion." A delusion cannot be corrected by everyday experience because *this* is the everyday experience of the paranoid person. It is, then, not so much a question of the kernel of historical truth (Freud, 1939) as it is a question of this kind of current truth becoming the constant repetition of the historical one. For the paranoid individual the only way out of his psychological cul-de-sac is to get past that which is hated and feared the most, to embrace the very thing he has repeatedly experienced as the rakshasa and at the very moment of embrace to experience that it is not.

In a somewhat similar vein, Meissner (1978), in discussing the difficulty of psychotherapy with paranoids concludes: "The therapist must bring the patient face-to-face with his ambivalence and must help him to bear his depression and disillusionment—patient and therapist must move in the direction of what is most painful to each, not away from it" (p. 131).

With all this in mind, the question becomes: how did Mr. Drew, at least fleetingly, find a way out of this psychological cul-de-sac of the paranoid?

How did he come to have his "central" experience at all? The answer has to be found in the therapeutic regression and emerging transference reactions. It seems that the dream interpretation the week prior to the central experience mobilized the yearning for the idealized selfobject. Although this in turn intensified the persecutory fantasy, somewhat, the patient nevertheless "broke through" these fantasies to experience something new. Perhaps the achievement of this significant inkling of a new beginning was possible because he was able to perceive the therapist's empathy; perhaps with that there was a deepening of his narcissistic transference (Ornstein, 1974).

That this therapeutic movement is very tentative is confirmed by his experience the following week in the medical-school lobby. He first imagines that he, too, is an important doctor; he holds his head up high; he "merges" with the idealized physician. However, he quickly retreats to his revengeful, paranoid position when he feels the merger will not be tolerated. In other words, he once again flees from the proverbial, absolutely terrifying repetition. The sequence of these two sessions highlights the ebb and flow of the mobilized transference and reflects on both the therapeutic work that has been done and that which still needs to be done. But it is the working-through process of such transference reactions allowing for transmuting internalizations that will ultimately provide a way out of the aforementioned cul-de-sac. It is perhaps the one experience that can potentially "correct" a paranoid delusion or, more accurately, lessen the need of such drastic constructs. And the empathic understanding of the very fragile tentative attempts at idealization are crucial to such a therapeutic endeavor. For, in the sense that an idealized selfobject is the precursor of guiding ideals, the successful emergence and resolution of an idealized transference eventually lead to mature forms of admiration for others and the capability of sustained enthusiasm. On the other hand, traumatic disruptions of such a transference can lead to fleeting episodes of fragmentation, narcissistic rage, burning envy, and a temporary delusionary construction of the omnipotent-object (Kohut, 1971)—in essence, a more or less fantasized persecutor.

As I stated earlier, Meissner believed that the paranoid patient must face his ambivalence and bear his disillusionment. What is suggested here, however, is that this disillusionment does not necessarily have to be born but can potentially be worked through vis-à-vis the selfobject transference. Furthermore, the exploration of Mr. Drew's "central" experience suggests that ambivalence need not be faced as if it were made up of two primal forces, love and hate; rather, what is behind the hate, the longing for merger with the idealized selfobject, can emerge in a potentially workable way in the therapeutic experience. To quote Kohut (1972): "Yet, underlying all of these emotional states [of narcissistic rage] is the uncompromising insistence on the perfection of the idealized selfobject and on the limitlessness of the power and knowledge of the grandiose self" (p. 642). There is nothing therapeutically optimistic about these statements, nor is there anything in them that lessens the painfulness of therapy that Meissner so poignantly addressed. Indeed, Mr. Drew's belief that hate can never turn back into love is the experience of the full measure of his disillusionment in a narcissistically perceived reality. The intensity of his hate is ultimately nothing less than the distorted perpetuation of his unending quest for primary love (Balint, 1968).

Of course, idealization can also be a defense. On this account Greenson (1967) states: "If one persists in analyzing the idealized transference as a resistance and gives no neurotic transference gratifications, ultimately the idealization breaks down. Then one can see an enormous rage and hatred in the patient as well as paranoid suspiciousness . . . It is this which the idealization covers up and which makes it so difficult to uncover" (p. 344). This statement is worth pondering because it is the exact opposite of what has been derived from analyzing Mr. Drew's "central" experience in which his rage and paranoia made it so difficult to see the underlying tentative idealizations. This contrast highlights the complexity of depth psychology and concomitantly the underestimated potential of iatrogenically retraumatizing patients in one way or another. Thus there are those situations in which the therapist does need to see the "rakshasa" in his patient, to understand how rage is so covered up by the patient's idealizations, and to help the patient dare to deal with the destructive fear of such anger. Yet there are those other situations in which the therapist must sense how the patient fears finding in him still one more "rakshasa" who is ready to spring should the patient stray too close with his idealizing longings or dare to risk a pathognomonic regression within the transference. In such situations, the therapist needs to see that perhaps at the very core of an almost unyielding repetition compulsion there is a glimmer of an earlier thwarted striving, a hope against hope which, if tended to therapeutically, has the potential to become the beginnings of a re-creation (Loewald, 1971).

## Summary

Using Mr. Drew's "central" experience as a pivotal point, a hypothesis of Tausk's about the paranoid mechanism was described and parallels with Mr. Drew's experience were drawn. Tausk's conclusion was that persons from whom the paranoiac has withdrawn his libido reappear to him as strangers. In Mr. Drew's case the converse seems to hold as well: a persecuting stranger whom the paranoiac invests with narcissistic libido reappears as a loving, idealized figure.

Next, Mr. Drew's "central" experience was reformulated in terms of the proposition Freud elaborated in the Schreber case to explore the paranoid mechanism. A comparison was then made.

The comparison led to two main conclusions. First, narcissism as a fixated driving force, as a striving that the persecutor *will* love again, and not just a regressive phenomenon, is at the core of the paranoid fantasy. Second, the restitutive and defensive aspects of a paranoid fantasy are inseparable. That is, a paranoid delusion is an attempt at restitution that is, itself, always defended against. When the defensive aspect breaks down vis-à-vis the clear emergence of an idealizing transference, the paranoid position is temporarily abandoned.

Finally, the clinical applicability of the study was briefly explored. The centrality of the emerging, very fragile idealizing transference and the patient's capacity to experience the therapist's empathy were examined. With this in mind, the concepts of disillusionment and ambivalence, and their central significance in the paranoid process, were reconsidered.

## REFERENCES

Balint, M. (1968), *The Basic Fault*. London: Tavistock Publications.

Blum, H. P. (1981), Object constancy and paranoid conspiracy. *J. Amer. Psychoanal. Assn.*, 29:789–813.

Castelnuovo-Tedesco, P. (1974), Stealing, revenge, and the Monte Cristo complex. *Internat. J. Psycho-Anal.*, 55:169–177.

Fenichel, O. (1945), *The Psychoanalytic Theory of Neurosis*. New York: Norton.

Freud, S. (1905), Three essays on the theory of sexuality. *Standard Edition*, 7:125–248. London: Hogarth Press, 1953.

————— (1911), Psycho-analytic notes on an autobiographical account of a case of paranoia. *Standard Edition*, 12:3–84. London: Hogarth Press, 1958.

————— (1924), The loss of reality in neurosis and psychosis. *Standard Edition*, 19:183–190. London: Hogarth Press, 1961.

————— (1939), Moses and monotheism. *Standard Edition*, 23:3–140. London: Hogarth Press, 1964.

Greenson, R. (1967), *The Technique and Practice of Psychoanalysis*. New York: International Universities Press.

Jaffe, D. S. (1968), The mechanism of projection: Its dual role in object relations. *Internat. J. Psycho-Anal.*, 49:662–677.

Kohut, H. (1957), Discussion of "Some comments on the origin of the influencing machine," by L. Linn. In: *Search for the Self*, ed. P. Ornstein. New York: International Universities Press, 1978, pp. 259–261.

————— (1971), *The Analysis of the Self*. New York: International Universities Press.

————— (1972), Thoughts on narcissism and narcissistic rage. In: *Search for the Self*, ed. P. Ornstein. New York: International Universities Press, 1978, pp. 615–658.

——— (1977), *The Restoration of the Self*. New York: International Universities Press.
Loewald, H. W. (1971), Some considerations on repetition compulsion. In: *Papers on Psychoanalysis*. New Haven, Conn.: Yale University Press, 1980, pp. 87–101.
Meissner, S. J. (1978), *The Paranoid Process*. New York: Aronson.
Ornstein, A. (1974), The dread to repeat and the new beginning: A contribution to the psychoanalysis of the narcissistic personality. *This Annual*, 2:231–248. New York: International Universities Press.
Schafer, R. (1972), Internalization: Process or fantasy? *The Psychoanalytic Study of the Child*, 27:411–436. New York: Quadrangle.
Searles, H. F. (1965), *Collected Papers on Schizophrenia and Related Subjects*. New York: International Universities Press.
Shapiro, D. (1965), *Neurotic Styles*. New York: Basic Books.
Tausk, V. (1919), On the origin of the "influencing machine" in schizophrenia. *Psychoanal. Quart.*, 2:519–566, 1933.
——— (1934), Ibsen the druggist. *Psychoanal. Quart.*, 2:137–141.
Waelder, R. (1951), The structure of paranoid ideas. *Internat. J. Psycho-Anal.*, 32:167–177.
Winnicott, D. W. (1960), Ego distortions in terms of true self and false self. In: *Maturational Processes and the Facilitating Environment*. New York: International Universities Press, 1965, pp. 140–152.

*January 1984*

# III

# CLINICAL STUDIES

# Clinical Contributions to the Theory of the Fictive Personality

JAY MARTIN, Ph.D. (Irvine, Calif.)

## Adult Identities and Fictive Formulas

Harry Nash, the hero of Kurt Vonnegut's short story, "Who Am I This Time?," is a clerk at a hardware store in North Crawford. Painfully shy, he "wasn't married, didn't go out with women—didn't have any close men friends either. He stayed away from all kinds of gatherings because he never could think of anything to say or do . . ." (Vonnegut, 1978, p. 20). Somebody in the town once remarked, Vonnegut tells us, "that Harry ought to go to a psychiatrist." But, the plain-speaking narrator of the story says, "I don't know what a psychiatrist could have turned up about him that the town didn't already know"; and, something of a psychoanalyst himself, the narrator adds that Harry's trouble was related to early abandonment: "he'd been left on the doorstep of the Unitarian Church when he was a baby, and he never did find out who his parents were" (p. 21).

What the gods take away with one hand, they give with the other—so the Greek maxim says. The "gift" that accompanied Harry's colorlessness was acting ability. He was extraordinarily versatile, equally skillful at taking the parts, successively, of Henry VIII, Abe Lincoln, and Queeg in *The Caine Mutiny Court-Martial*. Now the Mask and Wig Club has voted to do Tennessee Williams's *A Streetcar Named Desire* for the spring production. The director asks Harry to take a part. "Who am I this time?" he asks, eager

My work on this paper was supported by a grant from the Division of Fellowships, National Endowment for the Humanities; and by residence at the Rockefeller Foundation Study and Conference Center at Bellagio, Italy. In a somewhat earlier version this paper was awarded the Fritz Schmidl Memorial Prize of the Psychoanalytic Association of Seattle for the best paper involving applied psychoanalysis for 1982.

for a new identity. Harry is slated—naturally—for the Marlon Brando part, Stanley Kowalski. As soon as he picks up the playbook and starts reading, Harry is transformed and now seems "huge and handsome and conceited and cruel" (p. 24).

As the story unfolds, a colorless young woman who has come to town to help install some new telephone-company machines is persuaded to try out for the play. She accurately describes herself as "a walking icebox" (p. 24). "I wonder if you two would play the fight scene," the director says to Harry and Helene. " 'Sure,' said Harry, his eyes . . . on her. Those eyes burned up clothes faster than she could put them on. 'Sure,' he said, 'if Stell's game' " (p. 26). At first listless, she falls for Harry—or rather Stanley—like a ton of bricks as she plays this scene with him as Stella, his wife, and really lives out the part.

Toward the end of rehearsals, one of the townspeople takes pity on Helene and explains: "Once the show's over—whatever you thought Harry was evaporates into thin air" (p. 27). At first shocked, she plans carefully; and just after the last curtain, as Harry retreats into his invisible self, she presents him with a book—*Romeo and Juliet*—and gets him started reading. In a week they are married. Later, she tells the narrator, "In the past week . . . I've been married to Othello, been loved by Faust, and been kidnapped by Paris" (p. 135). Would they be in the next production?—he asks. "Who are we this time?" she says.

I do not know if Harry should have gone to a psychiatrist—after all, he did get a wife who seemed to have consummate taste for choosing exciting parts—but I do know two things: that some of the Harrys we shall look at do need treatment, and that long before Vonnegut writers were interested in Harry's kind of character.

I call it the "fictive personality," and I conceive of it as a personality disturbance in which, in the relative absence or weakness of *both* normal narcissism *and* object love, the self strives toward total identification with characters in literary, historical, or mass-media fiction: these characters transiently "fill in" the empty self by providing ready-made self-concepts—producing, on the surface, an illusion of real being, but all too often reflecting, beneath that, the reactive anger that arises from the early frustration that originally left the self helpless and empty, in search of parents at first and of authors subsequently.

In one of the world's greatest literary characters precisely this sort of being is represented. Don Quixote gives a remarkable, full exhibition of the fictive personality and thereby helps to begin to fill out the preliminary definition given above. The theme of his story is the confusion between illusion or fantasy and reality. As Waldo Frank says well in his introduction,

Don Quixote is "a man possessed, not a madman" (Cervantes, 1605, p. vi). What has "possessed" him is clear; his personality has been seized, captured, filled up, by the literature of chivalry. As one of Cervantes' prefatory poems to the novel has it, the Don is

> a Manchegan gentleman whose reading
> Had turned his head with tales of bleeding
> Knights-errant, damsels, love's surprises,
> And all the chivalry's disguises [p. 16].

He becomes so addicted to such reading that in order to buy books he sells off large parcels of his estate—"so great," Cervantes writes, "was his curiosity and infatuation" with chivalric tales. "In short, our gentleman became so immersed in his reading that he spent whole nights from sundown to sunup and his days from dawn to dusk in pouring over books, until finally, from so little sleeping and so much reading . . . [he] had filled his imagination with everything he had read, . . . all sorts of impossible things, and as a result had come to believe that all these fictitious happenings were true; they were more real to him than anything else in the world" (p. 27). At last, "he came to conceive the strangest idea that ever occurred to any madman in this world"—"he would go in quest of adventures, by way of putting into practice all that he had read in his books" (p. 27). To accompany his new, fictive being, he must give himself a new name (as the romance knight Amadis of Gaul had gone) and find a lady to whom he could consecrate his efforts.

All this is based on the traditions of chivalric literature, whose "authority and prestige" (p. 17) Cervantes said he had written the book to overthrow. Within the novel itself, the curate, barber, and housekeeper gain entrance to Don Quixote's study and sprinkle holy water about the room; then they burn his vast collection of romances, as if they could thereby exorcise the demon possessing Don Quixote's person. But the "demon" is his personality, and the books live on, as fictions, in him.

Literary critics, philosophers, and psychoanalysts have all recognized that the power of fictions resides in their ability to promote identifications. In a very ordinary, normal way, identification processes are involved in modeling, identity formation, values, the development of good ideals, personal maturation, and the growth of creative capacity.[1] But in the instance of the personality that I am looking at, the identification has a completely different quality, seeming almost to amount to possession. The identification does not stop at resemblance—it becomes total, incorporating the violent and

---

[1] It is important to differentiate the fictive personality as a disorder from the creative act of making fictions for an audience. In Martin (1984) I make this differentiation fully.

depressive aspects of the fictional character without self-examination, in a completely unscrutinized, indiscriminate manner. For the fictive personality, fictions do not simulate life, they are a *source* of life.

It is not surprising that creative writers have given us frequent representations of characters who are empty except for the fictions they take into themselves. A famous instance after Don Quixote is Goethe's *The Sorrows of Young Werther*. At the core of Werther's being is a conviction of will-lessness, emptiness. Werther says: "I stand, as it were, before a circus show. I see the little puppets move, and I ask whether it is not an optical illusion. I am amused with these puppets, or rather, I am myself one of them" (Goethe, 1774, p. 60). Georg Brandes (1936) tells how "young men sympathized, first in Germany, and later in many other countries, with Werther: they dressed and yearned and felt as he did" (pp. 214–215). Many of them committed suicide in complete identification with him. Werther gave scores of people an identity and a role to play—but that brought them to the brink, and over the brink, of the death which brought his identity, and theirs, to a conclusion.

Many other books come to mind in which the main theme is the way in which an empty, narcissistic person, or sometimes a child in whom identity formation has scarcely begun, "imports" into the self, as a preformed whole, a character from fiction or history. In *Wuthering Heights*, Cathy says, "I am Heathcliff." Emma Bovary, in Flaubert's novel, identifies with a whole series of romantic heroines. In *Crime and Punishment*, Raskolnikov wants to be, then acts *as if* he is, a Napoleon-like superman. In *Adventures of Huckleberry Finn*, Huck imitates Tom Sawyer, and Tom bases his actions upon the heroes of romantic adventure novels. Walker Percy's *The Moviegoer* exhibits the effects of film fictions upon personality. *Zelig* is a movie about the fictive personality process. Pirandello's *Six Characters in Search of an Author* and *Henry IV* are representative of modern drama in that, like so many other plays, these are concerned with empty persons seeking roles to play.

Certainly, we begin to get an idea of the individual varieties and wide cultural distribution of fictive personality; apparently, writers have identified a fairly permanent element of personality. A passage in Joseph Wood Krutch's *The Modern Temper* (1929) suggests that in part, indeed, some people and even whole societies have always composed themselves in relation to fictions: "Louis XIV tried to live as though he were the hero of one of Racine's tragedies; Sir Philip Sidney tried to live as though he were the hero of one of those half-pastoral, half-heroic prose romances of which he gave the world an example; Byron as though he were his own Childe Harold; and all the members of the society of King Charles II's day as though they were characters in one of Congreve's comedies" (p. 176).

Krutch remarks that literature provides "the various forms toward which various people of various societies have endeavored unsuccessfully to aspire" (p. 176). But what happens when, in the instances of the fictive personalities at which we have been looking, the endeavor *is* successful? Especially today, when mass communications, whence most of our fictions come, command more of a child's life than any other waking activity, including school, according to one survey (Schramm, 1961),[2] what happens to the personality when fictions are the chief material for emulation and the most abundant source for personality formation, and offer the most attractive appeals for love—that is, for "fictive love" rather than object love?

People with fictive personalities find it easy to discover selves to adopt when fictions are so plentiful in society. The theater and the profession of acting offer an instructive example of the pressure of plentifully available fictions upon even normal personalities. The British playwright John Mortimer (Walker, 1982) has recently said of a famous comic actor: "Acquaintances of the late Peter Sellers often felt they were meeting, in his private life, a blank sheet of paper. Without an assumed accent, a mustache, a funny walk or a set of false teeth, the actor knew, with depressing certainty, that he simply didn't exist" (p. 7). In him the actor's dependence on being someone else was carried to an extreme. But not surprisingly, many actors tend to exhibit fictive personality characteristics, perhaps brought forward, too, by training in modern techniques of encouraging "method" acting (Rule, 1973). I could give many examples of actors for whom life seems to exist only through adopting others' roles, but let me take two examples—one problematic, and one undoubtedly creative.

After several decades of playing the Lone Ranger on radio and television, in films and circuses, in 1979 Clayton Moore was obliged by the copyright owners to give up the part in favor of a younger replacement. He refused. He would not remove his mask—until at last a court decision forced him to drop his mask and, presumably, resume his "real" identity. But the Lone Ranger, he claimed, *had* become his true identity, displacing his original self. Wearing a masklike pair of dark sunglasses, Moore began to appeal to his audience to give him back his self. To crowds he told the story of "his" life with such an air of reality that one bystander was led to remark: "This guy *really* thinks he's the Lone Ranger." Moore himself says that he "fell in love with the character," and it "helped to make a better person of me . . . I tell the truth [according to] the Lone Ranger creed" (Marowitz, 1981, pp. 103–104).

---

[2] The "fictive personality" is, in relation to cultural materials, exactly the opposite from what Kris (1956) called "the personal myth." The patients discussed by him "do not borrow their autobiography from cultural tradition or any general mythology. They are the creators, and their myth is a personal one" (p. 300).

One of the recurring observations concerning Meryl Streep involves her ability to change her character considerably with her roles—to convey a whole new aura of personality with each part. The only thing she is really passionately demanding about, she has said of herself, is her work: "I can be as demanding within the boundaries of fiction as I want," she remarks (Rosenthal, 1981, p. 68). "Her approach," David Rosenthal wrote, ". . . is simply to assume the life of whomever it is she is about to portray. To become part of the landscape, as Meryl aptly puts it, to see a character's world and simply step right in. To disappear into the warped reality of acting fiction and emerge as someone else. To do so too well can be scary" (p. 77). Karel Reiss, the director of *The French Lieutenant's Woman*, observed that she is "liberated" by costumes. Accepting the British Academy Award for *French Lieutenant's Woman*, she said: "Call me in six years and the character will still be inside me. Usually it's difficult to get inside a character; this one is difficult to get out of" (Champlain, 1982, p. 28). No costumes were necessary when she played Sophie in the film made from William Styron's novel *Sophie's Choice*, but to prepare for the part Streep spent five months getting a linguistic costume—learning Polish. Everyone involved in the film, according to reports, was astonished "when, at the first reading around a table, Streep looked up to speak and it was Sophie who spoke. 'It was as if,' [Alan] Pakula says, 'Meryl Streep had ceased to exist' " (p. 28). During breaks on the set she continued, in conversation, to speak with a Polish accent.

I propose that fictive personality disorders have always existed and analysts have always treated them; but given the plentitude of fictions in contemporary culture, psychoanalysts are likely to be seeing an increasing number of patients now and in the future who fall somewhere along the continuum from relatively normal or sublimated fictionality to the other end of the scale—a rageful, even murderous, pathology of ficticity.

## Clinical Illustration #1: Melissa

When I started to work with Melissa she was thirty-four years old. Recently divorced she was the mother of several children. She had been in once-a-week therapy with an experienced psychiatrist, and he recommended her for analysis; in connection with her application for clinic treatment, she was interviewed by two senior analysts, who both agreed that she was capable of sustaining a psychoanalysis, with a high chance for a successful outcome.

Yet, though it was apparent that she needed treatment, to diagnose her illness was not so easy. In retrospect, my initial diagnosis already points to the problematic and ambiguous elements underlying her apparent needs. My first diagnosis was: hysterical personality, with underlying narcissism and obsessive-compulsive and masochistic features. "However," I added in my first report, "diagnostically this choice reflects the emphasis at this time, since she also shows other symptoms that would classify her as 'depressive neurosis,' 'anxiety neurosis,' 'sadomasochistic,' and 'passive-aggressive' behavior, and so on. In short, there is a wide spectrum of character and behavior neurosis."

One central feature did stand out at once, and has continued to be prominent: she feels empty and lacking in identity, and all of her symptoms congregate around a single empty core.

Even in the earliest hours of treatment, a primary conflict was apparent between her vividly experienced disappointments and her equally vital fantasies. To her the world seemed radically split. On the one hand, she was severely disappointed in her children, who demand too much of her; her former husband, who refuses to take care of her; her law school, which seems to require too much work of her; her mother, who, Melissa feels, criticizes her at every opportunity and makes her grovel; her brother, who is too distant from her; and her friends, who do not give her the continuous support she requires. Her satisfactions, it soon became clear, were confined to fantasy. She imagined having a secret friend, a romantic lover, a perfect house, an unending, unconditional supply of love and affection, and a career; her career would culminate in her triumph over all her enemies—mother, husband, children, and so on. For herself, however, there would be an endless flow of benefits and pleasures.

Whenever reality and fantasy came into conflict, it was clear, fantasy would win. She ran up debts. She resorted to shoplifting to get what she wanted. She overate compulsively. She lied on résumés, and she told lies to her husband and friends about her accomplishments. She developed, on demand, a whole battery of related illnesses, and she faked fainting spells and a suicide attempt. While of course these symptoms were multi-determined, they were fundamentally designed to make fantasy seem to triumph over reality, and to allow her to fill herself up.

I soon began to see that there was an intimate relation between her emptiness, her fantasies, her anger at real restrictions, and her self-defeating, acting-out behavior; and that the shifting diagnostic picture which I had observed very early was really a large picture which could be understood in terms of the concept of the fictive personality. The picture kept shifting precisely because it was all fictive, and her personality was the center and source of the fictions. I should have listened to her more carefully at the beginning. In the first session following our initial interview, she said, "I worked on and off in the beginning of my marriage, then I played at being a mother." To show me what she meant, she told me that though in a real way she did recognize that she had children and *was* a mother, she would sometimes watch herself taking care of her children in a mirror, and she knew that the reflected person was not real.

Soon she began to bring forth the idea that to understand the world required three keys. Her theory was that the world had three shapes, corresponding to her three favorite books: *Little Women, Gone with the Wind,* and *The Wizard of Oz.* All one had to do is to identify the proper book to be used to interpret the particular aspect of the world that any problem brought to hand, and the way of dealing with it would soon become evident. Never mind if it didn't work: the "key" remained right, though the world might be wrong.

It was no accident that all three of the books that served her had at their hearts—in Jo, Scarlett, and Dorothy—lost girls, alone and frightened, abandoned by men and yearning for new men, lovers or fathers, to save them—powerful wizards or forceful buccaneers. "I was Daddy's girl and could do no wrong," she said, both literally and also symbolically, many times. We soon took wing in a whirl of fictions. Other books with similar themes, such as *Mary, Queen of Scots, My Fair Lady,* and *Lulu's Window* were presented as modifications of the basic three. "I tend to live in a fantasy world," she said openly as early as session fourteen. "I play games. I do it almost all the time when I'm alone—for instance in my car, at night, or in the bathroom. And of course everything turns out right. I have a sick uncle who leaves me $50 million. I never grow old." Even in her dreams she was in the books she was reading. She wrote poems and analyzed them in her sessions—*those* were herself, rather than the unfamiliar self that managed a household or went to school. When she was depressed, she whispered to herself, "Scarlett O'Hara says, 'Tomorrow's another day!' " She knew that she wasn't Scarlett O'Hara most times, but she found the character irresistible and she slipped into it whenever possible: "Her similarity to me is enormous: she was aggressive, shocking, ungenteel. But look what was demanded of her! . . . When she needed her father most he had an accident and broke his neck." When Melissa felt alone, she gathered real or imaginary friends around her—like Dorothy, in threes. I was often cast in the role of the scarecrow, with no brains, but a friend nonetheless. This appeared clearly in the transference. She even saw me as playing a role, as if our real meanings were in the characters we played. "The role in which I see you," she said before the 100th hour, "has changed quite a bit . . . I said earlier that I saw you as an adversary, but I don't feel that way anymore. I see you very much as part of my support system. I'm beginning—though not totally—to feel comfortable, and I look to you for support, and so I was very angry with you on Wednesday because you let the session end just when I had gotten an important thought out. I knew the session was over, but I was angry. The image that came to me was you as the Wizard of Oz and also the Scarecrow, who helped Dorothy." (I felt that she was splitting the transference along the lines of her central conflict, seeing me as both the omnipotent and also the deprecated male figure, and I commented, "You'd like me to tell you the path to take and not leave you alone to fend for yourself, the way you felt your parents did.")

For her, everything was fiction. It was no accident that all of her central fictions involved costumes: she loved masks and masquerades of all sorts and even dreamed of becoming a nun, so appealing was it for her to wear a costume every day. She wanted to have a new name and consulted books, including the phone book, for appropriate names. Eventually, she chose a new name, that of her father's favorite actor.

In my interventions I hewed as closely as possible to the core of her ficticity, saying piece by piece and in many different ways: "You're really struggling for a special kind of love, the kind you hope will heal the hurts that little women and lost girls suffer. But when it doesn't come, you feel the old angers and bitter frustrations all over again at being lost and alone, and then comes the guilt of being angry at people you love and want to love you. So you can't seem to get back the love you missed, and you can't allow yourself to experience the love that is possible to an adult, here and now."

As these interventions accumulated and began to be accepted, she began to see fictions in the context of history—that is, fantasy in relation to experience. This showed up in the transference before the 100th hour. "I used to read a lot," she said. "Besides my all-time favorite, *Little Women*, I read all the other stories by Alcott. Not a day went by that I wasn't reading—I was always totally oblivious. I still get that way. Last night I had some time for reflection and I spent about an hour going through my high-school yearbook. . . . The books I see on your shelves, *The Decline and Fall of the Roman Empire, Poor Richard*, seem to be history instead of literature, and that surprises me. The kind of books I expected to see would be all the fictional classics." In fact, the majority of the books in my office are fiction—she was seeing the *history* in relation to the structural changes away from ficticity toward reality she was experiencing. Even the titles she saw—not the most prominent ones on the shelves—suggested she was edging toward the acceptance, depressing though it was to be, of her own sense of her impoverishment and fragmentation; and, thereby, giving vent to the rage over her abandonment.

Henry Adams, whose autobiography makes plain that his core identity and object attachments were thoroughly fictive, wrote in 1915:

But we, who cannot fly the world must seek
To live two separate lives; one in the world
Which we must ever seem to treat as real;
The other in ourselves, behind a veil [p. 88].

Melissa had treated the world *as if* it were real; now she began to come from behind the veil of ficticity and live in the world's reality.

A turning point in Melissa's understanding of herself through fictions came in the 180th hour of analysis. In a remarkable way, it came through an actual fiction. Her supreme fiction was that her father, though distant and seldom available, was really warm and loving. She had told me of her pseudo-attempt at suicide with pills, picturing her mother as distant and her father as caring for her, walking her around, making coffee for her, calling the doctor, and so on. By chance, she now came across a story which she had written about this incident when she was sixteen, and which she knew to be a direct narrative of what had happened. The reverse of what she remembered was recounted in her narrative. She had remembered it according to her fantasy, and reversed reality. This stunned her into a dramatic recognition of the distorting powers of her fantasy and the needs that drove it.

Her complaint, repeated many times over the next hundred hours, was that I had robbed her of the ability to live her other fantasy lives. Her storybook guides, *Little Women*, *The Wizard of Oz*, and *Gone with the Wind*, no longer seemed to explain everything. She began to be able to express anger toward her father. *Pari passu*, the psychophysiological reactions, phobias, compulsive lying, violent rages, and acting-out symptoms in general virtually disappeared. Certainly, under pressure she would still occasionally yield to the pleasures of ficticity, but now fiction was more and more a compensation for difficulty, not a way of life. During final exams in school, around the 325th hour, she said, "When I'm studying for exams I need some kind of release—for instance, I'm reading Agatha Christie's[3] mysteries. I know what it is about the mysteries: it's the whole way of life. The characters in her stories are wealthy and can do as they please. I conjure up a vision of people out on lawns sipping lemonade on a storybook day. I would absolutely love to live in that fashion, with enough money so that I wouldn't have to do anything I didn't want to do, and working could be a hobby. That's what I'd *like*. I'd like not to be under all these compulsions. Then I go back to studying, and it's o.k."

[3] For a helpful perspective on detective fiction as a source for fictive personality, see Rudolf Ekstein and Seymour W. Friedman (1959).

A few days after making the crucial distinction between fantasies that supplant reality to support a fictive identity and fantasies that are transiently compensatory or function as defenses on the level of sublimation, Melissa completed the movement from the fictive to the symbolic. Her decisive move from the realm of the imaginary was a definite sign of structural change. Now she reported a dream that began with all sorts of scary adventures, during which she hid in a suitcase. "After a while I climbed out of the suitcase, but I came out of the tail of a plane that had crashed: the tail was still sticking out of the water. I swam away. I wasn't sure what direction to take, but I decided to go east and thought, 'I'll just lie on my back and relax.' People came and they started to show *The Wizard of Oz*. I see the witch flying away. I realize it was all a fake, that I had been in a movie." In her associations she said: "After all her adventures Dorothy wakes up and finds it was all a dream, and she says, 'There's no place like home.' That's just me. Analysis has been a good adventure, and fantasies that once seemed real I know now are only fantasies. I feel like I've been born again and can get a real home now."

## Dynamic Aspects of the Fictive Personality

I wish to investigate additional clinical material, but before doing so, some further analysis of the dynamic issues involved is appropriate. Having a glimpse at the prevalence of this personality process in literature, in mass culture, and in one patient, we need to scrutinize the nature of the fictive personality in terms of its underlying dynamics.

Four analysts have quite separately launched investigations into the definition and description of this personality from four separate angles, describing different aspects of what, I would maintain, must be seen all together in order adequately to grasp its real character. Helene Deutsch's "as if" personality; Harry Guntrip's "schizoid emptiness"; Anna Freud's "altruistic surrender" considered as a defense; and Heinz Kohut's analysis of narcissism, provide, when taken together, a reasonably comprehensive understanding of the nature of the fictive personality.

Helene Deutsch (1942) did not, of course, invent the term "as if"—it had been used previously by the philosopher Hans Vaihinger in his book *The Philosophy of "As If"* (1911), which argued that since reality cannot be truly or totally known, human beings construct systems of thought to satisfy their needs and then reify their systems back into actuality, thus acting "AS IF" the real were the fictive systems they have created. Deutsch set forth her views in her 1942 essay "Some Forms of Emotional Disturbance and Their Relationship to Schizophrenia." Obviously, there is little similarity between

Vaihinger's use of the term metaphysically and her use of it to describe deep pathology, though it is not only possible but even desirable that I should fuse Vaihinger's and Deutsch's approaches in my own attempt to define the fictive personality as existing along a continuum from normal to pathological identifications.

Deutsch focuses upon "the individual's emotional relationship to the outside world" where "his own ego appears impoverished or absent," and where there is a paucity of "affective bonds and responses" (p. 262). This, as we have seen, is an integral feature of the fictive personality. Such an emotional disturbance, she says, takes two forms. In the first, the individual experiences an inner feeling of unreality. In the second, that feeling is projected defensively into the world, and existence "seems strange, objects shadowy, [and] human beings and events theatrical and unreal" (p. 263). What seems at first to be imaginative talent in such people, appears, under scrutiny, to be imaginative parasitism, mental automatism—the "borrowing," on the surface, of the talents or techniques of idealized others. Similarly, affective relationships look intense and varied, but investigation shows them to be "devoid of any trace of warmth." "As if" people seem to have vivid interior beings, but closer inspection shows that "inner experience" is excluded. "It is," Deutsch writes, "like the performance of an actor who is technically well trained but who lacks the necessary spark to make his impersonations true to life" (p. 264).

Deutsch is very clear about the dynamic source of the "as if" personality: though in appearance it looks like the sort of depersonalized coldness that results from the repression, say, of highly charged drives, "psychoanalysis discloses that in the 'as if' individual it is no longer an act of repression but a real loss of object cathexes" (p. 265). Thus the individual relates to the world, as I would put it, by transient fictive identifications. The self waits to be "filled up" by available object identifications, and any object appears as good as another. This makes the fictive personality equally capable of apparent nobility and apparent perfidy. Like the objects that pass before Plato's cave, casting their shadows on the walls within, objects in the world provide the shadowy selves, the fictions, that seize, one after another, the empty inner world. "Overenthusiastic adherence to one philosophy"—or partner, or moral system—"can be quickly and completely replaced by another contradictory one without the slightest trace of inward transformation—simply as a result of some accidental regrouping of the circle of acquaintances, or the like" (p. 266).

Despite the title of her work and its main thrust, Deutsch does not argue, ultimately, that the "as if" personality is confined to schizophrenia; rather, it exhibits a range. Yet every part of the range exhibits some "schizoid" characteristics, and it is here that Harry Guntrip's classification of "schizoid emptiness," in his 1968 book *Schizoid Phenomena, Object Relations and the Self*, is important.

"The schizoid person has renounced objects even though he still needs them" (p. 18)—this, in brief, is Guntrip's central theme. He assumes, correctly I believe, that the self drives toward good objects—relations, beliefs, commitments, institutions—by way of pleasure, achieved early in relations with parents and then confirmed and continued in relation to others. Lacking the capacity for such varied relations, the self cannot achieve completeness, which requires a balancing not-me; and instead, in my terms, reaches toward pseudo-relations, and thus a false self, in fictions—fictions that seem manipulable and manageable, that will not disappoint or disturb. But that route leaves the initial strivings unsatisfied; though objects are renounced, they are still desired, and this produces the central, hidden depressive conflict of the schizoid. Identification with fictions, transient, doubtful, and hesitant, has ceased to be a means of completing or satisfying the self—it is a means only of maintaining the boundaries of an ego by means of the containers provided by the fictions. Lacking the capacity for continuity in object love and thus in a self's inner commitment, the schizoid, Guntrip says, "is constantly 'in and out' of any and every kind of situation" (p. 59). One of my analysands said to me, "I feel that my symptoms are really just a scenario." Guntrip's descriptions of the result have, in general, the ring of truth: the schizoid, he writes, "usually has a rich and active fantasy life, but in real life is often tepid and weak in enthusiasm, is apt to suffer inexplicable losses of interest, and feels little zest in living. Yet deep inside he has particularly intense needs. He can live in imagination but not in the world of material reality from which he is primarily withdrawn into himself. He wants to realize his dreams in real life; but if he finds a dream coming true externally he seems to be unaccountably unable to accept and enjoy it, especially if it concerns a personal relationship" (p. 59). Fundamentally, of course, Guntrip is wrong in characterizing the schizoid's fantasy life as "rich": it is just the reverse. Normal fantasy provides a preparation for action or sublimation; schizoid fantasy is devoted to maintaining the distance between the self and the outer world.

In describing the picture presented by the fictive personality, I want now to turn toward its defensive aspect. This was very effectively designated by Anna Freud (1966) by the phrase "altruistic surrender" in the tenth chapter of *The Ego and the Mechanisms of Defense*. In altruistic surrender Anna Freud sees the combined operations of projection and identification—to these we might add masochism, "masochistic surrender"—for purposes of defense. Gratification is achieved, not directly, but through projection of one's own wishes onto another, followed by identification with the gratification of this other. Freud describes a young governess who, as a child, had wished fervently for beautiful clothes and many children. Though as an adult she wore modest dress and remained unmarried and childless, she fulfilled her original desires by taking an active interest in the clothes of her friends, being an insatiable matchmaker, and caring for many children in her profession. "It looked," Anna Freud writes, "as if her own life had been emptied of interests and wishes . . . Instead of exerting herself to achieve any aims of her own, she expended all her energy in sympathizing with the experiences of people she cared for. She lived in the lives of other people, instead of having any experience of her own" (p. 125).

"Altruistic surrender" most usually involves relatively inconspicuous, "normal" forms of projection and identification. But when employed defensively by an "as if" personality that needs to fill up the void of schizoid emptiness with grandiose fictions, then the constellation of the fictive personality emerges. Identifying with malleable fictions rather than with demanding—and threatening—real objects, the empty self projects outward its aggressive, disappointed impulses as if they were "out there" instead of "in here."

The fictive personality process is certainly related to the narcissistic disorders, which, as Kohut (1977) has shown, should be distinguished from borderline states and treated psychoanalytically. To be sure, in the literary instances and clinical cases I have looked at, or will subsequently mention, in this paper, many borderline or even psychotic disturbances seem to be evident—Don Quixote is regarded by many as a madman; Raskolnikov is a murderer; my case descriptions are replete with borderline features: identity confusion, emptiness, impaired reality testing, suicidal thoughts, derealization, splitting, primitive idealization, and so on. But, after all, the picture is much more complicated: Don Quixote is also revered by many as a perfect chivalric gentleman; Raskolnikov repented and changed his ways completely; and the apparent borderline features of the patients referred to are at least partly related to the identities they adopt or "try on," and tend to be transient rather than permanent features of the personality. Kohut (1971, 1977) and Kohut and Wolf (1978) see borderline pathology as arising from a deficiency in the normal development of the structure of the self. "This deficiency," Tolpin (1980) maintains, "is subsequently dealt with through a variety of unconscious defensive measures that maintain the integrity of the self through a particularly rigid or distorted organization" (p. 301). The fictive personality process is one of these defensive measures, by which a rigid, fully formed fictive organization is imported from without to provide support from within for a noncohesive self (cf. Goldberg, 1978).

In this context, Kohut's (1975) postulate that narcissism and object love develop along separate lines is highly suggestive. The fictive personality, I have claimed, arises when there is a simultaneous disturbance of both normal narcissism and object love. Those whose personalities are channeled into ficticity develop an array of fictive identifications which extend from the self to the world: both are conceived of as fictive. It would seem, then, that in the case of fictive personality, development along either line is displaced and stunted—but is neither fragmented nor shattered (as in borderline or psychotic states), and can be made to resume development when the fictions and their origins are treated in psychoanalysis.

In summarizing, we may conclude that the basic dynamic-defensive aspects regulating the fictive personality localize it in the area of the narcissistic disorders. Each from a separate angle, Deutsch, Guntrip, Anna Freud, and Kohut described a part of what is, taken together, a significant component of narcissism. When relatively sublimated, devoted to autonomy through fantasy, and transformed into productive work, a fictive behavior-and-thought orientation supports healthy narcissism; when combined with borderline personality, fantasy employed defensively, and anxiety, ficticity becomes dangerous.

Creative writers, as we have seen, first described the fictive personality, and therefore it should not be at all surprising that the psychoanalysts who have contributed most to the understanding of the fictive personality should all have turned to discussions of literary works in direct connection with their theories of ficticity. Helene Deutsch devoted an essay to "Don Quixote and Don Quixotisms" (1937), in which she treats the hero of the novel clinically in terms similar to those she uses in her discussion of the "as if" personality. Later, in her essay on the imposter (1955) she cites Thomas Mann's novel *The Confessions of Felix Krull* as providing an apt illustration of her clinical points. In his book, Guntrip devotes a long central section to a discussion of Henry James's life and works as good examples of the operations of the schizoid personality. Anna Freud, too, found the chief confirmation of her theory of altruistic surrender in a work of literature. Freud (1966) remarks that in her view "the finest and most detailed study of . . . altruistic surrender is to be found in Edmond Rostand's play *Cyrano de Bergerac*" (p. 132). The hero, Cyrano, helps his friend—and rival—Christian to woo Roxane, the woman they both love, since Cyrano, due to his huge nose, feels himself unworthy of being loved. Cyrano exemplifies the fictive personality; in conversation, he "speaks" poetry, even in rhyme: he composes as he duels, turning aggression into fiction. He believes that contemporary writers such as Corneille, Molière, and Swift have borrowed their work from him. He lives in a completely fictive world and there—far removed from real object love—he seeks his satisfaction. Isolated from love, he yet desires it; still, he flees from the opportunity to possess it. Kohut's first psychoanalytic paper (1957), too, concerned Thomas Mann's *Death in Venice*; in this article Kohut studied the disintegration of artistic sublimation—that is to say, the destruction of Aschenbach's ability to *create* literary fictions, leading him to experience and *treat himself* as a fiction—a fictive personality.

Since identification of aspects of the fictive personality through creative and psychoanalytic writings should help to deepen our understanding of the clinical issues involved, it is now appropriate to turn more intensively to additional clinical examples.

## Clinical Illustration #2: Terry

Terry came into analysis at a time when his marriage was dissolving; quite consciously, he chose psychoanalysis over joint counseling with his wife. He justified this route by the assertion that he could save his marriage only if he could get an adequate perspective upon himself. Though this was true, it was not, as I was to learn, all of the truth: he experienced powerful urges to be isolated, and psychoanalysis offered him an opportunity to isolate himself from his wife, in their separate treatments, no less than he had already isolated himself in his marriage, and, in general, in his life—from parents, from friends, from employers, and from his children. It was not long, of course, before this isolating wish appeared in the transference. He struggled with his wish to disclose himself, in order to advance in analysis, which conflicted, of course, with his more fundamental and certainly older wish to remain distant. What soon began to emerge was his core belief that he was empty, that when all was said and done he really had nothing to disclose—or, at most, he had to disclose that he could not experience himself as really having any vital inner life. His first dream in analysis was that he stepped over a depression in the ground, then behind him he saw the crack open up until it became a vast abyss. Where there had seemed to be solid ground there actually was only a vast nothingness. This early he was saying, as he said later in many different ways, that his "depression" was over the fact of his emptiness just beneath the surface. Terry had had previous therapy in connection with several years of exhibitionism which nearly culminated in an arrest. His exhibitionism consisted of showing his penis to women who walked past his car at stop signs or crosswalks. He kept the windows rolled up, and he was always poised to drive away. Thus he showed his outside, but he kept perfectly remote from any actual involvement with threatening inner urges.

As he began to convey a relatively broad picture of his background and the way he felt about it, he placed in the center and foreground his belief that he had never had any meaningful relations with anyone, except briefly, perhaps in an illusory way. He had some feeling that once his parents had been interested in him, but that was only a vague feeling: all his detailed memories were that they had been distant from him (and taught him distance as a way of life) in different ways. His father he sees as omnipotent and demanding, sometimes a robot, sometimes a godlike figure, disapproving and depreciating. "Frosty" is the word Terry uses to sum up the impression his father gave him. The word he uses for his mother is "spaced": he sees her as removed, dreamy, unresponsive to her son. He believed that his mother and father would have preferred to have had a girl. Based upon generalization of this early experience, he saw everyone in his later life in exactly the same terms.

This showed up in the transference in the 59th session in relation to the analysis of a missed appointment. He very clearly connected his wish to present an attractive false (or fictive) surface with the conviction that beneath the surface was a vast gap: "I'd *like* to paint some rosy picture because sooner or later I know you'll get tired of all this shit. I'm beginning to count on your support and I'm not sure I like that . . . I don't feel I've ever been able to rely on anyone for very long . . . I'm always afraid that I'm going to be left out . . . Even in here I find it impossible to open up completely and be unconcerned about how I'll appear." In Winnicott's familiar terms, he used a "false self" not to conceal or protect a "true self" but to cover up the *absence* of a true self or fundamental core. His associations are very strikingly filled with images of empty containers: space ships, tunnels, suits of armor, empty ships, mine shafts, bags, and bottles. His body is the shell; the empty inside *is* himself. "I must be trying to fill up a gap that was never filled up when I was a child," he said accurately in hour #254.

He has remained, in all his personal relations or professional activities, on the level of Deutsch's "as if." He has never really been able to commit himself to any job: he has merely occupied several jobs for brief periods. In his marriage, he has never experienced his activities *as* those of a husband; he sees himself acting, in a role, "as if" he were a husband. Sometimes he reminds himself that he has children and tries to act "as if" he were a parent, but even this feeling soon passes, and his children complain about his indifference. He is a man on the margin, the circumference, of everything.

He has given, on numerous occasions, very full portrayals of his schizoid feelings of emptiness and pretense, such as those described by Guntrip. These vividly portray how it feels to be a fiction to oneself:

I see myself now as a patchwork collection of defenses, tricks, illusions, with no dignity. Now, since the defenses are tumbling and we get nearer to me I get more and more concerned: there isn't a me. The sum total of me is in the illusions, and I'm afraid when we strip all these away, there won't be anything there. I'm—just tricks and illusions. Maybe the fact I speak of "I" means there is a me, but it's so small it's totally insignificant. I was born and my body grew, but I never did. I think that all my attempts—if I had any, and I *must* have had some—to develop were squelched, and I became convinced I was nothing and so I had to acquire pseudo-characteristics, costumes, whatever it was "they" wanted from me. I found that out right in the beginning. But I couldn't please "them" with the fakes either. I never satisfied—that's my essence. Anything to the contrary is an illusion, like a circus or a magic act, a play, "make believe." So every new relation is a challenge to see how long I can confound them—showing images or reflections of things that don't exist. It's like I died when I was a child—but that's my secret, I came back to fool everybody. Everybody thinks I'm still there—but I do it with mirrors. *How deep is a reflection?*

The French psychoanalyst Marcel Czermak, in speaking of the phenomena of "mental automatism," which is one of the impressions given by the fictive personality, speaks of these people as "living by copying gestures, to the point where they have become—can we still say subjects?—marionettes of pure seeming fabricated by various random parts, mimicked from people who have crossed their paths" (Schneiderman, 1980, p. 181). "Marionettes of pure seeming"; it is a fine phrase, one we shall have reason to remember when we hear of children who see themselves as like Pinocchio or as manipulated by wizards of humbug in Oz. Czermak's whole description fits Terry perfectly. How deep *is* a reflection? It is a ghost, only a "pure seeming"—a nothing—what my patient fears he will become. Should he give up his fictions, he fears, he will give up his self. Such a patient is purely theatrical. He lives through the lives—or, more terrifyingly, through the deaths—of others.

Terry, like Melissa, helps us to see the route to satisfaction taken by altruistic surrender, as described by Anna Freud. The identification is not with others who achieve real satisfaction from the patient's sacrifice, but instead consists of the satisfaction in identification with fictional characters. The defense of isolation, operating powerfully in Terry, keeps his identifications "inside": he identifies with his fantasies. But he sees himself as altruistically sacrificing himself for others: "I play the martyr," he said (hour #246), "I go without and do without. My wife has five or six times as many clothes as I do. Most of the time I do not eat lunch—I feed on doing without. I must have constant approval—and how can I get approval without giving? I even give to strangers, or my customers: I do little favors for them. I 'forget' to bill them. I'm the one who suffers."

Terry's fantasies derive directly from fictions. For more than two hundred hours, he kept the sources of his fundamental fictive identifications concealed. Unable to generate his own fantasies, he borrowed them from others. While Melissa's core fictions came from fairly respected books, Terry's derived wholly from comic strips. The difference in cultural level may give us some hints that the urgency to borrow fictive identities pressed upon Terry at an earlier age that it did upon Melissa.

At about the 200th hour he began to tell me that his earliest life ambition, which I knew was to be a pilot, derived from the comic strip *Terry and the Pirates*, and that he had once idolized the creator of the strip, Milton Caniff. Terry had actually tried to enter the Air Force Academy and envisioned a career as a flier. The image of the pilot enclosed in his cockpit, alone, isolated high above others in the sky, perfectly enacts, of course, his image of how his parents related to him: "frosty," "distant," "spaced." Sexually, he is extremely attracted to Oriental women, a preference that he traces to the "Dragon Lady" in the comic strip; he has an Oriental girl friend and often fantasizes about Oriental women.

Three other comic-strip characters proved to have been even more attractive objects of identification for him. These were the Lone Ranger, Superman, and Captain Marvel. All three have in common the fact they are isolated, influencing human affairs but ultimately remaining uninvolved in them. In all three there is a fundamental contrast between their appearances and their internal capacity. For the weak young man who becomes Captain Marvel when he pronounces the magic word "Shazam!"; or for Clark Kent, who is transformed from a "mild-mannered" reporter to an aggressive fighter against crime, there is no connection between his "real" appearance and his "more real" inner identity. Even the Lone Ranger wears a mask like an outlaw but does only good deeds. All three are figures who are allied with superego impulses: these help to defend Terry against feelings of shame and guilt and self-accusation, feelings that could easily overwhelm him without such objects for projective identification. Finally, all three characters behave in a fundamentally altruistic fashion, finding their satisfactions in the satisfaction of others, but never seeking anything for themselves. These, then, are characters who correspond very closely to Terry's distorted definition of identity, which he seeks to realize, in fantasy, through modeling all of his actions after these characters in comic-strip fictions. "I used to identify strongly with them when I was a kid," he said. "Their identities always remained secret. From time to time they appeared—they exposed themselves, did good deeds, and disappeared again. They were strong and gentle, the personifications of good. I like that. I want to do good."

Terry replaced his exhibitionist behavior with the compulsive search for women whom he could pick up from the street. His fantasy is that he will be able to locate women who will accept a ride in his car and then immediately fall in love with him and propose having sex with him. The woman will tell him all her most secret thoughts, admire his body unconditionally when he undresses, and make love to him, all the while never asking him to reveal anything of himself; and then they will part, and he will never see her again. "What I'd like them to say afterward," he remarked, "is 'Who was that masked man?' They would never forget me, and always think of me with longing, but they would never know anything about me." He envisions himself as making love with the vigor of a superman. These fantasies are never fulfilled, of course; and so after spending three or four hours in a day searching for their fulfillment, he often settles for a prostitute, whom he pretends he does not pay; and more often than not, he is unable to perform sexually.

Once Terry was able to talk about the identities that were most real to him—namely, the ones he had borrowed from fictions—he made rapid (but painful) strides in acknowledging the inadequacy of these secret identities. After more than 270 hours in treatment, he remarked: "I'm feeling like I have to learn to be myself and not an invented person."

It is important, I think, to give an illustration of how the analyst can work with fictive identity formations. When any patient discloses and discourses on the origins of his neuroses against a background of their genesis and development, in relation to his parents, or as arising from conflict, trauma, or past or current life situations, the analyst must, of course, interpret these through the transference since he is debarred from direct knowledge of the sources. However, when the patient associates his distress with that of a fiction shared by the analyst and analysand, there exists not only the transference, but also the agreed-upon "givens," facts of the fictional source as a background for interpretation. The analyst, this is to say, cannot usually see the distortions in the patient's representation of a parent, for instance; but he can, much more easily, see the distortions in the analysand's comments on a fiction which he has transferred into his own being. In a much more explicit way than through the transference, the analyst is able to distinguish between what is accurate and what is distorted or emphasized or omitted in the associations. He is able, to use Donald Spence's (1982) terms, to work with both "narrative truth" and "historical truth," as well as "transference" truth, in the context of the representation of the self as fictive.

In the 347th hour of analysis Terry talked about having visited a prostitute and being disgusted with himself. His feeling was that he was seeking "comfort," but from what or for what he could not say, and he was disgusted with himself. "How did the idea of finding a prostitute arise?" I wondered. "I was at the shop," he said, and I felt I had to get out. So I did. I went to the bookstore to buy a book, *The Lord of the Rings*. Then I felt I couldn't go back to the shop, so I drove around, and I saw this girl and picked her up. I had second thoughts about it the minute I did it." He said he hadn't gotten any pleasure from the sex—in fact, he didn't have intercourse with the girl. He said it was "all a pile of shit" and seemed to be telling the story generally in the manner of an adolescent, and in a few moments he showed explicitly what his identification was. It was with Holden Caulfield, hero of *The Catcher in the Rye*, one of the most famous books of the last thirty years: "Last night," Terry said, "I went to bed and slept for a couple of hours, then I awoke and lay there for about forty-five minutes. I got up and I read *Catcher in the Rye*. I identify so closely with this kid. I feel exactly as Holden Caulfield feels. We both are completely alone." At this point, I decided that I would pick up on his assertion of "exact" or total identity between himself and Caulfield in order to see what needs compelled him to see himself "as if" he were Holden. I believed I now understood the point of view from which he perceived his episode with the prostitute. I said, "Holden didn't fare any better with a prostitute." He said he knew that it was so—he had "the same" feelings of disappointment and guilt that Holden had experienced. "I wonder if you see any reasons why else you identify with Holden?" I asked. Terry associated:

I see, I experience, the confusion in his mind, and his desperation. He invites every cabby he meets to have a drink with him. Even a little girl in the park, a friend of his sister's, he invites for chocolate. First he goes one way, then another. The girl he asks to marry him he thinks is a royal pain in the ass anyway. He's so confused and frightened—I identify with that. I don't have any target, any direction. I don't seem to be effective at anything. This morning when I got up I felt I didn't want to come here—then five minutes later I couldn't wait to come. I'm depressed but I'm not allowed to be. ["You won't allow yourself," I said.]

Look how Holden tried to do lots of things, some crazy things, even, so he wouldn't have to feel depressed. His parents—just like mine—wouldn't allow him; mine wouldn't allow me, they didn't want to hear about it. I'd just like someone to give a damn about me. [I had heard his emphasis on Holden's parents' coldness as a distortion which he shares with Holden and also as Terry's projection of his own feelings into Holden, but I felt that the emotional focus was on his confusing depression and solitude, which is also Holden's problem; and so I said, "That's Holden's problem too."] It seems to be. That's why I identify with him. Our situations are so similar. He's been a failure at school and nobody gives a shit. He's trying hard not to give a shit too.

[Here, Terry's weak ego boundaries allow him to express his own feelings and need to defend against emptiness through attributing them to Holden. He continues in this expressive, revelatory vein:] I keep saying to myself, there's one big difference: Holden is sixteen and I'm forty-two, and I feel just like him. *He's* trying to find himself. He's trying to make some adjustment between himself and the world he doesn't understand, and he finds himself different from everyone. He wants so badly to fit in, and yet he can't find any place that's comfortable. I guess I'm saying that's *my* problem. What I see in the book is myself. We seem to be different from everyone else, incompatible. If I meet anybody who seems slightly to care to be sympathetic, I'll react just like Holden—I'll ask her to run away with me. [Terry had come close to doing that recently with a woman he had met only twice. I responded: "You did that with Ann, in effect."] Yes, exactly. I seem so much like Holden. I make myself like that. Holden is me. When I read *Catcher in the Rye*, and I've read it many times, I don't read it with an open mind; I put myself in it. It's not difficult: I see me in him.

Certainly there have been other occasions on which Terry experienced more transient feelings of identification. Not surprisingly, when angry, he expressed a feeling of similarity to the Super Tylenol killer, followed by identification with the "copy-cat" poisoners. On another occasion, when lonely and frightened, he said, "The real me is just a frightened, hidden-away child like Anne Frank. I'm in a prison, forgotten, unnoticed . . . I am this little kid with a long nose because I've lied so long. I'm vulnerable, like a little girl sitting in the corner among the ashes." Here, of course, a series of fictive identifications from fairy tales and children's books helps to give the analyst insight into the patient's feelings from several angles—perhaps most centrally of all conveying the idea that he sees himself as unreal.

Analysis of the fictive personality through both its permanent and its more transient identifications involves interpretation on several levels: (1) the patient's interpretation of himself through his choice of fictions; (2) the patient's distorting projections of his own impulses back onto the fiction; (3) the patient's interpretation of the analyst within this fictive frame. Working in this fashion with fictive identifications allows the analyst to expand the transference situation and to give depth and complexity to the analysis.[4]

[4] In his *Female Sexuality and the Oedipus Complex* (1975) Nagera gives an example of his work with Miss A., which corresponds to the work I have done with Terry. Miss A.'s identification with Nana, the prostitute in Emil Zola's novel, provided a route through which he analyzed her oedipal conflicts. Nagera writes: "When such fantasies came into the transference and she wanted to play Nana the prostitute with the analyst, we could ascertain not only the strength of her sexual wishes but her fear of losing control, of prostituting herself, of being able to seduce the analyst and other males. She referred with much visible anxiety to her fear of ending like Nana" (pp. 91–92).

Terry's identification with Holden Caulfield revealed an important aspect of his fictiveness and also conveyed his confused loneliness and reactive anger. This particular character from Salinger's popular book *The Catcher in the Rye* has served as a fictive model for others besides Terry. I would argue that the analysis of fictive personality in Terry can aid in the understanding of some aspects of the violence occurring in contemporary society. Some of this violence, I maintain, can be traced to the fictive-personality formations increasingly evident in today's social scene.

## Application of the Analysis of the Fictive-Personality Process to the Study of an Assassin: Mark David Chapman

When Mark David Chapman shot John Lennon five times with a .38 revolver at the entrance to the Dakota apartment under the banner of J. P. Salinger and in the name of Holden Caulfield, a fictive personality was thrust upon the world in terror.

Immediately following the shooting, Chapman took off his coat and sweater, apparently so that the police, when they arrived, would see he was not armed and intended no further harm; and then he took his copy of *The Catcher in the Rye* out of his pocket and started to read calmly. During the initial hearings, when asked why he had killed Lennon, he often remarked, in what he seemed to think was an answer, that the meaning was to be found in Salinger's book. He was, he said, the "Catcher in the Rye" for his generation, and he talked at length about the innumerable, complicated similarities that he saw between himself and Holden Caulfield during Holden's three days in New York which form the substance of the novel. He told psychiatrist Daniel Schwartz, who prepared material for the defense, that earlier on the day of the shooting he believed that immediately upon killing Lennon he would turn into Caulfield and cease to exist in his own identity. It seems, at least in part, that he really believed this to have happened, since at his sentencing in late August, 1981, he told Judge Dennis Edwards, Jr., that he had only a few words to speak before he would begin a vow of silence (one he has apparently kept). These are what he promised to be "my final spoken words": "I keep picturing all these little kids, and nobody's around—nobody big, I mean—except me. And, I'm standing on the edge of some crazy cliff. . . . I'd just be the catcher in the rye." The words, of course, are recited directly from the novel. Chapman's final testimony was that he had ceased to exist, or rather that he had found his true identity—in somebody else's fiction.

His whole career seems to have been based upon the drive toward finding himself in others. Tony Adams, the director of the DeKalb YMCA where

Chapman worked and formed his first plan for a life's career as a YMCA worker, said that Mark "would do anything to please me." The girl he was passionately devoted to, Jessica Blankenship, provided a fully formed set of values for him: he joined her religion and became fully persuaded of its perfection; he dressed and ate and drank as she did; he imitated her nonviolence: he went to the college she recommended. But it was not the qualities of the persons that he identified with, it was object identification itself that he was seeking: as Helene Deutsch had put it, any object would do. For, at the same time, he had been influenced by other friends to get into drugs—"he did anything he could get his hands on," one friend said: he idealized another friend who toted a pearl-handled revolver, and he later took pistol training and became a security guard. Before the killing, he said, he was fighting with "good and evil spirits." Out of this internal conflict he had tried to commit suicide; he failed, but he said: "My life is gone." He was becoming ready to adopt his final fictions.

In Chapman the "good" and "bad" identifications of the "as if" personality or the "in and out" behavior of the schizoid rested more fundamentally upon a thoroughgoing commitment to fictiveness. He became obsessed with Norman Rockwell's painting *Triple Self-Portrait*, which shows Rockwell looking in a mirror as he paints his reflection on a canvas. This was Chapman's central problem: Where is the "I"?—is it in the fictive, painted, observer artist, the fictive mirror, or the fictive art? There seemed no other alternatives, no arena in which he could really be "himself." Out of this confusion he began to identify with John Lennon. He played the guitar, he collected Beatles records, he married a Japanese-American woman (like Yoko) who helped to support him. When he quit his last job six weeks before the murder he signed his final worksheet with the name "John Lennon." He hung around the Dakota. He told a taxi driver who picked him up in front of the apartment that he had just dropped off the tapes of a new album that Lennon and Paul McCartney had made that day. On the day of the murder, he approached Lennon to autograph his latest album, *Double Fantasy*, and he made certain that a photographer snapped his picture with Lennon. He urged the photographer to remain on the scene until Lennon returned. "You never know," he said, "something might happen." The photographer left; but Lennon came back—to the fictive *Catcher in the Rye* and his real .38.

Based on Schwartz's testimony at the sentencing, we can say with fair certainty what had happened (Schwartz, 1981). Having failed to kill himself, Chapman's identification with Lennon turned increasingly sinister. He projected his own suicidal wishes onto the object of his identification. Then, to kill the bad things in himself, he had only to kill his double, Lennon.

Recently, he had come to consider Lennon a "phony," a wealthy business-man, a betrayer of his generation's ideals, an imposter. To kill Lennon would be to kill his "bad" side, therefore; and then, Chapman believed, his good side, the Holden Caulfield in him, would fully emerge. He would be able to become his good fiction.

"You and I," Schwartz told the judge, "try to model ourselves after somebody, . . . we will not run the risk of believing that we are that person" (p. 15). But Chapman did. Eventually, he projected his own hatred and inward sense of phoniness onto Lennon, so that he could view himself as pure and honest. Now, pure, he spoke directly to God. Eventually, God told him to plead guilty and allowed him to become Holden Caulfield, and to speak Holden's words. He *had* killed phoniness, he *had* murdered evil, he *had* rid the world of death: he *was* the catcher in the rye.

To be sure, Terry is very far from Mark David Chapman's psychotic fictiveness. But the identification processes and the shared identification with Holden Caulfield help us to pass from the in-depth understanding of a patient to the analysis of a event in culture.

At this point I want to turn to two clinical cases more briefly presented: the first involving a childhood trauma; and the second, a young man who was able to turn his fictive personality formations to creative use through work in writing a book.

## Clinical Illustration #3: Peter

Peter was referred for analysis at the age of five following an episode of hallucinatory psychosis which was preceded, six weeks earlier, by the view-ing of a television rerun of *The Wizard of Oz* (1939).

In light of the materials that soon emerged, in which the connections between separation fears, abandonment, unsteadiness of identity, and a growing fictiveness of self are clear, it will be helpful to state at once that Peter had experienced continuous threats to a conviction of his permanency and cohesion due to the fleeting, transient character of his childhood. He suffered a double loss around the age of one; first his family moved from an apartment to a home; and second, his mother went to work in his father's office while Peter was left with a sitter. Shortly after this, Peter experienced sleep disturbances. A year later, the home was sold, and the family moved to a duplex. Somewhat more than a year and a half later, the family moved from Los Angeles to New York, taking three weeks to go by auto. During the next eighteen months in New York Peter was unsettled, watching tele-vision for about four and a half hours each day and showing little inclination to go out into the cold. When Peter was four his mother gave birth to another baby, a boy. During the return trip to Los Angeles, Peter injured his penis, an episode which frightened him a good deal. On arrival back in Los Angeles, the family stayed with Peter's maternal grandmother; only a week before, his maternal grandfather had died and the family was mourning. His playmates were his cousins, whose mother and father had recently divorced. Two weeks before the hallucinatory episode, Peter was sent to kindergarten; a week before the episode, Peter's father returned to New York for a visit, and his mother came down with the flu. With his cousins, he went to a marionette show, "The Magic Lady," where he met the main actor and narrator, who was a friend of his uncle's. Three days later his father arrived home at 2:00 A.M. At 4:00 A.M. Peter woke in terror.

His fantasy was that he was being attacked, and his main terror was that he was going to be taken away, into a magic land, where he would become an unreal, "pretend" being. His mother recorded some of his talk during this time:

> I am a boy, a real boy. I want you to go away. Witches are not allowed. The queen, I promised, I promised, I promised, I would do it. No, I don't want to be make believe. I am a boy. Boys don't wear lipstick. Boys don't get flowers. I am my mommy's and daddy's boy. No, don't get rid of anyone. . . . you can't make magic. Don't make my food magic. No, you can't do that. You can't get rid of anyone. Don't get rid of me [Call, 1975].

What tends to be missing in other cases is precisely—and abundantly —available here: the exact instant, experienced as a hallucination, when both the realm of the self and the world of objects become so tenuous in themselves and in their connections that both become painful "make-believes," fictions. Peter's experience is like Dorothy's in *The Wizard of Oz*—for both, the fantastic is identical to the real. Quite clearly, Peter sees himself, his food, and his very being becoming unreal make-believes, while those whom he wishes to love turn into magic witches and fantastic queens. The real boy is being transformed into a fiction, mommy and daddy recede into the distance, and the witch is preparing to take him to the Land of Make-Believe where everything is changed: boys there wear lipstick, get flowers, and eat magic food.

What has happened, obviously, is that a series of losses and separations occurring just before the onset of these hallucinations revived an earlier fault line, a crack, in object and self relatedness most likely connected with the frequent moves made by the parents and by his mother's return to work during Peter's second year. On top of his long experience with television fantasies, seeing *The Wizard of Oz, Pinocchio*, and a magic show shortly before the hallucinations provided fictive materials by which the personality thus fragmented and detached from its image of itself as whole and of others as real would see itself in terms of the palpable reality of the available fictions.

Peter's case is so close to the primary dissolution of person and objects—extending into ficticity the forming concepts of the grandiose self and idealized parents—that it allows us to see the fictive personality taking shape before our eyes. It helps us, also, to see what otherwise we could not have guessed: the fictive personality formation *is* a solution in every sense. It expresses an overwhelming fear of annihilation, reflecting an internal conviction that there really *are* neither selves nor objects. At the most primitive level, this is a belief that the mirror reflects nothing, the mirror is empty. The primary concern is ultimately with protection against annihilation. When the self sees itself as a fiction, one of the means of restoring the self is to fuse with the fictions—among those available—that are closest to the fears and embrace them. Peter defends himself from becoming unreal by fusing with fictions. It *is* better, the self seems to say, to be a fiction than to be nothing. André Green has compared the schizophrenic to one of the *morts-vivants*, the vampire, who has no reflection in the mirror. The case of Peter, as he turns toward fictions, exhibits how psychotic that moment, internally experienced, must be.

## Clinical Illustration #4: Arthur

Severely depressed, confused, and feeling "lost and stuck," Arthur began treatment at the age of thirty-one. He talked fairly easily about his background. He presented his father as being like a Damon Runyon character, tough-talking, aggressive, shrewd, and distant. Arthur believed that his brother was favored by his father, since his brother, an attorney, was "sharkish," like his father. As a consequence, from as early as he can remember, Arthur formed a very close, infantilizing attachment to his mother. Even as late as his high-school years, he would spend afternoons lying with his mother on her bed, watching television and holding hands. At present he dreams copiously, and in many of his dreams, he has explicit intercourse with his mother; this would seem both to express the punitive aspects of his attachment and to hint at an infantilized superego. In a self-destructive aspect of his oedipal conflicts, he attached himself to a narcissistic woman who had been living with a man much older than herself for the last eight years. As the culmination of the tensions arising out of this *menage à trois*, the older lover tried to kill Arthur with a kitchen knife. When this was aborted, Arthur passionately embraced him and addressed him as "Dearest father!"

Early on, his mother prophesized that Arthur would achieve glory and greatness as an artist; in doing so, he would of course justify her and defeat his businessman father, who soon mocked him as "being in the playpen with writing," proclaiming loudly that Arthur would always "be a flop."

Lacking a cohesive center of self-esteem to support a sense of self, and experiencing the persons in his world as aggressive toward him either through criticism or overstimulation, Arthur sought a self in romantic fictions. Arthur early on turned to stories and movies as the source for self and object representations. Through the romantic myth of the suffering artist he managed to give some form and structure to his sense of lostness, his masochism; through the corollary myth of the alienated artist he gave controlled expression to this sense of emptiness and isolation; and through the myth of the artist as an attacker of bourgeoisie values, he gave himself permission to express his rage and disappointment with his father. Finally, through the image of the artist as frustrated lover, he expressed his dual wishes to attach himself to and to remain distant from his mother. He saw the woman with whom he was destructively involved as "a fairy-princess who is a sick-o," pretty accurately expressing his idealizing-deprecating conflicts concerning his mother. In general, the accumulated evidence is that his whole portrait of his childhood and of his mother and father is based on romantic literature, ultimately upon such fairy-tale literature in which the beautiful princess is captured and confined by a dwarf or evil giant and must be saved by the beautiful young male hero.

He represents his world and his own place in it through fictive identifications, not only in portraying his past, but also in interpreting his present. Transiently, when he feels confused he sees himself as living in a Kafka-esque world. When depressed, he interprets the world through placing himself in the role of a Chekhov character, seeing himself as a melancholy observer of human foibles—though, in fact, he is poorly equipped as an observer due to the strong influence upon him of predetermined fictive formulas and stereotypes. When he is gripped by passivity, he sees himself as Goncharov's Oblomov, a character who refused to leave his bed.

He expresses his hopes by placing himself in a kind of Hall of Fame of Great Writers which he has constructed in his head. He sees himself as residing in the company of such writers as Tolstoy, Dostoevsky, and Flaubert, and asserts that, as his mother thought, his destiny really does lie with his "being great." Thus he alternates between archaic feelings of fraudulence and the grandiosity which—almost—covers up these despairing feelings of emptiness and lostness. No wonder he brings his diary to sessions and reads from it, as if reading about a literary character or from a biography of a famous writer.

His central fictive identifications are, first, with Prince Hal (in Shakespeare's *Henry IV*, Parts 1 and 2, and *Henry V*, in which Hal succeeds his father as king); and second, with Frank Cowperwood in Theodore Dreiser's *The Titan* and other characters in novels. Both Prince Hal and Cowperwood, of course, rise out of obscurity and neglect, then burst suddenly upon the world as persons who achieve mastery, power, and success against enormous odds. Arthur sees himself in this company, too.

Unlike the other patients whom I have discussed, Arthur has actually made some success in transforming the impulses leading to fictive identity into actual creative work, instead of devoting himself wholly, as the others did, to the creation of an identity that would guard against the threat of personal dissolution. The difference seems to have been made by a lucky attachment that he made to a successful and well-known older writer during his college years in the East. This writer has remained in correspondence with him and has continued to give him encouragement, and thus seems to have given Arthur the impetus to develop a minimal, but effective, set of ego ideals around the image of the working writer. This friendship laid the basis for the move which Arthur made: from imitation of fictional characters, to identifications with writers who produce fictions. After a year of treatment, in which he developed an idealizing transference, he showed clear signs of increased productivity, the ability to complete work, and a definite diminishment of fantasies designed to feed his hitherto ravenous fictive identity.

At this point, a year into treatment, however, Arthur developed two new identifications, which, in his mind, he connected closely. The first identification was with the Japanese author Yukio Mishima, author of *The Sailor Who Fell from Grace with the Sea* and many other books. Himself deeply conflicted about whether his main identification was with the West, the new, and art; or with Japan, tradition, and politics, Mishima turned from the first set of values to the second. He organized a proto-fascist private army modeled on the Samurai code, and he attempted to return Japan to its seventeenth-century traditions. Frustrated in his aims, he committed suicide by cutting his stomach open in the ritual Japanese manner.

Arthur identified primarily with Mishima's skill as a writer. But underneath that, some of his own ambivalence and suppressed anger showed through in his choice of Mishima as a model for himself. Sometimes Arthur felt that he, too, should strike a blow against the shallowness of modern society, as Mishima had tried to do; at other times, depressed over separations or what he believed to be lack of progress in treatment, he felt that the only solution for him was to commit suicide, as Mishima had succeeded in doing.

At the same time, Arthur also saw himself as just like Paul Schrader, the film writer who wrote *Taxi Driver*. Arthur admired Schrader's success and felt that he himself had had the "very thoughts" which Schrader had put into the mouth of his main character, Travis Bickle. In due course, Arthur's fairly similar identifications with what he knew of Mishima's and of Schrader's lives (in Schrader's case, he knew very little) were analyzed along the lines of his narcissistic ambivalences, and both his grandiosity and his suicidal thoughts diminished considerably; the latter disappeared entirely. Arthur carried with him, at the end of this piece of analysis, his original respect for Mishima as a writer, and he saw Schrader as an appropriate model for how to write successful screenplays.

Arthur's case illustrates both: (1) how an older writer can serve as a real model to transform fictive personality identifications into work as a fiction writer; and (2) how a properly conducted analysis can reverse the pathological aspects of some fictive personality identifications, and turn them to use.

## John Hinckley and *Taxi Driver*

Arthur's case is, like Terry's, helpful in allowing us to get a perspective upon what extreme reactions may develop when neither satisfactory models nor analysis are available. John Hinckley, who attempted to assassinate President Reagan, also identified very closely, and much more extremely than Arthur, with Travis Bickle, the hero of *Taxi Driver*. He bears a similarity to Mark David Chapman, too, in that he also identified strongly with John Lennon. "I don't know why I even go on living," Hinckley said into a tape recorder a few weeks after Lennon's death. "The dream is over," he continued, "as Lennon said ten years ago, but it's really over now." After his own attempt at assassinating the president, Hinckley responded to a question about whom he admired. "I don't admire any political leaders, except perhaps Mr. Reagan. The only person I ever idolized . . . was John Lennon, and look what happened to him" (Hinckley, 1981, p. 51). And he added: "Anything I do in 1981 will be totally for Jodie's [Foster] sake." Agents who searched his room after the attempted assassination found an unmailed letter to Ms. Foster in which he promised to command her attention for the "historic deed" he was about to commit. By killing the president, he believed, he would become united with her. He did in fact tell *Newsweek* that before the assassination attempt she intimidated him, but "now I think we are equal and rather compatible. Don't you agree?" (Hinckley, 1981, p. 50). When she said on a videotape played during the trial that she had no relations with him, he ran out of the courtroom. He could only face fiction.

He was ready to kill any political figure, it seems: anyone would do. A month earlier he had planned to kill Senator Edward Kennedy and actually went to his office at the Capitol. He bought a Charter Arms .38 pistol, the same make and caliber gun that Chapman had used to kill Lennon; it was important that the gun be the same: somehow that would make up for Lennon's death. At the core of his otherwise fragmented mind and behavior was a central identification with the character Travis Bickle, the part played by Robert DeNiro in *Taxi Driver*, a character who stalks a presidential candidate, intending to assassinate him, and then becomes obsessed with a teen-age prostitute—played in the film by Jodie Foster. Hinckley sent Foster a note similar to that which Bickle sends her in the film: "Just wait, I'll rescue you very soon." From Yale!

He wrote to *Newsweek*: "Travis keeps telling Jodie that he wants to help her escape all of these sordid characters that are ruining her, but she doesn't understand what he is talking about and resists him. I know exactly how Travis felt." When *Newsweek* asked him about all the guns in his possession, he said that he personally was in favor of gun control, but "I bought so many handguns because Travis bought so many handguns. Ask him, not me." Hinckley said of Bickle: "If there were more people like Robert DeNiro played in the movie . . . there wouldn't be any problem controlling crime." He believed that the showing of Ms. Foster's films on TV were meant as a secret message to him.

Like someone collecting scrapbooks, Hinckley seems to have collected a variety of fragmentary identifications to support his central one with Bickle. In his room before the shooting he assembled photographs of Lee Harvey Oswald and song lyrics by Lennon, and he thought about his resemblance to Hitler—"an unimportant, common person who rose to eminence," he noted—and to Charles Whitman, who went on a shooting spree at the University of Texas in Austin in 1966. He himself had become little more than a scrapbook, the composite of his fictions. He had some awareness of this; for when the editors of *Newsweek* asked him whether books and movies influence the way people behave "in real life," he replied enthusiastically: "Yes, Yes, Yes. The line dividing life and art can be invisible." He called books and movies "hypnotizing" and "magical." When he shot at the president, psychiatrist William T. Carpenter testified, Hinckley felt as if he were "just there, living out an experience," in which the participants "were bit players"—a fictive experience, the only kind he could have.

"What a glorious opportunity for a man to immortalize himself by killing Abraham Lincoln!"—John Wilkes Booth said two years before his own crime (Dusseau, 1982, p. 243). He insisted that Lincoln should be killed in a theater, where Booth could jump upon the stage shouting *Sic semper tyrannis*, like Brutus. For him, as for Chapman and Hinckley, the assassination was a performance, theater, psychodrama, not actuality. So was its aftermath. No wonder that the televised vigil in memory of Lennon was reviewed in the *New York Times* by the paper's theater and book critics, not its news reporters. What fictive characters perform must be fiction, and they need to be seen as actors.

## Conclusion

There are many differences among Vonnegut's Harry; Don Quixote, knight errant; the suicidal Werther; harmless Clayton Moore; the patients Melissa, Terry, Peter, and Arthur; and the murderers Raskolnikov, Chapman, and Hinckley. All perform as they do, however, in accordance with the fictional objects of their identifications, the available fictions that fill up their empty selves and allow them to seem real so long as their fictions remain alive.

Many other issues might be pursued in investigating the nature and meaning of the fictive personality: its origin and development; its relation to borderline and narcissistic disorders; its connection to creativity; the nature of transitional phenomena in it; treatment considerations, and so on. I have treated some of these elsewhere (Martin, 1982, 1983), but in this paper my main concern has been to define the fictive personality and to describe it clinically, leaving more theoretical issues for other and subsequent investigations.

In the present paper I intended to make a clinical contribution to the problems and varieties of identification with fictions. Both for the individual and for society, the issue is how to find and then choose vital, fertilizing, creative identifications. This is what Sammler (in Saul Bellow's *Mr. Sammler's Planet*) thinks about as he walks down Broadway, looking at the variety of people:

> All human types reproduced, the barbarian, redskin, or Fiji, the dandy, the buffalo hunter, the desperado, the queer, the sexual fantasist, the squaw, bluestocking, princess, poet, painter, prospector, troubadour, guerrila, Che Guevara, the new Thomas à Becket. Not imitated are the businessman, the soldier, the priest, and the square. . . . They sought originality. They obviously were derivative. And of what—of Paiutes, of Fidel Castro? No, of Hollywood extras. Acting mythic. Casting themselves into chaos, hoping to adhere to higher consciousness, to be washed up on the shores of truth. Better, thought Sammler, to accept the inevitability of imitation and then to imitate good things. The ancients had this right. Greatness without models? Inconceivable. One could not be the thing

itself—Reality. One must be satisfied with the symbols. Make it the object of imitation to reach and release the high qualities. Make peace therefore with intermediacy and representation. But choose higher representations. Otherwise the individual must be the failure he now sees and knows himself to be [pp. 135–137].

In the clinical cases I have presented, the analysands learned to give up "acting mythic" or living bad fictions. In analysis, they began, painfully, to begin to make "higher representations."

## REFERENCES

Adams, H. (1915), Buddha and Brahma, *Yale Rev.*, 5:88.
Bellow, S. (1970), *Mr. Sammler's Planet*. New York: Penguin, 1979.
Brandes, G. (1936), *Goethe*, trans. A. W. Porterfield. New York: Crown.
Call, J. (1975). Unpublished manuscript.
Cervantes, M. (1605), *Don Quixote de la Mancha*, trans. S. Putnam. New York: Viking, 1949.
Champlain, C. (1982), "Sophie's" on location in Flatbush. *Los Angeles Times Calendar*, May 16, p. 28.
Deutsch, H. (1937), Don Quixote and Don Quixotisms. In: *Neurosis and Character Types: Clinical Psychoanalytic Studies*. New York: International Universities Press, 1965, pp. 218–225.
———— (1942), Some forms of emotional disturbances and their relationship to schizophrenia. In: *Neurosis and Character Types: Clinical Psychoanalytic Studies*. New York: International Universities Press, 1965, pp. 262–281.
———— (1955), The imposter: Contributions to ego psychology of a psychopath. In: *Neurosis and Character Types: Clinical Psychoanalytic Studies*. New York: International Universities Press, 1965, pp. 319–338.
Dostoevsky, F. (1866), *Crime and Punishment*, trans. C. Garnett. New York: Harper & Bros., 1951.
Dusseau, J. L. (1982), *Tertium Quid*: A third something in a muddied puzzle. *Perspectives in Biol. & Med.*, 25:238–253.
Ekstein, R. & Friedman, S. W. (1959), The function of acting out, play action and play acting in the psychotherapeutic process. *J. Amer. Psychoanal. Assn.*, 7:581–629.
Freud, A. (1966), *The Ego and the Mechanisms of Defense*, New York: International Universities Press.
Goethe, J. W. von (1774), *The Sorrows of Young Werther*. In: *Great German Short Novels and Stories*. New York: Random House, 1952.
Goldberg, A. (1978), *The Psychology of the Self: A Casebook*. New York: International Universities Press, pp. 165–262.
Guntrip, H. (1968), *Schizoid Phenomena, Object Relations, and the Self*. New York: International Universities Press.
Hinckley, J. (1981), Answers. *Newsweek*, October 12, pp. 50–51.
Kohut, H. (1957), *Death in Venice* by Thomas Mann: A story about the disintegration of artistic sublimation. In: *The Search for the Self*, vol I. ed. P. H. Ornstein. New York: International Universities Press, 1975, pp. 107–130.
———— (1971), *The Analysis of the Self*. New York: International Universities Press.
———— (1975), Remarks about the formation of the self. In: *The Search for the Self*, vol II. ed. P. H. Ornstein. New York: International Universities Press, 737–770.
———— (1977), *The Restoration of the Self*. New York: International Universities Press.
———— Wolf, E. (1978), The disorders of the self and their treatment: An outline. *Internat. J. Psycho-Anal.*, 59:413–426.

Kris, E. (1956), The personal myth: A problem in psychoanalytic technique. In: *Selected Papers of Ernst Kris*. New Haven & London: Yale University Press, 1975, pp. 272–300.

Krutch, J. W. (1929), *The Modern Temper*. New York: Harcourt, Brace.

Lebovici, S. & Widlöcher, D. (eds.) (1980), *Psychoanalysis in France*. New York: International Universities Press.

Marowitz, S. (1981), Myth and realism in recent criticism of the American literary West. *J. Amer. Stud.*, 15:95–114.

Martin, J. (1982), Two lectures on the fictive personality. Delivered to the Annual Joint Meeting of the Southern California and Los Angeles Psychoanalytic Institutes. Unpublished.

—— (1983), Fictive personality, transitional phenomena, and infant development. Delivered to the Second World Congress of Infant Psychiatry, Cannes, France.

—— (1984), Infant development: Fictive personality and creative capacity. In: *Frontiers of Infant Psychiatry*, ed. E. Galenson, J. Call, and R. Tyson. Vol. 2, in press.

Nagera, H. (1975), *Female Sexuality and the Oedipus Complex*. New York: Aronson.

Rosenthal, D. (1981), Meryl Streep: Stepping in and out of roles. *Rolling Stone*, October 15, p. 17.

Rule, J. (1973), The actor's identity crisis. *Internat. J. Psychoanal. Psychother.*, 2:51–76.

Schneiderman, S. (1980), *Returning to Freud*. New Haven and London: Yale University Press.

Schramm, W. (1961), Mass media and educational policy. In: *Social Forces Influencing American Education*. Chicago: University of Chicago Press.

Schwartz, D. (1981), Psychiatric testimony. The sad secrets of an assassin's mind: Mark David Chapman. *Rolling Stone*, October 15, pp. 13–15.

Spence, D. (1982), *Narrative Truth and Historical Truth*. New York: Norton.

Tolpin, P. (1980), The borderline personality: Its makeup and analyzability. In: *Advances in Self Psychology*, ed. A. Goldberg. New York: International Universities Press, pp. 299–316.

Vaihinger, H. (1911), *The Philosophy of "As If,"* trans. C. K. Ogden. New York: Harcourt, Brace.

Vonnegut, K. (1978), Who am I this time? *Sat. Eve. Post*, December, pp. 20 ff.

Walker, A. (1982), *Peter Sellers*. New York and London: Macmillan.

*January 1983*

# Clinical Notes toward the Understanding and Intensive Psychotherapy of Adult Eating Disorders

RICHARD D. CHESSICK, M.D., Ph.D. (Evanston, Ill.)

No vital function in early life plays such a central role in the emotional household of the organism as does eating. The child experiences the first relief from physical discomfort during nursing; thus the satisfaction of hunger becomes deeply associated with the feeling of well-being and security. . . . Another emotional attitude of fundamental importance, which becomes linked early in infancy with eating and hunger is possessiveness, with all its implications, such as greed, jealousy, and envy. . . . Knowledge of these fundamental psychological facts is necessary for the understanding of the emotional background of neurotic eating disorders.

—Franz Alexander (1950)

The adult eating disorders as they present in clinical practice can be placed on a spectrum ranging from severe anorexia on the one end to superobesity

Presented at the Chicago Institute for Psychoanalysis Conference on Behavior Disorders, November 19–20, 1983. This paper is dedicated to the fond memory of a friend, inspiring teacher, and psychoanalytic pioneer, Dr. Franz Alexander.

on the other, with all sorts of oscillations and variations in between. This paper will discuss the psychological aspects of eating disorders as presented by medically otherwise healthy adult patients in the clinical practice of intensive psychotherapy, toward the purpose of better understanding and treatment of such patients.

# I. Understanding

Weiss and English (1957) remind us that some families are quite "oral" in their orientation to life. A treat for such a family will be a good meal rather than creative work or play. They talk incessantly about food and the various ways it should be cooked, and other interests in life suffer proportionately. Everything about the offering and receiving of food is endowed with a high emotional value. Kolb and Brodie (1982) and Shainess (1979) point out that obesity often develops in a family setting in which the parents compensate for their own life frustrations and disappointments through the child; the mother is the dominant family member and holds the obese child by anxious overprotection, including pushing food. The mother frequently has high expectations for the child's ability to compensate for the failures of the parents. The obese child is one who has passively accepted the indulged role without rebellion, and has been taught to substitute food for love and satisfaction.

Hamburger (1951) described four different types of hyperphagia. One group of his patients overate in response to nonspecific emotional tensions such as loneliness, anxiety, or boredom. Another group overate in *chronic* states of tension and frustration, using food as substitute gratification in unpleasant life situations over long periods. In a third group, overeating represented a symptom of underlying psychopathology—most frequently, depression. The final group, in which overeating took on the proportions of an addiction, was characterized by a compulsive food craving unrelated to external events. Clearly, any generalizations about the psychological problems in eating disorders must be cautious indeed, because we are dealing with a group or variety of conditions, even within subgroups such as what the *Diagnostic and Statistical Manual of Mental Disorders* (1980, p. 67) calls "simple obesity."

Numerous reports on emotional disturbances among the obese have flooded the literature. The better the study, the less the evidence for distinctive psychological features. For example, Stunkard (1980) studied the negative body image in obese persons, who characteristically complain in psychotherapy that their bodies are grotesque and loathsome and that others view them with hostility and contempt. He writes that although "it seems reasonable" to suppose that all obese persons have derogatory feelings about their bodies, emotionally healthy obese persons have no such body-image disturbances, and only a minority of obese persons in treatment for other conditions such as neuroses show this. This important clinical observation is also made by Powers (1980).

The obesity of persons who were obese in childhood—so called "hyperplastic obesity," "juvenile-onset obesity," or "developmental obesity"—differs from that of persons who became obese as adults ("hypertrophic obesity") in that the juvenile type tends to be more severe, more resistant to treatment, and more likely to be associated with emotional disturbances. However, Stunkard (1975) and others disagree with the common notion that "middle-age obesity" develops slowly and gradually; actually it occurs in a series of weight spurts, as each stressful period in middle age is accompanied in predisposed persons by excess eating. Although many obese persons report that they overeat and gain weight when they are emotionally upset, Stunkard (1975) explains that it has "proved singularly difficult to proceed from this provocative observation to an understanding of the precise relationship between emotional factors and obesity" (p. 777). Obesity at a later stage can become a rationalization for failure, and the overweight person's attitude toward himself is further complicated by the current profound Western cultural distaste for obesity, especially in women (Wooley and Wooley, 1980).

Numerous authors have reported that the obese child becomes filled with grandiose daydreams as he suffers daily defeats in his major aspirations. These fantasies are usually conscious or disavowed, and they differ from those of the psychotic because the obese person is to some extent aware that they are unreasonable. In the psychotherapy of adult obese patients Ingram (1976) reports how these expansive and narcissistic features emerge coincident with weight reduction. Overeating appears protective in some cases against an incipient psychosis; such patients may develop a full-blown psychosis when they undertake to lose weight by vigorous dieting.

Stunkard (1975, 1980) describes about 10 percent of obese persons, most commonly women, as manifesting a "night-eating syndrome," characterized by morning anorexia and evening hyperphagia with insomnia. This syndrome, once precipitated by stressful life circumstances, tends to occur daily until the stress is alleviated. A "binge-eating syndrome," he says, is found in about 5 percent of obese persons, characterized by sudden compulsive ingestion of very large amounts of food in a very short time, usually with great subsequent agitation and self-condemnation. In these two syndromes, a mere 15 percent of obese cases, it is easier to outline psychodynamics involving orality and ambivalence. Yet Bruch (1973) claims that in her experience such night eaters are rare and binge eaters are much more common.

This leaves a large majority of obese persons in whom the disorder seems to be more subtle and all-pervasive. It is this large group who is more characteristically described as food addicts who have built in the use of food as a substitute for defects in psychic structure. Overeating has become an indispensable part of their life pattern, and vigorous weight reduction exposes such patients to unbearable tensions—which is why vigorous treatment aimed at weight reduction alone seldom is successful and even if successful is seldom maintained for very long. Frosch (1977) places these patients among the "character impulse disorders," emphasizing their intolerance of tension or frustration, based on developmental interference with their capacity for "anticipation" and confidence. Similarly, Garfinkel, Moldofsky, and Garner (1980) and Casper, Halmi, Goldberg, Eckert, and Davis (1980) demonstrated a high incidence of impulsive behaviors in the bulimic subgroup of anorexia-nervosa patients.

Psychoanalytic recognition of food addiction goes back to Rado (1926), who also coined the important concept of "alimentary orgasm"; the arguments for obesity as representing an addiction to food are updated and reviewed by Leon (1982). Today Rado's conceptions have fallen into eclipse, but common observations and reports of obese patients about eating show that Rado's notion of the relatively slower and longer lasting "alimentary orgasm," a diffuse feeling of well-being that extends throughout the organism, complete with a sense of repose and faraway look in the eyes, can indeed serve in such patients as a short-circuit avoiding sexual and more complex adult interpersonal intimacies. Clinical experience also confirms his contention that "a long series of foods and delicacies can be worked out, forming a regular gradation from ordinary foods up to pure intoxicants," for this is frequently spontaneously reported by patients. I have investigated the drug end of this gradation and the "pharmacogenic orgasm" in a previous publication (Chessick, 1960), and Woollcott (1981) presents an excellent recent discussion of this, emphasizing the "basic fault" in such patients which leads to a "fusion-individuation conflict," in some ways similar to the pathology of the borderline patient.

In discussing the addict Kohut (1971) writes,

> His psyche remains fixated on an archaic self-object, and the personality will throughout life be dependent on certain objects in what seems to be an intense form of object hunger. The intensity of the search for and of the dependency on these objects is due to the fact that they are striven for as a substitute for the missing segments of the psychic structure [p. 45].

He goes on to explain that in the personalities of addicts,

> The trauma which they suffered is most frequently the severe disappointment in a mother who, because of her defective empathy with the child's needs . . . , did not appropriately fulfill the functions (as a stimulus barrier; as an optimal provider of needed stimuli; as a supplier of tension-relieving gratification, etc.) which the mature psychic apparatus should later be able to perform (or initiate) predominantly on its own. Traumatic disappointments suffered during these archaic stages of the development of the idealized self-object deprive the child of the gradual internalization of early experiences of being optimally soothed, or being aided in going to sleep [p. 46].[1]

Bruch (1973) described "reactive obesity," in which overeating serves as a defense against a deeper depression in the patient, and a variety of authors, such as Cantwell, Sturzenberger, Bourroughs, Salkin, and Breen (1977) have linked the eating disorders to depression, generating some hopeful reports (such as Pope, Hudson, Jonas, and Yurgelun-Todd, 1983) on the treatment of these disorders with antidepressant medication. Overeating in these patients represents a self-soothing effort to prevent disintegration to more profound archaic experiences that are repressed and are associated with the current depressive affectual situation. In Krystal's (1983) report these archaic experiences were often actual infantile disasters such as "colic, eczema, feeding, or sleeping difficulties" which are "covered over by a conspiracy of silence, related to the shared wish to undo the common misfortune." Thus overeating protects the patient against basic massive affect states of a primitive archaic nature which threaten to develop if the current stress situation continues unabated, or—following Kohut—against fragmentation of the sense of self.

The psychological link underlying the whole spectrum of the eating disorders from superobesity to anorexia is stressed by Wooley and Wooley (1980) and many other authors. Shainess (1979) vividly describes that link in psychoanalytic terms: "I feel convinced that the unconscious fantasies connected with food are that it is poison. The patient is trapped between the need to eat and to sustain life, and the paranoid projection in relation to food . . . the anorexic feels full after a few bites, while the obese always has room for more, no matter how much has been eaten" (pp. 230–231). The efforts not to eat are seen as a phobic avoidance of poison while

---

[1] Since this paper was written Kohut (1984) has called attention to the very obese Bismarck, who was enabled to reduce his "craving" for food, wine, and tobacco by a Dr. Schweninger who for fifteen years functioned as a substitute selfobject (pp. 19–20). This is based on a report by Pflanze (1972); it is interesting that the report does not indicate whether or not Bismarck actually lost weight when Schweninger entered his life.

overeating represents the need to retain food-as-mother, says Shainess. One obese patient of mine regularly referred to binge eating of bags of cookies as eating "bags of garbage," and clearly distinguished this from her ordinary and normal eating pattern. In all the cases, the whole eating pattern is disorganized, and the relationship of child to mother is acted out over food.

Ritvo (1976) stresses the aggressive aspects of this relationship, with roots in the "repressed oral sadomasochistic conflicts with the mother." Thus anorexia characteristically breaks out upon going away from home, and "It is the introjected mother whom the adolescent is starving for and trying to control and punish" (p. 132). He adds the important clinical point that the first turnings to men of such patients may be "primarily an effort to replace the loss of the mother" (p. 133).

The syndrome of so-called bulimarexia, a binge-purge cycle, has become popular now (Casper, 1983), with patients mostly in the teens and twenties, and about 5 percent male, though it can appear at any adult age. During the binge there is a sense of loss of control and guilt; during the purge, a restitution, catharsis, and reinforcement of the sense of control. Underneath all of these various eating disorders, whether anorexia, bulimia, or the binge-purge cycle, there lie—as Kohut might say—a nameless preverbal depression, apathy, a sense of deadness, and diffuse rage. In my clinical experience the massive rage appears as either paranoid fears or self-hatred with a distorted self-image, or migraine, or temper tantrums, or any combination of these, similar to the borderline patient. It may also appear as a curious compulsive ritual, devoid of pleasure, in which the patient eats up everything in sight. In all those patients, Bruch (1973, p. 100) points out, the fatness is only an externalization of the conviction of ugliness on the inside. As one of my patients said, "I eat to feel, to get some sensation as opposed to no sensation. When you have done you are uncomfortable, but that is a feeling. I make myself fat, I think, to mirror how I feel inside about myself—it broadcasts a message that says, 'Love this ugly person as I am'. It fits with my lack of trust in people and says, 'I'll make it hard for you if you want to be nice to me'."

The dramatic eating disorder, whether through "alimentary orgasms," masochistic infliction of self-starvation or unpleasant compulsive stuffing, or the binge-purge guilt and restitution circle, drains off the rage and paranoia (more or less) and focuses the patient's attention away from the empty, depleted self and onto preoccupation with gastrointestinal-tract sensations. In this manner some sort of sense of being alive is maintained. So on top of the depleted and fragmented nuclear core, the patient has built various protective rituals and soothing activities which, in the case of the eating disorders sometimes permit the patient to function in society.

But at the same time the patient must deal with the massive narcissistic rage or unconscious sadism. For example, Offenkrantz and Tobin (1974) discuss these patients as "depressive characters" and emphasize the great unconscious rage at important objects who are not providing the patient with what he unconsciously feels he needs—a rage that often gets turned on the therapist. Under this lies an "anaclitic depression" characterized by depletion and a hopelessness that sufficient gratification will ever be possible.

Glover (1956) also placed less emphasis on fixation in the oral stage and viewed addiction as a transition state between psychotic and neurotic phases, serving the function of controlling sadism and preventing a regression to psychosis, or fragmentation. He writes:

> The necessary formula appears to be that the individual's own hate impulses, together with identifications with objects towards whom he is ambivalent, constitute a dangerous psychic state . . . symbolized as an internal concrete substance. The drug is then . . . an external countersubstance which cures by destruction. In this sense drug-addiction might be considered an improvement on paranoia: the paranoidal element is limited to the drug-substance which is then used as a therapeutic agent to deal with intrapsychic conflict of a melancholic pattern [p. 208].

In this form of "*localizing* paranoid anxiety," adaptation is enabled to proceed, and the differences in choice of substance from the more benign, like food, to the dangerous, like chemicals, is postulated by Glover to be simply related to the degree of archaic sadism.

There is no reason for this additional postulate, since food can certainly be conceived of by the patient as a destructive noxious substance. This is best summarized and illustrated in a recent play by Innaurato (1977), *The Transfiguration of Benno Blimpie*, a nightmarish account of a grotesquely fat and lonely 25-year-old man, who relives the humiliating events of his life while preparing to end it by eating himself to death. Benno—who spent his childhood eating, daydreaming, and drawing—says, "Paintings, you see, aren't enough. When loneliness and emptiness and longing congeal like a jelly, nothing assuages the ache. Nothing, nothing, nothing." As the narcissistic rage erupts in the drama he depersonalizes and plans, "When I become so fat I cannot get into his clothes, and can barely move, I will nail the door shut. I will put his eyes out with a long nail and I will bite at himself until he dies" (pp. 16–17).

As the drama reaches a climax he concludes, "I couldn't cry: Benno couldn't scream. He lay there; and in that instant, time stopped. And feeling, it stopped too, and seemed to merge with time, and with space. My sense of identity seeped out of me into the cracks in the concrete" (p.

26). At this point, which Benno calls his "transfiguration" and Kohut would call an irreversible fragmentation of the self, Benno prepares to mutilate his body with a meat cleaver.

Patients suffering from anorexia have been separated by Dally (1969) into three subgroups, and various authors (Wilson, 1983) have stressed the heterogeneity of this syndrome as a "final common pathway" for many disorders. Thus anorexia, like obesity, can appear in clinical practice in a large variety of ways. For instance one group purges and induces vomiting; another group shows impulsive self-destructive behavior including suicide attempts, self mutilation, and alcoholism; and yet another group achieves the desired end of thinness solely by dieting. Halmi (1980) and Zales (1982) also report this substantial diagnostic heterogeneity within the anorexic syndrome.

The psychodynamics of anorexia in young women have long been known to include the impairment of development arising from an early unsuccessful mother-daughter relationship. The adolescent girl, faced with feminine individuation and threatened by the loss of dependency on the family, responds to the conflict in these cases by regression to an infantile maternal relationship with unconscious craving for blissful eating experiences. This is denied in the drama which is carried out by an oscillation between eating and severe dieting; the pursuit of thinness usually represents an act of hostile and defiant compliance by the patient against the mother.

Bruch (1975) has repeatedly stated that anorexia nervosa is more akin to schizophrenic development or borderline states than to neuroses. She admits that depressive features deserve special evaluation and may indicate a true depression as a primary illness, but she feels that the disorder expresses "the underlying despair of a schizophrenic reaction" (p. 802), and she argues that recognition of the underlying potentially schizophrenic core is essential for effective treatment. In my clinical experience one of the important differentiating features between classical anorexia nervosa, appearing rather suddenly in early adolescence, and the usually less lethal anorexia, developing in adult patients, is that in the latter the core is depressive rather than schizophrenic and points to Kohut's descriptions of the empty, depleted self and narcissistic rage, and also Kernberg's conceptions of "all-bad" self and object representations, heavily invested with powerful negative and self-destructive affects.

Most psychodynamic formulations concerning the cause of anorexia have centered around the phobic response to food resulting from the sexual and social tensions generated by the physical changes associated with early puberty. But even Fenichel (1945) was aware that anorexias developing in adult life "may have a very different dynamic significance." He explains that anorexia may represent a simple hysterical conversion symptom expressing the fear of an orally perceived pregnancy, or of unconscious sadistic wishes. It may be a part of an ascetic reaction formation in a compulsion neurosis. It may be an affect equivalent in a depression, in which the symptom of refusal of food makes its appearance before other signs of the depression are developed. It may be a sign of the refusal of any contact with the objective world as an incipient schizophrenia.

Thus Fenichel comes a long way from any simplistic formulation of anorexia, at least in adults. He mentions a case reported by Eissler which illustrates that anorexia in an orally fixated person, even from the point of view of classical psychoanalysis, is thought of as "only one symptom of a general disturbance of all object relationships" (p. 177). In a paragraph remarkably similar to the language of Kohut, though it was written about twenty-five years earlier, Fenichel writes that Eissler's patient "had not gone beyond an extremely archaic stage of ego development. The mother 'remained the most important part of the patient's ego.' The refusal of food represented the longing for the primary, still undifferentiated gratification by the mother and its sadistic distortion after frustration" (p. 177).

In trying to understand the eating disorders it is important to remember that there are *two* general kinds of functional disturbances. One of them consists of unwanted physiological changes caused by the inappropriate use of the function in question, which Fenichel labels an organ neurosis. The other kind of disturbance has a specific unconscious meaning, is an expression of a fantasy in "body language," and is directly accessible to psychoanalysis in the same way as a dream; for this category the term conversion neurosis is usually reserved. A certain percentage of what are called organ neuroses actually are affect equivalents; that is to say, they represent the specific physical expression of any given affect without the corresponding conscious mental experience. For example, anorexia in some cases is an affect equivalent of depression, as recent studies (Cantwell, Sturzenberger, Bourroughs, Salkin, and Breen, 1977; Casper and Davis, 1977) increasingly demonstrate.

In most cases of adult eating disorders a pathological discomfort rooted in unconscious problems generates a certain behavior, which in turn causes somatic changes in the tissues. The person's behavior which initiated these changes was intended to relieve internal pressure; the somatic symptom forming the consequence of this attitude was not sought by the person either consciously or unconsciously. For example, Fenichel (1945) mentions a paper by Wulff, written in 1932 and to my knowledge never translated. Wulff described a "psychoneurosis" seen more in women than in men and related "to hysteria, cyclothymia and addiction." This "neurosis" is characterized by a fight against pregenital sexuality. Sexual satisfaction is conceived of as a "dirty meal." Periods of depression in which the patients stuff themselves and feel "fat, bloated, dirty, untidy, or pregnant" alternate with "good" periods in which they behave ascetically, feel slim, and conduct themselves either normally or with some elation. The alternating feelings of ugliness and beauty and the oscillation in the body feelings seem to be similar to the feelings before and after menstrual periods, and to also have an exhibitionistic component.

Fenichel, like many authors after him, vascillates in his description of food addictions between conflict interpretation using classical psychodynamics, and his intuitive clinical knowledge that such interpretation is not sufficient to explain the compulsively addictive aspects of these cases. Following Rado, he recognizes "an oral-erotic excitement" involved in eating and believes that the food addictions are unsuccessful attempts to master guilt, depression, or anxiety by activity—though no real explanation is given as to how this works. Thus eating disorders for Fenichel become what he calls "character defenses against anxiety," in which certain basic infantile conflicts are mastered by working them out over and over again in the realm of food or denial of food. Current psychoanalytic textbooks such as Bernstein and Warner (1981) add little to these formulations.

Bruch (1973, 1974, 1975, 1979, 1982) developed her own therapeutic approach to eating disorders, but her concepts have the same sense of generalization about them as the old classical psychoanalytic formulations. She recognizes a problem involving self-esteem, narcissistic rage, depletion, and depression in these patients as well as a narcissistic power struggle with the parents—but she depends on interpersonal theory, using, more or less, a Sullivanian approach. This is criticized by various authors in the publication by the Psychosomatic Study Group of the Psychoanalytic Association of New York (Wilson, 1983), which presents in-depth case material from the formal psychoanalysis of anorexic patients, utilizing an object-relations orientation differing from that of both Bruch and Kohut.

It is only in the study of each individual case that we can know what is most important for that patient. Bruch recognizes that food refusal is a defense against the original fear of eating too much; she correctly recognizes that the behavior of the anorexic is an extreme caricature of what the normal person has to do in order to lose weight. She does not always emphasize the tremendous self-hatred in the anorexic and the powerful rage and depressive affect that are expressed by the eating disorders, and she stresses the schizophrenic-like aspects.

Bruch (1979) candidly admits, "Relatively little is known how this changeover takes place, from what looks like ordinary dieting to this inflexible self-destructive but hotly defended fixation on weight and food" (p. 72). Yet Kohut (1971) described stages of fragmentation of the self in severe borderline and schizophrenic patients where there is a reconstitution of the self but with certain parts of the body decathected and viewed as useless; such patients may indeed even cut off part of the body at this point. It is not hard to see how a fragmentation of the self in adolescents and adults can lead to a similar reconstitution where the useless part of the body self is the body fat; indeed Bruch (1979) points out from her vast clinical experience how many anorexics spend time looking in the mirror over and over again "taking pride in every pound they lose and every bone that shows. The more pride they take in it, the stronger the assertion that they look just fine" (p. 82).

Thus severe anorexia can be thought of as a pathological reconstitution of the fragmented self where—as sometimes occurs in schizophrenic and borderline patients—a part of the self becomes split off and utterly divested of libido in order to permit a shallow reconstitution of the rest; this de-cathected part is represented by the body fat which is then viewed as useless, unwanted, and in need of being cut off. Indeed, maintaining reconstitution of the self may require a continuing and dangerous cutting off of this useless body fat representing the unwanted part of the self, which would explain the persistence with which these patients starve themselves, as well as their rigid negativism toward treatment to the point where if they are force-fed they may commit suicide.

Severe pathological anorexia represents, as Bruch says, a grotesque mirror image of obesity. She maintains also that both are related to faulty hunger awareness. This leads to Bruch's claim that the lack of awareness of living one's own life is of fundamental significance for the development of severe eating disturbances; in my clinical experience also, this curious sense of being ineffective or being a child in an adult world is characteristic of patients with eating disorders.

Another clinical feature I have here emphasized—the deep inner emptiness, rage, and paranoid proclivities in such patients—as in the "case" of Benno Blimpie, is not given so much prominence by Bruch. For example, Bruch (1973) reports a case of a fat student nurse who was hospitalized for an acute schizophrenic episode and was observed to eat ravenously whenever she had an argument or felt threatened. Her explanation was that she was afraid that the hostility of others and their angry words would rattle around inside her and keep on wounding her. "By stuffing herself with food she would cover her sore inside, like with a poultice, and she would not feel the hurt so much" (p. 92). The deep intrapsychic dynamics involving cycles of introjection and projection or, alternatively, Kohut's concept of the depleted nuclear self and its disintegration products are omitted in Bruch's formulations.

It is clear from clinical experience that the eating disorders protect the patient from unbearable affects which then do appear if the eating disorder is stopped. It is the extremely negative self image and self hatred—or in Kohut's terms the depleted self with the disintegration product of narcissistic rage—that *precede* the development of obesity, as emphasized by Stunkard and Burt (1967), and by Powers (1980) and many others. This intrapsychic psychopathology forms the foundation for the various adult eating disorders, which then develop when the tension becomes unbearable, the faulty preoedipal self-soothing system becomes overwhelmed, and the self threatens to fragment or actually does so, as in *The Transfiguration of Benno Blimpie*.

## II. Treatment

It is generally agreed that obese patients are more difficult to treat than nonobese patients. In one study, for example, "More obese patients than nonobese patients terminated treatment prematurely, and those who remained in treatment showed less improvement in psychological functioning" (Kaplan, Freedman, and Sadock, 1980, p. 1880). Most authors are gloomy with respect to the efficacy of psychoanalysis and psychoanalytic psychotherapy for the treatment of eating disorders, but some recent studies (Rand, 1981; Zales, 1982; Rand and Stunkard, 1983) are more hopeful, and the New York group (Wilson, 1983) considers psychoanalysis often to be the treatment of choice for anorexia, which they view as masking an oedipal neurosis.

Stunkard (1975) claims there is no value in uncovering unconscious causes of overeating explained as neurotic conflict resolution according to the classical psychoanalytic model for the production of neurotic symptoms. The majority of cases of obesity represent a characteriologic pattern at the basis of which is a profound failure in the early selfobject relationship, in which food is used as a substitute for missing segments of the psychic structure. It is this structural defect which must be slowly and patiently repaired in psychoanalytic psychotherapy. As a clinical illustration, we may take Bruch's (1973) description of "thin fat people," borrowed from Heckel, who warned us already in 1911 that the loss of weight by a fat person does not represent a cure by itself. Indeed the patient may show much more serious psychopathology when the weight is lost, and the battle may shift from an attempt to reduce to an attempt to keep from gaining weight by an obsessive preoccupation with maintaining a semistarved appearance that is so popular among fashion models in our slimness culture. These un-happy, dissatisfied people are still representatives of an eating disorder. Their compulsion with staying slim is a common clinical sequel in cases of obesity treated with various forms of behavior modification or other symp-tom-focused therapies, which have in essence converted a miserable fat person into an even more miserable thin person—and in both cases a person who is preoccupied with eating. Clinically, these adult patients do not pro-gress to a malignant state of anorexia nervosa, but reach a certain miserable stability in their thinness.

The narcissistic aspects of adult compulsive eaters or dieters are especially striking, along with their very low sense of self-esteem, conviction of in-adequacy, and compensatory fantasies and daydreams of "astounding gran-diosity" (Bruch, 1973). Furthermore, there is a curious "all or nothing" attitude, so that when confronted with the fact that their unlimited aspi-rations are not obtainable, they are apt to give up, lie around at home, and simply eat and grow fatter! In clinical work with such patients it is dangerous to allow the patient to assume that if psychotherapy is successful and they achieve thinness, their grandiose expectations will somehow be realized—an attitude much reinforced by advertising in our culture. Actually, the in-ability of such patients to follow a diet acts as a safeguard against putting their narcissistic fantasies to the test of reality. Thus, as long as they are fat, they feel that they have it in their power now or in the future to set everything right by losing weight. The basic psychological problems do not come into full awareness until after effective reducing, so that remaining fat is an important defense against having to face their own narcissistic or borderline psychopathology. Reducing, when rigidly pursued or outwardly enforced, may precipitate a psychotic reaction or profound depression. Even Federn (1947) observed during the psychoanalytic treatment of schizophrenics that the psychosis was sometimes initiated and precipitated by intentional weight reduction.

In my clinical experience not one patient has substantially reduced weight and maintained weight reduction without experiencing an extremely dif-ficult and painful process. The inhibition of activity in obese persons is a more fundamental aspect of the disorder than the overeating because it expresses a disturbance in the total approach to life and manifests, as Bruch (1973) puts it, "a real lack of enjoyment in using one's body, or a deep-seated mistrust of one's ability of mastery" (pp. 314–315); in Kohut's terms it is a representation of the empty depleted nuclear self. Thus the known value of exercise in weight reduction has to do with the reversal of a lifelong pattern of passivity, emptiness, daydreaming, and inactivity.

That group of fat people who are compulsive eaters represents, as Hamburger (1951) pointed out, an important subgroup of eating disorders. These patients seem unable to leave food in the refrigerator, or ignore an unfinished piece of cake or box of candy with its cellophane wrapper broker; they must compulsively finish everything. Although I am aware of no specific publications on this subject, it has been my clinical experience that such patients are acting out a ritual of pleasing somebody else which hides a deep narcissistic rage. Thus they are pleasing either the disturbed, anxious overcontrolling mother or father who has made it clear that food is precious and every bit must be cleaned from the plate because "the people in Europe are starving," and who sadistically enforces this dictum, or the spouse—on whom the patient is pathologically dependent—who has a deeply neurotic need to see the patient eat up everything in sight. What these patients are doing, therefore, is compulsively repeating a pattern that brought them mirroring approval from the vital selfobject in the past and is being repeated in the present in order to maintain a false self, which is less unbearable than fragmentation and rage. The role of such compulsive rituals in controlling aggression is predominant, as I have mentioned.[2]

Pernicious familial interference with reducing regimens can therefore be expected. In the case of children and adolescents it is the parents who undermine the dietary regime, and in the case of married people it is quite frequently the spouse who has an unconscious vested interest in keeping the patient fat, and therefore undermines all his or her efforts to reduce. If this is so, the therapist may have to insist that other members of the family go into treatment if the case is to be successful. Reducing weight is made impossible if the patient is surrounded by continual pressure from the persons most important in his or her life, and on which the patient is often pathologically dependent, to remain obese. It is actually astonishing to what extreme family members will go to undermine psychotherapy and dietary regimens that at the same time they are paying for. Every kind of ancillary support group such as Weight Watchers or TOPS, as well as medical supervision of diet and exercise, should be encouraged and supported for these patients, and it has been my clinical experience that they really do help. Introduction of such "parameters" in the psychoanalytic treatment of obesity is also advocated by Ingram (1976).

Bruch (1975) insists that treatment of cases of anorexia is more likely to be unsuccessful when a therapist conceives of the disorder as expressing "oral dependency, incorporative cannibalism, and rejection of pregnancy" (p. 807). She prefers to focus on the patient's defective tools and concepts

[2] Other patients compulsively eat only certain selected foods such as sweet rolls or ice cream, etc. In these patients there seems to be a combination of an organ neurosis and a conversion disorder; I have been able in some cases to trace back the specific food that is compulsively ingested to a vital association with the longed-for lost parent.

for organizing and expressing his own needs and his bewilderment in dealing with others: "Instead of interpreting intrapsychic conflicts and the disturbed eating functions, therapy will attempt to help him deal with the underlying sense of incompetence, encourage correction of the conceptual deficits and distortions, and thus enable a patient to emerge from his isolation and dissatisfaction. The patients need help with their lacking sense of autonomy, their disturbed self-concept and self-awareness" (p. 807).

It does not follow from any of this, however, that the eventual understanding of the unconscious meaning of the disorganized eating patterns through traditional methods is a mistake in the intensive psychotherapy of eating disorders; all that follows is that classical psychoanalysis without parameters runs a serious risk of ignoring all that has been learned even since the time of Fenichel about the treatment of such disorders and that, as in the case of borderline patients, intensive psychoanalytic psychotherapy as I (Chessick, 1974, 1981) have described it, offers greater hope with these patients. Such therapy, as Bruch (1974, 1979, 1982) would agree, concentrates first on the building of structure—"an attempt to repair the conceptual defects and distortions, the deep-seated sense of dissatisfaction and isolation, and the conviction of incompetence" (1979, p. 143)—and secondarily—except in self-destructive emergencies or the early appearance of negative transference based on the projection of all-bad self and object representations as described by Kernberg (Wilson, 1983)—on conflict interpretation, and is consistent with Fenichel's characterization of most eating disorders as an organ neurosis rather than a conversion neurosis.

In my clinical experience the most serious problem in the intensive psychotherapy of the eating disorders is not that of a schizophrenic loss of reality testing, as Bruch suggests, but of a deep characterologic depression often with core paranoid features—manifested by a derogatory self image, cynicism, and hopelessness and reinforced by the long-standing nature of the condition—as well as a profound narcissistic rage that begins to show itself as the eating disorder itself is corrected. Thus a long and difficult intensive psychotherapy is to be expected in such patients because we are dealing with a profound preoedipal disorder characterized by severe early structural defects.

Two conflicts that must be faced eventually are also suggested here, following the views of Glover (1956) and Woollcott (1981) rather than Kohut's implication of a relatively nonconflictual use of the addictive substance for self-soothing. These are (a) the fear of the loss of individual autonomy in the blissful union with the mother, and (b) the addictive substance as a poisonous antidote for the purpose of neutralizing dangerous sadistic substances felt as within, representing the painful early bad experiences with the mother and producing the hateful self image. The best measure of basic change is in the reduction of the derogatory body-image distortion (Garner, Garfinkel, Stancer, and Moldofsky, 1976; Casper, Halmi, Goldberg, Eckert, and Davis, 1979; Casper, Offer, and Ostrov, 1981).

Most authors currently agree—with some notable exceptions (Wilson, 1983)—that insight into unconscious conflicts and symbolic meanings usually does not by itself lead to a cure of eating disorders. Some are so pessimistic about eating disorders as to insist that the psychosis which they feel underlies the overt clinical picture can never yield to *any* verbal form of treatment. Similar to what I (Chessick, 1977, 1982, 1983) have recommended in the early phase of the treatment of borderline patients, rather than transference interpretations most authors advocate paying minute attention to both discrepancies in the patient's recall of his past and to the way he misperceives or misinterprets current events and often responds to them in an inappropriate way, especially at the beginning of therapy. At first a kind of ego-building therapy is called for in which the therapist has to function as an accessory ego for the patient to help sharpen his powers of self-examination and engage him as a partner in exploration. Even the strict psychoanalysts in the New York group (Wilson, 1983) agree that "The analyst provides auxiliary ego strength and a rational superego" (p. 185).

Each episode within the eating disorder has to be studied in detail in at least two or three sessions weekly, preferably with the patient on the analytic couch, to uncover the specific sequence and psychodynamic meaning that led to the episode. Paranoid distortions and fuzzy reality testing need to be corrected by careful attention to the realistic situation and current details. As Bruch (1973) writes, such patients "suffer from an abiding sense of loneliness, or the feeling of not being respected by others, or of being insulted or abused, though the realistic situation may not contain these elements. The anticipation or recall of real or imagined insults may lead to withdrawal from the actual situation and flight into an eating binge" (p. 337). Even the confusion of body image is complicated (Powers, 1980), combining inaccurate perception of actual size or shape with an unrealistic negative self-appraisal often consolidated in adolescence.

Since such patients tolerate a silent psychoanalytic therapist very poorly, the therapist, at least at the beginning of treatment, must be willing to participate actively with the patient in discussion of the details of the patient's current situation; at the beginning of therapy the patient must experience the therapist as being practically useful and helpful in getting the patient to explore the details of and the solutions to the problems of everyday living. At the beginning of therapy this is usually more important than any interpretations that might be made. Krystal and Raskin (1970) call this "facilitating the establishment of a benign introject," in which the therapist is used "to create an object-representation which [the patient] can utilize for inspiration and achieving a major change in [his] identity and function" (p. 106).

At the same time the autonomy of the patient must be carefully preserved by the technique of not telling the patient actually what to do but getting him to explore in greater detail the options and also the inaccuracies in his perceptions and expectations. If this early phase of psychotherapy is properly traversed, an addictive transference to the therapist forms, often resembling the narcissistic transferences described by Kohut,[3] and the intensive psychotherapy shifts increasingly into an interpretive psychoanalytic mode.

Furthermore, in all cases of severe obesity or anorexia, outside help is necessary; the patient must get proper medical supervision of weight reduction and exercise, be encouraged deliberately to increase social activities, and participate in support groups (Casper, 1982). The temporary substitution of anxiolytic agents for binge eating is occasionally very helpful. I believe it is unrealistic on the part of a psychotherapist to think that by interpretations alone he is going to reverse a long-standing, deeply embedded, and effective archaic process of tension reduction in an adult patient, especially since, as Glucksman, Rand, and Stunkard (1978) point out, complex unexplored neurophysiological, histological, and endocrinological mechanisms are also possibly involved.

It is a grave clinical mistake to form a therapeutic contract at the beginning of treatment with any patient in which therapy is seen as aimed primarily at either the reduction of or the gaining of weight, or the cessation of a bulimarexic pattern. The patient must be firmly told at the beginning of treatment that the eating disorder represents symptoms of an underlying important emotional disturbance, and that the only function of the psychotherapy is to understand and try to ameliorate the disturbance itself. If this is successful then the gaining or losing of weight will be accomplished by the patient when the patient is ready for it and with a steady pressure from the therapist, but under no circumstances should change in weight or eating patterns be seen as the primary goal of an intensive psychotherapy.

No attempt should be made to minimize the difficulty of substantial weight reduction as well as of keeping the weight down once it is down. Thus a therapist should never convey to a patient a promise that once his

[3] Indeed, Glover (1956) labels the addictions "circumscribed narcissistic neuroses."

problems and conflicts have been analyzed and solved the fat will just melt away and stay away. Furthermore, as long as the body weight is within reasonable nutritional limits, no value judgment needs to be placed on the fact that the patient is "fat" or "skinny." No absolute "correct" or "ideal" weight should be predicted, and the final weight at which the patient stabilizes should be that with which the patient—not necessarily the therapist—seems comfortable and satisfied. It is even sometimes best to tell certain overweight patients to live with their weight, or even offer some supportive treatment to help them accept their obesity, rather than make the assumption—often based on cultural or medical prejudice—that every patient who is overweight should be vigorously treated. The same is true with certain "thin fat people" and certain mild anorexics who have achieved a stable condition.

The most serious special countertransference problem encountered in the intensive psychotherapy of eating disorders is frustration from the long and tedious treatment required. The deep, empty depression in many of these patients produces a painful sensation in the therapist, as his normal liveliness, enthusiasm, and human investment in the patient is often met by a silent and depleted response or narcissistic self-preoccupation. This brings repeated narcissistic disappointment to the therapist over years of time; any therapist who works with eating disorders must have ample independent sources of emotional supply and empathy in his personal life and must be free of the temptation to turn to his patients for gratification, soothing, or narcissistic massage. Such patients are the least likely to produce "strokes" for the therapist, and as the weight problem begins to correct itself they become "worse" as the anger, despair, projective proclivities, and intolerance to any frustration or humiliation show themselves more and more in the interactions with the therapist, as Ingram (1976) points out.

The therapist may deal with his frustration, hatred, and rage at such patients in a reaction formation, becoming a replica of the overanxious parent and shifting to a so-called supportive treatment because of excessive concerns about the patient's fragility. The situation this leads to, in my consultation experience, is that the patient gets control of the therapy and leads the therapist a merry chase by threats of suicide or psychosis or dangerously extreme fluctuations in weight. Because of the typical projection fantasy of these patients, as reported by Offenkrantz and Tobin (1974), that "the therapist needs the patient to become abstinent in order to alleviate the therapist's own sense of inner emptiness, lack of pleasure, and craving for relief," careful continuing self analysis is required to prevent externalization (Chessick, 1972) of this fantasy.

In the intensive psychotherapy of these disorders the therapist is often called upon to decide *when* recommendations of outside medical help, groups, and even anxiolytic drugs are appropriate and necessary. The danger, of course, is in pushing these out of countertransference disappointment, anger, and frustration, rather than in the service of the patient's actual need at the time. If this occurs, the patient reexperiences empathic failure with the "food-stuffing mother." Conversely, withholding these prescriptions when they would be appropriate is also a destructive manifestation of countertransference, so careful self-analytic investigation on each occasion is required.

When the time comes that the patient must take some realistic steps to change his life style, the previously compliant and cooperative patient begins to show a tough capacity to engage the therapist in a bitter struggle. The willingness of the therapist to enter into this struggle with the patient and still maintain an empathic and analytic interpretive stance is probably the crucial factor that determines whether or not the treatment will succeed. In these cases, as Nacht (Chessick, 1974) said, it is not so much what the therapist says as the person he really is that counts in psychotherapy. Developing the capacity to maintain empathic contact with and a deep sense of inner commitment to an extremely disturbed patient who is only very slowly responding to the treatment, and whose eating disorder seems deeply fixed, while at the same time resisting the temptation to soothe one's self by adopting a supportive or messianic role, is an extremely difficult accomplishment. It represents a serious test of the therapist's skills, capacities, training, and personal analysis. The case reported of severe anorexia treated by Mintz (Wilson, 1983) is a beautiful demonstration of this.

# Summary

In this paper I have reviewed the clinical experiences of myself and others gained in the intensive psychoanalytic psychotherapy of adult eating disorders. I have emphasized the narcissistic rage secondary to the failure of early selfobjects as producing a variety of the features of the eating disorders, including migraine, tantrums, self-destructive activity, paranoid proclivities, body-image disturbances, and compulsive rituals. Such rage floods a defective self-soothing apparatus, and the patient regressively turns to the drama of the eating disorders to gain temporary relief and to counteract threatened fragmentation of the self. Psychoanalytic psychotherapy of these disorders requires a combination of modalities, but insight into what has happened and into the unconscious fantasies, which differ in each individual case and determine the particular disorder pattern, is consistently required if lasting changes in the patient's life style are to be effected.

The defective self-soothing mechanisms must be repaired by appropriate idealization and transmuting internalizations, and the patient must be enlisted as a partner in developing better reality testing and a new life style based on a stronger functioning ego developed both through appropriate interpretations, and a more cohesive sense of self. This constitutes a long and difficult task for both the patient and the therapist, but it can be accomplished, and there is no reason to be pessimistic about the results of structure-building therapy aimed primarily at the resumption of psychic development.

## REFERENCES

Alexander, F. (1950), *Psychosomatic Medicine*. New York: Norton.
Bernstein, A. & Warner, G. (1981), *An Introduction to Contemporary Psychoanalysis*. New York: Aronson.
Bruch, H. (1973), *Eating Disorders*. New York: Basic Books.
———— (1974), *Learning Psychotherapy*. Cambridge, Mass.: Harvard University Press.
———— (1975), Anorexia nervosa. In: *American Handbook of Psychiatry*, Vol. 4. ed. S. Arieti. New York: Basic Books. pp. 787–809.
———— (1979), *The Golden Cage*. New York: Vintage Books.
———— (1982), Anorexia nervosa: Therapy and theory. *Amer. J. Psychiat.*, 139:1531–1538.
Cantwell, D., Sturzenberger, S., Bourroughs, J., Salkin, B., & Breen, J. K. (1977), Anorexia nervosa: An affective disorder. *Arch. Gen. Psychiat.*, 34:1087–1096.
Casper, R. (1982), Treatment principles in anorexia nervosa. *Adoles. Psychiat.*, 10:431–454.
———— (1983), On the emergence of bulimia nervosa as a syndrome. *Internat. J. Eating Disorders*, 2:3–16.
———— Davis, J. (1977), On the course of anorexia nervosa. *Amer. J. Psychiat.*, 134:974–978.
———— Halmi, K., Goldberg, S., Eckert, E., & Davis, J. (1979), Disturbances in body image estimation as related to other characteristics and outcome in anorexia nervosa. *Brit. J. Psychiat.*, 134:60–66.
———— Elke, E., Halmi, K., Goldberg, S., & Davis, J. (1980), Bulimia. *Arch. Gen. Psychiat.*, 37:1030–1035.
———— Offer, D., & Ostrov, J. (1981), The self-image of adolescents with acute anorexia nervosa. *J. Pediatrics*, 98:656–661.
Chessick, R. (1960), The "pharmacogenic orgasm" in the drug addict. *Arch. Gen. Psychiat.*, 3:545–556.
———— (1972), Externalization and existential anguish. *Arch. Gen. Psychiat.*, 27:764–770.
———— (1974), *The Technique and Practice of Intensive Psychotherapy*. New York: Aronson.
———— (1977), *Intensive Psychotherapy of the Borderline Patient*. New York: Aronson.
———— (1981), What is intensive psychotherapy? *Amer. J. Psychotherapy*, 35:489–501.
———— (1982), Intensive psychotherapy of a borderline patient. *Arch. Gen. Psychiat.*, 39:413–419.
———— (1983), Problems in the intensive psychotherapy of the borderline patient. *Dynamic Psychotherapy*, 1:20–32.
Dally, P. (1969), *Anorexia Nervosa*. New York: Grune and Stratton.
*Diagnostic and Statistical Manual of Mental Disorders* (1980), 3d ed. New York: American Psychiatric Association.
Federn, P. (1947), Principles of psychotherapy in latent schizophrenia. *Amer. J. Psychotherapy*, 2:129–147.
Fenichel, O. (1945), *The Psychoanalytic Theory of Neurosis*. New York: Norton.

Frosch, J. (1977), The relation between acting out and disorders of impulse control. *Psychiat.*, 40:295–314.

Garfinkel, P., Moldofsky, H., & Garner, D. (1980), The heterogeneity of anorexia nervosa. *Arch. Gen. Psychiat.*, 37:1036–1040.

Garner, D., Garfinkel, P., Stancer, H., & Moldofsky, H. (1976), Body image disturbances in anorexia nervosa and obesity. *Psychosomatic Med.*, 38:327–336.

Glover, E. (1956), *On the Early Development of Mind*. New York: International Universities Press.

Glucksman, M., Rand, L., & Stunkard, A. (1978), Psychodynamics of obesity. *J. Amer. Acad. Psychoanal.*, 6:103–155.

Halmi, K. (1980), Anorexia nervosa. In: *Comprehensive Textbook of Psychiatry—III*, Vol. 2. ed. H. Kaplan, A. Freedman, & B. Sadock. Baltimore: Williams & Wilkins. pp. 1882–1891.

Hamburger, W. W. (1951), Emotional aspects of obesity. *Med. Clin. N. Amer.*, 35:483–499.

Ingram, E. (1976), Psychoanalytic treatment of the obese person. *Amer. J. Psychoanal.*, 36:227–235.

Innaurato, A. (1977), *The Transfiguration of Benno Blimpie*. London: T. Q. Publications.

Kaplan, H., Freedman, A., & Sadock, B. (1980), *Comprehensive Textbook of Psychiatry—III*. Vol. 1. Baltimore: Williams and Wilkins.

Kohut, H. (1971), *The Analysis of the Self*. New York: International Universities Press.

——— (1984), *How Does Analysis Cure?* Chicago: University of Chicago Press.

Kolb, L. & Brodie, H. (1982), *Modern Clinical Psychiatry*. Philadelphia: W. B. Saunders.

Krystal, H. (1983), Adolescence and the tendencies to develop substance dependence. *Psychoanal. Inquiry*, 2:581–618.

——— Raskin, H. (1970), *Drug Dependence: Aspects of Ego Function*. Detroit: Wayne State University Press.

Leon, G. (1982), Personality and behavioral correlates of obesity. In: *Psychological Aspects of Obesity*, ed. B. Wolman. New York: Van Nostrand Reinhold, pp. 15–29.

Offenkrantz, W. & Tobin, A. (1974), Psychoanalytic psychotherapy. *Arch. Gen. Psychiat.*, 30:593–606.

Pflanze, O. (1972), Toward a psychoanalytic interpretation of Bismarck. *Amer. Histor. Rev.*, 77:419–444.

Pope, H., Hudson, J., Jones, J., & Yurgelun-Todd, D. (1983), Bulimia treated with imipramine. *Amer. J. Psychiat.*, 140:554–558.

Powers, P. S. (1980), *Obesity: The Regulation of Weight*. Baltimore & London: Williams & Wilkins.

Rado, W. (1926), The psychic effects of intoxication. *Internat. J. Psycho-Anal.*, 7:396–413.

Rand, C. (1981), Psychoanalytic treatment of obesity. In: *Psychological Aspects of Obesity*, ed. B. Wolman. New York: Van Nostrand Reinhold, pp. 177–191.

——— Stunkard, A. (1983), Obesity and psychoanalysis: Treatment and four-year follow-up. In press.

Ritvo, S. (1976), Adolescent to woman. *J. Amer. Psychoanal. Assn.*, 24:127–138.

Shainess, N. (1979), The swing of the pendulum—from anorexia to obesity. *Amer. J. Psychoanal.*, 39:225–235.

Stunkard, A. (1975), Obesity. In: *American Handbook of Psychiatry*, Vol. 4. ed. A. Arieti. New York: Basic Books. pp. 76–86.

——— (1980), Obesity. In: *Comprehensive Textbook of Psychiatry—III*, Vol. 2. ed. H. Kaplan, A. Freedman, & B. Sadock. Baltimore: Williams & Wilkins. pp. 1872–1882.

——— Burt, V. (1967), Obesity and the body image II. *Amer. J. Psychiat.*, 123:1443–1447.

Weiss, E. & English, O. (1957), *Psychosomatic Medicine*. Philadelphia: W. B. Saunders.

Wilson, C. (ed.) (1983), *Fear of Being Fat*. New York: Aronson.

Wooley, S. & Wooley, O. (1980), Eating disorders: Obesity and anorexia. In: *Women and Psychotherapy*, ed. A. Brodsky & R. Hare-Muslin. New York: Guilford Press, pp. 135–158.

Woollcott, P. (1981), Addiction: Clinical and theoretical considerations. *This Annual*, 9:189–206. New York: International Universities Press.

Wulff, M. (1932), Über einen interessanten oralen Symptomenkomplex und seine Beziehung zur Sucht. *Internat. Z. für Psychoanalyse*, 18:281–302.
Zales, M. (1982), *Eating, Sleeping and Sexuality: Treatment of Disorders in Basic Life Functions.* New York: Brunner/Mazel.

*December 1983*

# Complicated Mourning

## VAMIK D. VOLKAN, M.D. (Charlottesville, Va.)

Accommodation to a loss by death unfolds in expectable stages when complications do not 'interfere. The aim of this paper is to familiarize the professional whose work brings him in contact with the bereaved with these stages and to help him assess signs of complication, whether they appear in the acute or the chronic stage of mourning. Complications in the latter culminate psychodynamically in one of two pathologies—(reactive) depression or established pathological mourning. The emphasis here will be on a definition of the metapsychology and the clinical picture of the latter and the description of a brief, but intensive form of psychotherapy especially effective for patients suffering established pathological mourning. I have termed this form of treatment "re-grief therapy." The psychoanalysis of persons with complicated mourning is also explored.

## Recognizable Stages of Mourning

Investigators studying the sequential behavior patterns of persons who had just suffered the loss of a "psychologically important other" by death have synthesized these patterns into schemata. Significantly, in spite of certain theoretical differences, I find all of these schemata to be generally similar from a phenomenological point of view. Pollock (1961), for example, describes the mourner's reactions as occurring in two states—the acute and the chronic. He holds further that the first stage includes three sequential steps of its own in which the mourner successively experiences shock, ac-

A shorter version of this paper was presented at the Conference on Psychoanalytic Psychotherapy, The Treatment of Depression, Chicago Institute for Psychoanalysis, November 20, 1982.

companied by denial of the death; acute grief (affective) reaction; and separation reaction, which reflects withdrawal of psychic interest in the internal representation of the dead.

In Pollock's schema, this acute stage is followed by a chronic one in which the bereaved demonstrates "various manifestations of adaptive mechanisms attempting to integrate the experience of the loss with reality so that life activities can go on" (p. 352). Pollock seems to equate his chronic stage with Freud's (1917) work of mourning. Most observers suggest that the work of mourning may require approximately a year, although Freud speaks in terms of a year or two.

Other systems of classifying the sequential phases of mourning, though failing to make any clear distinction between an acute and a chronic stage, incorporate essentially the same phenomena. Among such schemata that of Bowlby and Parkes (1970) is well-known. They recognize four stages in the mourning process. The first, characterized predominantly by numbness, usually lasts from a few hours to a week. During this time, numbness is interrupted by outbursts of intense distress and/or anger. Bowlby and Parkes see the second stage of bereavement as one of yearning and searching for the lost figure. They indicate that this stage may persist for months, or even years, during which the mourner will not only long for the one he has lost but be aware of an urge to search for him actively. A phase of disorganization follows, which is succeeded by a fourth and final stage, one of at least some degree of psychological reorganization that is related, I believe, to the development of adaptive mechanisms described by Pollock.

Though I think Pollock's division of the responses to death into two general stages is correct, I will not use his terms "acute" and "chronic" to refer to them. With their reference to time, the terms "acute" and "chronic" are best used here to refer to the persistence of any sign or symptom. To avoid semantic difficulties, I will speak rather of the *initial stage* and of the *work of mourning*, which is, in effect, the second and longer stage.

The initial stage includes the period of numbness and shock; denial of the death, followed by the splitting of ego functions with respect to the perception of the death; the activation of certain images of the dead and of inner patterns of relationship to them; and the experience of painful emotions accompanied by weeping. It is well recognized that the initial state is associated with anger (Pollock, 1961; Schuster, 1969; Volkan, 1981), the appearance of which during and at the end of this phase is psychologically necessary. This anger serves the ego's need for mastery of immediate shock and panic and indicates that the ego has now begun to interpret and integrate—at least to a significant extent—the impact of the loss in time and space. The experience of anger at being abandoned by the one now dead requires a recognition of the actuality of the death, a crucial event in the course of mourning.

If no complications supervene, one can expect the manifestations of initial grief to disappear within two to six months after the death, depending, of course, on the circumstances of its occurrence. During this period, signs of the initial stage not only follow one another but may suddenly disappear and reappear again, until the mourner, after acknowledging his anger, settles into the next stage, the prolonged work of mourning with its piecemeal advances. The work of mourning includes a slow-motion review of the mourner's relationship to the dead person; the struggle to keep or to reject a close tie with his representation of the one lost; and an initial regressive disorganization that is followed by a new inner organization able to test reality more fully for confirmation that the death, with all its psychological implications, has indeed taken place.

Before proceeding, it must be made clear that we are concerned here with adult mourning only, since there is considerable controversy in psychoanalytic literature and theory as to whether—or when—a child is capable of mourning. I agree with Wolfenstein (1966, 1969) that the experience of adolescence is a prerequisite of the ability to mourn in the adult sense. A gradual psychic withdrawal from one's parents or their representations—which, I might add, can never be complete—occurs during normal adolescence and serves to introduce the individual to the stages of psychic separation that mourning in the adult sense requires.

Because mourning, once initiated, moves as we have seen through recognizably differing stages—some of which include a variety of possible phases within themselves—one may assume that if the passage through any one of these is complicated, the individual may become fixated at that particular stage. In that event, the clinical characteristics expectable in any phase of that stage will usually be exaggerated, and the clinical picture will become even more complex as it reflects impulses (and defenses against them) regarding the complication itself. My own clinical research suggests that whenever a complication contaminates the chronic stage (Volkan, 1981), the psychodynamic processes of the mourner will culminate either in (reactive) depression or in what I have named *established pathological mourning*. Although the identification and treatment of the latter are the main concerns of this paper, it is important first to understand aspects of uncomplicated mourning and then to compare them with the (reactive) depression that may also develop in complicated mourning.

## The Completion of Mourning

A crucial aspect of uncomplicated mourning is that it has a conclusion on the practical level, so grief does not dominate the life of the bereaved indefinitely. Thus in the "normal" progression of events during the work of mourning, the bereaved reviews first acutely and then in piecemeal fashion the ongoing significance of the representation of the one lost to him; he both strives to bring the dead back to life and dreads encountering him again. These contrary impulses both to "resurrect" and to "kill" the lost object reflect the ambivalence that characterized the mourner's relationship to the dead person when he was still alive. In the end, both libidinal and aggressive ties to the representation are sufficiently loosened so that the mourner feels free to invest psychic energies formerly directed toward the dead in new objects. The mourner then usually achieves identification with the adaptive ego-alien aspects of the dead person's representation and so enriches his own ego. As Greene (1965) has indicated, one cannot assess the degree of the resolution of grief until the end of the second year—until the first anniversary of the loss, the first vacation or birthday without the presence of the deceased, or some other milestone has been experienced.

Obviously, a mourner never altogether forgets the dead person who was so highly valued in life and never totally withdraws his investment in his representation. We can never purge those who have been close to us from our own history except by psychic acts damaging to our own identity. It is, however, "normal" for the mourning process to have a beginning and a conclusion. In the practical sense it starts with a loss (in this context, the death of an important person) or with the realistic or fantasied threat of a loss; it ends when the mourner no longer has a need to reactivate the representation of the dead with exaggerated intensity in the course of daily living.

The process of relinquishing it has proceeded like the slow healing of a wound (Engel, 1961), and an open lesion has gradually been closed and covered over, though not without leaving its scar.

## Factors Influencing Initial Reactions to Death

It is important to recognize that initial responses to death will depend on several factors, including the mourner's ego maturity and the nature of his previous relationship with the one who has died. The circumstances under which the death occurred are also significant—whether the death was sudden and unexpected; whether it was violent or peaceful; whether the dead was seen as heroic in life and so is possibly understood as now transported to some kind of comforting Valhalla. The kind of arrangements made for the funeral rites and burial and the nature of the mourner's participation in them also influence initial reactions and require our attention when studying and treating the dynamics of bereavement.

It has long been recognized (Freud, 1917) that when the relationship between a mourner and the one he mourns had been ambivalent and stormy, the mourner's reactions are apt to be complicated by a variety of component feelings. The more loving the relationship had been, the more likely it is that the mourner will experience sadness but no guilt, and that this sadness, like love, will be personal and intimate, and thus, though less complicated by conflictual emotions, much more difficult to express than depression (Smith, 1971).

The death of an aged person or a chronic invalid is less shocking than a sudden, entirely unexpected death. The unanticipated death of a child is the most extreme example of the latter, and I believe that a mother never fully recovers from the sudden death of her small, healthy child, no matter how many creative/adaptive mechanisms she may find to endure her loss. As the child was both young and healthy, the mourner has been denied all access to what Lindemann (1944), who long ago provided us with a classical description of acute grief, called *anticipatory mourning*. By this he referred to the process of gradual accommodation that one makes to the loss of a significant other whose life is clearly coming to a close, and to the possible passage through some, or even all, of the stages of grief that may in such circumstances take place before the actual event of death. Such anticipatory grief may even be worked through before the event in a fantasied situation, at times with disruptive results. I had one young woman patient, for example, whose husband had been sent to Vietnam soon after their marriage; she was certain that he would not return alive. Later I learned the origin of her fatalistic anticipation. As a young girl my patient had suffered the sudden loss of someone close to her. So vivid was her fantasy of her husband's "inevitable" sudden death that when he did return from Vietnam unharmed and without a scratch, she perceived him as a stranger, a virtual "ghost" to whom she felt no relationship and did not want to be married, and they were soon divorced.

I have found that a *violent* death is often unconsciously connected with the mourner's aggressive drive derivatives and so fosters a guilt that precludes any expression of the angry and aggressive reactions that are "natural" and necessary after the death of an important other. Difficulties can also emerge in the initial stage when the dead person was too greatly idealized to be "killed," and the expected stages of mourning cannot be initiated. Both of these factors cause complications when an idealized leader dies suddenly, perhaps as the victim of his enemies, or when the mental representations of slain soldiers viewed as saviors are memorialized in the minds of those who mourn them. Here aggression and the need to "kill" the hero are both denied. I (Volkan, 1979), have described this situation as I saw it in my fieldwork on the island of Cyprus after the war there in 1974.

As suggested above, I (Volkan, 1970) have noted elsewhere on the basis of my clinical experience that the type of funeral, the nature of the mourner's participation in it, and even the type of coffin chosen for burial can influence the initial responses of a mourner. In regard to the latter, if the unconscious fantasy of the dead returning is strong, and if a lightweight coffin is chosen (i.e., light enough to fail to hold the body down), the mourner may unconsciously react to fears of the coffin's inadequacy. As for rites and religious services, as numerous psychoanalytic studies have revealed, these are attempts to deal with the common psychological components of the initial stage of grief, among them the emergence of aggressive feelings. Thus the mourner should be allowed to participate fully in whatever mourning rituals his culture and religion support. Ironically, it often happens that the persons most likely to have difficulty in coping with their grief, such as the young, are not made participants in the funeral rites. For example, a teen-aged boy who has just lost his father will, as the oldest surviving male, often be declared the head of the family and, paradoxically, be kept busy and thus "protected" from playing any active part in the funeral service itself.

I observed this in a patient of mine named Solomon who was a young teen-ager when his father died. The rather extended Jewish religious rites for the dead man were well under way when his mother decided that young Solomon should be sent to the country "to get fresh air." While in the country he caught a snake, which he then kept in a glass bottle with some sort of acid fluid. Having been interrupted in the religious ceremonies for his father, he was forced to create his own ceremony for "killing"—and thus mourning—his parent. The dead snake represented the dead man, and the son made a daily ritual of observing its progressive deterioration in the bottle. His unfinished psychological business with his father was so complicated, however, that he could not proceed through the mourning process successfully. As the snake rotted away the patient himself fell victim to severe dermatitis. His skin became infected, causing him considerable pain and inconvenience. Although one cannot know all the factors in the etiology of Solomon's skin trouble, it is safe to assume that his dermatitis reflected a significant identification with his decaying father—and that his removal from the funeral rites at least contributed to the complications that developed in his mourning process.

It should be added that one cannot overlook the effect of any drastic change a death may have brought about in the *real* world of those who survive it, such as the loss of a home or of financial support, and their symbolic effect on the inner world of the mourner.

The influences on the initial response to death mentioned thus far are rather readily observable ones. Clearly, only searching psychological examination such as that which occurs in the course of psychoanalytic treatment can reveal any perception of the loss by death idiosyncratic to the mourner, and its condensation for him in the representation of important psychic events, such as those related to separation and/or castration anxiety. If one is to understand the patient's responses on this level he must grasp the symbolism the individual patient is using.

## Complications of the Initial Stages of Mourning

Complications of the mourning process may begin immediately after the death. As Deutsch (1937) demonstrated, the rejection of emotion after a death implies the presence of such complications. Although the bereaved is fully aware of the historical reality of the death, it is possible for him to deny it emotionally, and he may remain fixated in the initial stage of mourning. I (Volkan, 1981) have described another even more severe type of death denial. In this type, which I term "total denial," not only are expected emotions absent, but also any conscious acknowledgment of the occurrence of death. Any such failure to grasp reality, if long adhered to, is usually dramatic enough to come to the attention of relatives and friends, who then take steps to "push" the bereaved into mourning, perhaps with the aid of a priest, clergyman, or rabbi. Total denial of a death is thus seldom allowed to continue long enough to require psychiatric attention. Although there are exceptions, only 2 out of 150 patients referred to me in sixteen years for symptom formation triggered by a death were still fixated in total denial. Such patients, when encountered, are always astonishing. One of these, a young man seen a month after his younger brother's death in an automobile accident, reported that he had no reason to grieve since it was only in his dreams that his brother had died. This man was not psychotic except for this focal break with reality.

In the initial stage one more frequently sees exaggerated outbursts of anger. The mourner's ego cannot tolerate the knowledge that most of this anger is directed toward the dead person who, by dying, inflicted such a grievous, seemingly unbearable wound. Such anger may be widely diffused, or it may be displaced onto one specific person. My research has shown, however, that there is no correspondence between the degree of initial anger and the chronicity of any complications that may arise in mourning. The person who seems to be having an overly dramatic angry response may just as dramatically recover from his anger state and follow a more usual course of mourning.

Numbness, a common immediate reaction to the news of a death, as we have noted, may recur intermittently in the initial stage. Indeed, if the mourning is chronically complicated, the clinical picture may include persisting episodes of numbness, although other characteristics will predominate. Wahl (1970) has written about other such "normal" grief manifestations. For example, preoccupation with the image of the dead—either in dreams or in waking consciousness—may later become chronic, and these manifestations may be seen years after the death of an important other. It is difficult to determine whether the resulting clinical picture reflects a fixation in the initial stage or the condensation of the complications of both the initial stage and that of the work of mourning. I believe the latter to be true.

## Complications in the Work of Mourning

I have found in my research that the patient who displays great disturbance in the initial stage of grief is not necessarily destined to develop complications in its chronic stage. Indeed, I (Volkan, 1981) have observed that sometimes persons showing very dramatic initial reactions to loss settle readily into the lengthy, piecemeal process that is the work of mourning.

I hold that chronic complication of the work of mourning and even chronic complication of the initial stage will, in the long run, eventuate in one of two kinds of pathological psychodynamic constellation—either (reactive) depression or established pathological mourning. These may be either patent or hidden behind symptoms of other recognizable illnesses or syndromes, for example, conversion hysteria. I believe, however, that all other recognizable disturbances to which a mourner is subject will manifest themselves within the psychodynamic framework of one of these two constellations, and that, once treatment has begun, one pattern or the other can be identified. Since my clinical experience has taught me that established pathological mourning may respond to a distinct therapeutic approach, identifying accurately the type of pathology that has developed in complicated mourning becomes crucial. As we will see, distinguishing between the two forms depends basically on determining what the mourner does with his representations of the one he has lost. I further believe from my experience with mourners demonstrating either pattern that the resolution of other psychic conflicts cannot proceed until the patient has been freed from complications in the work of mourning.

Although these two pathologies differ, it must be noted that regression is common to both. Indeed, regression in the uncomplicated work of mourning is necessary and is undertaken in the service of the new psychic organization that will appear once mourning is ended; such regression can be expected to include the use of introjective-projective mechanisms. The new psychic organization will, as indicated above, include both healing identifications with certain aspects of the deceased and adaptive mechanisms (Pollock, 1961; Rochlin, 1965) for dealing with an external world in which the lost one is no longer sought. Blos (1979) relates regression in the service of such development to the second individuation phase of adolescence. He contends that in adolescence regression in the service of development results in "the disengagement of libidinal and aggressive cathexes from the internalized infantile love and hate objects" (p. 179) and "brings the more advanced ego of adolescence into combat with infantile drive positions, with old conflictual constellations and their solutions, with early object relations and narcissistic formations" (p. 180). Recognizing this, it is clear why Wolfenstein (1966, 1969) developed the hypothesis, noted above, that passage through adolescence is a necessary precondition for the ability to mourn in the adult sense described here.

Just as some adolescents cannot manage second individuation with adaptive results, some mourners cannot mourn without establishing pathological conditions. In such cases reactivated introjective-projective mechanisms lead to pathological formations rather than to the enrichment of the ego.

## (Reactive) Depression

In order to distinguish established pathological mourning from the (reactive) depression that may also develop in complicated mourning it is necessary to review the characteristics of the latter. The psychodynamics of depression caused by a death include an indiscriminate *total* identification with both the positive and negative traits of the ambivalently regarded (both positive and negative) representation of the deceased, which is then assimilated into the mourner's self-concept. From the phenomenological point of view, the patient, unlike the individual in psychotic depression, undergoes no gross identity change as a result of this identification; yet his self-concept is nevertheless strongly affected. Since the individual has necessarily identified with ego-alien traits of the dead person, the total and indiscriminate identification that occurs in (reactive) depression is inevitably disruptive to the self. The ambivalence with which the depressed mourner simultaneously hates and loves the representation of his dead—with whom he has identified himself—evokes within him a struggle between a desire to honor and a desire to destroy himself. The self thus becomes the internal battleground for tensions formerly existing between the deceased and the mourner. I believe that Fenichel's (1945) study, summarizing the work of

Abraham (1911, 1916), Freud (1917), and Rado (1956), remains the best statement of this classic psychoanalytic understanding of (reactive) depression.

## A Case Example

A clinical vignette will illustrate the psychodynamics of this process. After her parents' divorce, a young girl tried, at least unconsciously, to take her mother's place with her father; this attempted oedipal triumph induced guilt feelings. Subsequently, her father killed himself after an unsuccessful love affair by "blowing out his *brains*" with a shotgun. The girl then went to college where she studied so diligently that she became known as "a brain," although she never consciously connected this nickname with her father's manner of dying. Its significance was forced to the surface only later when, while she was still a student, the sight of a museum display purporting to show the shattered, gray brain matter of a suicide who had shot himself through the head triggered a depression.

In the course of treatment it became clear that the girl had tried to repair the damaged mental representation of her lost father by herself becoming "a brain," but that in incorporating the positive qualities of a brain she had also identified with her father's "bad" part. As long as she could maintain the illusion that her father's representation was repaired she did not exhibit overt depressive symptoms, but confronted by the grisly exhibit, she was made to *lose* all hope of reconstructing her father. At this point her identification with her father's negative part became total, and she then became overtly depressed and suicidal. The extent of this patient's disruptive identification with her father's representation can be seen in even the manifest content of a dream she reported when she began treatment, one in which she wore her father's shoes.

## Established Pathological Mourning

### Introjects

As stated above, established pathological mourning differs from (reactive) depression in the way in which the mourner relates to the representation of the deceased. The representation is indeed taken in—introjected—but in the form of an object representation that is experienced by the patient as retaining boundaries of its own. This representation does not meld into the mourner's self-representation, but continues to have, as it were, an autonomous existence. These unassimilated object representations are usually called introjects in psychoanalytic literature when they exert exaggerated influence on the self-concept of the persons who possess them. Such transformation of an object representation into an introject occurs in a crisis (Schafer, 1968); for example, when, in order to modify the distressing situation after death, an ongoing representation of the dead person becomes urgently needed. Usually, in established pathological mourning, this "crisis" arises from the mourner's hope that the dead will return and his need to "kill" him in order to complete his mourning.

We now include in the category of established pathological mourning all persons—including schizophrenics and children—who speak clearly and often of these introjects. An example of this from my experience is a patient, in this case a middle-aged man, who continued for many years to have conversations, as he drove to work each day, with the "head" of his long-dead half-brother, which he felt resided within his chest. It is necessary to remember that although such mourners firmly refer to their introjects as thought they were immutable foreign entities lodged within their breasts, these patients are simply using their inner symbolic system to describe a dynamic-affective-cognitive psychological process.

An understanding of the psychological issues involved is essential. The individual caught up in established pathological mourning has not yet succeeded in identifying fully with the one he has lost—either in the total and disruptive identification of full-blown depression or the enriching selective identification characteristic of healthy mourning. Instead, he chronically maintains a relationship with his introject of the deceased (usually as it appears in part-object form, i.e., as a face or voice) that is halfway between healthy identification and (reactive) depression. Since such an introject originates chronologically before either the "normal" resolution of mourning or the development of depression, it has the potential for developing into either one. The introject cannot, however, serve in the uncomplicated work of mourning until it is no longer regarded with ambivalence. Insofar as the person fixed in a state of established pathological mourning clings to the introject in the hope of resolving his ambivalence, he can be said to be "striving toward" healthy identification. Unlike the depressed mourner, he has not surrendered all hope of resolving the ambivalence, and it is this attendant quality of hope that is the real significance of the introject in established pathological mourning. Because the introject offers a representation separate from that of the patient, he retains a representation of the dead with which the possibility of dialogue continues, and so the ultimate hope of resolution of the relationship is sustained.

## LINKING OBJECTS AND PHENOMENA

Although the person in established pathological mourning stays in contact with the representation of the dead internally, through the introject, he also maintains external contact with it by using what I (Volkan, 1972, 1981) call linking objects or linking phenomena. A linking object is some-thing—usually inanimate—actually present in the environment that is psy-chologically contaminated with various aspects of both the dead and the self of the mourner. In other words, it symbolically stands for aspects of both self and object representations, as well as for elements of the mourner's ego ideal and superego, and functions as an external meeting ground for those representations that offer the illusion of reunion between the mour-ner and the deceased. Linking phenomena also exist and serve in the same way, but do not have material existence; a musical tune with special sig-nificance would be an example.

Just as not every object image or representation of the deceased is an introject, so, although many things have this potential, not every keepsake or memento cherished by a mourner should be seen as a linking object possessing a significant investment of symbolism and magic. A person may focus on a "last-minute linking object" that gained its special significance because it was at hand at the moment when he learned about the death, or when he first viewed the body. For example, one patient was about to put a stack of records on his player when the telephone rang, signaling a call that turned out to be a death message, and the set of records continued to be invested with the unique affect of that moment. Most linking objects, however, are chosen any time fairly soon after the death. The mourner may or may not be consciously aware of the magic his linking object holds for him until his attention is directed to it in treatment.

Our experience shows that linking objects, other than "last-minute" ones, are usually selected from among four other possible categories. Things habitually used by the dead in the past, perhaps something he or she wore, such as a watch, may serve as linking objects. For example, one patient used the watch of his father, who had died of multiple sclerosis and whose initials, M.S., were carved on the back of the watch. A second category includes things through which the deceased had extended his senses—for example, a camera, which is an extension of sight. Thus, a young man who had given his dying father injections kept the father's broken camera, which had an attachment that resembled a syringe, in his closet after the father's death. Symbolic or realistic representations of the dead person's appear-ance, such as a photograph, form a third type. An example would be a young man who put his father's picture in a cover—representing a cof-fin—and placed this under a leaking pipe. His father had died from overtaxing his heart while swimming, and his picture went on "swimming" under the leaking pipe. The last group we have noted consists of gifts from or to the mourner before death took place. A young woman whose linking object was of this type used a nightgown she had given her mother, who died wearing it.

Whatever it may be, the linking object is not put by the mourner to its customary use; a watch is not worn, a record is not played. Rather, the object is carefully put—often even locked—away. The mourner must know at all times exactly where it is, and from time to time he will take it out and, in ritual fashion, handle it or gaze at it until he experiences an eerie feeling of reunion.

Elsewhere (Volkan, 1972, 1981) I discuss in detail the relationship and distinction between linking objects, transitional objects, fetishes, and other "magical" objects. My concern here is the recognition that the linking object serves as an external bridge between the representation of the mourner and his representation of the deceased, just as the introject serves as an internal bridge. Both remain under the "absolute" control of the mourner himself, so that he can maintain the illusion either of bringing the dead back to life or of "killing" him. As a result, the mourner remains in a limbo between the two possibilities. In this, established pathological mourning more directly reflects a fixation in the work of mourning itself than does (reactive) depression.

## THE CLINICAL PICTURE

Thus far I have approached established pathological mourning from the point of view of a metapsychological understanding of the functions of both introjects and linking objects and their use in the mourning process. Such theoretical understanding is required for the correct diagnosis necessary to successful treatment. There are, however, clues to the presence of established pathological mourning on a descriptive level—such as the mourner's continued search for the deceased and the accompanying dread of being successful in this search—that emerge during observation and treatment. For example, one young man would be so struck from time to time by the resemblance of some older man seen on the street to the father he had lost ten years earlier that he would believe the man might actually be his father. In one sense he recognized the impossibility of this, but he could not restrain his impulse to hurry to pass the older man so that he could turn and get a good view of him. Time after time, he felt that a man whose back resembled his father's might, in fact, turn out to be the dead man. When, with quickened pace, he was able to pass such a man and look more closely, seeing that he had been wrong, he could thus "kill" his father. In another case, he once heard of a man who bore his father's name and felt compelled to travel to his home to see for himself that it was not his father.

From a psychodynamic point of view this young man was *splitting* (Freud, 1940) his ego functions. He *knew* that his father was dead. Part of his behavior, however, implied that he *did not know* that his father was dead. This type of splitting protects the ego from a global break with reality, on the one hand, and allows, on the other, "gratification" from the continued exaggerated investment of the libidinal and aggressive drive derivatives in the representation of the dead. Holding onto introjects and/or linking objects supports such split-off functions of the ego by allowing the individual to maintain the belief that death has not occurred (the libidinal gratification is possible) and that one *still* can "kill" (the aggressive gratification is possible).

Unlike the "normal" mourner, the one in a state of established pathological mourning continues to be preoccupied with the deceased, or with aspects of death, and such preoccupations dominate his daily life. The subject of *reincarnation* becomes interesting, for example, though the sophisticated may "sublimate" such interest in scientific hypotheses. Some such mourners become compulsive about reading obituary notices, betraying not only anxiety over their own death, but a hope that in the absence of current mention the death that so preoccupies them can be dismissed and the deceased "killed." The preoccupations that fill the mind of one in a state of established pathological mourning can be morbid indeed. One man's invalid wife had died after a long illness. Two years later, her husband, who had fallen into this type of pathological state, had her remains taken from her original place of burial and reinterred beneath his bedroom window so that she could be close to him. After a while the reverse aspect of his ambivalence toward her asserted itself, and he had her returned to the cemetery. He became a patient when he proposed a third disinterment. More often, however, such a mourner denies the existence of the grave, or, if he visits it at all, does so in a ritualized manner. Furthermore, he will continue to speak of the deceased in the present tense, surprising others, for example, by saying of one long dead, "He *has* curly hair."

The therapist may find it useful in his formulation of a diagnosis to inquire into the patient's conscious awareness of having an introject or linking object. Because it absorbs the impulse to "kill," the latter is contaminated with exaggerated aggression, and the patient has a need to distance it. Thus he may lock his linking object in a closet. This distancing of the linking object helps the clinical observer differentiate it from the fetish proper. It also aids him in distinguishing established pathological mourning from (reactive) depression. The introject and linking object, by maintaining the hope of keeping the dead alive, absorb the mourner's guilt, preventing the patient himself from becoming the battleground as he does in depression. As a result, there is little or no lowering of self-esteem in persons with established pathological mourning. It is also through this absorption of guilt that the linking object militates against suicide.

## TYPICAL DREAMS

Diagnostic clues appear in the dreams of patients with established pathological mourning. Their *manifest* content can be of several kinds, of which I have found three main types:

(a) "Frozen" dreams, to use a term with which many patients themselves describe dream images of still tableaux, are completely without motion. These may occur in a series, one tableau following another as though the dreamer were watching the projection of a series of slides. One patient used the analogy of watching slices of bread fall out of a package. The patients' associations to such still tableaux vividly represent their fixation in the work of mourning.

(b) These patients may also have dreams in which the dead person is seen as alive, but engaged in a struggle between life and death. Thus he may be seen lying in a hospital bed, trapped under the rubble of a collapsed building, or sitting in a burning vehicle. The dreamer tries to save him—or to finish him off. Interestingly, both persons in the dream are usually undisguised. This may be because the ego's censoring capacity has already been overtaxed by the strength of the conflict involved in the mourner's ambivalent relationship with his representation of the dead. Another explanation may be that the ego concentrates on a struggle to "save" or to "kill," so that symbolization of the characters involved is secondary. In these dreams, the situation's outcome remains indeterminate because the patient invariably awakens before it is resolved.

(c) Dreams of the dead body in which something indicates that death is only an illusion are also characteristic. The body seen in its casket may be sweating, for example, or one long buried may show no sign of decay. Such dreams are not unusual among uncomplicated mourners during the months immediately after the death, but for them these dreams either cease or the body begins to change in appearance to fit the reality. The mourner in established pathological mourning, however, will continue to dream of the undecayed body, even many years after death.

## A CASE EXAMPLE

Again, a clinical vignette is useful. The case of Phyllis illustrates on a descriptive level how established pathological mourning differs from the (reactive) depression described in the case of the daughter of a suicidal victim. This case story first appeared in *Linking Objects and Linking Phenomena* (Volkan, 1981).

Phyllis was in her early twenties when a mentally deficient sister five years her junior died. The sister had lived in the family circle until puberty when, fearing that their daughter might become pregnant, her parents had sent her to an institution. She had returned home for weekend visits, however, and on one such visit she fell on a stairway and broke her neck, dying instantly.

At the time of the accident Phyllis was out with "an exciting new date." She had experienced the usual shock reaction when she learned of the accident, but later recalled that for a few days afterward she had had "unwelcome thoughts" recalling how the event had interrupted the fun she had been having. During that period she had exhibited irritability that those around her attributed to grief, but which she herself recognized as deriving from her rage that her sister's death had spoiled her pleasure. She attributed her guilt to the "selfishness" of this anger. She had episodes of weeping, but at the funeral and in the time following she could not help but wonder how soon it would be seemly for her to again go dancing with her new boyfriend, who had made a condolence call.

During the next few weeks, Phyllis was flooded with memories of the ways in which her dead sister had so often spoiled her fun, as well as with recollections of her own childhood fantasies of curing her. She felt renewed guilt over having supported her parents in their decision to place her sister in an institution. Within three months, however, she felt she had adjusted fairly well to the tragedy and her guilt feelings disappeared.

It was at about this time that Phyllis was driving in the country with a woman friend when their car hit a horse that had strayed onto the road. The horse was thrown into the air by the impact, and the fall to the ground broke its neck. Horrified, the two women got out of the car, and while her friend went to a nearby house to call the authorities, Phyllis watched the animal thrash about in the throes of death. Helpless, she was convinced that fate was playing a gruesome trick on her, and as she noticed some rocks by the roadside she told herself that she "would have to be as hard as these rocks" to bear so savage a reprise of her sister's death. As the horse gave its last gasp she picked up one of the stones, a flat one, kept it in her hand for a while, and then dropped it into her pocket. When she reached home, she placed the stone in a box in her bedroom closet.

Phyllis still had the stone when she became my patient five years later, although by then she had moved into an apartment with another girl. She recognized that the stone held some kind of magic for her and felt compelled to keep it. Although she disliked looking at it, she had to know at all times where it was. She consciously connected it not only with her sister's death but also with the accident that had killed the horse. The stone was a relic of the horse's final moment of life, and, intellectually, she was aware as well that its flatness reminded her of her sister's flat chest, and that its hardness had something to do with the hardness she believed she herself needed to endure the tragedy of these violent deaths. A further association emerged when she recalled, with both affection and guilt, how her family had defensively joked about her handicapped sister, one brother saying that the sister "had rocks in her head."

Phyllis realized that in her mind the two deaths were interchangeable. For a year after the accident she was preoccupied with a slow-motion picture of the horse hurtling through the air and plunging to the ground, which would then switch to an image of her sister huddled at the bottom of the stairs, the latter derived from descriptions of the scene as related by family members present at the time. She was in fact so preoccupied with these images that she was obliged to give up her work as a secretary and to take a vacation of some months before resuming work elsewhere.

By then the image of her sister at the bottom of the stairs seemed literally to be buried within her chest. From time to time she would reactivate it at work. The image had its own autonomy, so that she could relate to it in different ways. In her mind's eye, for example, she might kick the dead girl to bring her back to life. Sometimes, however, the violence of this fantasied act would cause her to feel guilty, so that she would then try to arouse her sister more gently. Sometimes her sister's image appeared to her spontaneously; at other times it was triggered by idiosyncratic associations. For example, the sexually charged term "necking" would be associated with the sister's and the horse's broken necks and would reactivate the introject enough to bring it into her full waking awareness; "frozen" images of her sister persisted in her dreams.

At home, she still looked for her sister whenever she was reminded of her. On the other hand, she dreaded the possibility that she might find her there on a weekend visit as in the past. Once, while she was in her apartment, she heard a noise outside, as though something had fallen from a nearby tree. She felt compelled to look to see if it were her sister, even though intellectually she knew that this was impossible.

Phyllis felt "normal" except for her preoccupation with death and her sister's image. She continued to use the present tense when speaking of her sister, and during the year before coming to see me she had joined a "religious" group that emphasized achieving contact with the dead. Unlike the depressed mourner, she did not experience lowered self-esteem or self-reproach, but she felt that if her sister had not died her own life would have taken a different and more productive course. Phyllis was right that her life might be more productive, but it was not the death per se, but her "frozen" state in the work of mourning that prevented this. In her ongoing preoccupation with the stone, with her dead sister's body image, in her fantasized violent or gentle interactions with her introjected representation of her sister, Phyllis was clearly engaged in a continuing conflict between seeking and dreading to find—"killing" or not "killing"—the dead girl.

## Re-grief Therapy

Up to this point I have focused on defining established pathological mourning by describing its phenomenological and metapsychological characteristics as well as by distinguishing it from the (reactive) depression that can follow death. Understanding this difference is essential when planning treatment—indeed correct diagnosis is the first step, as established pathological mourning may respond to a particular approach on the part of the therapist.

One of the first tasks to confront a therapist treating established pathological mourning will be that of developing a formulation of the multiple psychological factors that have caused his patient to become "frozen" in his work of mourning. Psychoanalytic studies have shown that the clinical picture presented on the surface is the symbolic expression of conflictual material—from different levels of the patient's development. The psychodynamic constellation of established pathological mourning may be due to the reactivation of unresolved, or poorly resolved, conflicts of the separation-individuation phases. In other patients, however, a similar clinical picture may be owing to unfinished psychological business with the dead on an oedipal level. Thus an initial assessment of the patient's general psychic organization will be necessary.

In our work at the University of Virginia (Volkan, 1970, 1972, 1981; Volkan, Cilluffo, and Sarvay, 1975; Volkan and Josephthal, 1980), we have found that selected patients with established pathological mourning may respond favorably to a brief form of psychotherapy that aims to reintroduce the patient into the usual mourning process. We named this type of treatment "re-grief therapy." Since he has become "fixated" along the way, it may be easier to free such a patient to return to the normal work of mourning than it is to work through the more conflicted psychological constellation of a patient who is depressed. In "re-grief therapy" the patient is seen intensively three to four times a week, but the therapy lasts for only a few months.

Inasmuch as the patient with established pathological mourning is in a state of chronic hope that the dead will return—but simultaneously wants equally to "kill" him in order to complete his mourning—he is preoccupied with being in psychological contact with his introject. During the initial phase of re-grief therapy, the therapist, after taking a careful history, helps his patient to distinguish ideas and feelings that belong to the representation of the one he has lost from those that are truly his own, using what have been called *demarcation exercises* (Volkan and Showalter, 1968). The therapist is well-advised to refrain from excessive questioning of his patient while taking his history, which is best accomplished in a nondirective exchange. This type of history taking may itself, with help from the therapist, enable the patient to begin differentiating his own thoughts, attitudes, and feelings from those under the influence of his introject. In any case, the patient in established pathological mourning will inevitably broach the subject of death and of his lost one.

Demarcating the introject, so to speak, enables the therapist to help his patient see what he has taken in and thus determine what he feels about the introject, as well as which of its aspects he wants to reject. It is important here to note again that although the patient himself may employ the kind of vivid symbolic terminology discussed above in referring to his intro-ject—speaking of the introject as a foreign body or as possessing a discrete inner presence—what is being described is, actually, an affective-cognitive-dynamic *process*. The therapist treating patients of the kind under discussion must, therefore, be sufficiently experienced to keep from engaging with his patient in purely intellectual gymnastics.

Following the demarcation exercises, which may require some weeks, the therapist, while avoiding premature interpretation at this point, initiates the exploration of reasons why the patient became fixated and unable to work through his grief. He encourages the mourner to repeat his account of his past, specifically as it pertains to the deceased, helping him to recall circumstances of the final illness or fatal accident that caused the death, the conditions in which he learned of it, his reaction to seeing the body, the events of the funeral—indeed all events associated with the loss. Again, instead of asking question after question to elicit this information, the experienced therapist will indirectly stimulate the patient to initiate these topics himself, achieving better results by allowing the verbalization of such material to coincide with the expression of the feelings it inevitably arouses.

If the therapy is going well, anger usually appears at this point—at first diffuse and directed toward others, and then directed toward the dead. Abreactions—what Bibring (1953) describes as "emotional reliving"—may also then occur, demonstrating to the patient the actuality of his unacceptable, and therefore repressed, impulses toward the representation of the person who is now dead. As the patient procedes to re-grieve, it can be assumed that impulses, such as death wishes toward the person who is now dead, will surface, and the patient's readiness to have them interpreted and to lessen his guilt feelings can be assessed. Using his understanding of the psychodynamics motivating his patient's need to keep the lost one alive, the therapist through clarifications and interpretations then helps the patient to gain insight into unconscious aspects of his relationship to the one lost.

As stated above, the patient with established pathological mourning typically continues to use the defense mechanism of splitting the ego functions. At an appropriate time his attention is called to this by helping him to focus on precisely how he became aware that the dead person was, in fact, no longer living. This focusing will have positive results only if it occurs at an emotionally suitable time, and is not experienced as a purely intellectual exercise. The patient himself may show genuine surprise at the ambiguity of his recollection, and may blurt out something like: "I thought he was not breathing any more. But at the same time I thought his chest was moving. It is crazy! He was dead and not dead!" Thus the therapist has helped him to revisit the point at which the splitting took place, and so to re-evaluate reality.

It is characteristic of our patients' experience that the funeral rites had not gone well. Often the patient did not see the coffin lowered into the ground. Asked at an appropriate time, "How do you know that he is buried?," the patient will surprise himself by realizing that one part of his awareness never believed that the burial had actually been completed. He is then likely to feel anger at those who prevented his participation in the funeral ceremony. By this time it has been made clear to the patient that while he felt, and indeed knew, that death had occurred, he had paradoxically continued to behave as though nothing had happened. The most important step to be undertaken in this phase of confrontation, clarification, and interpretation of death-related impulses, fantasies, and wishes—and the defenses against them—is that of focusing on the linking object. As its nature and significance are being explored, the therapist will make a formulation about the choice of the particular object from among the many possibilities. Because it has physical existence, with properties that reach the senses, the object has greater "magical" impact than that possessed by the introject. Once the patient grasps how he has been using it to maintain "absolutely" controlled contact with his representation of the dead, as well as to postpone mourning and keep the process of grief frozen, he may be ready to use the object for a therapeutic purpose, to reactivate his mourning further.

It is suggested that he bring the linking object to a therapy session, where it is at first typically avoided by the patient. With the patient's permission, the therapist may keep it in the therapy room, pointing out that its magical properties exist not in the object left behind but in the patient's perception of it. Finally introduced into therapy, it is placed between patient and therapist long enough for the former to feel its spell. He may even be asked to touch it and to report anything that comes to mind. Even now I am surprised at what intense emotion is congealed in these objects, and caution others about this. Such emotion serves to unlock psychological processes until now contained within the linking object itself, and emotional storms so generated may continue for weeks. At first diffuse, emotions involved gradually differentiate themselves, and the therapist, with his patient, can then identify anger, guilt, sadness, and so on. Whether the patient chooses to discard it altogether or not, the linking object will then at last lose its magical power.

Clarifications and interpretations concerned with death and the deceased, and the sharper focus on these subjects effected by the introduction of the linking object into treatment, lead to the final phase of mourning—disorganization, which is followed by reorganization in which sadness—(without guilt)—appears. Patients who had never before visited the grave of the one they lost do so now, as if to say goodbye; some who had not had a tombstone put in place are now able to make the proper arrangements. At this point many patients spontaneously plan some kind of memorial ritual for the one they have lost. Many consult priests, ministers, or rabbis for religious consolation as, toward the conclusion of the re-grief process, they begin to accept the death.

I have been successful, with suitable patients approaching the end of their therapy, in using the manifest content of their *serial* dreams to identify their place within their re-griefing. Pollock (1961) and I (Volkan, 1981) have both pointed out that the phases of the work of mourning are accurately reflected in the manifest content of these dreams. For example, someone with established pathological mourning may dream of a field covered with green grass. As his grieving is reactivated he may see this field again, but now with a ditch scoring the grassy green slope. When he actually "kills" the dead person he may again see the same field in a dream, but in this version he will be pushing the one lost, who seems alive but deteriorated or damaged in some way (for example, the lost one may be confined to a wheelchair), into the ditch. In the final dream of this series he sees the grassy field again undisturbed, as though the dead person now at last lies securely beneath the grass-covered ground. Patients then experience a sense of the introject's having left them in peace. They feel free, even excited at this point, by the lifting of their burden, and begin to look for new objects for their love.

## THE TRANSFERENCE PHENOMENON IN RE-GRIEF THERAPY

I believe that to elucidate some of the important meanings of a patient's loss intellectually will not be greatly beneficial if his related emotions are not engaged and incorporated into this ideation. Throughout treatment, patients experience a variety of powerful emotions as they gain insight into their inability to allow the dead person to die; this insight is arrived at through the clarifications and interpretations offered them, the therapy being designed to loosen the hold of their investment in the representation of the dead person and reactivate the arrested mourning process. The use of the linking object in particular provokes intense emotional outbursts that, without interpretation engaging close scrutiny by the patient's observing ego, are not curative. The link to the representation of the dead, externalized into the linking object, must be brought through the patient's engaged understanding into the realm of his inner experience.

In spite of the use of a special device (the linking object) in re-grief therapy, the transference relationship becomes the vehicle whereby insight into ambivalence grounded in conflict between longing and dread may be gained, and resolution finally effected. The therapist should actively, directly, and instructively oppose any initial shame—or excessive control—with which the patient may conceal the complications of his grief, and encourage his direct exploration of feelings and fantasies about the person he has lost, and the internal and external relationship he maintains with him. Through his activity the therapist offers himself as a new object for the patient's consideration, aiming, as in traditional psychoanalytic therapy, to develop a therapeutic alliance without encouraging an *infantile* transference neurosis. Rado (1956) uses the term "interceptive interpretations" to describe the interception of the development of infantile transference neurosis through premature interpretation of the transference phenomenon. I use a modified form of this when I think the transference threatens to develop into a ripened infantile transference neurosis. Transference—but not transference neurosis—is inevitable and may prove therapeutic by providing close and intimate contact within the therapeutic setting as conflicts are understood. At times the patient may relate to his therapist as he had related to the one he mourns, and thus make it possible to work through in a focal way the conflicts he had not resolved with the one lost. The fresh grief caused by separation as therapy terminates can be put to appropriate use.

Although re-grief therapy is brief inasmuch as it lasts for some months rather than for years, it is intense, intimate, and certainly not superficial.

## Established Pathological Mourning and Psychoanalysis

The therapeutic spectrum in our research ranged from what we regarded specifically as "re-griefing" to psychoanalytic psychotherapy, or, beyond that, to psychoanalysis proper (Volkan, 1981). There are time-tested ways of conducting proper Freudian analysis with suitable patients, whether the initial diagnosis be hysterical neurosis, character disorder of a high level, or established pathological mourning. The patient's conflicts are dealt with by interpretations within and during the working through of the transference neurosis. The patient in established pathological mourning will at some point in his analysis become aware of the reasons he has been unconsciously and symbolically defending against "killing" the one he mourns. Different patients have different reasons for keeping the dead "alive." A patient may have narcissistic need of the deceased's representation in order to maintain his own sense of self; or his need may be oedipal, the presence of the dead being necessary if he is to advance developmentally. These needs clash with derivatives of such wishes as that to deny dependency or to gain oedipal triumph by "killing."

We should also take into consideration in analysis the influence of infantile pathogenic fantasies still available in the complicated mourning process, especially when the dead person's representation is an external depository of a character dominant in them. For example, one young woman fell into established pathological mourning after the death of a boyfriend younger than she. Her analysis showed that some of her dominant behavior patterns were affected by a pathogenic infantile fantasy, and by her defense against the wishes to which it gave expression. At two years of age the birth of a brother had been traumatic for her because of external attendant circumstances; she fantasied ridding herself of the baby she saw as the cause of her unhappiness by consuming him as she would consume ice cream. We reconstructed this fantasy in her analysis from her dreams, her transference constellations, and the reappearance of the fantasy in a current version—thoughts of cannibalism that had come when during a train ride she had been physically close to a mother and her crying baby.

Her analysis further revealed that the boyfriend she had lost represented her younger sibling; as long as she controlled their relationship and "adored" him she could defend against her murderous wishes. She was jolted by the gratification of her aggressive drive by his death and the loss of a character featured in her infantile pathogenic fantasy.

Although I suggest that it is not necessary in treatment of established pathological mourning to modify basic rules of psychoanalysis, two issues do need consideration:

1. The clinical picture of established pathological mourning may appear in persons of different personality makeup. One having a low-level character organization and presenting characteristics of established pathological mourning on the surface is probably not a good candidate for re-grief therapy or for psychoanalysis proper, but he may benefit from long-term treatment with modified psychoanalytic techniques. I point out elsewhere (Volkan, 1981) how the results of psychological testing may identify those for whom re-grief therapy is suitable; one may consider them good candidates for psychoanalysis also. The choice may depend on such external factors as the higher cost of the latter, but the evaluation of internal considerations is more important. Do the underlying pathologies need resolution *now*? Can the patient's ego adaptively contain the underlying pathologies once the complicated mourning is resolved? I have reported how some patients elect to undergo psychoanalysis after completing "re-griefing."

2. The presence of established pathological mourning, even in the patient suitable for psychoanalysis, interferes with effective resolution of the other psychopathologies, especially when linking objects are *secretly* used. A seeming paradox here needs attention: although pre-existent psychopathologies such as dependence and aggressivity have caused the patient to react to loss in a pathological way, the complicated mourning must be ameliorated before the antecedent pathologies can be analyzed.

One young man I treated cherished as a linking object a gold chain with a St. Christopher medal he had felt compelled to buy though he was not a Catholic after the death of the "good-father" figure who had met all his narcissistic needs and nourished his self-esteem. The patient's narcissistic personality organization stemmed from a traumatic early relationship with his mother. The meaning of the dead man's representation became clear once the patient was in analysis. It was something he continued to depend on to supply his narcissistic needs. He gradually became aware during his analysis of his need to keep the older man "alive" and his dread of having to acknowledge his dependence. This was all reflected in the transference. There had been little change during the first two years of analysis in this patient's personality organization, but then he disclosed the secret of the golden linking object he always wore, even when making love or taking a shower. In previous sessions it had been concealed beneath his shirt, but once its part in the drama of his object relations was analyzed, he was able to "let go" and to disclose much anal material connected with gold and secrecy, and to work through in the transference neurosis reactivated early trauma.

Thus far I have dealt with maladaptive aspects of established pathological mourning, and pathologic aspects of linking objects. It should be remembered, however, that some people accommodate to the psychodynamics of established pathological mourning by using linking objects creatively—or, indeed, by *creating* them. The continuation of "magical" communion with the dead can be seen in such cases as serving the purposes of creativity in adaptive ways.

## REFERENCES

Abraham, K. (1911), Notes on the psycho-analytical investigation and treatment of manic-depressive insanity and allied conditions. In: *Selected Papers*, ed. D. Bryan & A. Strachey. New York: Basic Books, 1960, pp. 137–156.
———— (1916), The first pregenital stage of the libido. In: *Selected Papers*, ed. D. Bryan & A. Strachey. New York: Basic Books, 1960, pp. 248–279.
Bibring, E. (1953), The mechanism of depression. In: *Affective Disorders*, ed. P. Greenacre. New York: International Universities Press, pp. 13–48.
Blos, P. (1979), *The Adolescent Passage*. New York: International Universities Press.
Bowlby, J. & Parkes, C. M. (1970), Separation and loss within the family. In: *The Child in His Family*, vol. 1, ed. E. J. Anthony & C. Koupirnik. New York: Wiley Interscience, pp. 197–216.
Deutsch, H. (1937), Absence of grief. *Psychoanal. Quart.*, 6:12–23.
Engel, G. L. (1961), Is grief a disease? A challenge for medical research. *Psychosom. Med.*, 23:18–22.
Fenichel, O. (1945), *The Psychoanalytic Theory of Neurosis*. New York: Norton.
Freud, S. (1917), Mourning and melancholia. *Standard Edition*, 14:237–258. London: Hogarth Press, 1957.
———— (1940), Splitting of the ego in the process of defence. *Standard Edition*, 23:271–278. London: Hogarth Press, 1964.
Greene, W. A. (1965), Disease response to life stress. *J. Amer. Med. Wm. Assn.*, 20:135–140.
Lindemann, E. (1944), Symptomology and management of acute grief. *Amer. J. Psychiat.*, 101:141–148.
Pollock, G. H. (1961), Mourning and adaptation. *Internat. J. Psycho-Anal.*, 42:341–361.
Rado, S. (1956), Adaptational development of psychoanalytic therapy. In: *Changing Concepts of Psychoanalytic Medicine*, ed. S. Rado & G. E. Daniels. New York: Grune & Stratton, pp. 89–100.
Rochlin, G. (1965), *Griefs and Discontents: The Forces of Change*. Boston: Little, Brown.
Schafer, R. (1968), *Aspects of Internalization*. New York: International Universities Press.
Schuster, D. B. (1969), A note on grief. *Bull. Phila. Assn. Psychoanal.*, 19:87–90.
Smith, J. H. (1971), Identificatory styles in depression and grief. *Internat. J. Psycho-Anal.*, 52:259–266.
Volkan, V. D. (1970), Typical findings in pathological grief. *Psychiat. Quart.*, 44:231–250.
———— (1972), The linking objects of pathological mourners. *Arch. Gen. Psychiat.*, 27:215–221.
———— (1979), *Cyprus: War and Adaptation: A Psychoanalytic History of Two Ethnic Groups in Conflict*. Charlottesville, Va.: University Press of Virginia.
———— (1981), *Linking Objects and Linking Phenomena: A Study of the Forms, Symptoms, Metapsychology and Therapy of Complicated Mourning*. New York: International Universities Press.

——— Cilluffo, A. F., & Sarvay, T. L. (1975), Re-grief therapy and the function of the linking object as a key to stimulate emotionality. In: *Emotional Flooding*, ed. P. T. Olsen. New York: Human Sciences Press, pp. 179–224.

——— Josephthal, D. (1980), The treatment of established pathological mourners. In: *Specialized Techniques and Psychotherapy*, ed. T. B. Karasu & L. Bellak. New York: Brunner/Mazel, pp. 118–142.

——— Showalter, C. R. (1968), Known object loss, disturbance in reality testing, and "re-grief work" as a method of brief psychotherapy. *Psychiat. Quart.*, 42:358–374.

Wahl, C. W. (1970), The differential diagnosis of normal and neurotic grief following bereavement. *Psychosomatics*, 11:104–106.

Wolfenstein, M. (1966), How is mourning possible? *The Psychoanalytic Study of the Child*, 21:93–123. New York: International Universities Press.

——— (1969), Loss, rage, and repetition. *The Psychoanalytic Study of the Child*, 24:432–460. New York: International Universities Press.

*April 1983*

# The Function of Play in the Process of Child Psychotherapy: A Contemporary Perspective

ANNA ORNSTEIN, M.D. (Cincinnati)

Play, as a universal phenomenon, has been the subject of studies utilizing a variety of theoretical frames of reference. Like dreams, play functions as a window through which the investigator or therapist can take a glimpse at the workings of the mind. Also like dreams, play not only provides a window through which we can investigate the mind but "it is a major growth center of the psyche" (C. Stewart, 1981, p. 92). But, unlike a dream, in the case of play, the therapist can also respond, interact with the player, and thereby effect its outcome. It is for this latter reason that play therapy in its various forms—psychoanalytic, relationship, behavioral—has become a form of treatment for children.

The interest in play came with the interest in learning more about the inner world of the child. Psychoanalysis, as this was applied to the treatment of children, played an important part in these investigations as did academic psychology, especially following Piaget's pioneering research into cognitive development. By investigating the intricate interplay of the child's sensorimotor and cognitive-perceptual endowment with his physical surround, Piaget—observing the play of his own children—arrived at far-reaching conclusions regarding the mode by which the child constructs his reality. Jung, Freud, and Piaget gave us the theoretical tools to observe, to organize, and to interpret the child's play, in terms of both its emotional and its cognitive dimensions.

Presented at a Panel on Play Therapy, sponsored by the Youth Guidance Center of the Framingham Mental Health Association, Boston, March 10, 1984.

349

Since play as a natural phenomenon encompasses and can provide insight into the emotional as well as the cognitive realm of the mind, it has taught us a great deal about the development and function of the psyche. We have learned that play, games, and cognitive development are functionally related (Sutton-Smith, 1963), that play is the primary precursor of creativity (Winnicott, 1971a), that play has the capacity to moderate affect and anxiety either retrospectively, as after traumatic experiences, or in anticipation of such events as hospitalization and surgery. Also, play promotes the development of the capacity to delay by providing substitute gratification. For this reason, play is considered, especially by developmentalists, to be a form of rehearsal for life. Since, during play, the child is in control of his physical surround and can use his imagination, he can "rehearse" anticipated relationships and events that could otherwise prove to be overwhelming. It is in this process that the child discovers himself, his potentials, and his limitations (Frank, 1955).

Self-discovery is the essence of sandplay, an analytic activity in which child and adult patients "create" a symbolic world with small figures in a box of sand. Sandplay, practiced by Jungian analysts, is based on the original work of a Swiss analyst, Margaret Loewenfeld. The foundation of this concept of treatment was that, given the right tools, children would find their way to communication of their inner experiences. "Children, everywhere, have always turned spontaneously to their native soil, and to the miniaturizing of the world about them as fundamental tools with which to accomplish the indispensable early molding of their interior earth, the ground of their existence, and the structuring of the inner world of their imagination" (L. Stewart, 1981, p. 22).

Freud (1920) himself reported on only one psychoanalytically informed observation of play concerning the reaction of one of his grandchildren to his mother's absence. The child repeatedly threw away a wooden reel and retrieved it with the help of a string attached to it. Freud explained this play as the child's effort to master the pain of loss related to his mother's absence; the play provided an opportunity for active mastery over a passively endured experience. The conceptualization of play, especially that of repetitious play as a form of working through a loss or other forms of traumatic experiences, is one of the outstanding principles that Freudian psychoanalysts have retained in their listening perspective regarding children's play. Waelder (1933), in a systematic exposition of the psychoanalytic theory of play, included the pleasure principle as well as functional pleasure in his conceptualization. In the therapeutic situation, however, analysts consider neither the pleasure principle nor functional pleasure to be as important a motive for play as the repetition compulsion. This is to be expected. Children in the offices of psychotherapists are symptomatic children; the joy has gone out of their play. Instead of functional pleasure, we witness fear, hesitation, undue caution, or a degree of drivenness and compulsivity; the play becomes not only joyless but highly routinized, lifeless, totally lacking in spontaneity. This quality in play is particularly noticeable in the more disturbed child for whom play, in the customary sense of the word, has been replaced by rituals and routines without which the child becomes anxious and nonfunctional.

Such was the case with eight-year-old Tommy. After spending a day in school where he could barely contain his restlessness and was constantly reprimanded for vigorously chewing on his fingers and sucking on his pencils, upon returning home he would compulsively arrange his toy cars and buses in a specific order. Any interference with the highly ritualized bus play caused him great distress. The fear of missing his bus and not being able to return home was one of the reasons why his play had a driven and compulsive quality. It is in clinical situations such as Tommy's that we recognize how the child attempts to master, through play, a potentially overwhelming quantity of anxiety. Such efforts, however, offer only temporary relief, and, with time, the play becomes increasingly more compulsory.

Winnicott was an exception to the emphasis on play as a vehicle for mastery, as an activity that is dominated by repetition compulsion. Winnicott distinguished between "play" and "playing": play being a structured activity, limited by place, time, and equipment, while "playing" was a creative experience, a state of mind in which a child or adult has the freedom to have his imagination soar; that is, in which he has the capacity to be "playful." Winnicott (1971b) recommended that the therapist's attention not be directed toward the *content* of the play as much as toward the inhibitions that interfere with spontaneity and playfulness. In this effort, he did not consider interpretations to be of importance and stated that "psychotherapy of a deepgoing kind may be done without interpretive work" (p. 50). In this conceptualization the therapeutic potential was supposed to be *created* in the very act of therapist and child playing together; psychotherapy with play was meant to facilitate the child's creative potential. For Winnicott, the role of a facilitator was not restricted to the therapist but extended to the child's emotional environment in general: "I draw attention to the fact that description of the emotional development of the individual cannot be made entirely in terms of the individual, but that in certain areas, and this is one of them, perhaps the main one, the behavior of the environment is part of the individual's own personal development and must therefore be included" (p. 53).

## Interpretations in Play Therapy

One of the most lively controversies regarding the therapeutic use of play occurred between Melanie Klein and Anna Freud in the 1940s. The essential aspect of their controversy concerned itself with the roles of transference and interpretations in the analyses of young children where play was the major avenue of communication. Mrs. Klein maintained that even a very young child (she reported on the successful analysis of children as young as age two) can develop transferences and can use interpretations as long as the child's analysis is completely separated from his/her home life. "For only under such conditions is he able to overcome his resistance against experiencing and expressing thoughts, feelings and desires which are incompatible with convention, and in the case of children, felt to be in contrast to much of what they have been taught" (p. 127). In Mrs. Klein's opinion, interpretations—that is, the verbalization of the unconscious meaning that the analyst attributes to the child's play—were to bring about a *direct contact* with the child's unconscious. In addition to the cathartic effect of play, the major therapeutic impact was to be derived from acquainting the child with the *real meaning* of his play behavior. With this technique, she hoped to "teach" the child about the existence of the unconscious. Although this highly intellectual approach to the analysis of children, in which play was used in a manner similar to the free association of adults, has been repeatedly questioned, it still appears to have an impact not only on the analysis but also on the psychotherapy of children. The impact of this approach has been felt in the relatively heavy reliance on the therapist's verbalizations of what she[1] believes the unconscious meaning of the child's play to be, without such "interpretations" either being confirmed or negated by the child. It is important to note that Klein's and Winnicott's technical recommendations regarding the usefulness of interpretations are diametrically opposed even though, in the literature, one frequently finds Klein and Winnicott linked in their theoretical positions.

Anna Freud took issue with Melanie Klein's technical approach. This controversy is well-known and I do not intend to repeat it here. My reason for referring to it in this context is only to indicate that, while Miss Freud did not question the possibility of children developing transferences or children making use of interpretations, she did advocate a period of time that was to precede analysis proper, a period during which the child was to secure "a positive attachment to the analyst." For Anna Freud, as for Melanie Klein, verbalization (that is, the translation of primary-process to secondary-process communication) was an essential aspect of a child's analysis.

---

[1] In this paper the therapist will be referred to as "she," the patient as "he."

Erikson, a student of Anna Freud's, made some of the most important contributions to the psychoanalytic theory of play and its use in the analysis of children. Erikson (1940) distinguished among three separate but closely linked spheres in the child's emotional life: (1) The child's own body and its functions, he called "auto-sphere"; (2) the toy scene, "micro-sphere" (an arrangement of small objects in such a way that their configuration signifies a configuration of conflicting forces in the child's life); and (3) the relationship to the real persons, including the therapist, the "macro-sphere" (pp. 577–578). The distinction among the three spheres has clinical significance; it is in the transition from the micro- to the macrosphere that "play disruption" occurs most frequently. Erikson explained play disruption primarily as an increase in instinctual tension, as the child, in the course of play, approaches unconscious conflicts. I would suggest, however, that play disruption may occur not only in relationship to such purely intrapsychic events but may well occur also when the therapist, in her eagerness to make the unconscious conscious, offers interpretations that draw the child's attention to his (usually disturbed) relationships in his macrosphere.

In spite of the risk of play disruption, Erikson recommended systematic interpretations of the meaning of play as he saw the therapist's efforts at "making explicit some of the implicit (preconscious) steps of selecting, associating, and reasoning" (p. 560) as the essential aspect of the curative process of play. In this sense, Erikson used a child's play very much the way analysts of adult patients use dreams for the interpretations of transference and resistance. At the same time, Erikson recognized the limitations of interpretations and may have given the cathartic effect of play a greater significance than is obvious on first reading. "To play it out," he said, "is the most natural autotherapeutic measure childhood affords" (p. 561).

Whether through catharsis or through "repeated interpretations that further the verbal communication of inner dangers and the establishment of a supremacy of conscious judgement over unmanageable or completely repressed tendencies" (p. 564), Erikson recognized (similarly to Winnicott and myself) that psychoanalytic treatment finds a powerful obstacle in the fact that the child is constantly changing under the influence of extratherapeutic factors. "Therapeutic influences act at best as accelerators and inhibitors on a continuum of maturational processes which *in their normal or, let us say, extraclinical manifestations, for the most part have never been properly studied and described.* The intricate changes observed during a child's treatment therefore are too easily explained as a function of treatment" (p. 571; Erickson's emphasis). He also observed that chances for the improvement of the child were better where "the mother too has an opportunity to relieve in conversation her ambivalence toward the child and is prepared to respond to his improvement" (p. 563).

In summary, then, we could say that the most controversial aspect of psychoanalytic play therapy relates to the question of interpretations and to the degree to which the family is included or excluded in the child's treatment. Analysts have decided on this question in keeping with the particular model of the mind that aided them in their therapeutic efforts. Melanie Klein, for example, whose approach to the analysis of children was guided by the topographic model, and who considered the child's play to be equivalent to the free association of adults, recommended precise and extensive interpretations of the unconscious meaning of play to be the most essential aspect of the child's analysis. This was in keeping with the theory of cure determined by the topographic model: To get well, the unconscious had to be made conscious without, as yet, the full appreciation of resistances. In Mrs. Klein's theoretical frame of reference, communication with the parents was not only not desirable but contraindicated. This was in keeping with her expectation that even very young children develop transferences and can use interpretation as long as this is done in the privacy of the analyst's office. Anna Freud, on the other hand, working with an ego-psychological perspective, paid special attention to the child's resistances to interpretations. Although interpretation was no less central in the analysis of the nonverbal child, she gave special attention to the timing of her interpretations and recommended a period of preparation in which the analyst "courted" the child and established a therapeutic alliance with him.

As for Winnicott's and Erikson's attitudes toward interpretations, Winnicott advocated that the therapist, in his effort to promote spontaneity, creativity, and playfulness, does not need to offer interpretations that address the content of the play. On the other hand, Erikson, I believe, was correct in observing that "playfulness does not work until (and then as long as) pressing purposes and fears have lost their compelling power" (p. 575).

The use that therapists can make of play that facilitates the emergence of the child's internal experiences has to be differentiated from merely playing games with children. Playing games that are governed by rules and regulations has long been associated with the latency-age child, the age at which the child is in the process of repressing infantile fantasies and is therefore resistant to engaging in free play. However, this does not mean that games do not provide diagnostic and/or therapeutic opportunities. It only means that these opportunities are of a different order from a creative immersion in play that stimulates conscious and unconscious fantasies.

The capacity to observe rules has been considered to represent a developmental achievement: the resolution of the Oedipus complex and the internalization of relatively autonomous superego values. While this may be true for the nonsymptomatic child, children who are symptomatic, especially children with relatively severe obsessional symptoms, are dependent on the observance of rather rigid rules. These are not necessarily the rules of the game but are more likely to be idiosyncratic. An inability to adhere to the rules of a game or the need to establish idiosyncratic rules may indicate a developmental lag or the presence of psychopathology in a latency-age child. However, an inability to follow the rules of a game or the establishment of idiosyncratic ones has to be distinguished from cheating. John Meeks (1970), in a thoughtful paper on children who cheat at games, offers clinically useful explanations for this behavior, outstanding among them being the child's narcissistic vulnerability. Cheating can be a way in which the child protects himself from an intolerable drop in self-esteem. Meeks recommends that, as a piece of pathological behavior, cheating should be allowed to emerge fully before the therapist intervenes. "Early prohibitions against cheating tend to force the child to manage his wish to cheat entirely by superficial conformity. The underlying fantasy and meanings are then lost to understanding" (p. 159). I agree with this recommendation and would consider it as one of the few therapeutic advantages that playing games may offer. Allowing the cheating behavior to emerge, understanding its meaning, and responding to it interpretively distinguishes the therapeutic use of a game from the kind of playing with a child that has no discernible therapeutic benefits.

## The Function of Play in Child-centered Family Treatment

Play therapy has been synonymous with psychoanalysis for the young child. The questions raised have been psychoanalytic questions: the presence or absence of transferences, the relative value of interpretations, and whether or not contact with the parents interferes with or promotes the child's analysis. However, placing play into the context of child psychotherapy rather than psychoanalysis raises still further questions. The questions that the child therapist asks of herself relate to (1) the nature of the psychopathology of the children therapists most frequently see in their offices; (2) the frequency of therapy hours; and (3) the social and emotional milieu in which most of patients live.

The children we see in our offices currently, most of them only once weekly, are not children whose egos are strong enough to utilize interpretations and achieve insight into the nature of their difficulties so as to make changes in their behavior. The majority of our child patients suffer from various degrees of structural defects and deficits rather than from well-delineated intrapsychic conflicts and compromise formations. Differences in the nature of the psychopathology, changes in the child's social and

emotional milieu, and the reduction of the frequency of treatment hours
have led to the application of a watered-down version of psychoanalysis
and a gradual disillusionment in the efficacy of the individual treatment
of the child. The failure to develop a theory of treatment that would be
more specifically suited for the psychotherapy of children who suffer from
structural deficits rather than from primary intrapsychic conflicts has resulted in the application of various trial-and-error techniques. The use of
play has been no exception; playing with the child and periodically offering
a "hit-or-miss" interpretation rested on the shaky theoretical ground that
time spent with the child would "somehow," perhaps through identification
with an accepting, nonjudgmental adult, prove to be therapeutic. This form
of "child psychotherapy" has been unrewarding to therapists and without
demonstrative therapeutic benefits and has resulted in the slow abandonment of the individual treatment of children during the last twenty years.
Its place has been taken primarily by the various family-treatment modalities. This was to be expected. Even if the psychotherapy of children had
been conducted more systematically and more successfully, it would still
have to be questioned whether or not children of any age can make use
of insight into the nature of their difficulty when they continue to live
under, at times, severely pathogenic circumstances.

Family therapy, however, introduced a technique that accords the symptomatic child a very different position in the treatment process from that
of individual treatment. In family therapy, the symptomatic child is considered to be the recipient of family pathology, and it is on the family
pathology that the therapist focuses her interventions. What I am proposing
instead is a form of treatment that does not sacrifice the in-depth understanding of the symptomatic child but, along with giving the child the
opportunity to reveal the unconscious source of his difficulties through
play, involves the child's emotional environment in the treatment process
as well. This is a form of treatment in which the therapist, while trying to
understand the child in depth in individual sessions, uses this understanding not only to offer the child interpretations but more importantly to help
the family—through the appreciation of the unconscious motives of the
child's behavior—to become therapeutic toward the symptomatic child. I
described this form of treatment in detail in earlier publications (Ornstein,
1976, 1981).

The concern with the environment's empathic availability to the symptomatic child can be found in Winnicott's as well as in Erikson's statements
regarding the therapeutic use of play. Winnicott continued to emphasize
the child's ongoing need for a "facilitating environment," and Erikson
(1940) made frequent references to the same with such statements as "the

clinical problem seems to be solved *only* by the establishment of permanent and sufficient everyday release channels and not by a momentary release under special conditions" (p. 563).

The process of child-centered family treatment is a complex one: It means to provide the child with sufficient safety to reveal his fears, hopes, and expectations and at the same time, for the therapist to be empathically responsive to members of the family most intimately connected with the child. In the following, I shall elaborate on this approach by (1) examining the play situation in the context of child-centered family treatment; (2) discussing the theory that facilitates the integration of the insight that the therapist gains from the child's play with the treatment of those members of the family who play the most crucial roles in the child's emotional development; and finally (3) demonstrating the technique of this treatment method with the help of a clinical vignette.

(1) To enter the child's inner world, to have him play out his fears, fantasies, hopes, and expectations, is a considerable therapeutic task in itself. Creative child therapists (Winnicott's squiggle game, Richard Gardner's storytelling) have described special techniques that can unlock the door to the child's fantasies, be these conscious or unconscious. My own thinking regarding the therapeutic use of play has been greatly aided by Erikson's description of play disruption. This is what seems to happen: the therapist, watching the child approach the play equipment, expects the child to begin to play spontaneously. After some hesitation and with some help from the therapist, the child may begin to play, periodically glancing at the therapist to pick up a clue as to what is expected of him. But with good luck, the child eventually does "get lost" in the play, externalizing his inner world bit by bit either with the therapist's help or without it. The therapist, in the meantime, tries to facilitate the emergence of material that will touch on the conflictual and painful aspects of the child's life which would help her understand the intrapsychic sources of the child's troubled behavior. She may even carefully "guide" the child into the direction of the painful and the conflictual. No matter how carefully this is done, however, as soon as the therapist enters the play with her own agenda, she runs the risk of play disruption. In addition, should the therapist venture an interpretation of the meaning of the child's behavior, the chances of a play disruption are even greater.

An example is that of four-year-old Kathy who arranged her doll play in such a manner that the children in the dollhouse slept at a considerable distance from the parents. One of the children woke up in the middle of the night, and Kathy, in the name of the doll, called for the mother doll. The therapist was to fetch the mother doll, which she dutifully did; an interaction ensued in which the baby doll and the mother doll both appeared unhappy. This "encouraged" the therapist to say that in her fear and frustration the baby doll hit the mother doll in the leg. Kathy suddenly became scared, put her fingers into her mouth, and refused to continue the play. For the therapist, the recognition of her mistake came too late: this was a play disruption which would take some time to repair. Hitting her mother when angry was one of the reasons that Kathy was brought for treatment: an unhappy, clinging child, she had more recently become abusive toward her younger sister and mother.

One could argue that the therapist's timing was off, that the intervention was made prematurely, and that play disruption could have been avoided if the therapist's comments had been made after she had been sure of a therapeutic alliance or of a "positive attachment." But I don't believe the question was that of timing; rather, the question was the purpose of the intervention. What was the therapist trying to accomplish by introducing into the microcosm a piece of information that belongs to the child's macrocosm? Was she trying to induce the child to talk about the symptomatic behavior, in this case about hitting her mother? Trying to induce the child to speak about the symptomatic behavior is different from getting to know the child so that the therapist can understand better the *source* of the anger and frustration that has led up to the abusive behavior. By focusing directly on the troubled behavior, the therapist disrupted the play because the child ceased to experience the therapist's office as a safe place where feelings could be revealed. Instead, the child feared that once more he would be reprimanded for his behavior. The play disruption here was not related to the therapist abandoning the metaphor. Rather, the disruption occurred because, rather than facilitating the elucidation of relatively spontaneous play that could reveal the unconscious motives for the disturbed behavior, the therapist focused on the behavior itself. Once the play is disrupted, it is difficult to re-establish the sense of safety in which the child can continue to reveal himself. I would suggest that, in order to make maximum diagnostic use of the play, it is best if the therapist makes every effort to facilitate its natural flow, that she not focus on the child's symptomatic behavior and not move out of the microcosm to the macrocosm unless the child does so.

One could argue that play activity in which the therapist refrains from "guiding" the child into the area of his symptomatic behavior, and does not translate the child's symptomatic behavior into its "real" meaning, may have a cathartic effect and may possibly be of diagnostic value but is unlikely to have a therapeutic effect. This is a valid argument and indeed, in child-centered family treatment, the child's play has primarily a diagnostic and only secondarily a therapeutic value. In this form of treatment, the therapist can make the best use of the insight that she gains by "translating" this insight for the parents in a way that helps them to be in tune with the motivational forces that are the source of the child's troubled behavior.

(2) The processing of psychological data is a challenging task under all circumstances, but it is particularly difficult when the therapist has to integrate clinical data generated by more than one person. In the child-centered family treatment, where various members are involved in the treatment process, it is useful to conceptualize the treatment as a single process. Such a conceptualization is supported by the observation that various aspects of the treatment are contributed by various members of the family. While it is the child's symptoms, it is the parents' motivation for change which brings the family to the professional. The therapeutic alliance is based initially on parental motivation which eventually has to evolve to include all participants in the treatment process. Also, while the child's capacity to utilize insight is limited, the parents (in order to effect changes in themselves in their relationship to the child) have to achieve considerable insight into their own as well as the child's difficulties.

The conceptualization of the treatment of the parents with that of the symptomatic child as a single process is facilitated by a theoretical model that can encompass this kind of complexity. The model I am suggesting is that of the "self-selfobject unit," in which the child's self is assessed in relationship to his selfobject environment. This model signifies that the child's self cannot be defined without the effect that his selfobject environment has on its functioning, nor can the selfobject environment be defined without its meaning to the developing self. The self as it develops within the context of selfobject environment is considered to be an open system. I believe Anthony (1970), speaking of the development of children within the context of a family, had this in mind when he observed that "the dichotomies of internal and external, intrapsychic and interpersonal, individual and familial exist largely in the minds of the observer—a splitting created by the traditional theory and perpetuated in traditional practice" (p. xxxii). The concept of the selfobject bridges the traditionally established sharp line of demarcation between internal and external, intrapsychic and interpersonal, and thereby becomes a useful tool for the conceptualization of the treatment of the child within the context of the family.

The model of the self-selfobject unit is derived from Heinz Kohut's theory of the self and its development in relationship to the various selfobject functions, provided by the empathically responsive emotional environment of the child. Kohut's discovery of the selfobject transferences alerted child therapists to those parental functions which, because of their silent presence, by and large, have been taken for granted. With these discoveries, we are now in a position to recognize those clinical conditions in children that are the consequences of the absence or partial failure of certain specific parental responses to the child's ordinary narcissistic developmental needs for affirmation, validation, and a feeling of merger with the omnipotence and power of the parent. The recognition of selfobject transferences in the analyses of adults and the subsequent systematic formulation of a psychology of the self (Kohut, 1971, 1977) have made it possible to correlate failures in specific areas of parenting with the nature of the child's psychopathology. This correlation, in turn, has enabled child therapists to be more precise in their child-centered treatment of parents.

Using the stability and cohesiveness of the child as the overriding point of orientation in determining the nature of the child's psychopathology, we recognize three broad categories of psychological disorders in children. At one end of the spectrum are the childhood neuroses where the child's self is considered stable—an increasingly rare diagnostic finding. At the other end of the spectrum are the psychoses. The self here has never attained cohesiveness but has remained fragmented and archaic. It is in the third group, in the middle of these two extremes, that we recognize the primary self-disorders of childhood. This is a group of children who have traditionally been diagnosed as suffering from neurotic behavior or personality disorders, many of whom were diagnosed as suffering from childhood depressions, drug abuse of adolescence, and a whole array of developmental deviations and arrests. It is this group of patients, in the middle of the diagnostic spectrum (children who suffer from various degrees of self-pathology) that psychotherapists see most frequently in their offices.

Many manifestations of self-pathology in childhood are related to the child's efforts to deal with disappointments related to parental failures in empathy. These are discreet failures, not easily detectable by the external observer, and more often than not, totally unconscious to the parents. Even subtle breaches in parental empathy, however, can lead to the formations of defense organizations and behavioral patterns which serve to protect the child from re-experiencing the pain of traumatic disappointments. Such defense organizations, which become integrated into the growing psyche, attain a degree of rigidity that does not readily yield to changed parental attitudes. This explains the need for the child to be given the opportunity to experience and express feelings, wishes, and fantasies that only the safety of the therapist's office can provide. Many would argue that such an opportunity is in itself therapeutic, and I would agree. Still, I prefer to consider such opportunities to have primarily a diagnostic and only secondarily a therapeutic value. I do so in order to emphasize that the therapist cannot attribute undue importance to her words, no matter how successfully facilitating and accepting these are, when the child has to return to an environment in which a similar acceptance of his feelings cannot be expected. And, as I indicated earlier, even if the child achieves insight into his feelings and can connect these with his behavior, this rarely leads to a change in behavior. Using the model of the self-selfobject unit and conceptualizing the child's psyche as an open system, we recognize the continued developmental need for parental selfobject responses. Such responses have to be available in the child's everyday life-experiences and preferably in relation to the primary caretakers; the proud glance or an encouraging word by a parent cannot be replaced by the most comprehensive and well-timed interpretations.

Should the therapist be successful in establishing empathic contact with the parents and help them understand their troubled child in depth, she has achieved two interrelated goals: the parents, instead of responding to the child's manifest behavior in a way that further aggravates his condition, can now tune in and respond on the level of the child's subjective experiences; they have been helped to recognize their own therapeutic potential. By increasing parental in-tuneness and avoiding parental responses to the child's manifest behavior, the family is being helped to create a therapeutic atmosphere in the home where, barring further upheavals, the child is assured progressive development. The greatest challenge in such a treatment situation is for the therapist to remain in empathic contact with every member of the family and for her to remain interpretive; a therapist is not asked to take sides, she is asked to understand and to explain. Not to take sides appears to be the greatest challenge to child therapists, who, more often than not, are deeply identified with the child and are tempted to "educate" the parents in their parental responsibilities. Giving advice and educating the parents, however, appear to increase parental guilt and defensiveness and may have serious consequences for treatment: the parents, unable to follow the advice because of their own imperative emotional needs and because they do not feel heard by the therapist become increasingly resentful toward the child for making them feel inadequate as parents. By experiencing their own inadequacy and helplessness more painfully, the parents, instead of tuning in on the level of the child's subjective experiences, are likely to become more punitive in relationship to his troubled behavior. It is for this reason particularly important that, before explaining to the parents the deeper roots of the child's troubled (and troubling) behavior, the therapist assess the parents own self-development so that she can respond to them therapeutically rather than with an implication of criticism. In all of this it is important that the therapist remember that the symptomatic child has an adverse effect on family life and that therefore the parents' current attitude and behavior toward the child cannot be mistaken for what may have been originally, that is, genetically, responsible for the child's symptomatic behavior.

(3) In the following, I shall describe a clinical vignette that demonstrates the therapist's task in a child-centered family treatment. The clinical vignette is that of seven-year-old John[2] whose mother called the therapist after she was told that the child would be expelled from school unless she sought treatment. The school described Johnny's behavior as uncontrollable; he was provocative with his peers and his teachers, throwing pencils when the teacher turned her back or snatching things away from his peers and taunting them. The mother, who was a working woman and had recently gotten married after divorcing Johnny's father when her son was two years old, resented the frequent trips to school and the complaints that she felt she couldn't do anything about. She felt hurt and abused by the child.

During the first joint interview, the mother complained about John's behavior at home as well as in school. The child, listening, hung his head and restlessly shuffled his feet under his chair. When spoken to, he shrugged his shoulders at first but then grumbled something about the way things had changed at home since the arrival of the new father. As the mother continued to complain without even briefly considering the child's feelings either about her being out of the home or about the new father, the therapist felt her anger rising. It was very important for her not to speak until she had her feelings under control. The therapist had to find a way to convey to the mother that she understood her frustrations, especially in view of Johnny's very provocative behavior. Only when the therapist could understand *and accept* the mother's state of mind could she expect the mother to hear her child's pain. At this time, however, the mother was too angry, too deeply hurt by the child's indolence to hear him even if the child could have articulated his feelings.

The next few interviews were spent with Johnny alone. The child needed a "safe space," an opportunity to make contact with his feelings. This was to be an opportunity for child and therapist to articulate Johnny's feelings jointly and for the two of them to plan the way in which they could communicate these to his mother and stepfather. In the therapist's office, Johnny approached the toys cautiously. Eventually, he settled on finger-painting and constructing some animals out of papier-mâché. Once he found what he was interested in, he became involved with the activity. The

---

[2] This case was described in greater detail and from a somewhat different perspective in another publication (A. Ornstein, 1976).

therapist made several attempts to engage the child in a conversation, but he answered her questions only in monosyllables. She also tried to identify his feelings from the pictures he made with the fingerpaints, and though he did not seem to object to her comments, he did not elaborate on the contents of the pictures. One of the pictures showed a house burning down so fast that it could not be saved. The other one was a glob of black paint that he called "a monster." When the therapist said that these pictures seemed to show how he felt inside—filled with fury like the fire, hopeless in this rage, and like a monster, all black and bad inside—John did not answer but continued to paint. There was no play disruption but no elaboration on his fantasies either.

The therapist's chance of gaining a deeper insight into the child's provocative, mischievous, and angry behavior came when he finished his first papier-mâché animal, a snake. When the therapist promised to keep the snake for him, Johnny tried to impress her with how little he cared whether she kept it or not. Unfortunately, the snake disappeared, probably destroyed by a careless janitor. As John walked into the office the following week, he looked around the office eagerly, still insisting that he couldn't care less whether the snake was there or not.

After this episode, the child's behavior changed markedly in the office. He became frantic, moved from one activity to the other, made impossible demands on the therapist, and regularly destroyed everything he made, insisting that nothing he did was any good. Interpretations to the effect that she understood his anger, since she had failed to protect what he made, did little to calm him. (The possible symbolic meaning of the snake could not be approached until the more immediate issue of the loss of something *he* made and gave to the therapist for safekeeping was dealt with.) The incident was useful as it exposed the possible sources of John's provocative and angry behavior. It indicated that the provocative behavior may serve to protect him from being retraumatized whenever he felt dismissed in school or at home.

The therapist then suggested that the two of them invite mother and stepfather so that they could all talk about Johnny's feelings together. In essence, the therapist told the parents that, for reasons that still had to be understood, Johnny was much more sensitive to slights, to being dismissed, than even he realized; his provocative behavior protected him from knowing how much it mattered to him what people felt about him. For example, he had to pretend that it did not matter whether or not the therapist or his mother cherished the things that he had made or paid attention to him. At the beginning, the therapist only tried to help the parents see that *there was a reason* for the child's misbehavior, one that the parents, too, could understand. The stepfather was quick to pick up on this, while the mother continued to focus on John's "badness." However, there was a small change in the content of her complaints. She spoke much more about her feeling hurt by John, his failure to understand how hard life had been for her, since she had to raise him without a father. She cried some, and the therapist noted that this touched the child deeply and made him feel ill at ease. She commented on the importance that his mother's feelings had for John and that when he felt that he was a "bad boy," not pleasing her, he became anxious and did things that got him into further trouble. By provoking others, he hoped to overcome his frustration, hurt, and sense of helplessness.

The details of this treatment process are not pertinent to my thesis. I only wanted to indicate what I meant by "translating" the motives for the child's behavior to the parents and the way in which such translation has to be done with the therapist's awareness of the parents' present-day emotional state, and with regard to their own hurt and helplessness. In the course of this treatment both the mother and the teacher remembered instances in which the child "erupted" following some incident that did not appear significant at the time, but could retrospectively be recognized as an instance in which he felt that his mother or the teacher didn't take him, or what he said, seriously.

Mother and stepfather as well as teacher were worried that the therapist's emphasis on understanding the child was a demand on them "to give in" to his behavior. This, too, had to be clarified, and they recognized that "giving in" could have been one more way in which John felt dismissed. However, once understood and the deeper sources of his behavior appreciated and responded to, John's provocative, attention-getting behavior diminished considerably.

The joint interviews with the family, however, did not terminate the child's individual sessions. This form of treatment has to evolve into a process, and the focus on the child has to be retained. The therapist was aided in this by conceptualizing the treatment as a single process and organizing her data with the help of the model of the "self-selfobject unit." By doing so, she was able to interpret to the mother her need for the child to affirm her in her motherliness and her frustration that John, with his behavior, "labeled" her, in a way, as a "bad mother." Problems related to the mother's or stepfather's job, or problems related to their relationship that did not affect their attitude and behavior toward the child, were not taken up in the family sessions. This made the treatment more "focal" than family treatments usually are and assured that the child's difficulties would be understood and responded to in depth.

# Summary

A review of the psychoanalytic literature on play reveals that in the therapeutic situation play has been considered to serve multiple functions: an opportunity for catharsis, for working through, as well as an opportunity for the child to experience and to reveal feelings that young children in particular cannot articulate. In my survey of the literature I focused specifically on the role of interpretations in psychotherapy where play is a major avenue of communication. In response to changes in the child's social and emotional milieu, changes in the frequency of therapy hours and in the frequency with which our child patients exhibit structural deficits rather than primary intrapsychic conflicts, I proposed the child-centered family treatment: a method of treatment in which the depth-psychological understanding of the child is not sacrificed but in which the insights that the therapist gains into the inner world of the child (sometimes through play and sometimes through a therapeutic dialogue) are "translated" to the parents. Rather than depending on the effect of her words, the therapist through this translation aims at creating an empathic therapeutic milieu in the child's home in which the parents respond to the child's fears, wishes, and anxieties rather than to his manifest behavior. The theoretical foundation of this approach to the treatment of young children and their emotional environment is provided by the model of the "self-selfobject unit"—a model based on Heinz Kohut's theory of the self and its relationship to its selfobject environment. In this model, a child depends on the ongoing empathic responsiveness of his emotional environment for his development; no insight by the child into his difficulties can substitute for these crucial (affirming and validating) developmental needs.

Finally, I described a fragment of a clinical vignette in order to demonstrate the technique that is involved in this form of child psychotherapy and the place of play in this treatment process.

## REFERENCES

Anthony, J. (1970), Editorial comment. In: *The Child in His Family*, ed. J. Anthony & C. Koupernik. New York: Wiley, pp. xxxi–xxxii.

Erikson, E. (1940), Studies in the interpretation of play. *Genetic Psychol. Monogr.*, 22:557–671. Provincetown, Mass.: Journal Press.

Frank, L. (1955), Play in personality development. In: *Therapeutic Use of Child's Play*. New York: Aronson, 1979, pp. 71–77.

Freud, A. (1946), The role of transference in the analysis of children. In: *The Psychoanalytic Treatment of Children*. London: Imago Press, pp. 28–37.

Freud, S. (1920), Beyond the pleasure principle. *Standard Edition*, 18:3–66. London: Hogarth Press, 1955.

Klein, M. (1955), The psychoanalytic play technique. In: *Therapeutic Use of Child's Play*. New York: Aronson, 1979, pp. 125–140.

Kohut, H. (1971), *The Analysis of the Self*. New York: International Universities Press.

———— (1977), *The Restoration of the Self*. New York: International Universities Press.

Meeks, J. (1970), Children who cheat at games. *J. Amer. Acad. Child Psychiat.*, 9:157–170.

Ornstein, A. (1976), Making contact with the inner world of the child. *Comprehen. Psychiat.*, 17:3–36.

———— (1981), Selfpathology in childhood: Clinical and developmental considerations. *Psychiat. Clin. North Amer.*, 4:435–453.

Stewart, C. (1981), The developmental psychology of sandplay. In: *Sandplay Studies*. San Francisco: C. G. Jung Institute, pp. 39–92.

Stewart, L. (1981), Sandplay and the C. G. Jung Institute of San Francisco. In: *Sandplay Studies*. San Francisco: C. G. Jung Institute, pp. 1–4.

Sutton-Smith, B. (1963), Play in cognitive development. In: *Therapeutic Use of Child's Play*. New York: Aronson, 1979, pp. 17–25.

Waelder, R. (1933), The psychoanalytic theory of play. *Psychoanal. Quart.*, 2:208–224.

Winnicott, D. (1953), Transitional objects and transitional phenomena. *Internat. J. Psycho-Anal.*, 34:89–97.

———— (1971a), Playing, creative activity, and the search for the self. In: *Playing and Reality*. New York: Basic Books, pp. 53–64.

———— (1971b), Playing a theoretical statement. In: *Playing and Reality*. New York: Basic Books, pp. 38–52.

———— (1971c), *Therapeutic Consultations in Child Psychiatry*. New York: Basic Books.

*April 1984*

# Narcissistic Injury and the Occurrence of Creativity: Freud's Irma Dream

STANLEY M. KAPLAN, M.D. (Cincinnati)

In this house on July 24th, 1895,
the Secret of Dreams was revealed to
Dr. Sigmund Freud

In a letter to Fliess on June 12, 1900, Freud (1887–1902) wrote, "Do you suppose that some day a marble tablet will be placed on the house, inscribed with these words:" (p. 322). He was referring to the above inscription and the summer place, Bellevue, where he had interpreted the now-famous dream of Irma's injection. Freud had dealt to some extent with his own and his patients' dreams before; however, this was the first dream he subjected to a complete and exhaustive interpretation. He saw Bellevue as the place where ". . . the Secret of Dreams was Revealed." As Schur (1972) put it, ". . . that day, July 24, 1895, represented a milestone in a development of the new science" (p. 85). Certainly, the interpretation of the Irma dream was one of Freud's important creative acts. The noteworthiness of the analysis of this dream has also been discussed by Erikson (1954), Leavitt (1956), Grinstein (1980), Keiper and Stone (1982), and others.

The Irma dream is reported in detail in "The Interpretation of Dreams" (1900), and although Freud, admittedly, prudently stopped short along some of his lines of association, he still provided a rich account that enables us to appreciate the circumstances in which the dream occurred and the impact events had on him at the time. We, therefore, are given an opportunity to gain some understanding of the psychological conditions that favored this scientific, creative act. While this information is not likely to answer questions relating to the psychological bases of creativity, it may facilitate our understanding of why some creative acts occur at particular times in the lives of creative people. In other words, it may throw light on the conditions that can favor the instigation or mobilization of creativity.

Heinz Kohut (1978) has contributed significantly to our understanding of aspects of creativity, notably the timing and the forces promoting it. In his paper, "Creativeness, Charisma, Group Psychology: Reflections on the Self-Analysis of Freud," he suggests that the basic narcissistic configuration of the psychic organization involved in the sequence leading to the creative activity of some creative people is a fluid one. The sequence includes

> periods of narcissistic equilibrium (stable self-esteem and securely ideal-ized internal values: steady, persevering work characterized by attention to details) are followed by (precreative) periods of emptiness and rest-lessness (decathexis of values and low self-esteem; addictive or perverse yearnings: no work), and that these, in turn, are followed by creative periods (the unattached narcissistic cathexes which had been withdrawn from the ideals and from the self are now employed in the service of the creative activity: original thought; intense, passionate work). Translating these metapsychological formulations into behavioral terms, one might say that a phase of frantic creativity (original thought) is followed by a phase of quiet work (the original ideas of the preceding phase are checked, ordered, and put into a communicative form, e.g., written down), and that this phase of quiet work is in turn interrupted by a fallow period of precreative narcissistic tension, which ushers in a phase of renewed creativity, and so on (pp. 815–816).

Important in this conceptualization is the disrupted narcissistic equilibrium with its associated detachment of cathexes from derivatives of the omnip-otent grandiose self and the idealized other which are made available for creative activity. Kohut gives some evidence that these stages occurred in Freud's work. He further provides us with an understanding of Fliess's role as an "idealized archaic omnipotent figure" serving for Freud as either a confirming other within the context of a mirror transference or a source of strength available from an idealizing transference.

Kohut's intriguing hypothesis about creativeness implies a somewhat reg-ular, though fluid sequence of events. It would seem reasonable to assume that this sequence would be modified and influenced by the meaningfulness to the creative genius of events that he or she encounters in life. Events experienced as narcissistically disrupting should affect the existing equilib-rium, releasing disturbing amounts of narcissistic cathexes that have to be dealt with. The usefulness or deleterious effects of these energies will de-pend, among other things, upon such factors as the degree of narcissistic trauma experienced, the integrity of the system regulating the individual's self-esteem, and the availability of selfobjects at the time. A fragile, relatively incohesive self may become totally incapacitated because of fragmentation, while another more firmly anchored self may be able to respond with a healing creative act, providing, of course, that the necessary basic creative ability is there. The precise balance of factors leading the potentially creative person to respond in either of these two directions would be difficult to define in quantitative terms.

There are interesting examples of creativity following narcissistically traumatic events. Such an event in the life of August Strindberg was pivotal in his career as a writer. Failure was certainly no stranger to the early life of this talented, but clearly narcissistically vulnerable man. His mother, a domestic servant who came from humble parentage, had been his father's mistress before she became his second wife. By contrast, Strindberg's father was part of an aristocratic shipping family, but he had fallen on bad times by the time of their marriage. According to Sprigg (1949), "To add to the humiliation of the irregular union, he had gone bankrupt and August was born when his father's fortune was at its lowest ebb. The family could not hold up its head among the neighbors" (p. 2).

A significant turning point in Strindberg's life occurred when he was about twenty years old. Although by then he had seriously considered or embarked upon several careers which had come to naught, with the encouragement and assistance of a Jewish physician, Dr. Lamm, who recognized his brilliance, he ultimately decided to study medicine. After some period of study and apprenticeship, he went to Uppsala for his preliminary examinations. He failed them. Strindberg was angered and humiliated. Although he could have returned after another year to repeat the exams, he abruptly shifted his interest to the theater where he sought a career as an actor. With new vitality and confidence, he threw himself into this venture. After spending a limited amount of time at the Dramatic Academy, he sought work on the stage not only confident in his ability but generally disdainful of his fellow actors. After one brief role in a play, he persistently insisted upon being auditioned for a leading part. It was reluctantly granted. He failed miserably. Quoting Sprigg (1949), "He was sternly advised to go back to the Dramatic Academy, and walked out into the street weeping with rage and humiliation . . . He went home to his lonely attic, took an opium pill and lay on his bed half hoping to die" (pp. 33–34).

Strindberg awoke with a variety of personal memories and scenes from a story he had recently read. "And then, as if it were involuntarily, the action began; he saw the characters on a stage and heard them speak, and as the hours passed found that he had witnessed the whole performance of a play. He wrote until exhausted, then collapsed on to the bed. Soon energy was restored, and at the end of four days he had written a two-act domestic comedy. He felt an extraordinary relief, 'as if a long pain were over, an abscess lanced at last!' Instead of dying, he had been born again; out of chaos had come creation" (p. 35). Thus an abrupt narcissistic injury played an important role in the initiation of this brilliant playwright's career. Fortunately, although the play was rejected, the enthusiasm of the friends he assembled to read it to and the publisher he sent it to facilitated the restoration of Strindberg's cohesive self and, therefore, the continuation of his playwriting.

There are interesting points of comparison between these events in Strindberg's life and the events leading to Freud's first complete dream interpretation, that of Irma's injection.

In the Preamble to the discussion of the dream, Freud (1900) relates that he had been treating a young lady, Irma, who was a close friend of the family, during the summer of 1895. The treatment had ended in only partial success and with some disagreement between him and his patient about what step she should take next. Her "hysterical anxiety" had been relieved, but some somatic symptoms persisted. Later during the summer, Otto, a dear friend and medical colleague, visited Freud. Otto had just returned from a stay with Irma and her family at their summer resort. When Freud inquired about Irma's condition, Freud reports that the manner in which Otto responded annoyed him; he had the feeling that Otto was being critical of him. That evening Freud wrote out the case history of Irma "with the idea of giving it to Dr. M. (a common friend who was at that time the leading figure in our circle) in order to justify myself" (p. 106). Freud had the dream that night or the following morning.

To recount the dream:

A large hall—numerous guests, whom we were receiving. —Among them was Irma. I at once took her on one side, as though to answer her letter and to reproach her for not having accepted my "solution" yet. I said to her: "If you still get pains, it's really only your fault." She replied: "If you only know what pains I've got now in my throat and stomach and abdomen—it's choking me"—I was alarmed and looked at her. She looked pale and puffy. I thought to myself that after all I must be missing some organic trouble. I took her to the window and looked down her throat, and she showed signs of recalcitrance, like women with artificial dentures. I thought to myself that there was really no need for her to do that.—She then opened her mouth properly and on the right I found a big white patch; at another place I saw extensive whitish grey scabs upon some remarkable curly structures which were evidently modelled on the turbinal bones of the nose.—I at once called in Dr. M., and he repeated the examination and confirmed it . . . Dr. M. looked quite different from usual; he was very pale, he walked with a limp and his chin was clean-shaven . . . My friend Otto was now standing beside her as well, and my friend Leopold was percussing her through her bodice and saying: "She has a dull area low down on the left." He also indicated that a portion of the skin on the left shoulder was infiltrated. (I noticed this, just as he did, in spite of her dress.) . . . M. said: "There's no doubt it's an infection, but no matter; dysentery will supervene and the toxin will be eliminated." . . . We were directly aware, too, of the origin of the infection. Not long before, when she was feeling unwell, my friend Otto had given her an injection of a preparation of propyl, propyls . . . propionic acid . . . trimethylamin (and I saw before me the formula for this printed in heavy type) . . . Injections of that sort ought not to be made so thoughtlessly . . . And probably the syringe had not been clean [p. 107].

All the associations will not be detailed here, but some will be cited to develop the points to be made.

According to Freud, the events of the preceding day that instigated the dream were the manner in which he experienced the news his friend and colleague, Otto, had given him about the current condition of Irma's health, and his working late into the night writing Irma's case history principally to "justify" himself in the eyes of this "leading figure" in their medical circle (Freud, 1900). Schur (1972) identifies Dr. M. as Breuer. Otto, according to Schur (1972), was Osker Rie, an intimate friend and junior colleague who had in former years worked under Freud. As mentioned above, Freud clearly states that Otto's remarks that "she's better, but not quite well," were experienced as a (unempathic) "reproof" of the manner in which Freud had dealt with Irma which had upset and annoyed him. It was that night that Freud wrote the lengthy case history and had the dream, the first that he exhaustively analyzed.

Freud (1900) said this about the dream: "The dream fulfilled certain wishes which were started in me by the events of the previous evening (the news given me by Otto and my writing out the case history). The conclusion of the dream, that is to say, was that I was not responsible for the persistence of Irma's pain, but that Otto was. Otto had in fact annoyed me by his remarks about Irma's incomplete cure, and the dream gave me my revenge by throwing the reproach back on to him. The dream acquitted me of the responsibility for Irma's condition by showing that it was due to other factors—it produced a whole series of reasons" (p. 118).

The analysis of the dream (and, perhaps, even the writing of the case report for Dr. M.) seems to have been a creative act stemming from the attempt to deal with the narcissistic injury that followed Otto's "reproof." In support of this is Freud's (1900) comment, "I was conscious that my friend Otto's words, or the tone in which he spoke them, annoyed me. I fancied I detected a reproof in them, such as to the effect that I had promised the patient too much; and, whether rightly or wrongly, I attributed the supposed fact of Otto's siding against me to the influence of my patient's relatives, who, as it seemed to me, had never looked with favour on the treatment" (p. 106).

Leavitt (1956), in his paper on the dream of Irma's injection, comments on the effects of Otto's remark on Freud's self-esteem. "The impact on Freud's self-esteem, since he was highly conscientious, must have been traumatic indeed, and especially so in view of the fact that his heart and aptitudes had never been in clinical medicine" (p. 442). Leavitt's paper mainly deals with the way in which this dream reveals Freud's ambivalence toward Fliess.

Freud (1900) reflects upon "revenging" himself on Otto. He comments: "But Otto was not the only person to suffer from the vials of my wrath" (p. 119). He took revenge, also, on his "disobedient patient" and on Dr. M. Obviously, the narcissistic disturbance and the resulting narcissistic rage described here are not comparable quantitatively with that which Strindberg experienced. In fact, they are at different levels of experience. Yet qualitatively they have similarities, and both lead to creative acts—by Strindberg, the writing of a first play which initiated a brilliant career as a playwright; by Freud, the discovery of "the Secret of Dreams."

At this time in his life, Freud was vulnerable. He was involved in establishing the credibility of his scientific discoveries and especially his new and innovative approach to the treatment of some types of mental disorders. ". . . in spite of all my inevitable ignorance, I was expected to produce therapeutic successes" (p. 108). There were many doubters of his work including Breuer (Dr. M.), his senior colleague to whom he had previously turned for "assistance and support." Freud cites an example of this in his associations relating to turning to Breuer when he encountered serious problems treating a patient with sulphanol. Breuer seems to have been used by him to some extent as an idealized selfobject although by then a strain in their relationship had already developed (Jones, 1953). Kohut (1978) points out the greater role Fliess played in this regard, but Fliess was not always immediately available because of the geographic distance that separated the two men. Also, Schur (1972), in his excellent discussion of the Irma dream, points out the traumatic impact that Fliess's bungled surgery on Irma had on Freud. Schur's thesis is that the dream served the purpose of protecting the relationship with Fliess by means of displacement of blame onto Otto. Nevertheless, the preparation of Irma's case history, which went on "far into the night" (p. 108), could have been an intense effort on Freud's part to sustain Breuer's favorable opinion of him as well as that of his close circle of associates, all of whom could provide the kind of confirmation one ordinarily needs when one is exploring new scientific areas.

Freud's relationship with Irma and her family was also significant. Irma, a friend of the family, was soon to attend a party at the Freud household at Bellevue. He comments: "It will be readily understood that a mixed relationship such as this may be a source of many disturbed feelings in a physician and particularly in a psychotherapist. While the physician's personal interest is greater, his authority is less; any failure would bring a threat to the old-established friendship with the patient's family" (1900, p. 106). A greater narcissistic investment in the patient's response to treatment is likely under such circumstances.

Freud's association to "trimethylamin" which occurred as a visible chemical formula in the dream is interesting. It led Freud to associations about Fliess who believed that this substance was one of the products of sexual metabolism. Freud mentions that Fliess was ". . . a person whose agreement I recalled with satisfaction whenever I felt isolated in my opinions" (p. 117). As mentioned above, Otto's comment about Irma's condition evoked in Freud a feeling of being professionally isolated which was dealt with by turning his thoughts to selfobjects for soothing reassurance. In regard to the series of organic compounds that came to mind in his associations to "trimethylamin," it is interesting to note that according to Jones (1953) Freud worked for a year in a chemistry lab where he was unsuccessful. "Although he rather liked chemistry he had no success in it, and he later poke of this wasted year as an unfruitful one, the recollection of which was humiliating. Indeed, he afterwards termed 1882 'the gloomiest and least successful year of my professional life' " (p. 59).

Kohut (1978) hypothesizes and provides some evidence that during the precreative period there is "a decathexis of the self as the narcissistic energies detach themselves and become available for the creative task" (p. 817). In this regard, he suggests that Freud's cigar smoking was a manifestation of precreative narcissistic tension. He cites a letter to Fliess of June 12, 1895, in which Freud writes, "I have started smoking again, because I still missed it (after fourteen months abstinence), and because I must treat that mind of mine decently, or the fellow will not work for me" (p. 121). This was written six to seven weeks prior to the analysis of the dream of Irma's injection. Could Freud's return to smoking have been an evidence of the precreative restlessness occurring before the accomplishment of this creative act which was then ignited by Otto's remarks which caused a further abrupt decathexis of the self?

Freud described fluctuations in his abilities to do intellectual work—his mood being the important determinant. In a letter to Fliess (Jones, 1953) on December 24, 1899, he wrote: "I can quite clearly distinguish two different intellectual states in myself: one in which I take very good notes of everything my patients say and even make discoveries during the (therapeutic) work, but apart from it I cannot reflect or do any other work; the other in which I draw conclusions, write down notes, and am even free to take an interest in other things, but in which I am actually further away from the business in hand and do not pay close attention to what is going on with the patients" (pp. 344–345). According to Jones (1953), "The significant point is, however, that happiness and well-being were not conducive to the best work. That depended on an internal and rather unpleasant, disturbance, a rumbling from below the surface. As he remarked himself: 'I have been very idle because the moderate amount of discomfort necessary for intensive work has not set in'" (p. 345). All work, of course, is not creative; nevertheless, these reflections by Freud (1900) are pertinent here.

Another significant personal dream that Freud reports early in "The Interpretation of Dreams" is the "Dream of the Botanical Monograph." The dream is brief: "I had written a monograph on a certain plant. The book lay before me and I was at the moment turning over a folded coloured plate. Bound up in each copy there was a dried specimen of the plant, as though it had been taken from a herbarium" (p. 169).

This dream is used by Freud to illustrate the role of recent and indifferent material in dreaming. Freud recalls that he had seen a new book in the window of a bookshop with the title, *The Genus Cyclamen*, which was "evidently a *monograph* on that plant" (p. 169). His associations to this dream led to a monograph he had written some years before on the coca plant, the source of cocaine, and this, in turn, reminded him that it was Koller and not he who had received credit for discovering the local (ophthalmic) anesthetic properties of cocaine. For this, Koller was properly acclaimed. Freud expresses chagrin, for he had indicated in his paper that cocaine possessed anesthetic property, but he had not been thorough enough to pursue the matter. According to Jones (1953), Freud had hoped to gain some measure of fame from his work with cocaine.

The stimulus to the Botanical Monograph dream was a narcissistically disrupting event of the evening before. He had walked home with Dr. Königstein who was involved in the cocaine discovery by virtue of having been the first to use it for ophthalmic surgery. While they were talking, Dr. Gärtner and his wife joined them. Gärtner was one of the authors of a Festschrift honoring Stricker, the director of a laboratory with which Gärtner was associated. The book listed the accomplishments of former members of this laboratory among whom was Koller who was cited for having discovered the anesthetic properties of cocaine. In fact, Gärtner had assisted Koller in his animal experiments on the use of cocaine as a local anesthetic agent for the eye (Grinstein, 1980).

Freud (1900) provides us with the meaning of the dream which he likened to the dream of Irma's injection. "What it meant was: 'After all, I'm the man who wrote the valuable and memorable paper (on cocaine)' " (p. 173). It seems clear that the events that proved to be the stimulus for the dream were a narcissistically disrupting reminder that fame had eluded him because of his failure to follow through. One might conclude from this that the resulting freed narcissistic cathexis evoked a wish-fulfilling dream of being seen as the true discoverer, thereby protecting his sleep. Also, one has to consider that the interpretation of this dream had a creative element. Freud gave it a position of importance by citing it so early in "The Interpretation of Dreams" and using it to illustrate for the first time several significant dream processes he had discovered.

Freud describes an interesting daydream he had the morning after the Botanical Monograph dream. He had not by then interpreted the dream—he did so that evening. The daydream was to the effect that should he ever develop glaucoma, he would go to Berlin, to Fliess's house where he would be operated on "incognito" so that the ophthalmic surgeon would have no knowledge that he was indeed the discoverer of the use of cocaine as an anesthetic or, as he puts it, "had a share in the discovery" (p. 173). This daydream provides two means of diminishing narcissistic tension: reunion with Fliess, an idealized archaic omnipotent figure; and a grandiose, exhibitionistic fantasy (albeit denied, i.e., being "incognito") relating to being the discoverer of the ophthalmic use of cocaine.

When he associates to the Count Thun dream in chapter 5 of "The Interpretation of Dreams" (1900), Freud provides us with some understanding of his ambitions and his sensitivity to evidences of failure. He recalls having "disregarded modesty" and urinating in the presence of his parents in their bedroom. His father reprimanded him with the words: "The boy will come to nothing." Freud speculates: "This must have been a frightful blow to my ambition, for *references to this scene are still constantly recurring in my dreams* [Freud's emphasis] and are always linked with an enumeration of my achievements and successes, as though I wanted to say: "You see, I *have* come to something!" (p. 216; emphasis added).

Otto's "rebuke" may well have echoed the admonition, "The boy will come to nothing." Revenge was taken on Otto and Dr. M. in the Irma dream much as it was taken on his father in the Count Thun dream. Freud's conclusion about the meaning of the Botanical Monograph dream was that it meant: "After all, I'm the man who wrote the valuable and memorable paper [on cocaine]." In other words, he is saying, "You see, I have come to something."

Erikson (1954) implies that Freud's dreaming the dream of Irma's injection was a creative act. In other words, he had the dream in order to discover. It is unlikely that all creative acts are instigated by narcissistically disrupting events, or that all narcissistic acts lead to creativeness. In fact, Charles Kligerman (1980), in his article "Art and the Self of the Artist," suggests that in addition to the artists described by Kohut, i.e., those with wide narcissistic shifts, there are those like Bach who seem to fuse the three phases described by Kohut "into a smooth-running, reliable process analogous to an autonomous ego function: if you will, he operates like an expert craftsman who has perfected his skill and employs it every day, without undue creative turmoil" (p. 390). In his view, whenever the type of artist Kohut describes "is threatened by a loss of self, be it structural deficit or a temporary enfeeblement, he attempts to feel whole again by offering his product as a perfect self to be confirmed by an admiring world" (p. 389).

Other examples of creativity could be cited here that followed upon the heels of narcissistic injury. It is as though the experiencing or offering of the "product as a perfect self" is used as a counterbalance to the experiencing of oneself as inferior or flawed.

## REFERENCES

Erikson, E. H. (1954), The dream specimen of psychoanalysis. *J. Amer. Psychoanal. Assn.*, 2:5–56.

Freud, S. (1887–1902), *The Origins of Psychoanalysis: Letters to Wilhelm Fliess, Drafts and Notes*, ed. M. Bonaparte, A. Freud, and E. Kris. New York: Basic Books, 1954.

———— (1900), The interpretation of dreams. *Standard Edition*, 4 & 5. London: Hogarth Press, 1958.

Grinstein, A. (1980), *Sigmund Freud's Dreams*. New York: International Universities Press.

Jones, E. (1953), *The Life and Work of Sigmund Freud*, vol. 1. New York: Basic Books.

Keiper, A. & Stone, A. A. (1982), The dream of Irma's injection: A structural analysis. *Amer. J. Psychiat.*, 139:1225–1234.

Kligerman, C. (1980), Art and the self of the artist. In: *Advances in Self Psychology*, ed. A. Goldberg. New York: International Universities Press, pp. 383–396.

Kohut, H. (1978), Creativeness, charisma, group psychology: Reflections on the self-analysis of Freud. In: *The Search for the Self*, vol. 2. ed. P. H. Ornstein. New York: International Universities Press, pp. 783–843.

Leavitt, H. C. (1956), A biographical and teleological study of "Irma's Injection" dream. *Psychoanal. Rev.*, 43:440–447.

Schur, M. (1972), *Freud: Living and Dying*. New York: International Universities Press.

Sprigg, E. (1949), *The Strange Life of August Strindberg*. London: Hannish Hamilton.

*February 1984*

# IV

# APPLIED
# PSYCHOANALYSIS

# Shakespeare's King Lear: A Poetic Attempt to Understand Madness as a Fragmentation of the Self

## FRANCO PAPARO, M.D. (Rome)

> *Edgar.* . . . Men must endure
> Their going hence even as their coming hither;
> Ripeness is all.
> —*King Lear*, V.ii.9–11

Heinz Kohut (1978), in his correspondence with Eric Heller on "Psychoanalysis and the Interpretation of Literature," has stressed the value of applying the new psychoanalytic psychology of the self to the study of artistic creation. The aims of my paper can be summarized as follows.

First I shall try to corroborate a remark made by Freud (quoted by Trilling, 1950) and endorsed by Winnicott many years later. According to Freud and Winnicott, when we find something new in our work with our analysands, we soon realize that great poets and philosophers made the same discovery much earlier. A second aim, but not a secondary one, is to stimulate my readers to pick up Shakespeare's *King Lear* and immerse themselves in it. They can thus enjoy the pleasure of discovering or rediscovering the richness and beauty of the text and the depth of the psychological insight of a genius, who could be considered, as I hope to demonstrate, a self psychologist *ante litteram*. Last but not least, I hope to show that the study of Shakespeare's masterly description of the steps and stages in the process of King Lear's madness as fragmentation of the self enhances the empathic understanding of our most disturbed patients in the clinical situation.

379

Hyman Muslin (1981) has recently written an interesting paper, "King Lear: Images of the Self in Old Age." His stimulating ideas have served as the point of departure for my own study of the Shakespearean text. Muslin states that "In this play, held by many to be the greatest of all of Shakespearean tragedies (Hazlitt, Dowden, Coleridge, Granville-Barker), we immediately become caught up in the emotional turmoil of the father-king whose needs for self-support as he enters his declining years are neither recognized nor gratified. (A subplot in the play, involving the Duke of Gloucester and his sons also deals with the disruptions of the relationship between father and child and its tragic consequences)" (p. 143).

The reader can refer to Muslin's work for a survey of the classical psychoanalytic literature on *King Lear*. For my part I will only briefly comment on Muslin's central hypothesis but will focus my attention on the theme, hinted at but not fully developed by Muslin, of Lear's madness as a process of fragmentation of the self.

I agree with Hyman Muslin's hypothesis that the main motive of the play is not, as Coleridge put it, "parental anguish through filial ingratitude." An accurate study of the Shakespearean text shows something more complex than that. Completely absorbed by his self needs, "Lear . . . is incapable," Muslin says, "of recognizing his favorite daughter's self-limits" (p. 146). In fact, he turns from Cordelia to his older daughters, Goneril and Regan, who have chosen to flatter him. On the other hand, Goneril and Regan "have ample instigation for their reactive rage" (p. 146) since Lear has openly declared his preference for Cordelia, the only daughter whom Lear addresses as "our joy."

In the subplot, the bastard son Edmund aims to deprive his legitimate half-brother Edgar of Gloucester's favor. But Edmund, too, like Goneril and Regan, has had his share of injuries to his self-esteem.[1]

This, after all, is not simply parental anguish through filial ingratitude; rather, *there are reciprocal failures of empathic understanding between parents and children that lead to a vicious circle of injury and rage.*

I have chosen to ignore several aspects of *King Lear* as a tragedy. For instance, I will completely overlook Gloucester's character and the conflicts among him and his sons, despite their utmost importance in the dynamics of the drama.[2] My paper will be deliberately devoted to the study of Shakespeare's poetic presentation of the gradual process through which mount-

---

[1] Introducing Edmund to Kent, at the start of the play, Gloucester calls him half-jokingly "whoreson" and mentions that ". . . yet was his mother fair; there was good sport at his making . . ." (I.i.21–22).

[2] I hope my work will inspire the study of Gloucester's simulated suicide as a poetic forerunner of the modern psychodrama.

ing anxiety and rage, stimulated by a series of traumatic events, come to overburden Lear's self cohesion and result in the breaking up of his nuclear self and his madness.[3]

The admirable presentation of Lear's gradual change of mood, from serene confidence to spiteful rage, begins when Cordelia answers Lear's question ("what can you say / to draw a third more opulent than your sisters," I.i.84–85) with the famous laconic words, "Nothing, my lord." In sudden rage, Lear urges her, "Nothing will come of nothing, speak again." He is deeply upset by Cordelia's declaration: "Unhappy that I am, I cannot heave / my heart into my mouth. I love your majesty / according to my bond, no more, no less" (I.i.90–92).[4] Then Lear tries to blackmail her: "Cordelia! Mend your speech a little / lest you may mar your fortunes" (I.i.93–94). At her refusal, he explodes and attempts to defend himself from the narcissistic injury by irately disclaiming his ties with her.

> *Lear.* Let it be so! Thy truth then be thy dower:
> For, by the sacred radiance of the sun,
> The mysteries of Hecate and the night,
> By all the operation of the orbs
> From whom we do exist and cease to be,
> Here I disclaim all my paternal care,
> Propinquity and property of blood,
> And as a stranger to my heart and me
> Hold thee from this for ever . . .
>
> (I.i.107–115)

As a direct consequence of Lear's disowning Cordelia, Lear divides her part of his kingdom between Goneril and Regan and their husbands Albany and Cornwall. We observe a Lear self-assured and almost exalted.

> *Lear.* With my two daughters' dowers digest the third.
> Let pride, which she calls plainness, marry her.
> I do invest you jointly with my power,
> Pre-eminence, and all the large effects
> That troop with majesty. Ourself by monthly course,

---

[3] We can find a few references to Lear's personality before the beginning of his tragic breakdown. In the last lines of I.i. Regan says, "he hath ever but slenderly known himself." And Goneril says, "The best and soundest of his time hath been but rash."

[4] Why does Cordelia not comply with Lear's request of infinite love? I agree with Muslin (1981): "The failure of Cordelia to recognize her father's need for admiration is, in essence, her resistance to self-transformation" (p. 153). In my opinion, she refuses to comply because she wants to be "true," to maintain her identity, and she cannot afford to give up the idealized image of the father and to transform herself into her father's caretaker by accepting his fantasy "to set rest on her kind nursery" (I.i.122–123). On the other hand, as Muslin writes, "Cordelia's resistance to her father's challenge can, of course, be understood as her anxiety, that is, becoming her father's consort, an oedipal triumph, which she rejects" (p. 153).

> With reservation of an hundred knights[5]
> By you to be sustained, shall our abode
> Make with you by due turn. Only we shall retain
> The name and all th'addition to a king; the sway,
> Revenue, execution of the rest,
> Beloved sons, be yours: which to confirm,
> This coronet part between you.
>
> (I.i.127–138)

In spite of Lear's apparent self-assurance, when his most trusted supporter, the Earl of Kent, insists on interceding in favor of Cordelia, the wrathful Lear resorts again to the same defense against the narcissistic blow given by Kent's rebellion. He angrily bids Kent "out of sight"[6] and relentlessly banishes him.[7]

The dramatic action then shifts to Goneril's house, where Lear, with his retinue of a hundred knights, is to spend the first month. Shakespeare introduces us to a Goneril bitterly complaining about the "riotous" behavior of the knights. She "will not speak to Lear" when "he returns from hunting" and gives orders to her steward Oswald.

> *Goneril.* Put on what weary negligence you please,
>          You and your fellows . . .
>
> (I.iii.13–14)

> And let his knights have colder looks among you;
>
> (I.iii.24)

We find here a wonderful example of the "use of empathy for inimical purposes" (Kohut, 1980). In fact, it can be inferred that Goneril knows how vulnerable her father is to negligence and lack of acknowledgment of his person. Soon afterward Lear is onstage talking to a knight.

> *Lear.* Thou but rememberest me of mine own conception: I have per-
>         ceived a most faint neglect of late; which I have rather blamed as
>         mine own jealous curiosity than as a very pretence and purpose of
>         unkindness: I will look further into 't . . .
>
> (I.iv.65–69)

We hear Lear blaming his own "jealous curiosity."[8] In other words Shake-

---

[5] See, below, my hypothesis about the meaning of the retinue of a hundred knights.

[6] Many critics have pointed out that images referring to eyes, vision, and sight occur frequently in *King Lear*. They have also stressed the metaphoric meaning of Gloucester's physical blindness as opposed to Lear's mental blindness.

[7] Kent will appear in the following scenes in disguise.

[8] It is interesting to note that "curiosity" is one of the 116 words that is used by Shakespeare in *King Lear* but not in his earlier work. Such words, according to G. Taylor, reflect the influence of Florio's translation of Montaigne's *Essays* on Shakespeare (see Arden edition, p. 235).

speare imagines that Lear is well aware of his hypersensitivity to slights. I see in this scene a touching picture of a person, who, though wounded in his pride and self-esteem, tries to use his own self-calming functions in order to keep his balance.

However, when Oswald enters, Lear asks him:

O! you sir, you, come you hither, sir. Who am I, sir?

*Oswald.*    My Lady's father.

*Lear.*      "My Lady's father," my Lord's knave: you whoreson dog! You slave! You cur!

(I.iv.76–79)

Of course, Lear expects Oswald to reply, "the King," and at Oswald's answer Lear loses his temper. He acts out his rage by striking Oswald and tripping him with the help of the disguised Kent.

At this point in the tragedy the Fool comes on the stage. In my opinion he represents a dramatic dislocation of an insightful endowment of Lear's self, an inner voice, which with wit and humor[9] tries to hold Lear together in an attempt to counter the threatening disintegration of the self.[10] I will quote only two brief samples of interactions between Lear and the Fool.

*Lear.*    Dost thou call me fool, boy?

*Fool.*    All thy other titles thou hast given away; that thou wast born with.

(I.iv.145–147)

*Lear.*    When were you wont to be so full of songs, sirrah?

*Fool.*    I have used it, Nuncle, e'er since thou mad'st thy daughters thy mothers; for when thou gav'st them the rod and puttest down thine own breeches

(I.iv.167–170)

Goneril enters and harshly laments the Fool's insolence and the knights' misbehavior, for which Lear himself may be held responsible. Lear reacts with a speech that could be reproduced in a modern textbook of psychiatry as a reliable description of a short-lived experience of depersonalization heralding a psychotic breakdown.

*Lear.*    Does any here know me? This is not Lear:
          Does Lear walk thus? speak thus? Where are his eyes?

[9] On wisdom and humor as transformations of narcissism, "which aid man in achieving ultimate mastery . . . to tolerate the recognition of finiteness in principle and even of his impending end," see Kohut (1966, pp. 456–457) and *The Analysis of the Self* (1971).

[10] The Fool disappears from the drama when, at the end of the tempest, all the defenses fail and Lear becomes mad.

> Either his notion weakens, his discernings
> Are lethargied—Ha! Waking? 'Tis not so!
> Who is it that can tell me who I am?

*Fool.*     Lear's shadow.[11]

(I.iv.223–228)

Later Goneril insists that his knights are disordered and "deboshed" and asks Lear "a little to disquantity" their number. The injured Lear decides to leave Goneril's house and says with regret:

*Lear.*                                        . . . O most small fault,
> How ugly didst thou in Cordelia show!
> Which, like an engine, wrench'd my frame of nature
> From the fix'd place, drew from my heart all love,
> And added to the gall. O Lear, (Lear,) Lear!
> Beat at this gate that let thy folly in,
> And thy dear judgment out! . . .

(I.iv.264–270)

The metaphor of the "frame of nature" being "wrenched from the fixed place" suggests "the figure of a building that is thrown off its foundation by a powerful mechanical contrivance."[12] We also observe Lear repeatedly calling himself by name and beating his head. This could be considered "an attempt to counteract through self-stimulation a feeling of inner deadness and depression" (Kohut, 1977, p. 5).

Violent wishes and fantasies of revenge help Lear to hold himself together. He entertains the idea of a retaliation: *Goneril.* ". . . may feel / how sharper than a serpent's tooth it is / to have a thankless child / . . ." (I.iv.285–287). He imagines that, when Regan hears about Goneril's harsh treatment of her father, "with her nails She'll flay thy [Goneril's] wolvish visage" (I.iv.305–306). (For a discussion of the dynamics of search for revenge after a narcissistic injury see Kohut, 1972.)

During the following scene Lear and the Fool are left alone on the stage. The Fool continues to exert the function of the witty, self-critical inner voice of the shattered Lear.

*Fool.*     Canst tell how an oyster makes his shell?
*Lear.*     No.
*Fool.*     Nor I neither. But I can tell why a snail has a house.
*Lear.*     Why?

---

[11] "In this context the term shadow shows that Lear is now a bleak, two-dimensional remnant of his former self" (J. Kirsch, 1966, p. 218).

[12] G. Kittredge (quoted by Kenneth Muir, preface to Arden edition, p. 48).

| | |
|---|---|
| *Fool.* | Why, to put's head in; not to give it away to his daughters, and leave his horns without a case . . . |

| | |
|---|---|
| *Fool.* | Thou shouldst not have been old till thou hadst been wise. |

(I.v.25–30, 41–42)

Lear's fear of fragmentation cannot be denied any longer. Thus Lear invokes heaven to help him to master it.

| | |
|---|---|
| *Lear.* | O! let me not be mad, not mad, sweet heaven; <br> Keep me in temper;[13] I would not be mad!— |

(I.v.43–44)

In the second act Lear arrives at Gloucester's castle to find that his messenger (the disguised Kent) has been put in stocks. This reveals a tremendous disregard toward Lear himself. Initially, Lear refuses to believe that Regan and her husband have ordered the outrage. Lear is so angry that he tries again to stimulate his own psychic resources, this time by soothing the feelings that are about to choke him.

| | |
|---|---|
| *Lear.* | O, how this mother swells up toward my heart;[14] <br> Hysterical passion, down, thou climbing sorrow! <br> Thy element's below. Where is this daughter? |

(II.iv.54–56)

Lear asks to speak to Regan and her husband Cornwall and receives the answer that they are weary and sick. He angrily threatens.

| | |
|---|---|
| *Lear.* | Go tell the Duke and's wife I'd speak with them, <br> Now presently: bid them come forth and hear me, <br> Or at their chamber door I'll beat the drum <br> Till it cry sleep to death. |

(II.iv.113–116)

And again the attempt to repress a physical expression of his anxiety.

| | |
|---|---|
| *Lear.* | O me, my heart, my rising heart! But down! |

(II.iv.118)

Regan eventually meets her father and, to his scorn, supports Goneril's behavior. The climax is reached when Goneril herself arrives and Regan takes her by the hand. In the discussion that follows, Regan and Goneril are allied in the request for a substantial reduction of Lear's retinue.

[13] Temper refers to the correct balance of the four humors of the human body (see Melchiori, 1976).

[14] The idea was prevalent during Shakespeare's times that the womb (*mother* in English and *hystera* in Greek) could migrate toward the heart and the throat, causing feelings of choking.

*Goneril.*                                                                    Hear me, my lord;
                What need you five-and-twenty, ten, or five,
                To follow in a house where twice so many
                Have a command to tend you?
*Regan.*                                                                    What need one?
*Lear.*         O, reason not the need; our basest beggars
                Are in the poorest thing superfluous.
                Allow not nature more than nature needs—
                Man's life is cheap as beast's. Thou art a lady;
                If only to go warm were gorgeous,
                Why, nature needs not what thou gorgeous wear'st,
                Which scarcely keeps thee warm. But, for true need—
                                                                    (II.iv.258–268)

It is the superfluous that gives man's life its meaning! As gorgeous dresses are symbols of Regan's status, so the hundred knights are symbols of Lear's status, and he cannot give up this external aid to his shaken identity.[15]

In order to resist the slights received by his unempathic and hostile daughters Lear invokes the gods "to touch him with noble anger." Again he expresses ideas of terrible vengeance and tries to refrain from weeping.

*Lear.*                                                             . . . You think I'll weep;
                No, I'll not weep.             [*Storm heard at a distance*]
                I have full cause of weeping; but this heart
                Shall break into a hundred thousand flaws
                Or ere I'll weep. O Fool! I shall go mad.
                                                                    (II.iv.289–293)

Now the storm and tempest inside Lear find an echo in the elements of nature outside. A little later, Lear walks bareheaded in the storm and vehemently addresses the natural forces with the omnipotent fantasy of dominating them and thus controlling the disintegration taking place within himself.

*Lear.*         Blow, winds, and crack your cheeks! Rage! Blow!
                You cataracts and hurricanoes, spout
                Till you have drench'd our steeples, drown'd the cocks!
                You sulphurous and thought-executing fires,
                Vaunt-curriers of oak-cleaving thunderbolts,
                Singe my white head! And thou, all-shaking thunder,
                Strike flat the thick rotundity o' th' world,
                Crack Nature's moulds, all germens spill at once

---

[15] I have described elsewhere (Paparo, 1981) a young girl, a narcissistic personality disorder, who was reluctant to go to the beach in summer and to wear a bathing suit. She was aware of her need for formal clothes as a support to her weak sense of identity.

(III.ii.1–9)

We can easily see that verbs indicating fragmentation, breaking, fracture, and so forth occur frequently in this part of the play "to make them paradoxically connective elements in the verbal tissue of the tragedy" (Melchiori, 1976, p. xliii; my translation). In the short quotation I have quoted here there are "crack" at line 1, "cleaving" at line 5, "shaking" at line 6, "strike" at line 7, and again "crack" at line 8!

Now the disguised Kent begs Lear to shelter himself from the tempest by entering a hovel.

| | |
|---|---|
| *Kent.* | Here is the place, my Lord; good my Lord, enter. |
| | The tyranny of the open night's too rough |
| | For nature to endure.                     [*Storm still*] |
| *Lear.* | Let me alone. |
| *Kent.* | Good my lord, enter here. |
| *Lear.* | Wilt break my heart? |

(III.iv.1–6)

| | |
|---|---|
| *Kent.* | Good my lord, enter here. |
| *Lear.* | Prithee, go in thyself; seek thine own ease: |
| | This tempest will not give me leave to ponder |
| | On things would hurt me more. But I'll go in. |

(III.iv.22–25)

In my opinion a second defense mechanism is ascribed by Shakespeare to Lear's remaining outside in the storm: "he will have his thoughts distracted from the ingratitude which will otherwise break his heart" (Muir, 1972, p. 107).

A famous monologue follows. It illustrates, in my view, a third desperate attempt on Lear's part to integrate the external storm with his effort to keep a certain degree of cohesion and continuity within his own experience.

| | |
|---|---|
| *Lear.* | Poor naked wretches, wheresoe'er you are, |
| | That bide the pelting of this pitiless storm, |
| | How shall your houseless heads and unfed sides, |
| | Your loop'd and window'd raggedness, defend you |
| | From seasons such as these? O! I have ta'en |
| | Too little care of this. Take physic, Pomp; |
| | Expose thyself to feel what wretches feel, |
| | That thou mayst shake the superflux to them, |
| | And show the Heavens more just. |

(III.iv.28–36)

Here Shakespeare shows great psychological perception. He poetically portrays Lear trying to strengthen his harassed identity through a fleeting identification with his own underprivileged subjects. Lear still pretends to be a king, while he imagines what these wretches feel when exposed to a pitiless storm and acknowledges his unfulfilled duties of charity toward them as well as his own former carelessness and artificiality.

Eventually, Lear enters the hovel with the Fool and Kent, and here they find Edgar who, banned by his father, feigns madness and pretends to be Tom o' Bedlam.[16] At first sight Lear believes that "nothing could have subdu'd [Tom's] nature / to such a lowness but his unkind daughters" (III.iv.69–70). Lear continues to insist on his conviction notwithstanding Kent's confutation. Thus again Shakespeare gives us the picture of a defense. Lear, in order to emphasize his own person, attributes to Tom the same awful "pass" in which he finds himself. After an exchange of words with the Fool and Tom, who exhibits his assumed madness through crazy speeches, Lear reaches a climax[17] and addresses Tom.

Lear.    (Why,) thou wert better in a grave than to answer with thy uncovered body this extremity of the skies. Is man no more than this? Consider him well. Thou owest the worm no silk, the beast no hide, the sheep no wool, the cat no perfume. (Ha!) Here's three on's are sophisticated. Thou art the thing itself! Unaccommodated man is no more but such a poor, bare, forked animal as thou art. Off, off, you lendings! Come, unbutton here.

(III.iv.100–108)

In Shakespeare's circumstantial account of the very moment of Lear's "losing his wits," Lear acts out a need to be naked by tearing off his "lent" clothes. This sequence gave me an aha! experience. I think I understood for the first time, after many years of working with severely disturbed patients, why psychotic people in an acute phase so often undress themselves. This aberrant behavior, as depicted by Shakespeare, may represent a last attempt to avoid a breaking point by placing reliance on one's own uncovered body as "the thing itself," i.e., the firm "animal" basis of human existence.

Soon afterward Shakespeare offers us the touching picture of a delusional Lear. In the hovel, Lear's misperceptions and hallucinations allow him to act out a court trial against his evil daughters. Kent, Tom, and the

[16] Edgar is naked and has "grimed" his face with filth. Bedlamites were poor people, discharged from Bedlam's hospital in London, who wandered begging charity. (See Gentili, 1978, p. 118.)

[17] As W. Empson comments, "madness has come. No doubt the appearance of the wild Edgar . . . is the accident that made him unable to shun it any longer" (quoted in Muir, 1972, p. 109).

Fool, invested by Lear, as king, to be judges in the trial, enter into the delusion.

Lear.       I'll see their trial first; bring in their evidence.
            [*To Edgar*] Thou robed man of justice, take thy place.
            [*To the Fool*] And thou, his yokefellow of equity,
            Bench by his side. [*To Kent*] You are o'the commission;
            Sit you too.

                                                              (III.vi.35–39)

Lear.       Arraign her first. 'Tis Goneril! I here take my oath before this
            honourable assembly she kicked the poor King her father.

                                                              (III.vi.46–48)

In his paper "On the Mechanism of Paranoia" Freud (1911) wrote: "*The delusional formation, which we take to be the pathological product, is in reality an attempt at recovery, a process of reconstruction*" (p. 71; Freud's italics). In this passage Freud had in mind the delusional reconstruction of a lost world. Shakespeare's poetic imagery suggests to me an attempt at the delusional reconstruction of a kingly self.

Toward the end of the fourth act all the attempted defenses have failed to halt fragmentation and to restore cohesion to Lear's self. Lear is now depicted as utterly fragmented. The sequence of Lear's associations before his acknowledgment of the blind Gloucester, is revealing.

Lear.       No, they cannot touch me for coining. I am the King himself.
Edgar.      O thou side-piercing sight!
Lear.       Nature's above art in that respect. There's your press-
            money.—That fellow handles his bow like a crow-keeper.—Draw
            me a clothier's yard.—Look, look! a mouse!—Peace, peace! this
            piece of toasted cheese will do't.—There's my gauntlet; I'll
            prove it on a giant.—Bring up the brown bills.—O, well flown
            bird! I'th' clout, i'th' clout! Hewgh![18] Give the word.
Edgar.      Sweet marjoram.[19]
Lear.       Pass.

                                                              (IV.vi.83–94)

In his comment on this soliloquy Kenneth Muir (1972) writes: "Lear's mad speeches have an undertone of meaning, and although he leaps from one subject to another it is often possible to see that there is a subconscious connection between them. *Coining*, which was a royal prerogative, leads to the thought of *press money*. This suggests watching recruits at target practice

[18] An imitation of the sound made by the arrow (see Arden edition).
[19] The password itself is related to the theme of madness; in Shakespeare's time marjoram was considered a remedy for diseases of the brain.

and war. War suggests *peace*, which in turn suggests *piece*, and also a challenge and brown *bills*. *Bills* suggest *bird*, bird suggests an arrow in flight, and its target" (p. 103).

If we examine Lear's speech and contrast it with the speeches of feigned madness made by Edgar (disguised as Tom o' Bedlam), we are struck by the difference.[20] It is my hypothesis that Shakespeare uses Lear's erratic speech to portray lost cohesion of the self and fragmentation. The fragments are constituted by single thoughts and pieces of past experience.[21]

Let us now discuss the moment when Cordelia's soldiers, following her orders, have found Lear wandering about— . . . "As mad as the vex'd sea; singing aloud" . . . —(IV.iv.2) and have taken him to her camp. A doctor helps Cordelia in assisting her father. He gives Lear some simple operatives, "whose power will close the eye of anguish." After a long sleep, Lear wakes up dressed in fresh garments.

| | |
|---|---|
| *Doctor.* | [*To Cordelia*] Please you draw near.—Louder the music there![22] |
| *Cordelia.* | O my dear father! Restoration hang |
| | Thy medicine on my lips, and let this kiss |
| | Repair those violent harms that my two sisters |
| | Have in thy reverence made. |

                                                            (IV.vii.25–29)

Lear's gradual awakening is poetically described. He tries to orient himself in space and time and to take possession of his body while he is testing his own perceptions.

| | |
|---|---|
| *Lear.* | Where have I been? Where am I? Fair daylight? |
| | I am mightily abus'd.[23] I should die with pity |
| | To see another thus. I know not what to say. |
| | I will not swear these are my hands. Let's see. |
| | I feel this pin-prick. Would I were assur'd |
| | Of my condition! |

                                                            (IV.vii.52–57)

Following the doctor's advice, Cordelia addresses Lear.

[20] It is interesting to compare this sample of Lear's speech to the classical examples reported by Eugen Bleuler (1952) as "indirect and clang-association and freely flowing thought processes" in patients he described as typical cases of schizophrenia (pp. 14–40).

[21] The mouse is probably a visual hallucination.

[22] The employment of music in the treatment of madness was a fairly common practice in the sixteenth century. It is, in my opinion, worthwhile to quote in this context Heinz Kohut's (1957) thoughtful discussion of the function of music during the various phases of schizophrenia. He writes: "If the comfort of soothing regression in the form of music is provided, a movement toward the recathexis of memories of friendly voices may be initiated and the musical sounds may, in some cases, become the first emotionally significant representatives of a regained reality" (pp. 252–253).

[23] Lear is probably afraid that he is hallucinating Cordelia's image.

*Cordelia.*                                          O! look upon me, sir,
And hold your hand in benediction o'er me.
No, Sir, you must not kneel.

(IV.vii.58–59)

*Lear.*        I fear I am not in my perfect mind.

(IV.vii.63)

Do not laugh at me;
For as I am a man, I think this lady
To be my child, Cordelia.
*Cordelia.*                                          And so I am, I am.[24]

(IV.vii.68–71)

Why can Cordelia now soothe Lear and help to restore him to cohesiveness? Perhaps it is easier for Cordelia to respond appropriately to his need for comfort when he is decompensated whereas the empathy required when he is an exalted, demanding monarch was beyond her capacity.

I will conclude this necessarily cursory and schematic account of Shakespeare's empathic understanding of the psychological process through which an injured old man falls apart and eventually "acquires wisdom by going mad" (Muir, 1972) with a short comment about one of the last scenes of the play, in which Cordelia and Lear have been arrested.

*Lear.*        No, no, no, no! Come, let's away to prison;
We two alone will sing like birds i'th' cage:
When thou dost ask me blessing, I'll kneel down
And ask of thee forgiveness: so we'll live,
And pray, and sing, and tell old tales, and laugh
At gilded butterflies, and hear poor rogues
Talk of court news; and we'll talk with them, too—
Who loses and who wins; who's in, who's out—
And take upon's the mystery of things,
As if we were God's spies; and we'll wear out,
In a wall'd prison, packs and sects of great ones
That ebb and flow by th' moon.

(V.iii.8–18)

This beautiful speech conveys to me not the image of an "integrated and optimistic Lear" (Muslin, 1981, p. 149), but that of a tranquil wise man. Lear has painfully gone through a transformation of his self which allows him to branch away from worldly values and interests (e.g., he has overcome

[24] Ruskin remarked that "All Cordelia is poured forth in that infinite *I am* of fulfilled love" (quoted in Arden edition, p. 179).

his desire for vengeance) and to achieve "that human attitude we call wisdom" (see Kohut, 1966).

Before the curtain falls, I want to add a few words in conclusion. Heinz Kohut has often stressed that functional psychoses are severe primary disorders of the self. Kohut thought that an inborn tendency to permanent or protracted fragmentation of the nuclear self might render schizophrenic people not analyzable (Kohut, 1971, 1972, 1977; Kohut and Wolf, 1978). Upon rereading the above, I realize that what I have reported might be viewed as a sort of supervision of the "treatment" by Shakespeare of a psychotic (schizophreniclike) episode in an old man. In so doing, I have used the theory of self psychology as the main frame of reference. Shakespeare was an extraordinarily gifted and expert depth psychologist and dramatist, and he cured his patient, although Lear eventually died on the stage at the end of the tragedy.

With the development of our theory and the refinement of our practice (I often repeat that there is nothing more practical than a good theory, and self psychology *is* a good theory), we have enormously improved our ability to achieve therapeutic success in less severe primary self disorders (earlier considered not analyzable, as is currently the case with psychoses). I hope the same might happen with, at least, some forms of psychosis, once we investigate them more thoroughly from our point of view. Shakespeare might prove to be an inspiring teacher, leading us in our research to extend self psychology creatively to the psychotherapeutic treatment of psychotic persons. In addition, we may discover something about prevention as well (of psychosis in old age, for example).

## REFERENCES

Bleuler, E. (1952), *Dementia Praecox or the Group of Schizophrenias*. New York: International Universities Press.

Freud, S. (1911), The mechanism of paranoia. *Standard Edition*, 12:70–71. London: Hogarth Press, 1958.

Gentili, V. (1978), *La recita della follia*. Turin: Einaudi.

Kirsch, J. (1966), *Shakespeare's Royal Self*. New York: Putnam's.

Kohut, H. (1957), Observations on the psychological functions of music. In: *The Search for the Self*, vol. 1, ed. P. Ornstein. New York: International Universities Press, 1978, pp. 235–254.

———— (1966), Forms and transformations of narcissism. In: *The Search for the Self*, vol. 1, ed. P. Ornstein. New York: International Universities Press, 1978, pp. 427–460.

———— (1971), *The Analysis of the Self*. New York: International Universities Press.

———— (1972), Thoughts on narcissism and narcissistic rage. In: *The Search for the Self*, vol. 2, ed. P. Ornstein. New York: International Universities Press, pp. 685–724.

———— (1977), *The Restoration of the Self*. New York: International Universities Press.
———— (1978), Psychoanalysis and the interpretation of literature: A correspondence with Erich Heller. *Critical Inquiry*, 4:434.
———— (1980), Reflections on *Advances in Self Psychology*. In: *Advances in Self Psychology*, ed. A. Goldberg. New York: International Universities Press, pp. 473–544.
———— Wolf, E. (1978), The disorders of the self and their treatment: An outline. *Internat. J. Psycho-Anal.*, 59:413–425.
Melchiori, G. (1976), *Re Lear di Shakespeare*. Milan: Montadori.
Muir, K. (1972), Preface to the Arden edition of *King Lear*. New York: Methuen.
Muslin, H. (1981), King Lear: Images of the self in old age. Typescript. Also published in *J. Mental Imagery*, 5:143–156.
Paparo, F. (1981), Il trattamento dei disturbi narcisistici della personalita e del comportamento secondo H. Kohut. *Neuropsich. Infant*, 240–241:577–586.
Shakespeare, W. *King Lear*. The Arden Edition. New York: Methuen, 1975.
Trilling, L. (1950), *The Liberal Imagination*. New York: Viking Press.

*January 1984*

# Wordsworth on Teaching a Child to Lie: Some Thoughts on Creative Fictionalism

JEROME KAVKA, M.D. (Chicago)

William Wordsworth, author of the indelible phrase "the child is father to the man," deserves the psychoanalyst's attention not only because he was one of the most perceptive writers about childhood, but also because he has come to be seen as an increasingly "more complex and more complete artist whose underlying theme is self-examination" (Everett, 1959, pp. 338, 350).

For these reasons he has been regarded as a forerunner of Freud. Reading Wordsworth brings Freud to mind because "nothing appealed to him more than to trace the subtler appreciations of adult life to the deep rooted instincts of childhood." He believed, furthermore, that "nothing that passes into the deep reservoir of the subconscious mind can be lost . . ." (Patton, 1966, p. 153).

In a masterful essay on the poet, Lawrence Durrell (1973) links Wordsworth tightly to Freud, perhaps to the point of exaggeration. Although Durrell himself may not have prompted assessments by psychoanalysts, his view is increasingly shared by many sophisticated literary scholars, Christensen (1946), Trilling (1951), Ferry (1959), Douglas (1968), Onorato (1971), and Hartman (1977) among them. Finally, the poet's major and most successful works, so evidently autobiographical, are yielding their secrets.

To Durrell, "everything—even [Wordsworth's] less successful work—becomes significant and enriching." In one of his lesser-known works Wordsworth reveals his exceptional perceptiveness as a psychologist of children. "Anecdote for Fathers," the enchanting sixty-line ballad, first published in 1789, shows how the art of lying may be taught. This poem has been regarded as "affording the earliest indication of the poet's psychological interest in childhood" (Durrell, 1973).

Anecdote for Fathers
shewing how the art[1] of lying may be
taught

I have a boy of five years old
His face is fair and fresh to see;
His limbs are cast in beauty's mould,
And dearly he loves me.

One morn we stroll'd on our dry walk,
Our quiet house[2] all full in view,
And held such intermitted talk
As we are wont to do.

My thoughts on former pleasures ran;
I thought of Kilve's delightful shore,
My[3] pleasant home, when Spring began,
A long, long year before.

A day it was when I could bear
To think, and think, and think again;
With so much happiness to spare,
I could not feel a pain.

My boy was by my side, so slim
And graceful in his rustic dress!
And oftentimes I talked to him,
In very idleness.

The young lambs ran a pretty race;
The morning sun shone bright and warm;
"Kilve," said I, "was a pleasant place,"
"And so is Liswyn farm."

"My little boy, which like you more,"
I said and took him by the arm—

[1] In the 1800 version, "practice."
[2] In the 1802 version, "home."
[3] In the 1802 version, "Our."

"Our home by Kilve's delightful shore,
"Or here at Liswyn farm?"

"And tell me, had you rather be,"
I said and held him by the arm,
"At Kilve's smooth shore by the green sea,
"Or here at Liswyn farm?"

In careless mood he looked at me,
While still I held him by the arm,
And said, "At Kilve I'd rather be
"Than here at Liswyn farm."

"Now, little Edward, say why so;
My little Edward, tell me why";
"I cannot tell, I do not know."
"Why this is strange." "Why this is strange,"
                                    said I.

"For, here are woods and green-hills warm;
"There surely must some reason be
"Why you would change sweet Liswyn farm
"For Kilve by the green sea."

At this, my boy, so fair and slim,
Hung down his head, nor made reply;
And five times did I say to him,
"Why? Edward, tell me why?"[4]

His head he raised—there was in sight
It caught his eye, he saw it plain—
Upon the house-top, glittering bright,
A broad and gilded vane.

Then did the boy his tongue unlock,
And thus to me he made reply;
"At Kilve there was no weather-cock,
"And that's the reason why."

---

[4] In the 1800 version:

At this, my boy hung down his head,
He blush'd with shame, nor made reply;
And five times to the child I said,
"Why, Edward, tell me why?"

Oh, dearest, dearest boy! my heart
For better lore would seldom yearn,
Could I but teach the hundredth part
Of what from thee I learn.
[Brett and Jones, 1963, pp. 63–66]

Edward (Basil, Jr.) was the son of Basil Montagu, Wordsworth's fellow student at Cambridge. Montagu's first wife died there in childbirth in 1793. Two years later, William and his sister, Dorothy, took the orphaned boy into their home, where he remained under their care for two or three years. Durrell regards the adoption of the child as an important phase of Wordsworth's life. "He is my perpetual pleasure," wrote Dorothy Wordsworth of the boy. The poet complained about his moral character: "He lies like a little devil" (Knight, 1907, p. 103).

Despite the Wordsworths' benign influence, the boy ultimately deteriorated. He became mentally ill, failed in his pursuit of a career, and continued to lie. In later life he complained that the Wordsworths had illtreated him. As it happened, the Wordsworths also were unable to deter the unfavorable course of another child under their influence, the son of their poet-friend Coleridge; more about this later.

Most litterateurs regard the "Anecdote" poem as a didactic work with the sole aim of teaching adults not to press children. Some critics, who miss the poet's subtlety, see the poem as simplistic or frolicsome, even unimaginative. In modern terms, we could say that Wordsworth speaks to the issue of optimal empathy on the part of the parent; if one expects too much, and at the wrong time, one forces the child to prevaricate in order to maintain self-esteem. In Wordsworth's 1800 revision, the boy not only hung his head in silence but also "blush'd with shame" when pressed repeatedly. Here the poet reveals his deep empathy with the child's feelings of disapproval, a characteristic response to the interjection, "Why?" In this observation alone, Wordsworth showed exceptional understanding of the influence of elders on their charges; he was revolutionary in seeing the parental contribution to the child's behavior so directly.

Wordsworth was inclined to idealize the pleasures of his childhood, usually denying the pain and certainly the consequences of his own parental losses. But now the orphan's presence brought forth unhappy feelings, which the poet tried valiantly to suppress. (After his own children died, Wordsworth would again feel the poignancy of loss.)

The entire poem is tinged with anxiety as if the hypomanic defense is a thin veneer covering up deep longings for a maternal (self) object. When the boy's insistent preference for the mother threatens to bring unpleasant affects to the surface, the adult begins to press him. He holds the boy's arm as if he were forcibly cajoling the child's love—his gesture actually an expression of the poet's own need for a "selfobject."

If we read the poem carefully, we wonder about Wordsworth's sensitivity to the child's lying and what it may have meant for the poet to be involved in prevarication.

Before confronting the child, the poet pleasantly muses about Kilve by the shore. The adjectives suggest strong affects, and the poem wavers between increasingly anxious evocations from the past and current euphoria. The poet felt so good that he could bear any pain, he says. Literally? How about the pain of remembrance? The note of hypomania suggests a defense against emerging longings aroused by the presence of the orphan boy. The poet gives no indication that he himself was a double orphan at the height of his own puberty. (We now know that the poet had already been responsible for "orphaning" a young woman, his illegitimate daughter in France; she accompanied him on beach walks during his occasional visits.)

In the poem, the child was obviously torn between satisfying the elder and still being true to his own feelings. Apparently, he preferred the shore to the farm, but to avow this would hurt his male caretaker's feelings.

What is it the boy cannot admit and does not even know he is concealing? By his absurd answer, he avoids the embarrassment of admitting that he misses the woman in his life: Dorothy Wordsworth (or, more likely, his own mother). The boy's strange response indicates his knowledge of having lost his mother early and his symbolic wish to be united with her.

The child's response when pressed is not simply a lie; within the lie is an unavowed, disguised truth. The weather-cock stands for the male, Wordsworth, the caretaker to whom he should feel grateful, yet doesn't because of the poet's unempathic queries.

This poem demonstrates forcefully and beautifully what may happen between two people—both of whom have lost their parents—in intimate transaction. Surely, Wordsworth strongly identified with his charge. He was just eight when his own mother died and fourteen at his father's death. Yet, by the time he began caring for the orphan, Wordsworth had creatively transformed his own childhood depression into his commitment as a poet.

Many critics have been able to detect longings for his mother not only in the thematic content of his poetry, but in the formal aspects of his creativity as well.

In a literary analysis that closely parallels mine, Jean Brenkman (1976) uses a linguistic approach. To her, "The pain, fond regrets," and emphasis on "a long, long year," along with the absence of any reference to the wife, indicates that she is separated from them and is dead. Being at Kilve

represented being "near the womblike waters with his mother," while Liswyn farm is associated with "separation from mother." To Brenkman, also,
"the lie like a slip of the tongue contains a kernel of truth . . . this young
boy prefers the place and time before he became separated from nature
and from his mother, which are often in Wordsworth's poetry equatable
moments" (p. 9).

Wordsworth was perceptive enough to know that he had erred in pushing
the child—though he didn't understand what the error was. He even sighed
with relief at the end perhaps because his own repression barrier, which
was dangerously close to being breached, remained intact. It was almost
better for both man and child to ignore the issue of mother loss.

It is fascinating that Wordsworth did the pushing in the area of his own
pain, the mother loss. But, rather than making the connection clear, he
emphasized the negative moral influence of forcing children to premature
closures. This in itself is not an unworthy contribution. But children prevaricate to solve their narcissistic dilemmas, an action that has far-reaching
significance in its relation to creativity.

In a sense Wordsworth may be alluding to the issue of creative fictionalism, the art of poetry. He could well have understood that beneath overt
fiction lies the truth—this may indeed by his theory of poetry making. This
is what the child was doing, creating fiction. But more on this later.

The care that the poet and his sister gave the orphan facilitated certain
transference reactions commonly seen in adoptees:

> Young Basil Montagu . . . has been something of a problem . . . he took
> to abusing his father, and also, to Montagu's horror, the Wordsworths.
> He stated that when living with them they had treated him with such
> cruelty that he was constantly employed in most menial occupations and
> but for the pity of the poor villagers who privately supplied him with
> such pittance as they could ill spare, he should have starved. In fact,
> Wordsworth's early description of him—"he lies like a little devil"—was
> still true.
>
> Montagu took his own peculiar methods of curing this propensity in
> his son . . . "by reading Wordsworth's works, to eradicate his opinion of
> Wordsworth." Apparently his efforts were not without effect, for Basil
> after a few weeks confessed that he was lying, and hoped that his father
> would permit him to proceed to Grasmere and atone to W. W. for the
> misrepresentations that had been made. . . . Basil continued to calum-
> niate his father . . . after he returned to London. His diseased mind was
> never cured, and the rest of his life was a tragedy of illness and unhap-
> piness [Moorman, 1965, pp. 237–238].

Even though the father forced his son to disavow his lies, there is some suggestion of truth in them: he had not been accurately cared for in the past because the transference implications of the boy's complaints had not been apparent. Like the boy's father, Wordsworth, too, began to force the child in the poem, but unlike the father, and probably because he himself was an orphan, he was able to catch himself and put a stop to the pressure, if not understand it.

## Psychoanalytic Views on Lying and Related Behavior

More than a century after the publication of Wordsworth's "Anecdote," Freud in his 1913 essay on children's lies showed the way to analyze them by examining deep motivational factors which included the Oedipus complex as well as pregenital and narcissistic conflicts. He described a seven year old who lied to conceal her love for her father. She had suffered a narcissistic humiliation when her father refused her expressions of tenderness; Freud noted the persistence of anal eroticism in the elaboration of her lie. Ironically, Freud himself repeated the narcissistic blow by refusing the young patient's gift of flowers.

A ten-year-old patient of Freud's with an "unusually strong attachment to her father" (p. 308) boasted in order not to belittle her father, whom she was valiantly idealizing. Freud's discovery of the suppression of hidden incestuous love by a child vulnerable to narcissistic humiliation opened the way to more fruitful understanding of children's lying.

Wordsworth, indeed, recognized overt parental contributions to the lies of children, but he also implied the child's covert motivation. His "Anecdote" suggests that he would have agreed with Freud who said, "we should not think lightly of such episodes in the life of children" (p. 309).

Even a cursory review of post-Freudian literature on lying, secrecy, and other forms of prevarication, such as malingering (Eissler, 1951), simulation (Sadow and Suslick, 1961), and pretense (Barchilon, 1973), reveals that self-esteem regulation is paramount. Even authors who analyze largely in structural terms and attempt to demonstrate the contribution of libidinal fixations and failures of oedipal resolution are obliged to take into account the issue of narcissistic equilibrium, just as Freud himself had done.

In psychoanalytic studies that emphasize structural analysis, lying tends to be seen as defensive and maladaptive. Where the emphasis is on self-esteem regulation, lying may be seen as an adaptive function of a weak ego-structure—an adaptation needed to maintain narcissistic equilibrium.

At a scientific meeting, on April 7, 1909, Otto Rank presented a paper "On the Psychology of Lying," in which he linked children's lies with the need to conceal masturbation. Sigmund Freud disputed such a connection when not supported by the facts of analysis. Freud said: "it is by no means a matter of course for the child to lie; it is a matter of course for the child to tell the truth." Further, "in lying, the child imitates the adults, who conceal the sexual facts from him, and who lie by giving him false information about these facts; it is from this that the child assumes his right to lie" (Nunberg and Federn, 1967, p. 203).

At the same meeting, Alfred Adler argued that lying is necessary for the preservation of a certain psychic equilibrium, a point of view taken up by some modern psychoanalysts—Ekstein (Ekstein and Caruth, 1972), for example. The issue of narcissistic equilibrium, emphasized by some of Freud's colleagues, was noted by the master himself in his paper on infantile mental life written four years later.

The issues and the questions raised in the earliest psychoanalytic conferences on the subject of lying are still in debate: (1) How much is lying a manifestation of a (structural) conflict based on libidinal fixation? (2) Are there not always underlying issues of self-esteem regulation present in lying behavior? (3) Is the analytic importance of lying behavior to be considered largely in the context of a transference setting?

Until recently, assessments of lying behavior followed Freud's structural point of view and were interpreted as involving pregenital fixations, as for example, in the anal stage of development (Freud, 1913; Dickes, 1968; Hoyt, 1978) and as evidence of unresolved oedipal conflicts (Freud, 1913; Greenacre, 1958b; Weinshel, 1977).

> . . . the child's first successful lie breaks the tyranny of parental omniscience, i.e., the child begins to feel that it has a "mind of its own," a private identity unknown to its parents. Tausk places this momentous occurrence early in the sequence of normal development, in the period of toilet training. The relation of "secrets" to the function of "secretion" is obvious; the child learns that he can mislead the person doing the training, that he can hold back, that he can keep something to himself. . . . the basic form of the secret is anal [Hoyt, 1978, pp. 231–232].

> While this paper has emphasized the importance of the oedipal problems in the production of imposture, it should be stressed again that one might better refer to these as the effects of an oedipal phase than the effects of the oedipal relationships. The acting out of the impostor is largely an attempt to achieve a sense of reality and competence as a man more than to claim the mother in any deep sense. From the material of my analytic cases it seemed indicated that the mother might be a phallic mother and insofar as the child was closer to her than to the father and identified with her phallus, this increased the whole quality of illusion with which the impostor paradoxically struggles for some self-realization [Greenacre, 1958b, p. 112].

In Weinshel's (1977) three case histories, "all of whom had more than adequate super-ego functioning," episodes of lying occurred in the context of an ongoing transference neurosis. They (1) represented a re-enactment of an aspect of each patient's oedipal conflict; (2) permitted the recovery of old memories revealing unconscious oedipal wishes while simultaneously protecting those wishes by acting as a "screen"; and (3) were a vehicle for aggression directed to the oedipal object for having "lied" to the patient.

Some analysts have been prevarication as involving the whole ego apparatus, somewhat as an adaptive device (Eissler, 1951; Sulzberger, 1953; Sadow and Suslick, 1961; Margolis, 1966).

[Malingering] is always a sign of a disease often more severe than a neurotic disorder because it concerns an arrest of development at an early phase. [Malingering lies] between alloplastic and autoplastic disorders . . . it does not (in contrast to neurotic disorders) leave any single structure in the personality unaffected [Eissler, 1951, pp. 252–253].

The keeping of a secret is not simply an act of omission but rather constitutes a task involving the whole ego [Sulzberger, 1953, p. 43].

[Simulation may be] defensive in an intact and integrating rather than deteriorating ego . . . [Simulation is a] symptomatic compromise between unacceptable impulses and unconscious super-ego structures [Sadow and Suslick, 1961, p. 458].

A few analysts (Kris, 1956; Weinshel, 1977) see the screening function of personal myths as a form of lying which may be adaptive despite the obvious narcissistic component.

I will now quote from several unrelated papers, all based on clinical experience and analysis of the transference, which suggest that imposture can be a highly adaptive form of mastery. In these studies, issues involving self-esteem regulation are paramount.

R. Grinker, Jr. (1961), found lying in the therapeutic situation to have both structural and narcissistic elements. Lying was "used by the ego in the service of mastery of earlier traumata, [that] the fraud and deceit were secondary to the main goals . . . ego expansion and a new sense of identity." Lying somehow decreased the "feeling of ego incompleteness" that was present. Furthermore, Grinker found other adaptive factors present through which the patient sought to "evoke love and sympathy in the object," to "seek revenge by deceiving the object," and to re-create "feelings of the past" (p. 452).

Finkelstein's case (1974) of a twenty-three-year-old analysand shows strongly the direct influence of the parents on the lying behavior.

. . . the chief characteristic of the transference appeared in his continual lying to me [p. 102].

As we explored his lying to me, Teddy revealed through associations that he was re-living in the transference his lying relationship with his parents. He was offering me an opportunity to condone his lies, support his self-deception, and enjoy his self-idealization, as well as his idealization of me, in order to form with him a narcissistic "mutual admiration society" [p. 103].

. . . remains an infantile, passive, narcissistic character [p. 105].

. . . emphasize his general disturbance in regulation of self-esteem [p. 108].

In the history of patients who ridiculed their analyst, Barchilon (1973) found ambivalent parents who betrayed their trust by providing mixtures of "real and faulty knowledge, contradictory affects, truth and lies." He concluded that such "mockery directed at grown-ups indicates a change from a helpless, passive attitude into an active one and shows courage."

Helen Beiser (1970), in discussing children who cheat at games, pointed to the adaptive value of dishonesty: self-esteem is at stake; there is a desire to maintain a fantasy of omnipotence. Like Barchilon, she saw the need to mock parental figures as adaptive.

It became clear to Ekstein and Caruth (1972) in their work with schizophrenic patients that "what is important is the process of secreting, not the content of the secret" (p. 207). They credited Freud with explaining that "the child's first lie . . . his first secret, is one of the first signs of his beginning capacity for separation and individuation" (p. 200).

To Ekstein and Caruth, to withhold secrets is to develop a mind of one's own; lying isn't simply resistance; that would be an oversimplification. However, even though the conscious secret is a form of deliberate resistance, they agree with Greenson (1967) that it is "something to be respected and not crushed, coerced or begged out of the patient" (p. 202).

It appears that Wordsworth implicitly recognized that his own coercive approach not only did not enhance the self-esteem of the child under his care, but also added another to a long line of narcissistic humiliations.

In a paper on secrets, Meares (1976) emphasizes "the positive or creative value of certain hidden ideas" (p. 258). To him, "the core of the self may be felt as a series of hidden ideas" (p. 261). "In sharing," therefore, "there is a risk of losing that which is 'mine' " (p. 260). Secrets become disclosed "in a developing dialogue with others who can be trusted to share and respect them" (p. 259).

Goldberg (1973), who established a developmental line for truth-telling instead of for lying, came to a similar position:

> . . . we must conclude that truthfulness consists of telling the facts to someone whom one wishes to know them. It involves both the capacity to do so acquired in the course of development plus the judgment to behave with maximal adaptiveness to the situation. It is not necessarily a higher order of behavior nor an ethical good. The final outcome of the developmental line of truth-telling is thus an admixture of facts and fictions that best meet the situation [p. 111].

> . . . psychic stresses may result in fragmentation of the self, which leads to noncohesiveness and may be manifested as lying [p. 108].

> . . . the lack of truthfulness . . . not based on deliberate deception but on lack of self-object differentiation [p. 108].

> . . . lying is as much a part of normal growth and development as is telling the truth [p. 108].

Greenacre (1958b) synthesizes a variety of issues related to imposture, including narcissism, pregenital fixations, and oedipal failures, and by her emphasis on perception is able to draw a bridge from prevarication to creativity.

> It may be that vision and the reflection of oneself from and by others play a crucial part in early problems of identity, as well as the fact that the sadomasochistic excitement of imposturous states gives a heightening of sensation and perceptiveness with strong narcissistic libidinal investment, and that the sense of reality in these deformed characters depends more on this than on the depth of object relationships . . .

> It is not only the standards and values which need to be changed in such cases, but the ability itself to convert a narcissistic identification into a critically selective and internally structured set of ego ideals, which is ordinarily accomplished only through resolution of the oedipal problems at the beginning and later at the end of the latency period [p. 109].

In her recent philosophical study of the related subject of "deep skepticism," Sawyier (1981) concluded that one source of such skepticism was "a fierce protectiveness of one's inner self." Furthermore, she had much to say about a visual model for knowledge being of a more cognitive than psychological nature, in contrast to a "touch model" about which I will say more when we discuss Wordsworth's theories on the development of the self.

## Creative Fictionalism as Adaptive Lying

In Wordsworth's "Anecdote" we catch him at an important moment of awareness, the start of a developmental line regarding self-honesty, an issue examined by Ekstein, Caruth, and Goldberg in their work. The poet stops short of self-analyzing why he pushed the child, although at least he recognized what he was doing. His failure to deal with the subtle issues of his own maternal longings could well have interfered with the child's development of self-honesty.

Ironically, the Wordsworths also failed to deter the unfavorable course of the other child under their influence, Hartley, the son of Coleridge. In the poem Wordsworth wrote about that child, four years after "Anecdote," he shows even more insight into narcissistic vulnerability. The end of this poem is strangely reminiscent of E. A. Robinson's "Richard Cory," about which I wrote a few years ago (Kavka, 1976).

> On the ground of intimacy and affection we may almost count Coleridge's eldest child, Hartley, as a member of the Wordsworth Household. The poem to H. C.—Six Years old, composed in 1802, exquisitely conceived and elaborated, reveals not only an affection but an understanding of the child's nature, not unmingled with concern, which few parents could equal. The boy, Hartley, like his father, was a genius but, also like his father, a genius of unstable equilibrium. To any one acquainted with the pathetic outcome of the elf-like personality that inspired Wordsworth's poem, there are lines which become almost uncanny in their prophetic suggestion. Here is a poet whose observation of children was not of the casual kind [Patton, 1966, p. 141].

> H. C., after his father's death, settled at Grasmere in order to be near the Wordsworths who bestowed upon him the tenderest attention. He inherited his father's lack of will power and inconstancy in work, and from his college days at Oxford was the victim of intemperance. During his last years he spent much of his time in the taverns of the neighborhood [Wordsworth, 1904, p. 290].

To H. C.
Six Years Old
1802, 1807

O Thou! whose fancies from afar are brought;
Who of thy words dost make a mock apparel,
And fittest to unutterable thought
The breeze-like motion and the self-born carol;
Thou faery voyager! that dost float
In such clear water, that thy boat

May rather seem
To brood on air than on an earthly stream;
Suspended in a stream as clear as sky,
Where earth and heaven make one imagery;
O blessed vision! happy child!
Thou are so exquisitely wild,
I think of thee with many fears
For what may be thy lot in future years.
I thought of times when Pain might be thy guest,
Lord of thy house and hospitality;
And Grief, uneasy lover! never rest
But when she sate within the touch of thee.
O too industrious folly!
O vain and causeless melancholy!
Nature will either end thee quite;
Or, lengthening out thy season of delight,
Preserve for thee, by individual right,
A young lambs heart among the full grown flocks.
What hast thou to do with sorrow,
Or the injuries of tomorrow?
Thou art a dew-drop, which the morn brings forth,
Ill fitted to sustain unkindly shocks,
Or to be trailed along the soiling earth;
A gem that glitters while it lives,
And no forewarning gives;
But, at the touch of wrong, without a strife
Slips in a moment out of life.

Wordsworth more than made up for his failure in this minor, though even more poignant poem in the elaboration of his longings in "Tintern Abbey," "The Excursion," and, most of all, "The Prelude"—the broadest view of his capacity to sublimate narcissistic conflicts. Here he shows profound insights into the quality of selfobject attachments and even a theory of self-development that is quite sophisticated, suggesting that self-cohesion begins quite early in the mother-child relationship and is enhanced by important sensual experiences.

Still, we should not underestimate "Anecdote," a forerunner to the poet's later, richer ideas. One critic notes that Wordsworth went beyond being concerned about associations in a state of excitement and appears to have introduced the motivational impact of affects, especially in regard to the formation of the self:

In the preface to Lyrical Ballads as printed in 1800, Wordsworth actually states that his "principal object" in writing the poems was "to make the incidents of common life interesting by tracing in them . . . the primary laws of our nature: chiefly as regards the manner in which we associate ideas in a state of excitement" [Nesbitt, 1970, p. 161].

Wordsworth, like Coleridge, emphasized the importance of affects in the establishment of the self. He regarded the senses themselves as creative, and his term for the creativity of the senses was *creative sensibility*.

Like Coleridge, he appreciated that touch was for the infant more than a momentary contact of the flesh, and the source of more than sensuous comfort [Walsh, 1960, p. 33].

The child learns to know by learning to feel; he learns by sensation, by sensory contact with his mother . . . The first exercise of its powers is to combine the parts of the mother into a whole person. Quite literally, the child's first poetic act is the creation of his mother [Christensen, 1946, pp. 361–368].

But what mother is created and denied in the poetic act?

Psychoanalysts who have studied lying behavior tend to split into two camps: those who see it as defensive and maladaptive, and those who see it as adaptive in the maintenance of narcissistic equilibrium. Similarly, litterateurs who have used depth psychology to understand Wordsworth's autobiographical reconstruction, especially in "The Prelude," fall into the same two camps. I will focus, however, on those who have explicitly elaborated a self-psychological approach, one that resonates with the implications that appear to be present in Wordsworth's work itself.

Onorato (1971), for example, feels that Wordsworth, the orphaned child, was traumatized by the double parent loss and was probably lied to, as was the religious custom (the parents are in heaven, etc.). Onorato says, "it was not vanity that caused him to hesitate and observe himself instead of man, nature and society, but profound self-doubt." He is, however, referring to Wordsworth's self-development and demonstrates it in asking how Wordsworth sees what a mother does for an infant: " 'she' connects his feelings of belonging in the world with the activity of his mind and seems like a function of it" (p. 76).

Onorato goes even further, as if he were aware of Kohut's concepts of the vertical split (1970) and the restoration of self cohesion (1977): "The successful joining of self and soul would repair a traumatically divided being and fulfill the feeling of 'something ever more about to be' " (pp. 71–72).

Douglas (1968), too, became aware that Wordsworth's mother was the self-object; "not the external mother whether good or bad, but the inner mother, the possessively absorbed object of love and need . . . correspondingly the feelings involved . . . less incestuous than . . . narcissistic" (p. 68).

Here, from the poet's own self-analysis, is a theory of the coherent sense of self emerging in the earliest contact between mother and child.

> . . . blest the Babe, . . .
> Upon his Mother's breast, who, when his soul
> Claims manifest kindred with an earthly soul,
> Doth gather passion from his Mother's eye!
> . . . . . . . . . . . . . . . . . . . . . .
> From this beloved Presence, there exists
> A virtue which irradiates and exalts
> All objects through all intercourse of sense.
> No outcast he, bewilder'd and depress'd;
> Along his infant veins are interfus'd
> The gravitation and the filial bond
> Of nature, that connect him with the world.
>
> ("The Prelude," II.237–264)

Onorato (1971) notes Wordsworth's description in "The Prelude" of an emerging self:

The infant's awakening mind, under the influence of his "one beloved Presence" is not just experiencing the coalescence of things, but of otherness as otherness. And self and soul are never to Wordsworth closer together than here in his talking of the Blest Babe—"when his soul/Claims manifest kindred with an earthly soul." "Soul" here is closer in meaning to fullness of self than anywhere else in Wordsworth's poetry [p. 6].

It is difficult to be as eloquent as the great poet, and one must marvel at the psychological sagacity of a genius who lived almost two centuries before the elaboration of self psychology. Furthermore, Wordsworth anticipates Kohut's theories by suggesting that the coherent sense of self begins much earlier than we are wont to believe: it begins early in infancy and is firmly entrenched through the sense of touching, which is more "experience near" than the sense of seeing.

And all this from a highly traumatized youngster. But to what extent did Wordsworth fail in his psychological development where he succeeded as a poet? Did he, in fact, entirely succeed as a poet? We know that his work diminished in depth as the years wore on. In what ways were his narcissistic transformations unsuccessful, and what has this to do with lying and deception?

### Creative Fictionalism as Narcissistic Transformation

Let me praise some modern literary scholars who have devoted much attention to Wordsworth. I was deeply gratified to discover what little need there was for apologias about psychoanalytic reductionism; not only is psychoanalysis sympathetically accepted by many scholars, but it is found most useful, and critics on a highly sophisticated level apply ego psychology and now include self psychology, albeit of their own invention. They anticipate Kohut, as Wordsworth did (or because Wordsworth did!).

Onorato deserves special praise. He writes of the poet's metaphors: "Life is a journey . . . from the self-less . . . condition of birth to the special self-hood of a poet, from the thoughtlessness of general sensations to that of specific sensations and thoughts, and from irrecoverable states of feeling to those spiritual regions beyond thought of which poets sometimes write . . ." (p. 17).

Rapturous prose indeed, as Onorato subtly distinguishes remembrance from creative fictionalism:

> In a poetic autobiographical account of the growth of a poet's mind, it would be useful to emphasize the inventive sense along with the recollective sense of the I-speaking character, and remember that the poet is creating a character, is "characterizing" himself, by using both Memory and Imagination . . . what we ordinarily associate with the imaginative invention of a character in literature is being used as the sustained activity of self-invention [p. 6].

Yet Onorato is also tuned in to that which might reflect failure in the poet, either as a person or as a poet: "Wordsworth's pre-occupation with himself, his self-elaborating egoism," and "his inability to finish with satisfaction, or even to finish" (p. 5).

Together with another sensitive critic, Read (1931), Onorato points to the contrived way of rendering one's self and one's story through poetic creation. He notes Freud's emphasis on concealment rather than revealment and even suggests a form of acting out by way of creativity that would be consistent with the acting out defined as a form of remembering.

> When Wordsworth uses a metaphor like the "sunlight of memory," he is consciously and beautifully simplifying what can be remembered and he is unconsciously denying what cannot be clearly recollected [Onorato, 1971, p. 125].

Read (1931) cautions about idealization in autobiography:

> . . . the fully developed man of thirty-five is recollecting the child of

seven or eight. To what extent are his recollections guided and influenced by his present ideals? Considerably, I should say, especially in view of the nature of those ideals, and the importance that is assigned in them to the period of childhood. . . . the very process of poetry involves idealization, or more exactly the universalization, of individual experience. . . . the simple psychological truth that self visualization is nearly always self-aggrandizement [pp. 48–49].

Phyllis Greenacre's work emphasizes the libidinal-phase development of the creative individual and his innate sensitivity and perceptivity. She refers to the increased range of outer objects, including body sensations, as the field of "collective alternates" because they substitute for the warmer personal human objects. "All object relationships," she writes, "may be felt and expressed with a vast increase in their symbolic representations and . . . the tendency to anthropomorphism in observation and thought is increased and usually lasts throughout life" (p. 539).

Read (1931) reminds us of the poet's highly sensitive predisposition to later defects of character:

His mother dies when he was eight, his father at fourteen. . . . Indeed before his mother's death William had already developed peculiarities of character which caused her some anxiety . . . he himself relates that an intimate friend of his mother's once told him that he was the only one of the five children about whose future life his mother was anxious; and he, she said, would be remarkable either for good or for evil. "The cause of this was," continued Wordsworth, "that I was of a stiff, moody, and violent temper; so much so that I remember once going into the attic of my grandfather's house at Penrith, upon some indignity having been put upon me, with an intention of destroying myself with one of the foils which I knew he kept there. I took the foil in my hand, but my heart failed" [pp. 44–45].

After 1805, under the pressure of loss, Wordsworth became rigid. Tragically, the loss of his own children through illness added to his burdens. He was never successful in rearing any children to his satisfaction, and that included the subject of our poem, and he was disappointed that children under his charge failed to live up to his academic expectations.

Douglas (1968) demonstrates in his analysis that narcissistic issues played a greater role in Wordsworth than sexual ones.

Ferry (1959) saw Wordsworth's peevishness as a failure:

. . . the poetry after about 1805 is generally quite inferior to the poetry written before that time [pp. 172–173].

. . . for the most part there is a shocking debilitation in his work. The symptoms of it are plain, too: a flat and moralistic and not often very passionate adaptation of Christian and classical vocabularies; a tendency to increased garrulity; a soberly cheery optimism about the relations of man and nature, man and God, combined with a sort of peevishness against railroads and a zeal for capital punishment [p. 173].

... He says a "deep distress" "humanized" his soul, and is this not at once a kind of confession that the love of nature had not led to the love of man, and the declaration of a new aim and new interest which his imagination was not equipped to sustain? It sustains it, to be sure, in passage after passage of the late poetry which has to do with human death, for this remained for Wordsworth what it has always been, the most poignant of human experiences. But the imagination—Wordsworth's imagination—could by no means attach itself to human life in other ways nor detach itself from its old interests; and its old interests, whether he knew it consciously or not, had failed. His genius was his enmity to man, which he mistook for love, and his mistake led him into confusions which he could bear. But when he banished the confusions, he banished his distinctive greatness as well [p. 173].

## Summary and Conclusions

I have attempted to show with the aid of literary support that lying behavior is not simply a result of a structural conflict; that fundamental narcissistic issues are involved came out in the earliest discussions by psychoanalysts on the subject, at a scientific meeting in 1909.

It appears that lying is a manifestation (symptomatic) of the failure of self-cohesion. The therapeutic implication is that when the defects in self-cohesion are repaired, symptomatic lying becomes less necessary or unnecessary; when it is used, it is not entirely maladaptive, but signifies a defect in self-cohesion.

Creative fictionalism is my term for the narcissistic transformation that uses fiction and poetry for the mutual purpose of concealment and revelation, albeit disguised. It is somewhat akin to Kris's concept of the personal myth in autobiography. (I am regarding all fiction as essentially autobiographical.) Idiosyncratic concealment invites psychoanalytic detection, which should touch upon the nature and strength of the instinctual forces, the characteristic ego defenses, but also upon those horizontal and vertical splits serving concealment. Poetic concealment may be the artist's compromise with the pain of reality and its constant doses of trauma. Whether there is an aesthetic bonus may depend on how gracefully or successfully the artist carries out his purpose. Just as Wordsworth admired the child's lies, or capacity to lie, so may we admire his own poetry (lies?).

My analysis of Wordsworth's early minor poem suggested that he had limitations as a father; he was somewhat aware of this but didn't understand the nature of it. He attempted to do no harm, but his failure to facilitate the thriving of children in his charge, literally as well as figuratively, was deeply disappointing to him.

The analysis of this early poem permits anticipation of Wordsworth's later failures insofar as it demonstrates a thwarted solution; denial is operative, and the necessary process of working through his childhood depression remained unfinished. All of his later losses occurred in an already narcissistically vulnerable child in the adult, and in a sense Wordsworth knew he would never work through his childhood depression.

As an art form, the narcissistic transformation of his unresolved losses into poems of great interest and beauty suggests that he achieved a creative and useful adaptation, but developmentally this form of adaptation continued to act as a barrier, ending up in the rigidity of his adult character.

## REFERENCES

Barchilon, J. (1973), Pleasure, mockery and creative integration: Their relationship to childhood knowledge. A learning defect and the Literature of the Absurd. *Internat. J. Psycho-Anal.*, 54:19–34.

Beiser, H. (1970), Discussion of "Children who cheat at games," by J. E. Meeks. *J. Amer. Acad. Child Psychiat.*, 9:1.

Brett, R. L. & Jones, A. R. (eds.) (1963), *Lyrical Ballads, Wordsworth and Coleridge.* London: Methuen.

Brenkman, J. (1976), The Uncommon language of the lyrical ballad. Unpublished manuscript.

Christensen, F. (1946), Creative sensibility in Wordsworth. *J. English and German Philology*, 45:361–368.

Dickes, R. (1968), Some observations on lying, a derivative. *J. Hillside Hosp.*, 17:94–109.

Douglas, W. W. (1968), *Wordsworth: The Construction of a Personality.* Kent, Ohio: Kent State University Press.

Durrell, L. (1973), *Wordsworth Selected by Lawrence Durrell.* Middlesex, Eng.: Penguin Books.

Eissler, K. R. (1951), Malingering. In: *Psychoanalysis and Culture*, ed. G. B. Wilbur & W. Muensterberger. New York: International Universities Press, pp. 218–253.

Ekstein, R. & Caruth, E. (1972), Keeping secrets. In: *Tactics and Techniques in Psychoanalytic Therapy*, ed. P. Giovacchini. New York: Aronson, pp. 200–215.

Everett, B. (1959), The prelude. *Critical Quart.*, 1:338–350.

Ferry, D. (1959), *The Limits of Mortality: An Essay on Wordsworth's Major Poems.* Middletown, Conn.: Wesleyan University Press.

Finkelstein, L. (1974), The impostor: Aspects of his development. *Psychoanal. Quart.*, 5:85–114.

Freud, S. (1913), Infantile mental life: Two lies told by children. *Standard Edition*, 12:303–311. London: Hogarth Press, 1958.

Goldberg, A. (1973), On telling the truth. In: *Adolescent Psychiatry*, Vol. 2. ed. S. Feinstein & P. Giovacchini. New York: Basic Books, pp. 98–112.

Greenacre, P. (1958a), The relation of the impostor to the artist. In: *Emotional Growth.* Vol. 2. New York: International Universities Press, pp. 533–554, 1971.

—— (1958b), The impostor. In: *Emotional Growth.* Vol. 1. New York: International Universities Press, pp. 93–112, 1971.

Greenson, R. R. (1967), *The Technique and Practice of Psychoanalysis*, Vol. I. New York: International Universities Press.

Grinker, R. R., Jr. (1961), Imposture as a form of mastery. *Arch. Gen. Psychiat.*, 5:53–56.

Hartman, G. H. (1977), A touching compulsion: Wordsworth and the problem of literary representation. Georgia Rev., Summer, pp. 345–361.

Hoyt, M. F. (1978), Secrets in psychotherapy: Theoretical and practical considerations. *Internat. Rev. Psycho-Anal.*, 5:231–234.

Kavka, J. (1976), The suicide of Richard Cory: An explication of the poem by Edwin Arlington Robinson. *This Annual*, 4:479–500. New York: International Universities Press.

Knight, W. (1907), *Letters of the Wordsworth Family*, vol. I, 1787–1855. Boston & London: Ginn & Co.

Kohut, H. (1960), Beyond the bounds of the basic rule. *J. Amer. Psychoanal. Assn.*, 8:567–586.

——— (1970), Narcissism as a resistance and as a driving force in psychoanalysis. In: *The Search for the Self: Selected Writings of Heinz Kohut: 1950–1978*, Vol. II, ed. P. H. Ornstein. New York: International Universities Press, pp. 547–562, 1978.

——— (1977), *The Restoration of the Self*. New York: International Universities Press.

Kris, E. (1956), The personal myth: A problem in psychoanalytic technique. In: *Selected Papers of Ernst Kris*. New Haven: Yale University Press, 1975, pp. 272–300.

Lind-Brenkman, J. (1976), *The Linguistic Imagination: Poetic Language Theory in Wordsworth's Lyrical Ballads*. Iowa City: University of Iowa Press.

Margolis, G. J. (1966), *Secrecy and identity. Internat. J. Psycho-Anal.*, 47:517–522.

Meares, R. (1976), The secret. *Psychiat.*, 39:258–265.

Moorman, M. (1965), *William Wordsworth: A Biography: The Later Years, 1803–1850*. London, Oxford, & New York: Oxford University Press.

Nesbitt, G. L. (1970), *Wordsworth: The Biographical Background of his Poetry*. New York: Pegasus.

Nunberg, H. & Federn, E. (eds.) (1967), *Minutes of the Vienna Psychoanalytic Society*. New York: International Universities Press.

Onorato, R. J. (1971), *The Character of the Poet: Wordsworth in "The Prelude."* Princeton, N.J.: Princeton University Press.

Patton, C. H. (1966), *The Rediscovery of Wordsworth*. New York: Gordian Press.

Read, H. (1931), *Wordsworth, The Clark Lectures 1929–30*. New York: Jonathan Cape and Harrison Smith.

Sadow, L. & Suslick, A. (1961), Simulation of a previous psychotic state. *Arch. Gen. Psychiat.*, 4:46–52.

Sawyier, F. H. (1981), On the psychology of radical skepticism. Presented to the Chicago Institute for Psychoanalysis, January 21.

Sulzberger, C. F. (1953), Why it is hard to keep secrets. *Psychoanal.*, 2:37–53.

Trilling, L. (1951), The immortality ode. In: *The Liberal Imagination: Essays on Literature and Society*. New York: Viking, pp. 150–159.

Walsh, W. (1960), Wordsworth and the growth of the mind. In: *The Use of Imagination*. New York: Barnes & Noble, pp. 30–51.

Weinshel, E. (1977), Some observations on not telling the truth. 21st Sandor Rado Lecture. Reported by J. Hoffman in *Bull. Assn. Psychoanal. Med.*, 16:3–31.

Wordsworth, W. (1904), *The Complete Poetical Works*. Cambridge, Mass.: Houghton Mifflin, The Riverside Press.

*January 1984*

# Opera and Human Emotions

SIEGMUND LEVARIE, Ph.D. (New York)

In this paper I intend to treat opera, not as a disease (as some people would have it), but as a symptom. In the history of music, opera is indicative of an attitude which has become so prevalent since the production of the first opera in Florence around 1600 that most people today are inclined to judge all music in operatic terms. The attitude I am referring to can best be diagnosed by its concern with "expression," "communication," "emotion," and the like. These terms are, of course, appropriate to music. The point I wish to make, however, is that the concept of music as communication is at best one-sided and limited; and that it is matched by another concept of opposite character which follows an older tradition and which, moreover, seems to come closer to the root of the art. Both concepts must be considered for a full understanding of the function of music. If I shall appear to favor the nonoperatic side, as it were, I am today primarily motivated by a desire to restore a balance that may have been disturbed by preceding presentations as well as by the general prejudices of the last few centuries.

I have labeled the operatic attitude as symptomatic of "music as communication." The opposite attitude is more difficult to describe in one word. In default of anything better, I shall follow a suggestion made by the composer Ernst Levy in using the term "music as monument." Try to take this word literally without entanglement in specific associations. "Monument" evokes the idea of something serving as a reminder of a human accomplishment, something enduring as a record of a creative achievement,

This paper was originally delivered as an address at the annual meeting of the American Psychiatric Association in Atlantic City on May 11, 1966. It has not previously been published. Siegmund Levarie, professor of music at the City University of New York, was a close friend of Heinz Kohut ever since they met in 1924. They went to school together, shared many experiences on both sides of the Atlantic, and jointly wrote the first article ever published by Kohut, "On the Enjoyment of Listening to Music" (Kohut and Levarie, 1950).

something existing for its own sake. The concept of art as monument would be immediately understood by an Oriental, for instance, whose traditional philosophy has not admitted individual communication into the realm of art. He reads in the *Upanishad*: "Man ought not to work for any why, not for God nor for his glory nor for anything at all that is outside him, but only for that which is his being, his very life within him" (iv.5,6). A commentator to this passage adds that " 'working for work's sake' sounds to modern ears like 'art for art's sake.' But 'art' has here no modern sentimental connotations. It represents the artist's understanding of his theme, the work to be done. 'Working for work's sake' means in freedom, without ulterior motive, easily. It means doing one's best at the moment. It stands for perfection in temporal works" (Coomaraswamy, 1956a, pp. 88ff.).

A parallel taken from biology might add clarity in its own manner. A flower exists without ulterior motive. Whatever it communicates to the beholder is incidental. I doubt whether anyone here would prefer to think of himself first as a means of communication and only secondarily as a "monument"—and I am including myself at this moment of attempted communication. The biological analogy seems justifiable: man creates a work of art in the image of God creating the world.

These two concepts of music are not mutually exclusive. On the contrary: each composition is both monument and expression. But the emphasis shifts. In our century, communication in every form—over the radio as much as on the analyst's couch—dominates our thoughts and actions. The advertising jingle on the radio is perhaps the extreme example of musical communication at all cost to the exclusion of other considerations. The jingle is expressive for a particular purpose, it appeals to the listener's emotions for a totally ulterior motive, and it readily sacrifices any inherent musical virtues to the desired and paid-for end. Yet even on this lowest level, the composition contains musically recognizable qualities of melody, harmony, and rhythm. Opera proceeds along similar lines on a much higher level; but the necessary sacrifice to emotion and expression is built by definition into even the best opera.

Perhaps I cân evoke the other side of music by relating some historic facts that surround the birth of opera. From about the year 1000, when Western polyphony came into being, to about the year 1600, when opera began its phenomenal rise, we hear very little, if anything, about music as communication or expression. Both aspects of music obviously existed then as they do now, but the emphasis was clearly on the interpretation of music as monument. Music theorists wrote voluminously, but none of them cared about "appreciation." They studied the monument, not the listener; the work of art, not its effect. The medieval visual representations of musical

scenes all confirm this general conviction. The paintings, drawings, and
sculptured reliefs you may have seen show exclusively, before the Ren-
iassance, the music being made, the singers and instrumentalists, but never
the audience. This is true even of the characteristic "angels' concerts,"
which convey the idea that paradise was filled with "doers" and not with
"consumers." When Dante asks the composer Casella whom he meets in
Purgatory for some music "to solace the soul," he promptly earns a severe
rebuke from Cato who shouts at him that this kind of standing around and
listening to music "non lascia a voi Dio manifesto," "let not God be manifest
to you" (ii.106–123). But what Dante still described as negligent self-indul-
gence gained force in the following centuries. The crisis of the musical
Renaissance culminated in the planned creation of opera by an aesthetic
club of intelligent Florentines at the end of the sixteenth century.

The discussion topic of this paper was developed on a highly conscious
and articulate level by the members of that club—the *camerata*, as it was
known. They wrote essays all of which deal with the conflict between the
monumental aspects of the older music and the emotional demands of the
new. Polyphony (which is now accepted as one of the major accomplishments of Western man, comparable in imagination and intellect to the
invention of calculus) was attacked by the *camerata* as "unworthy of a free
man for lacking the power to move a man's mind" (G. Bardi, ca.1580, p.
294). The new music, and the only one worth having, must be based on
communication, expression, and passion. The immediate result was the
condemnation of earlier musical achievements (such as the superior works
of the Netherlands composers) and the introduction of the new art form,
"opera." Listen to Vincenzo Galilei, the astronomer's father and an active
member of the *camerata*:

> Music exists primarily to express the passions with greater effectiveness
> and to communicate these passions with equal force to the minds of
> mortals for their benefit and advantage. Hence the rules thus far ob-
> served by composers as inviolable laws are directly opposed to the per-
> fection of the true music. These rules may be excellent and necessary
> for the mere delight the ear takes in the variety of harmonies, but for
> the expression of conceptions they are pestilent. Consider the composers
> until now. They aim at nothing but the delight of the ear, if it can truly
> be called delight. They have not a book among them for their use and
> convenience that speaks of how to express the conceptions of the mind
> and of how to impress them with the greatest possible effectiveness on
> the minds of the listeners; of this they do not think and never have
> thought since the invention of music. The last thing composers consider
> is the expression of the words with the passion that these require. I say
> that it is not enough merely to take pleasure in the various harmonies
> heard in a musical composition [pp. 306–307].

These words were written about fifteen years before Galilei's colleagues in the *camerata* translated his theoretical concern into action by writing and producing an opera. Describing the first opera performance, a *Dafne* by Peri and Caccini, an eyewitness reports in a letter that the chief aim of the venture "was to improve modern music and to raise it in some degree from the wretched state to which it had been reduced, chiefly by the Goths" (in Bardi, 1634, p. 364). The tone of this letter is echoed by a plaque on the Bardi palace in Florence, the first home of the *camerata*, which claims to this day that there the art of music was made sublime after having been barbarized by the foreign Flemings. Bear in mind that the barbarians referred to are composers like Johannes Okeghem, Josquin Desprez, and Adrian Willaert. These superior masters had written works which contained a life force that came from within. The new style, on the other hand, insisted on being representative. The *stile rappresentativo*, sponsored by the *camerata*, won the battle hands down. The rise of opera in the following three centuries is a clear symptom of the acceptance of music as a means of communication and expression. On the whole, we take this attitude for granted. The linking of art with human emotion is typical of modern man and the world around us.

Yet, four hundred years are a short span within the course of universal history. Although the Renaissance has been generally interpreted as "human progress," an opposite view is equally possible. The gain may have been the freedom of individual expression, but the price paid for it (which people other than psychiatrists too willingly overlook) has been the isolation of the individual from universal forces. In the twentieth century, we are still the heirs of the European Renaissance, whether we like it or not. The general assumption is that we like it. But opera taken as a post-Renaissance phenomenon might well be merely the most audible symptom of an artistic fall from grace. The late Ananda Coomaraswamy, curator of Indian art at the Boston Museum of Fine Arts, took a critical view of the alleged "progress." His knowledge of both the Western and Oriental philosophies of art enabled him to place his faith in "art as monument" above the popular notion of "art as communication." He writes:

It is demanded of the artist to be both a contemplative and a good workman. Contemplation is not a passion but an act: and where modern psychology sees in "inspiration" the uprush of an instinctive and *sub*conscious will, the orthodox philosophy sees an elevation of the artist's being to *super*conscious and *supra*individual levels. What is for the psychologist the "libido" is for the metaphysician the "divine Eros." There is also a sense in which the man as an individual "expresses himself," whether he will or no. This is inevitable, only because nothing can be known or done except in accordance with the mode of the knower. But the artist whom we have in view is not trying to express *himself*, but *that* which was to be expressed. Our conception of art as essentially the expression of a personality, our whole view of genius, all these things are the products of a perverted individualism and prevent our understanding [1956b, pp. 38–39].

Pushed into the background by the triumphal march of opera, the concept of music as a monument of universal truth rather than as an expression of personal emotion has yet remained alive in a kind of undercurrent. We hear it strongly in the organ works by Bach and the string quartets by Haydn, Mozart, and Beethoven. It finds poetic expression in the words of the nineteenth-century Austrian writer Adalbert Stifter, for instance, who sensed the correspondence of the inner and outer worlds. He writes: "Beethoven lifts the most beautiful unknown diamond out of your own heart and holds it, radiant and luminous, before your eyes" (I, 58). This kind of insight is not the prerogative of poets. The mathematician John William Sullivan had similar thoughts about "music as expression." About forty years ago he wrote: "Music, as an expressive art, evokes states of consciousness in the hearer which are analogous to states that may be produced by extra-musical means. It is usual to describe these states as 'emotions' but this word, unless carefully used, is misleading. No composition, for instance, can be adequately described as 'melancholy' or 'joyful.' Such emotions, if they enter at all into the total effect, never enter as isolated elements" (pp. 33–34).

While calling up these witnesses to bolster my argument, I have not forgotten that the audience for this paper consists largely of psychiatrists. Scientific research has thus far only scantily elucidated the connection between music and psyche, which obviously exists as a reality. Reiteration of the same old stories of David playing before Saul and of Pythagoras exorcising sickness through musical means have not yielded modern therapeutic results. Although some developments might be expected as your investigations continue, the approach will remain superficial unless music is considered in its totality as being a monument as much as a communication. A paper that I wrote some time ago jointly with Heinz Kohut hinted at some of the possibilities. Our essay, in the 1950 volume of the *Psychoanalytic Quarterly*, tried to clarify certain aspects of the enjoyment of listening to music. As one of our main points, we demonstrated that unorganized sound symbolizes primitive dread of destruction and that this fear is made unnecessary by the intelligible, though nonverbal, organization of sound in music. Elements in this organization are the clear-cut beginning and end; the use of tones rather than noises; a tonality to which the listener is conditioned; rhythm; repetition; traditional formal patterns; and familiar instruments.

You will have noticed that a key phrase like "organization of sound in music" is readily applicable to the concept of "music as monument." I submit to you, in summary, that musical experience is rooted in a correspondence between the structure of music and the structure of our soul. We apprehend music because there are processes in the outside world which are analogous to those in our mind. The crystallographer Victor Goldschmidt simply called these psychological processes "natural laws." Music is not, as some people would have us believe, primarily a process in which the sending party "expresses" and the receiving party "emotes." Music is, first and last, an event that happens in the soul. It is the resonance of our psyche to a monument. An inner spiritual structure corresponds to an outer physical structure. Music happens when both are attuned to each other.

## REFERENCES

Bardi, G. de' (ca. 1580), *Discourse on Ancient Music and Singing*. In: *Source Readings in Music History*, ed. O. Strunk. New York: Norton, 1950.

Bardi, P. de' (1634), *Letter to G. B. Dori*. In: *Source Readings in Music History*, ed. O. Strunk. New York: Norton, 1950.

Coomaraswamy, A. N. (1956a), *The Transformation of Nature in Art*. New York: Dover.

—— (1956b), *Christian and Oriental Philosophy of Art*. New York: Dover.

Kohut, H. & Levarie, S. (1950), On the enjoyment of listening to music. *Psychoanal. Quart.*, 19:64–87.

Galile, V. (1581), *Dialogo della musica antica e della moderna*. In: *Source Readings in Music History*, ed. O. Strunk. New York: Norton, 1950.

Stifter, A. (1959), *Feldblumen*. In: *Gesammelte Werke*. Wiesbaden: Insel-Verlag.

Sullivan, J. W. (1949), *Beethoven: His Spiritual Development*. New York: Mentor Books.

*October 1983*

# Originality and Creativity

## PINCHAS NOY, M.D. (Jerusalem)

The gift of creativity as an enduring personal trait is dependent on at least two different factors. First, there must be an urge, drive, or motivation to create something new; and second, there must be talent to carry out and materialize this creative urge.

These two factors, although expected to complement one another, are in fact independent. The evidence lies in the many individuals who are endowed with only one of the factors, and therefore never succeed in being really creative. We know many artists and scientists who are endowed with an outstanding talent and who possess many of the cognitive features claimed by psychological studies to characterize creativity, but who, owing to a lack of motivation to create something new and original, devote themselves only to performing, teaching, studying, or criticizing art or science created by others. We also know the opposite cases—those artists or scientists who are always driven by a strong motivation to create something new and original in their fields of activity, but owing to a lack of sufficient talent, never succeed in creating anything significant.

In several of my former studies (Noy, 1966, 1968, 1972, 1978) I dealt with the second factor responsible for creativity—the talents, cognitive processes, and personality features that enable their possessor to succeed in his creative endeavors. In the present study I intend to deal with the first factor, and to examine the urge, drive, or motivation that brings an individual to invest his efforts in an attempt to create something new and original. We know that such a motivation may express itself in only one isolated area—as in the case of the artist or scientist who is very original in his specific field of creation but does not display any originality in other fields—or it may express itself in several or all fields of activity. However, in both cases, originality—whether combined with the sufficient talent to

421

create something significant or not—usually appears to be habitual for a given individual, i.e., there is a tendency for originality that characterizes his responses and creative endeavors throughout his entire life.

In the present study we will examine the following four questions:

(1) What are the specific cognitive features characteristic of the tendency for originality?

(2) How do contemporary psychological theories explain the development and cultivation of the tendency for originality?

(3) What is characteristic of creative originality, i.e., of those original products that contribute creatively to the progress of art and science?

(4) What can contemporary psychoanalytic theory and clinical experience contribute to a better understanding of the dynamic background and the developmental course of the tendency for originality?

Modern psychology has invested a good deal of effort investigating the "creative process"—the mental processes involved in the creative act. Most students of creativity agree that the basis of any creative act, whether in science or in art, always involves the reorganization of available information in some new form. Koestler (1964) writes: "This act of wrenching away an object or concept from its habitual context and seeing it in a new context is . . . an essential part of the creative process" (p. 529). Parker (1963) describes creativity as "the act of seeking out, trying out and combining knowledge in new ways." Mednick (1962) defines the creative process as "the forming of associative elements into new combinations which either meet specified requirements or are in some way useful" (p. 227). Guilford (1967), who suggested the "transfer theory" to explain creativity, writes: "Novel thinking means that retrieved information is to be used in a new form or in new connections . . . A theory learned in certain connections is torn out of the context in which it was learned, for use in some new context" (p. 100); and De Bono (1969), using the term "lateral thinking," describes creativity as follows: "Lateral thinking has to do with rearranging available information so that it is snapped out of the established pattern and forms a new and better pattern" (p. 237).

Nobody, of course, would minimize the necessity of revealing new facts and enriching our stock of actual knowledge in any human scientific and cultural progress; but what seems to characterize most of the highest and most original creative acts is mainly the ability to approach the well-known facts from a novel and original point of view. By such a new look connections are detected between facts hitherto regarded as unrelated; novel problems for research are revealed in areas hitherto regarded as satisfactorily solved, and new means are created to express meanings hitherto regarded as inexpressible. Koestler (1968) claimed that Copernicus created a revolution in our cosmological view, even though "insofar as actual knowledge is concerned, Copernicus was no better off, and in some respects worse off, than the Greek astronomer of Alexandria who lived in the time of Jesus Christ . . ." (p. 73). "The essence of science," he states, "lies not in discovering facts, but in discovering new ways of thinking about them" (p. 235). Polanyi (1958) claims that Einstein, too, while announcing his Special Theory of Relativity in 1905, was "unaided by any observation that had not been available for at least fifty years before" (p. 11). Eissler (1971) is of the opinion that what distinguishes the genius from the merely talented is his ability to create new paradigms, new models of thought patterns to organize the known facts: "The discovery of these paradigms is, in science, the function of genius. Talents will perform permutations or combinations . . . or . . . clarify the consequences . . . In the literary field, the function of the genius is to create a new world that might even compete successfully with existing reality in the minds of many" (p. 249).

If we were to reduce these various statements into one definition, utilizing the computer model as applied in psychology today, we could say that what characterizes the genuine creative act is not the addition of novel information, but the use of new programs for processing the already available information. Thus the problem of originality could be reduced to the question: What makes a person process a particular piece of information with the aid of a novel program, instead of using the habitual ones?

Frank Barron (1955), one of the first to study originality as an isolated component of creativity, shows that originality is seldom manifested as a single nonexpected act; "some persons are regularly original, whereas others are regularly unoriginal." Therefore he suggests approaching originality as a relatively enduring trait of the personality, urging psychologists to study it not as an isolated mental act, but as a "personality disposition." Although Barron tries to relate this disposition to several other personality traits, it seems to me that we do not yet have enough solid evidence to speak about a "personality pattern." I would therefore prefer to approach the tendency for originality merely as a "cognitive style," thus leaving open the possibility that this tendency may manifest itself in quite different and diverse forms of personality structures. Let us see now what the characteristics of this cognitive style are.

Any of the functions of human thought—classifying and categorizing input data, discerning regularities and finding out similarities and repetitions, organizing experience, evaluating it against memory imprints, revealing discrepancies and solving the problems created, foreseeing future events and planning the proper behavioral acts to meet them—is dependent on some habitual ways of processing the information involved, i.e., on pre-

established programs. There are qualitative differences in the kind of programs people develop for any of the mental tasks and quantitative differences in the number of alternative programs they have at their disposal to
perform any of these tasks. For example, when a child begins to learn
arithmetic at school he has to develop the appropriate program to perform
any of the calculations required of him. But when we inquire of the children
how they perform a given calculation, we may find that although each of
them reaches the same correct result, each child uses a different program,
i.e., each represents the numbers in his imagination in a different form
and employs a different strategy for performing the calculation.

We can reveal another important difference as well: while one child,
after developing an appropriate program for performing a given operation
and being satisfied with the results, tends to stick to it for the rest of his
or her life, another, when confronted repeatedly with similar problems,
will try to find some new ways of solving them. The result will be that the
first, even if he does well at mathematics, will possess only a limited repertoire of calculating programs, whereas the second, who continues all his
life to experiment with new and alternative techniques of solving the same
problem, will finally accumulate a rich repertoire of programs and therefore be much more efficient in meeting new problems.

Hunter (1966) studied a mathematician named Professor Aitken, famous
for his special ability for rapid mental calculation. For example, when asked
to express as a decimal the fraction $\frac{1}{47}$, after 24 seconds he gave the
answer—0.0851063829787234042553191.4. Hunter claims that Aitken's
extraordinary achievements are made possible by his "repertoire of ingen-
ious calculation plans . . . When Aitken tackles a problem, his first priority
is to decide a calculative plan . . . Aitken has a large variety of calculative
plans at his disposal, and he can solve the same problem in several different
ways . . . He searches for that plan which will carry him to the solution in
the shortest time and with least difficulty" (p. 343). Aitken told Hunter that
at around the age of thirteen he became so fascinated with calculation that
he spent all his free time exploring complex problems and finding a new
technique to solve them each time. Finally, he succeeded in accumulating
such a huge stock of calculative programs that he had no difficulty in
solving the most complicated problem in the shortest time.

The same process, that of an indefatigable accumulation of organizing
programs, is what characterizes any person infatuated by a specific art,
science, or other "hobby." The chess player who spends hours and hours
in solving chess riddles, the musician who analyzes musical pieces of other
historical periods or cultures, the inventor who tests all kinds of machines—all are spending their time and efforts in experimenting with new

and alternative techniques to solve the problems in which they are interested, thus enriching their repertoire of programs in order to improve
steadily their ability to solve any new problem they may confront in the
future. Theoretically, any process of cognitive development, education, or
training can be described as such a cumulative process of continuously
adding new programs to organize experience and knowledge. In this process there are wide individual variations, both quantitatively, in the number
of programs each individual accumulates, and qualitatively, in the specific
areas of mental activity in which most of the efforts are concentrated. If
we were to arrange the various individual variations along a continuum,
we could delineate the two poles as two opposite cognitive styles, which I
would call the *restrictive* and the *prolific*. Individuals in the first group are
characterized by a rather limited repertoire of programs by which to organize their experience, solve their problems, and plan their responses;
they have a tendency to restrict themselves lifelong to the same redundant
strategies of thought, patterns of behavior, techniques for interpersonal
manipulation, and systems of values and beliefs. The others, at the opposite
pole, are characterized by a rich repertoire of diverse programs in one,
several, or all areas of mental activity, and are always eager to try out new
and alternative ways of organizing experience, new strategies of solving
problems, and new techniques of manipulating and adjusting to significant
others.

I am aware of the fact that this dichotomy may overlap several other
dichotomies suggested by other psychologists, such as "routine vs. adven-
turous thinking" (Bartlett, 1958), "convergent vs. divergent thinking" (Guilford, 1959), "the leveling vs. sharpening control principle" (Gardner,
Holzman, Klein, Linton, and Spencer, 1959), "field dependency vs. field
independency" (Witkin, Lewis, Hertzman, Machover, Meissner, and Wapner, 1954), but because it is based on quite a different principle of differentiation, it should not be confused with any of the others.

My thesis is that originality as an enduring feature characterizing a given
person can flourish only in the ground of the "prolific style." To clarify:
although not every person with such a style is expected to exhibit originality,
every person exhibiting originality habitually is assumed to belong to the
prolific style. Originality, therefore, must be regarded not as an isolated
mental act based on the occasional ability to see several phenomena from
an angle different from the usual, but as a habitual response based on the
permanent ability to use a much greater repertoire of organizing programs
than does the nonoriginal other. Thus, if the original person succeeds in
revealing connections between phenomena hitherto regarded as unrelated
(the great discoveries in science), in opening new questions in problematic

areas already regarded as solved (the openings of new areas for research), or in showing how meanings regarded as unexpressible can be expressed (the great advances in art), it is because when he approaches a new mental task, he comes equipped from the beginning with a greater armament of techniques and strategies than does his fellow who always succeeds in seeing only the conventional. Being equipped with many alternative programs to "attack" any of the tasks involved, he may, then, when flexible enough, shift from one point of view to another, discerning the phenomena in which he is interested from a different angle every time.

This *richness* in diverse and alternative organizing programs, and the *flexibility* to dissolve quickly the schemata created with the aid of one group of programs and to reorganize them anew with the aid of alternative programs, when extreme, makes for the special ability of the creative mind for original solutions. But to some extent, a considerable degree of richness and flexibility is required to attain any *change* in the patterns of behavior, systems of beliefs, or structure of personality. This issue is especially relevant for psychoanalysis, as we know that any lasting change to be attained as the result of therapy is dependent on the patient's capability to reorganize his experience, memory, and attitudes, utilizing other programs from those previously utilized. The patient in therapy naturally presents his habitual ways of understanding significant events, handling his impulses, experiencing his past, and responding to the behavior of others. The essence of any interpretation is the analyst's attempt to open the patient's mind to the possibility that the same events may eventually be understood differently, the impulse may be handled otherwise, the memory may have another meaning, or the other's behavior may be responded to in a different way.

Schafer (1982), speaking about the reconstruction of the past with the aid of interpretations, states: "each analytically revised account of the past is necessarily a reconstruction of that which has already been constructed differently" (p. 77). But it is clear that any such attempt to incite a patient to utilize organizing programs other than his habitual ones is first of all dependent on whether he at all possesses the sufficient number of alternative programs necessary for the reorganization of his experience, memory constructs, and beliefs, and for the employment of different strategies of thought and patterns of defense. If a patient belonging to the restrictive style is equipped only with a very limited number of organizing programs, it will be very difficult for him, if not impossible, to assimilate any interpretation. Schafer (1979), speaking about what he calls "principles of constructing experience" (which I would regard as identical to "organizing programs"), claims that any ability on the part of the patient to utilize interpretation effectively is dependent on his being equipped with a heterogenous system of such organizing principles: "It is this heterogenous composition that provides the fulcrum with the help of which it is possible to move the subjective world . . . The analysands of whom this is true can hear an interpretation as such, at least some of the time, however else they hear it (e.g., as criticism). Those who can't, are unanalyzable—at least during that attempt at analysis. Any theory of effective interpretation or therapeutic effect must allow for an interpretation's being heard in more than one way" (p. 882).

Any experienced analyst is well acquainted with both—the prolific and restrictive styles—and knows how they are expected to behave in the therapeutic situation. Those with the *prolific style* are generally among our most gratifying patients. Typically, such a patient, sometime in his last phase of analysis, after most of his resistances, regressive tendencies, and restraining defenses have been worked through, enters into what can be called a "creative phase." He then eagerly catches every interpretation, including those he rejected defensively in former phases of his analysis, is ready to examine them for all their possible vantage points, to produce plentiful associations connected to any of their multifaceted meanings, and even succeeds in surprising us by illuminating new meanings we had not considered at all. This work proceeds mostly in an atmosphere of laxity and playfulness, while the patient seems to enjoy his ability to wander flexibly through the diverse domains of meanings, getting new perspectives to relate to his past experiences and trying out new approaches in his behavior with others.

The patient with the *restrictive style* is the exact inverse, and therefore is included among our most frustrating patients. Typically, such a person can hardly respond to any interpretation, especially to those based on an attempt to re-examine a given phenomenon from a different angle from the reported one. Even when the analyst tries, while reflecting something back, to reformulate it only slightly differently from the original version, the patient rejects it, or simply responds with an "I don't understand what you mean." It always seems as though the patient, being bound to one context and strategy of thought, has no possibility of shifting his view and seeing things from a different angle or level, a shift essential for the assimilation of any interpretation. I think that these are the kind of patients Freud (1937) had in mind when he spoke about "depletion of the plasticity" in his paper "Analysis Terminable and Interminable," while detailing the various factors responsible for insoluble interminability. Likewise Rangell (1981), when he describes "an otherwise intelligent woman [who] ritualistically returns with 'I don't understand' to the most primitive explanations in a way that recalls Mahler's description of pseudo-imbecility in children" (p. 132); and Klein (1980) when he describes "Austistic phenomena in neurotic patients" as a "tendency to bring up some topic which the patient seizes upon with obsessional rigidity but which is never worked through because of the inability to take in interpretations and to deal with the problem" (p. 395). What pervades these descriptions, and many others scattered through the literature that are similar, is the sense of helplessness the analyst bears when treating an otherwise intelligent patient with a basic pathology mostly not exceeding the regular neuroses, who for some unknown reason shows no improvement—the years pass and nothing changes. To my mind, in most of these cases, it is the lack of a minimal stock of alternative organizing programs that make any reorganization of experiences, knowledge, and beliefs, and therefore any change, impossible to attain.

Psychologists interested in the cultivation of creativity and originality and psychoanalysts interested in improving techniques used in treating patients regarded as "unanalyzable" will certainly ask: "Can a cognitive style be modified?" In the present case the question would take the form: "If one takes into consideration all the transient factors that may cause a person to act as if restrictively, such as specific defenses, anxieties, or interpersonal conditions, would it be possible to modify cognitive organization so that a restrictive style will become closer to the prolific one?" No attempt will be made here to answer this question, but it is clear that it can be answered at all only if we have sufficient understanding of the following: What is the process by which these styles develop in vivo? How does each of them serve the adaptive aims of its possessor? What conditions are responsible for their stabilization? So, let us go on and focus on these issues, dealing with the processes that assumedly contribute to the development of originality, and leaving aside at present the problem of the eventual inducement of changes.

## Psychological Development Theories

Most developmental studies deal not with originality as an isolated component, but with creativity in general. The general approach pervading most experimental studies is the interpersonal one, attributing the development of creativeness to a specific childhood family constellation. Lytton (1971), summarizing the pertinent literature, presents a family profile of creative children:

> They would seem to be middle-class with father having considerable autonomy in his profession or business. The father thus provides a model of autonomy, as well as of general effectiveness and the parents, in turn, grant similar autonomy to their children. The mother will also often have

had a career in her own right before marriage. The parents exhibit enthusiasm for creative activities, encourage their children's curiosity and explorative urge and stimulate them to independent achievement. However, this is done without pressure for high standards or particular accomplishments, since autonomy here means that the parents do not intrude, but allow their children to develop at their own pace and in their own desired direction, even to the point of being tolerant of some backsliding to more infantile behavior. The children's autonomy may also be bought at the expense of some closeness and warmth in family relations. Nor is the family necessarily an entirely harmonious one: open expression of feelings and sometimes of disagreement will be a normal part of family life [p. 72].[1]

Only a limited number of psychologists, such as Barron (1963) and Weisberg and Springer (1962), who seem to be influenced by the psychoanalytic approach, try to explain the development of creativity (Barron also is concerned with the development of originality) using the adaptive point of view. According to this point of view the development of all cognitive techniques and strategies is regarded as reflecting the growing child's attempts to cope in the most efficient way with his inner needs and with the demands of his social environment. If we were to apply this approach to the explanation of the development of the above-suggested two cognitive styles—the restrictive and the prolific—the following developmental process could be described:

The maturing brain of the developing child enables him to meet every one of his phase-appropriate problems and conflicts by constructing new cognitive techniques and strategies, each adjusted to its specific task. This natural tendency of the maturing child—to "attack" new problems with the aid of novel techniques and strategies—requires constant reinforcement of the child by his caretakers. Children not provided with sufficient reinforcement may soon learn that after succeeding once to solve a problem or to cope with a situation in a given way, the best thing to do is to stick to this solution and not try and experiment with other solutions. Other children, in contrast, being sufficiently reinforced in their natural efforts to try out new solutions, will learn that finding a new way to solve a problem or cope with a situation can always be worthwhile. The first group tends to develop into the restrictive style, confining their cognitive activities throughout their lives to the same and repetitive techniques and strategies, whereas the others tend to develop into the prolific style, continuing always to widen and enrich their repertoire of techniques and strategies. By "reinforcement" we may include (1) all environmental conditions that *do* foster

---

[1] Reprinted by permission of the publisher, Routledge & Kegan Paul.

the attempts of the child to experiment with new and alternative ways of problem solving and coping, and (2) all those conditions that *do not* enable the child to stick to his repetitive techniques and strategies, but force him to search for new ways to cope and adapt. To foster his attempts, the child needs parents who are able to respect his emerging autonomy without imposing their beliefs and expectations on him, and who are ready to meet his experiments and actions favorably, regardless of how clumsy and inefficient they may be at the beginning.

In regard to the second group of conditions, those that force the child to search for new ways of coping, it would be interesting to mention MacKinnon (1961) who, in their study of creative architects, found that in their childhood their parents tended to move from one place to another much more frequently than did the families of less creative children. Thus we may assume that when a child *has* to adapt each time to a new physical and social environment, he cannot allow himself to stick to his habitual ways of coping, but is each time forced to revise his techniques and strategies in order to adapt to the new setting. We may assume that several other environmental conditions may have an influence similar to that of the frequent alterations of residence, which also force the child to develop a diversity of problem-solving and coping techniques. Such conditions may include frequent changes of his group of caretakers, impulsive and unpredictable parents, great discrepancies between the demands and behavioral patterns of the two parents, or between the parents and some of his sisters and brothers, etc. Each of these conditions contributes to the enrichment of the child's repertoire of organizing programs, and therefore to his eventual emergence as an original and creative individual.

One of the cognitive features that most intrigues the psychoanalytically oriented researchers of creativity is the openness of these gifted individuals to accept the irrational and to trust their unconscious as a reservoir of organizing processes to be utilized in their creative endeavors. Barron (1963) writes: "The creative individual . . . turns much more than do most people to the dimly realized life of the unconscious, and is likely to grant more than a usual amount of respect to the as yet unconscious forces of the irrational in himself and in others . . . the creative individual not only respects the irrational in himself, but also courts it as the most promising source of novelty in his own thinking" (p. 158). This "turning to the life of the unconscious" makes for what I would regard as the most interesting ability of the creative individual—the ability to enrich his secondary-process cognition with techniques and strategies derived from the primary process (an enrichment I described in detail in a former paper [Noy, 1978]).

Most of the psychologists who have written about this phenomenon tend to explain it along the same lines as they explain creativeness in general—as the outgrowth of a specific family atmosphere favorable to the child's free enactment of the primary processes in his thoughts and communications. Some of them, influenced by Kris's (1952) notion of the "regression in the service of the ego," stress the tolerance of such families to regression. Weisberg and Springer (1962), for example, write: "The development of such a mind, it is hypothesized, proceeds from an adaptive, reconstructive technique learned in early childhood, in which the child regresses comfortably, and does not use repression or withdrawal as a primary means of dealing with a chronically anxiety-producing environment" (p. 564). Others, less sure that primary-process enrichment is necessarily connected to regression, tend to stress the tolerance of the creative child's parents in accepting his imaginative and irrational communication as a possible explanation for the development of his ability to utilize his primary processes in constructing his products. This contrasts with the "rational" parents who always scold their child for speaking "nonsense" when he reveals the products of his imagination, letting him understand by this that free primary-process-thought activity is something he has to be ashamed of, and that he must do his best to suppress any manifestation of it in his overt communication.

When surveying the pertinent psychological literature, the psychoanalytically oriented reader cannot but get the impression that there is something naïve in the tendency to explain the development of creativity and originality only as an outgrowth of the nurturing family atmosphere in childhood, and the adaptive struggles of the maturing child. To clarify, this approach is not erroneous, but it certainly represents only one side of the many factors contributing to the development of creativeness in the individual. This one-sidedness stems, I believe, from two factors, one methodological and one ideological: (1) Most of the findings serving as a basis for the conclusions are derived from biographical material, superficial interviews, questionnaires, and in the best case, psychological tests; so that most of the significant dynamic information—the specific childhood conflicts, traumata, anxieties, and frustrations, the emotional attitudes of the parents, the exact patterns of the child's object relations—is missing. (2) The whole approach to the study of the development of creativity becomes more and more subordinated to the belief that creativity is, and has to be, the incarnation of man's striving for self-actualization. Maslow (1963), for example, opens his lecture on "The Creative Attitude" with the declaration: "My feeling is that the concept of creativeness and the concept of the healthy, self-actualizing, fully human person seem to be coming closer and closer together, and may perhaps turn out to be the same thing" (p. 1).

This belief pervades most of the developmental studies which, although describing the childhood of the creative individual as not always being the happiest, evidently believe it to be the healthiest. If one were to take the two opposing developmental lines, that directed toward the emergence of creativity and originality, and that leading to the development of the un-creative, conventional, habit-bound type of personality, the first is always regarded as the outcome of healthy, normal, and undisturbed develop-ment, whereas the opposite is seen as the result of some distorting and restraining influences which disturbed development in some of its earlier phases. This attitude is best expressed by Rogers (1954) in a paper which has already become a classic in the literature about creativity: "The main-spring of creativity appears to be the same tendency which we discover so deeply as the curative force in psychotherapy—man's tendency to actualize himself, to become his potentialities . . . it exists in every individual and awaits only the proper conditions to be released and expressed." Therefore "it is clear that they [the conditions for creativity] cannot be forced, but must be permitted to emerge" (p. 256). The conclusion one can derive from this approach is that when you are confronted with a creative, original, or prolific style of cognition, you need not bother to search for specific causes to explain its development, and certainly not in the domain of psy-chopathology; but if it is the opposite style that emerges, then it is evident that something has been going astray in the process of childhood devel-opment. Although, I am sure, that we all find this approach very attractive, I doubt if as psychoanalysts we can accept it without criticism. But let us pause here and deal first with another important issue—what do we mean by "creative originality"?

## Creative Originality

Originality is manifested in the tendency to produce something new—ideas, things, or means of expression and communication of experience that previously have not existed, or have not been used in the same context. But originality, in order to be regarded as creative, requires an additional factor: somebody else who is ready to "buy" the new product. Stein (1963) defines creativity as "that process which results in a novel work that is accepted as tenable or useful or satisfying, by a group at some point in time" (p. 218). Why "at some point in time"? In order to include creators whose novelties were rejected by their contemporaries, but "discovered" and accepted by some future generation. There are certainly many indi-viduals who, though definitely original, cannot be regarded as creative. We all know many scientists and artists who are always doing their best to emit something new and original, but who in fact produce nothing "creative" because nobody is ready to accept their ideas or products as tenable, useful, or satisfying. Others, in contrast, often not even trying very hard to be original, succeed in having their products accepted by some "significant group" as relevant, and sometimes are even lucky enough to be remembered in history as pioneers who opened a new era in science or a new style in art. Bach, for example, in whose compositions all subsequent music is already implied, never attempted to be original, and on the contrary was often blamed by his contemporaries for being conventional and "altmodist." The same is true of Cézanne, who is now regarded as the "father" of modern painting. Some people would certainly claim that the social acceptability of an original product is mainly a matter of chance. They would explain that in every area of science and art there are hundreds of creators, each contributing his original novelties; they believe that if a creator whose novelties were rejected by his contemporaries is privileged to be "discovered" by a future generation, his later acceptance was largely a matter of chance. The particular art or science, developing according to its inner rules, had reached a point where the novelties of Mr. X had become the accepted style. Other people, not giving the credit to pure chance, believe that if a creator is accepted many years later, it is because by his ingenuity he was able to foresee future developments. Books on the history of science and art are full of stories of geniuses who "were ahead of their time" and therefore "created for future generations." In my opinion, although I am not so sure that the genius in science or art is endowed with a prophetic power to foresee the future, his ability to be historically right can hardly be regarded as a matter of chance.

To develop the discussion, let me introduce here the concept of "social needs," stating that any innovation, in order to be accepted and integrated into the stream of an advancing science or art, has to be attuned to the needs of some social group. Scientific creativity is the attempt to pose new questions and to provide new ideas about how to understand, master, and modify nature, whereas artistic creativity is the attempt to find and construct new means for the expression of human experience, and to provide new formulas for organization and ordering it (see also Noy, 1979a). Any new idea can be accepted in science only if it provides the answer to a question that is relevant for someone, and any new means of expression or formula for organization can be adopted only if it serves to express, organize, or order something for which an artist is striving, but hitherto had no means of accomplishing.

Such a view is in line with recent developments in philosophy and in two new disciplines—the sociology of science and the sociology of art. The common understanding that governed philosophy for centuries was that any science or art is a closed system that develops according to its own inner rules and needs, driven forward by the creative genius who provides the new solutions and imposes his new rules on the scientific or artistic community. This concept was influenced by Kant (1790) who stated: "Genius is the talent (or natural gift) which gives the rule to art . . . Genius is the innate mental disposition [*ingenium*] through which Nature gives the rule to Art" (p. 188). Today, however, more and more philosophers are ready to pay attention to the interrelationship between science and art and the needs of the society in which the particular science or art flourishes. Habermas (1968), for example, is of the opinion that the very questions any science asks are dependent on the social interests of its particular culture and time.

To my mind, what characterizes creative originality is its possessor's ability to perceive the social needs directed toward his science or art and to respond to them creatively. As opposed to many scientists and artists who create novelty only for the sake of exhibiting their originality, the creative scientist or artist, while rebelling against the conventional to present his original scientific or artistic products, always remains attuned to the needs of a target group. Though it often seems as though he possesses the ability to foresee the future development of his science or art, this is not because he is endowed with any prophetic power. The new needs, in any of the transitional phases of science and art, emerge mostly outside of the awareness of the scientific or artistic community and are manifested at first as a growing dissatisfaction with the conventional, and as some dim yearning for the appearance of something new. Sometimes it may take several decades before these latent needs become evident enough to call for a scientific revolution or a new style in art. The creative genius, in his extreme sensitivity to the needs of his society, succeeds in identifying them immediately at their emergence, long before his contemporaries become aware that something is going to change. Being loyal only to his own perception (what we usually call "intuition"), he immediately stops what he has been doing when he feels that the needs have changed and directs his creative endeavors to meet the new demands. Thus it is not the future, but only the present that he is able to sense, but owing to his sensitive "antennae" he perceives that present to which we ordinary people are already blind and deaf.

The possession of such "antennae" to sense the emerging needs of his target group long before they become evident is also what characterizes the real *leader*; in contrast, the mere politician can see only the evident. He may appear to be "ahead of his time" when he persuades his people to invest their efforts in meeting the needs of tomorrow, instead of wasting them by coping with what he knows already belongs to yesterday.

All of them, the creative scientist, artist, or leader, equipped with "antennae" to sense their fellows' needs long before they themselves do, may often be partly or totally unaware of what it is that they are responding to. What betrays their sensitivity is, first, their deep sense of conviction that, even when they depart from any consensus to pursue their novel and original path, alone and deserted by all their colleagues, they are inevitably right; and, second, the proof of history that they have indeed been right.

Several years ago, as part of my attempts to interview creative people, I had the opportunity to speak with one of the most creative and original minds in our field. When I asked him about the way he develops his original ideas, he told me: "It usually begins with some general feeling that something cries out for revision and alteration. And then, when I begin to work on developing my own ideas, I become more and more anxious. I know that the more I depart from the common opinion, the more I will be attacked, excommunicated, and rejected by many of my best friends. It is like leaving a friendly and safe harbor to go out in a small boat into the stormy big sea. But what gives me the courage to proceed on my way is that, although I have no idea where I am going to land, I know deep in my heart that not far away is the other coast, and I am certain that I can reach it."

From all that has been said here one can get the impression that in the endless discussion of "does history create the genius, or is it the genius who creates history?" I am unequivocally in favor of the first alternative. But that is not exactly the case. I believe that there is an ongoing interrelationship between the work of the creative genius and the historical development of science and art. Although I do not believe that the genius can really instigate historical change, I think that by his ability to perceive changes and formulate them while they are still in their initial phase of emergence, he facilitates their emergence and accelerates the process itself. From this point of view, the genius in science or art can be compared with the analyst, and his creative work can be compared with the interpretations given to the patient. By understanding the meanings of what is still latent, and by knowing how to articulate the meanings and reflect them back in an intelligible form, both can assist their patients/audiences/communities to confront what they are still unable to see, to assimilate it, and to utilize it as a lever for the inducement of changes. Like the artist or the scientist, the analyst must be regarded not as the cause of the change but only as the catalyst that accelerates the process. However, as any chemist knows well, although it is never the catalyst that creates the process, without its interference the process may not proceed at all, and no change will occur.

Returning to the issue of interest to us in the present study—the cognitive or personality features characteristic of the individual endowed with the ability for creative originality—we recognize that we are confronted here with something like a paradox. On the one hand, we recognize a person rebelling against every conformity, pursuing his original way without letting social co·.ventions impede him in his progress; but on the other hand, we see a person with the most sensitive antennae attentive to the tiniest social changes and able to respond to them long before anybody else. Therefore, the question that can be asked is: Why should a person be motivated to rebel against the generally accepted and agreed-upon conceptions of sci-ence or the conventional forms of art in order to renew them for the benefit of those who don't ask for change and many times even scornfully declare their resistance to any such change? To answer such a question, as with similar questions dealing with the motivations for creativity, we have to turn to psychoanalytic theories. Why? Because the answers to all other issues concerning creativity, such as the cognitive processes involved, the structure of the creative personality, or the developmental background of such personality, can also be provided, at least in part, by the other disci-plines of psychology and sociology; a reasonable answer to questions con-cerning motivation, on the other hand, can be provided only by psychoanalysis.

## Psychoanalytic Theories of Development

Everything said up to this point can assist us in understanding only the conditions for originality, i.e., the cognitive organization, personality pat-terns, and developmental background that make an individual capable of responding originally in places and situations where others are not able to do so. But what characterizes the original creator in science and art is that he not only *can* create original products where others cannot, but that he *must* do so. The scientist will spend days and nights on overcoming the obstacles to his original work, and the artist will never be satisfied with what has already been accomplished, and immediately upon finishing one original work will begin to plan the next. And, what is so curious about it is that he may even not enjoy doing this at all, but feels himself under the tyranny of some inner urge which compels him to create. Simenon, who is known as a highly prolific writer, said (as quoted by Storr, 1972): "Writing is not a profession, but a vocation of unhappiness" (p. 1). To understand this "must," to follow the origin of the compelling impulse to create some-thing new and original, we have to look into the *motivations* of the creative individual, and at the needs satisfied by the creative activity.

Psychoanalysis, as has already been mentioned, deals not with originality as an isolated component, but with creativity in general. As far as the motivations for creativity are concerned, the main problem occupying most psychologists interested in this issue is whether the motivations for creativity belong to the "normal" and healthy aspect of personality or stem from the psychopathological. For psychoanalysis such a question is practically irrelevant, because creative activity is no longer regarded as representing a drive, wish, or conflict, but is seen as a *solution* to some inner struggle. The basic struggle underlying creativity may be similar to those that may bring people to develop a neurosis, borderline, or even psychotic disturbance, but the creative activity as the solution to any of those disturbances is always regarded as a healthy one. This approach has its origin in the writings of Freud, who in the 23rd lecture of his "Introductory Lectures on Psychoanalysis" (1916–1917) described the artist as "in rudiments an introvert, not far removed from neurosis" who succeeds, in contrast to the neurotic, to find "a path that leads back from phantasy to reality" (p. 376); and in 1920, in a letter to Stefan Zweig, wrote: "Hysteria . . . is an expression of the same organic power which produces the genius of the artist." The adjectives used to describe the creative activity, as we find them repeatedly in modern psychoanalytic literature, are "restorative," "recuperative," "reparative," "compensatory," and so on—all adjectives reflecting the belief that the scientist or artist succeeds in his creative endeavors to find the path that may lead him from neurosis or psychosis back to healthy integration and adaptation.

But, although there is today a general willingness to understand creative activity as an attempt to overcome some basic inner conflict or developmental struggle, there is no agreement yet concerning the exact nature of this underlying conflict or struggle. Classical psychoanalysis, in line with the general approach of the beginning of the century, believed this conflict to be the oedipal one. In recent years, again with the general theoretical trend, the supposed underlying conflict has been gradually moving "downward" toward the various preoedipal conflicts and developmental struggles. The first member of that movement to see conflict in this way was Melanie Klein who, according to Hanna Segal (1981), "concludes that the anxieties of the depressive position and the reparative urge which they give rise to, lie at the root of creativity" (p. 81). Today the trend naturally goes in the direction of the self and narcissism. For Kohut (1966) "the creative activity itself deserves to be considered among the transformation of narcissism" (p. 259); and in *The Analysis of the Self* (1971), after presenting some examples, he states: "There is no need, however, to rely exclusively on such gross examples to serve as a proof for the narcissistic nature of the creative act" (p. 315). Gedo (1972), describing the analysis of a patient he considered to be a genius, writes: "In order to maintain his narcissistic balance he needed continuous proofs of his worth as a creator. It was the unending threat of a deficit in his self-esteem that made the creative act into an emotional necessity for him. Insofar as the creativity of genius provided him with matchless narcissistic replenishment, the opportunity to heal himself through work produced in him a daemonic impetus for the creative act. This relentless force, in turn, distinguished his creativity from that of lesser men. Like the Phoenix, he rose from his own ashes" (p. 202).

Niederland (1967, 1976) assumes that the specific narcissistic injury motivating an individual to compensate for it by creative activity is a severe disturbance in the image of the body-self:

> In my own work, I have focused attention on the presence of permanent and often severe injuries to infantile narcissism and its effect on the creative potentialities. In the cases observed, the narcissistic injury could be traced to feelings of incompleteness derived from early physical frailty or disability, protracted illness in childhood, congenital or early acquired malformations, and fantasied or factual anomalies . . . In a series of eight analytically studied artist-patients—all creatively active individuals—fantasies of being incomplete, misshapen ugly, or deficient could be observed. During creative work these feelings were replaced by sensations of completeness, of being strong, whole, and free from deficiency or inadequacy, punctuated by feelings of insufficiency when difficulties in their work arose [1976, pp. 195–196].

I fully agree with those writers who consider the psychoanalytic model of the self as the best model available today for the understanding of the phenomenon of creative activity, but I have some problems with the manner in which most of them tend to conceptualize the self. Let us, therefore, take a short detour to examine critically the prevailing psychoanalytic conception of the self.

It is common agreement, based on ample clinical evidence, that the more severe psychopathological situations, those usually grouped as "beyond the neuroses," represent a basic disturbance in the organization of the self. The problem is that from this notion the opposite conclusion, an erroneous one to my mind, is generally automatically derived: that every disturbance revealed in the organization of the self necessarily represents a narcissistic, borderline, or psychotic psychopathology. It is certainly correct that in the more severe psychopathologies a defect in organization of the self is always involved, but the inverse is *not* true—not every disturbance in the self will necessarily give rise to a severe psychopathology. Since in clinical practice we can see self disturbances that are represented by all kinds of psychopathologies, from transient neuroses to the most severe cases of psychosis, to say that somebody has a disturbance in some sector of his self, or to describe a given symptom as representing an attempt to cope with a defect in the organization of the self, certainly does not require diagnosing him as narcissistic or borderline.

This view, identifying self pathology with narcissism, borderline, or psychotic conditions, has its origin, at least in part, in the writings of Kohut. The impression one can derive from his writings is that two kinds of psychopathology exist: "self-pathology" and "structural pathology" (see Kohut, 1977, p. 225). The first, the more severe one, derives from preoedipal disturbances (narcissistic, borderline, and psychotic), and the second, from oedipal ones (neurotic). Each kind of psychopathology is assumedly connected to a different developmental task. Gedo (1976), in his lecture on "The Metapsychology of the Self," shows that according to Kohut's theory the first developmental task is to attain "self-cohesion": "Kohut . . . has established the degree of cohesiveness in the organization of the self as the basic criterion for the differential diagnosis among major groups of psychopathology: classical transference neuroses, the borderline and psychotic characters, and narcissistic personality disturbances. These criteria, based on degrees of self-cohesion, can be extrapolated into an epigenetic developmental psychology" (p. 168). The first developmental task is "self-unification, in which the primary identity is established, the main issues of psychic life can be seen as these of self-definition. Only after self-cohesion is accomplished does behavior begin to be regulated by the pleasure-principle" (pp. 168–169). Implicit in this theoretical approach is the belief that the struggle to organize a cohesive self is a task expected in normal development to be accomplished once and forever and to be finished before the beginning of the oedipal period. This belief is exactly what I have to disagree with, because I am convinced that the struggle to maintain a cohesive and well-integrated self, a self that provides us with a firm sense of unity and continuity and that serves as *the* center for internalization, identification, and object relation, is a never-ending struggle, occupying the healthy mind as well as the pathological one for its entire life.

In a series of papers dealing with the various aspects of the psychoanalytic theory of the primary process (Noy, 1969, 1973, 1978, 1979b, 1982), I advanced the idea that this task, to maintain the unity and continuity of the self, is the main function of the primary process. According to the theory the primary processes are defined as "self-centered," and they include all the mental processes whose function is to serve the self in its needs for assimilation, accommodation, and integration. The secondary processes are defined as "reality-oriented," and they include all the mental processes whose function is to enable the organism to deal with reality, such as per-

ception and inner representation of reality, control of reality-directed behavior, and communication with others. Both mental activities, the self-
centered and the reality-oriented, must continuously support and complement one another; therefore both must be developed and improved
throughout the individual's life, so that in no phase of life can the self-
centered activity be regarded as accomplished. The self as an island of
stability placed in an organism that has to act and adapt itself continuously
to an ever-changing reality requires ongoing organizing activity to *assimilate*
new experience, to *accommodate* itself to the changing demands of reality
which get more complicated with each consecutive developmental phase,
and to safeguard its *integration* against the various forces threatening its
cohesion. This organizing activity, accomplished through the operation of
the primary processes, proceeds on various levels of mental functioning,
such as the constant stream of pre- and unconscious organizing activity
accompanying daily reality-oriented rational reasoning (Kubie, 1966), daydreaming or contemplation, dreaming, and all kinds of artistic activity. All
of these activities are aimed at achieving the same goal—to serve the self
in its needs for assimilation, accommodation, and integration—but each
becomes specialized in order, more or less, to fulfill different aspects of
these functions. Artistic activity—the focus of the present study—holds a
unique place among all other self-centered activities, by fulfilling mainly
the functions of the self's interrelationship with other human objects. This
includes the expression and articulation of emotions and feelings, the exchange of emotional experience with others, the gaining of access into the
emotional life of others, and the reconciliation among the ambivalent
emotions aroused in interpersonal situations (see Storr, 1972; Noy, 1979a).

Before going on with the presentation of my views about creativity and
originality, let me offer a few words of reservation: my theory is based
mainly on what I have learned from studying *artistic* activity from the
psychoanalytic point of view. Although there is no doubt that most of the
motivations toward the two kinds of creativity—the artistic and the scientific—have the same origin, it may be that in the case of scientific creativity
other motivations are also involved about whose origin I as yet have no
idea. Therefore, when using the term "creativity" I mean mainly artistic
creativity, though I do include those aspects of scientific creativity in which
the similarity to artistic creativity can be proved.

My general thesis is that the motive for creativity is always a self-centered
one. In fact, because creativity is a compound activity driven by various
motives, such as the strive for perfection, the quest for originality, the
search for aesthetic form, and the need for articulation, we have to speak
about "motives" in the plural. Each of these motives presumedly has its

origin in one of the major developmental struggles of the self, or, in other words, each of the various component activities of creativity is related to one of the major needs of the developing self. The specific need to which originality is related is the need of the self for individuation,[2] the need to develop a sense of self experienced as something unique, separated, and different from all the other objects. This struggle for individuation is one of the major developmental tasks of early childhood and continues to occupy every person for his entire life, but in normal development we expect that enough sense of individuation has been created before maturity is reached, so that that task no longer demands too much mental investment. However, in cases where the creation of a sense of individuation was hindered for reasons we will discuss later, the struggle for individuation may continue throughout life as one of the central pursuits of the personality, and may have a major influence on all the individual's thoughts and deeds.

Practicing for years in a university community, I had the opportunity to work with many teachers and therefore learned a lot about their motivations to succeed in their lectures and writings. Everyone wants, of course, to succeed and earn a good reputation; but it is interesting to see how diverse are the motives that drive each of them to be "good." The major aim of some lecturers is to convince their students of the importance of the discipline they are teaching, and their success is measured accordingly by the number of followers they have managed to recruit. Others strive to exhibit their encyclopedic knowledge in the writings of the "great fathers" of their science, and to prove their loyalty to them, and so on. Among these various aims you will always find those lecturers for whom the most important aim seems to be to appear original at any price. One professor of history once told me: "I am satisfied after a lecture only if I have succeeded in enabling my students to see that that historical event they know well can also be understood from a quite different angle from what they previously believed." One always gets the impression that what is important for these teachers is not to exhibit knowledge, to prepare their students to pass their examinations well, to earn their admiration for being able to explain complicated material, and so on, but mainly to be remembered by their listeners as somebody *different* from the "crowd" of other teachers and *unique* in approach.

Sometimes this need to be original at any price may even impede a teacher's academic advancement. One patient, for example, who for years was unable to invest enough energy to complete any serious research wasted practically all his talent in his attempts to impress his colleagues and students

[2] Jung was the first to speak about "individuation" in relation to art, but for him this concept had a different meaning from the one accepted today in self psychology.

again and again with his bright and original ideas. He came to recognize his status (and to ask for psychotherapeutic aid) only after he opened a letter of recommendation sent to the committee that had to decide about his promotion and found that he was described by a distinguished colleague as "the jester of our profession." Similar examples of a wish to be perceived and remembered as "different" and "unique" are common among creative writers, poets, composers, etc., especially those known by their inclination to experiment with new forms and styles.

The question of interest to us is the following: what is the developmental origin of such a need to always appear different and unique? We may assume that if this need has already determined the development of the entire cognitive style, as in the case of genuinely creative individuals, its origin has to be very early in the process of cognitive development, i.e., in some early disturbances in the mother-child relationship or in other interpersonal relationships that have impeded the normal process of individuation. The problem is that in dealing with disturbances in early mother-child relationships we usually expect to find some *deficit*, some inability of the mother or another significant caretaker to respond appropriately to one of the basic needs of the child, such as the need for mirroring, empathic understanding, "refueling," etc. But in the cases where the disturbance is more or less localized in the process of individuation alone, we are confronted mostly with an *excess*, with a too-close emotional relationship, or with a mother too eager to satisfy all her child's needs. The main problem the child has to cope with throughout his formative years is therefore not abandonment or emotional neglect, but excessive intrusion, preventing the child from delineating his self as separate from the object representations of his mother and other significant others. We know, of course, that underlying the disturbances of "excess" may be psychopathological dynamics similar to those in the cases of "deficit," and that the reason for a mother to give her child too much may be only the other side of the same narcissistic pathology that may bring another mother to give less than needed. But I want to stress the fact that that is not always the reason for excess. Just as I am not ready to consider any disturbance in the organization of the self as identical with "narcissism" or "borderline," so I also do not think that any cause of "excess" necessarily reflects a severe psychopathology of the mother, or a serious disturbance in the mother-child relationship.

It is important to stress this point in order to understand why most developmental studies of creative individuals, such as those mentioned in the second section of this paper, provide an image of a normal childhood with "good-enough" parents, and do not point to any significant disturbances. The reason is that most psychological studies, as already mentioned, are based oh background information derived from questionnaires or a few interviews, whereas most disturbances of "excess" are not detectable by such superficial methods but can be revealed only after a considerable period of psychoanalysis or psychotherapy.

Therefore, to follow the developmental origin of the quest for originality and to learn in which of the early conflicts and developmental struggles they are really rooted, we will have to resort to analyzed clinical cases. But here we are confronted with another problem: the number of published cases is extremely low, because the more a person is really creative, the better known he is in his community, the more his therapist is, for ethical reasons, prevented from presenting his case. As I am also restricted for the same reason, I will describe parts of the story of a patient I heard about in a seminar in which I participated on one of my visits abroad.

A young musician, in his early twenties, was referred to therapy because of various neurotic symptoms, including serious disturbances in his relationships with the other sex. His superior musical talent became manifested quite early in his life, and his mother, herself an enthusiastic music lover, did everything in her power to foster his talent and was also his first dedicated teacher. Not only did she fulfill her own ambition through his success in music, but she also shared her love of music with her son, and used music as one of the dominant channels for emotional communication with him. All his childhood remained in his memory as one long and happy festival of music, in which he and his mother used to listen together, discuss the music, and sing and play together on the piano. Naturally, he went on to study music, became a good pianist, and at adolescence began his first steps in composition. After several years in which he continued to share with his mother every new musical idea he conceived, they gradually began to part ways. He went more and more in the direction of modern and electronic music and began to compose in a style totally alien to his mother and to his own former taste. She was at first bewildered; she was unable to understand what had happened to him, and even went for psychological consultation to ask if something could be done with a *Wunderkind* who began to lose his talent as he grew up. And then came the final ceremony at the Academy of Music where he won the first prize for the piece of music every graduate student had to compose for this event. His mother, invited as one of the distinguished guests, became the hero of the evening as all the teachers stood in line to congratulate her as the mother of "one of the most promising and original composers."

On that occasion she was finally forced to realize that her son had continued to be a real talent, even though with all her understanding in music, she could not enjoy anything he had created. The young musician, in later discussing this event with his therapist, stated: "When I saw my mother standing bedazzled in the hall, smiling shyly back at all the people congratulating her, I suddenly knew that from then on my music was mine alone. I realized how much she really hated every tone of what I composed, but I also knew how full of pride she was in being my mother. From now on she *has* to respect me for something to which she will never again have access." This event came to be the turning point in his relationship with his mother and with women. Whereas from adolescence on he became more and more involved in endless discussions and quarrels with her, he now gradually resumed his traditionally good emotional relations with her, and in time many of his problems in intersexual relationships also began to dissolve. It became clear that, after succeeding in fortifying an island of individuality for himself in one of the central sectors of his self, he could now give up the struggle in all the other sectors.

In connection with this case it would be interesting to quote one of the many findings from the study of Cambor, Lisowitz, and Miller (1962) who presented thirty of the world's foremost creative jazz artists:

> Nearly all of the musicians described themselves as leaving home and embarking on their career . . . between the ages of 16 and 21. This decision usually occurred during a period of tension, dissatisfaction, and uncertainty at home which was described as centering around the following two main conflictual areas: 1) An increasing uncomfortable relationship with the mother, who seemed unable to recognize the musician as an individual and who attempted to keep him a dependent, symbiotic child. At the same time the mother was encouraging her son and making excessive demands for unique accomplishments. 2) A competitive ambivalent relationship with the father, siblings, or peers [pp. 7–8].

The authors summarize their findings:

> Actually jazz became a substitutive continuation of their symbiotic childhood, offering dependency gratification through group identity and a sense of belongingness . . . an unconscious or partly conscious motivation . . . is a striving for a negative identity . . . This seems to be related to a rebellious desire to assume a goal or way of life exactly opposite from that expected of them or presented to them as most desirable by the family, other significant people, or society in general . . . All seemed to want to seek and defend a niche all their own, rather than to accept the excessive and conflicting ideals of overly ambitious parents [pp. 13–14].[3]

I assume that in the background of every creative individual displaying

[3] Reprinted with permission of the William Alanson White Psychiatric Foundation.

a lifelong intense desire for originality one can reveal an early massive emotional intrusion interfering with the natural process of self-individuation. The individual differences mainly lie in the extent of this intrusion and in the ability of the growing child to resist and overcome it. In cases where the intrusion is not too massive, or remains confined to one or several isolated sectors of the self, the child, if gifted enough, can use one of the talents he is endowed with to overcome it by developing an appropriate substitutive activity that will grant him the sufficient sense of individual identity. In cases where the intrusion is more intense, the child may succeed in evading it by splitting his self into a "false self" and a "true self." The first self develops in compliance with the expectations of mother, father, and the family, and the second, in accordance with the natural inclinations and talents of the individual himself. Winnicott (1965) states: "Only the True Self can be creative, and only the True Self can feel real" (p. 148). That means that only if the individual succeeds in maintaining a "free sphere" of true selfness besides the sphere dominated by the False Self can he use his natural talent and choose the solution of creativity and originality to attain some sense of self-individuation.

To demonstrate such a solution, let me present a short clinical vignette: A young man in his late twenties came to analysis with the aim of solving his dependency needs to his parents. Several years before he had begun a brilliant career in economics and politics, but in addition to these activities he used to paint in secret. It became clear that his main occupation represented his False Self, through which he succeeded in fulfilling all his family's expectations for a brilliant academic and political career, and his second occupation, that of painting, his True Self, through which he succeeded in expressing his hidden rich emotional life. Most of his analysis remained focused around his attempts to overcome his dependency needs and the necessity to get his parents' approval for all he did. But toward the end of the analysis he began to consider seriously the possibility of leaving his present successful occupation and of dedicating himself full-time to a career in painting, even though he realized that his family would regard that as a real disaster. It was also interesting to see how, by gradually dissolving the strict boundaries between the False and the True Selves, he succeeded in partly integrating the two occupations—utilizing his sensitivity for others in his political activities and using his ability for public relations to advance his artistic career (after he dared for the first time to come out with a public exhibition).

Alice Miller's (1979) description in "The Drama of the Gifted Child" is perceptive: these children are "sensitive, alert, and have many 'antennae,' [and] will quickly learn to adapt to the narcissistic needs of their parents . . . The result will be that, in spite of excellent performance, the child's own true self cannot develop" (p. 57). These are children who, in order to secure the permanent supply of their parents' love and respect, have renounced any attempt for self-individuation and development of their True Self, and continue for life to gratify their parents' needs and to fulfill their expectations. Even after reaching maturity and independence from the parents, they continue to comply with the expectations of society and remain forever dependent on the affirmation of the significant others. Miller found "an amazing ability on the child's part intuitively, that is unconsciously, to perceive and respond to this need of the mother or of both parents, i.e., to take on the role which had unconsciously been assigned to him . . . This ability is then extended and perfected. Later these children . . . eventually develop a special sensitivity to unconscious signals of the needs of others" (p. 49).

The question I would ask here is this: Is this grim developmental scenario, as Miller describes it, really the only one possible, or does another possibility also exist—a way for the child to continue to secure the supply of love and respect of others, but *without* sacrificing his individuality? I am sure that such a way does exist—that of creative originality. The gifted individual can use his sensitive "antennae," his special ability to sense even the unconscious needs of others, not for complying with the needs and expectations directed toward him today, but for gratifying the needs that others might have tomorrow. The gap created between the needs of today and those of tomorrow may then provide him with the sufficient "life span" for developing his own individuality, for utilizing his specific talents to fortify at least one sector of his self as unique and different from all the others.

From the psychosocial point of view, such a solution is indeed the best one we can imagine. The gifted individual, facing the dilemma of "how to attain self-individuality without endangering the love and respect of the significant others," chooses to rebel against the generally accepted and agreed-upon conceptions of science, or the conventional forms of art, not only for the purpose of destroying them, but in order to renew them for the benefit of all of us. And then, if he has really succeeded in widening the scope of one of the sciences, or in enhancing our ability to enjoy one of the arts, we are ready to grant him all the love and respect. But now, not only for the reason that he needs it, but also because we believe that he really deserves it.

## REFERENCES

Barron, F. (1955), The disposition toward originality. *J. Abnorm. & Soc. Psychol.*, 51:478–485.
——— (1963), The need for order and disorder as motives in creative activity. In: *Scientific*

*Creativity: Its Recognition and Development*, ed. C. W. Taylor & F. Barron. New York: Wiley, pp. 153–160.

Bartlett, F. C. (1958), *Thinking: An Experimental and Social Study.* New York: Basic Books.

Cambor, C. G., Lisowitz, G. M., & Miller, M. D. (1962), Creative jazz musicians: A clinical study. *Psychiat.*, 25:1–15.

De Bono, E. (1969), *The Mechanism of Mind.* New York: Penguin, 1976.

Eissler, K. R. (1971), *Talent and Genius.* New York: Grove Press.

Freud, S. (1916–1917), Introductory lectures on psycho-analysis. Lecture XXIII. *Standard Edition*, 16:358–377. London: Hogarth Press, 1963.

—— (1937), Analysis terminable and interminable. *Standard Edition*, 23:209–254. London: Hogarth Press, 1964.

Gardner, R., Holzman, P. S., Klein, G. S., Linton, H., & Spencer, D. P. (1959), *Cognitive Control: A Study of Individual Consistencies in Cognitive Behavior.* New York: International Universities Press.

Gedo, J. E. (1972), On the psychology of genius. *Internat. J. Psycho-Anal.*, 53:199–203.

—— (1976), New horizons in metapsychology, view and review. *J. Amer. Psychoanal. Assn.*, 24:161–180.

Guilford, J. P. (1959), Traits of creativity. In: *Creativity and Its Cultivation*, ed. H. H. Anderson. New York: Harper, pp. 142–161.

—— (1967), Intellectual factors in productive thinking. In: *Explorations in Creativity*, ed. R. L. Mooney & T. A. Razik. New York: Harper & Row, pp. 95–106.

Habermas, J. (1968), *Erkenntnis und Interesse.* Frankfurt: Suhrkamp.

Hunter, I.M.L. (1966), Mental calculation. In: *Thinking and Reasoning*, ed. P. C. Wason & P. N. Johnson-Laird. London: Penguin Books, 1968, pp. 341–351.

Kant, I. (1790), *The Critique of Judgement.* Oxford: Oxford University Press, 1952.

Klein, S. (1980), Autistic phenomena in neurotic patients. *Internat. J. Psycho-Anal.*, 61:395–402.

Koestler, A. (1964), *The Act of Creation.* London: Pan Books, Ltd.

—— (1968), *The Sleepwalkers.* London: Penguin Books.

Kohut, H. (1966), Forms and transformations of narcissism. *J. Amer. Psychoanal. Assn.*, 14:243–272.

—— (1971), *The Analysis of the Self.* New York: International Universities Press.

—— (1977), *The Restoration of the Self.* New York: International Universities Press.

Kris, E. (1952), *Psychoanalytic Explorations in Art.* New York: International Universities Press.

Kubie, L. S. (1966), A reconsideration of thinking, the dream process, and "the dream." *Psychoanal. Quart.*, 35:191–198.

Lytton, H. (1971), *Creativity and Education.* London: Routledge & Kegan Paul.

Mackinnon, D. W. (1961), The nature and nurture of creative talent. *Amer. Psychol.*, 17:484–495.

Maslow, A. (1963), The creative attitude. *Psychosynthesis Research Foundation Reprint*, no. 10. New York.

Mednick, S. A. (1962), The associative basis of the creative process. *Psycholog. Rev.*, 69:220–232.

Miller, A. (1979), The drama of the gifted child and the psychoanalyst's narcissistic disturbance. *Internat. J. Psycho-Anal.*, 60:47–58.

Niederland, W. G. (1967), Clinical aspects of creativity. *Amer. Imago.*, 24:6–34.

—— (1976), Psychoanalytic approaches to artistic creativity. *Psychoanal. Quart.*, 45:185–212.

Noy, P. (1966), On the development of artistic talent. *Israel Annals Psychiat.*, 4:211–218.

—— (1968), The development of musical ability. *The Psychoanalytic Study of the Child*, 23:332–347. New York: International Universities Press.

—— (1969), A revision of the psychoanalytic theory of the primary process. *Internat. J. Psycho-Anal.*, 50:155–178.

—— (1972), About art and artistic talent. *Internat. J. Psycho-Anal.*, 53:243–249.

—— (1973), Symbolism and mental representation. *This Annual*, 1:125–158. New York: International Universities Press.

—— (1978), Insight and creativity. *J. Amer. Psychoanal. Assn.*, 26:717–748.

———— (1979a), Form-creation in art. *Psychoanal. Quart.*, 48:229–256.
———— (1979b), The psychoanalytic theory of cognitive development. *The Psychoanalytic Study of the Child*, 34:169–216. New Haven: Yale University Press.
———— (1982), A revision of the psychoanalytic theory of affect. *This Annual*, 10:139–185. New York: International Universities Press.
Parker, D. H. (1963), *Schooling for Individual Excellence*. London: Nelson.
Polanyi, M. (1958), *Personal Knowledge*. London: Routledge & Kegan Paul.
Rangell, L. (1981), From insight to change. *J. Amer. Psychoanal. Assn.*, 29:119–141.
Rogers, C. R. (1954), Toward a theory of creativity. *ETC: A Review of General Semantics*, 11:249–260.
Schafer, R. (1979), Character, ego-syntonicity, and character change. *J. Amer. Psychoanal. Assn.*, 27:867–891.
———— (1982), The relevance of the "here and now" transference interpretation for the reconstruction of early psychic development. *Internat. J. Psycho-Anal.*, 63:77–82.
Segal, H. (1981), *Melanie Klein*. England: Penguin Books.
Stein, M. I. (1963), A transactional approach to creativity. In: *Scientific Creativity: Its Recognition and Development*, ed. C. W. Taylor & F. Barron. New York: Wiley, pp. 217–227.
Storr, A. (1972), *The Dynamics of Creation*. London: Secker & Warburg.
Weisberg, P. S. & Springer, K. J. (1962), Environmental factors in creative function. *Arch. Gen. Psychiat.*, 5:64–74.
Winnicott, D. W. (1965), Ego distortion in terms of true and false self. In: *The Maturational Processes and the Facilitating Environment*. New York: International Universities Press, pp. 140–152.
Witkin, H. A., Lewis, H. B., Hertzman, M., Machover, K., Meissner, P. B., & Wapner, S. (1954), *Personality through Perception*. New York: Harper.

*August 1983*

# INDEX

Abandonment of infantile aims, 89
Action, addiction to, 100
Activity-passivity conflicts, 158, 169-173
Actors and acting, 267
Addiction, 304-305
Adult identities and fictive formulas, 267-272
Aesthetics, 172n
Affective attunement, 107-108
Affective experiences, synthesis of, 109
Affects, 74
Affects depressive, 112-114
Affects differentiation, 108-109
Affects tolerance, 109-111
Affects, desomatization of, 110-111
Affects, false, 71
Aggression, 223
Aim of therapy, 67
"Alimentary orgasm," 304
Alter-ego countertransferences, 49
Altruism, 187
Ambitions, 101
Analyst's contribution to the transference, 31-33
Analytic situation, 87
Analyzability, 19, 148, 150, 151, 428
Anorexia, 308-309
Anxiety, disintegration, 63
Archeology, 20
Arithmetic, 424
Art, 416
Arthur, case of, 293-296
"As-if" character, 277-278
Assassination, 289
Attitudes, harsh parental, 102
Authority, 160
Autoerotism, 77

"Badness," 103
Basic regulation (first three months of life), 40-41
Benno Bimpie, the transfiguration of, 307-308
Bible, New Testament, 158-159
Binge eaters, 303-304, 306

Biography and criticism:
  Freud, Anna, *Normality and Pathology*, 77
  Freud Sigmund, *Irma's Injection Dream*, 367-376; *The Dream of the Botanical Monograph*, 374-375
Kohut, Heinz, 222
Strindberg, A., 369-371
Bismarck, 305n
Borderline states, 202

Camerata, 417-418
Catch 22, 259
*Catcher in the Rye*, 287, 289-291
Catholic church, 159
Change, 137, 179
Chapman, Mark David, 289-291
Character disorders, 59
  narcissistic, 92
Charisma, 161-165
Charm, negative, 225
Child development—Early childhood, 63-64
Children, "exceptional," 184
Clinical implications, 146-151
The completion of mourning, 325-326
Complications in the work of mourning, 329-331
Conceptualizations of transference, 20-27
Conflict, 70, 139-140
"Copy-cat," 288
Creative fictionalism as adaptive lying, 406-410
Creative fictionalism as narcissistic transformation, 410-412
Creative originality, 432-436
Crowds, 167
Cults, 156
Culture, 69-70
Czermak, Marcel, 284

Death instinct, 221
Death, reactions to—Mourning, 323
Defenses, 108
Depression (reactive), 331-332
Depressive disorders, 113

449

Compiled by Glenn E. Miller